3,13 A
     B
     C
3,17 B
3,18 A
     C
3,19 A
     C

4 capu

28 mi und top
to KCU

FIELDS AND WAVES
IN COMMUNICATION ELECTRONICS

Fields and Waves in Modern Radio
  Simon Ramo and John R. Whinnery

Handbook of Automatic Computation and Control
  Eugene M. Grabbe, Simon Ramo, and Dean E. Wooldridge, Editors

FIELDS AND WAVES

IN COMMUNICATION

ELECTRONICS

SIMON RAMO

President, Bunker-Ramo Corporation

JOHN R. WHINNERY

Professor of Electrical Engineering
University of California, Berkeley

THEODORE VAN DUZER

Associate Professor of Electrical Engineering
University of California, Berkeley

John Wiley & Sons, Inc., New York · London · Sydney

Library of Congress Catalog Card Number: 65-19477
Printed in the United States of America

PREFACE

This book is an intermediate level text on electromagnetic fields and waves. It clearly builds much on an earlier volume by two of the authors,* but has been modernized and updated by continuing use in a course at the senior level at the University of California on "Electromagnetic Fields and Waves."

There was once some argument concerning the need for the treatment of field and wave problems from Maxwell's equations in an electrical engineering curriculum. There is no such argument now, but there is much discussion of the level for such treatment and the proper manner of beginning. There is no single answer to this question since successful curricula can be built in a number of ways. The ideal perhaps is to include field concepts with the circuit concepts and physical electronics at the beginning, and to weave them all in continuously to higher levels throughout the curriculum. In most schools this ideal continuous blending is impractical, and at some point it is necessary to concentrate on the several parts.

This book assumes an introductory course in field concepts which can be satisfied by the lower division physics courses of many universities. It is likely, however, that in present electrical engineering curricula there will be some additional development of the field concepts before a course, based upon this book, is entered. It also assumes a background of calculus. Material on vector analysis, differential equations, fourier series, and matrices is included in a form suitable for review or a first introduction. It is a basic philosophy of the book that these introductions be given where the material is to be used, and related to real problems in fields and waves. Since it is also assumed that the typical reader will have had a course in simple electrical circuitry, many of the examples relate to circuit concepts. This is not essential, however, as the definitions of the circuit quantities are given and the base of a modern physics course in electricity and magnetism will suffice.

* S. Ramo and J. R. Whinnery, *Fields and Waves in Modern Radio*, John Wiley and Sons; 1st ed. 1944; 2nd ed. 1953. The first edition was prepared with the assistance of the General Electric Company when the authors were employed in its laboratories.

Recognizing that opinions differ on the proper manner of starting the study of fields and waves, the book is designed so that the first few chapters can be studied and/or taught in any order. We believe that the median student will benefit by a review of oscillation and wave fundamentals using simple circuit ideas, and also by a thorough review of static fields, before beginning dynamic field problems. It is also a basic philosophy of the presentation that each chapter begin with simple examples, then present the general formulations before applying these to a number of important practical problems. Additional flexibility in the use of the text results from some selection from the examples; usually the more advanced and specialized appear at the end of chapters and need not all be treated to continue with the main development of field and wave concepts. Problems of various levels are included, from simple exercises through rather difficult developments.

The thread of the development is generally clear from a study of the table of contents and will not be repeated here. It should be noted that although electromagnetic theory is an old and classic subject, it remains very much alive in its developments. Thus since the last revision of this book's predecessor,* nonreciprocal devices using anisotropic media such as ferrites or plasmas with magnetic fields have gained a standard place in communication engineering. Numerical methods of solving field problems have assumed greater importance with the availability of high-speed computers. Antenna technology has been revolutionized by the frequency-independent antennas, phased arrays, and greater use of lens-type radiators. The interaction of materials and waves has become central to many devices. Finally, with the development of the laser, standard electronic techniques and optical principles have been brought together even more than in the microwave range which often uses a combination of circuit, wave, and geometrical optics points of view. All these changes have been reflected in the preparation of this book.

We have many people to thank for their suggestions and their specific help. Colleagues at the Bell Telephone Laboratories gave general and specific advice during a visit of one of us (JRW) there this last year.

Of the instructors of the fields course at Berkeley, Professors Angelakos, Bevensee, Everhart, Silver, Süsskind, Welch, and White gave many helpful suggestions. Professor C. K. Birdsall especially gave detailed comments which played a major part in forming this book. Professors Shyh Wang of Berkeley and C. F. Quate of Stanford helped much on the materials portions.

Canoga Park, California
Berkeley, California
June, 1965

SIMON RAMO
JOHN R. WHINNERY
THEODORE VAN DUZER

CONTENTS

CONTENTS xi

I OSCILLATION
AND WAVE FUNDAMENTALS

I.01 Introduction

This book is concerned with electromagnetics, particularly that part underlying oscillations and waves. Before introducing the laws of electricity and magnetism for serious study, it will be desirable to discuss some ideas and mathematics that have to do with oscillations and waves generally. This will be done by using simple circuits and conventional uniform transmission lines as examples. When this is done, the objective is not to present the theory of circuits and lines as such. Indeed the theory underlying both comprises a good part of the book. The purpose of this chapter is to illustrate (and for some readers to review) a point of view toward oscillations and waves needed for the rest of the book. Specifically the objectives are:

1. To present a clear picture of the energy relations in oscillating systems.

2. To point out criteria relating energy properties of a system to bandwidth, impedance, etc., for later comparison with cavity resonators.

3. To clarify the concepts of waves, particularly in regard to such properties as phase velocity, reflection, and characteristic impedance.

4. To point out common properties of transmission lines according to the conventional distributed constant approach for later comparison with properties of waves in space and in wave guides.

5. To present or review some fundamental mathematics necessary for the study of oscillations and waves throughout the book.

6. To develop approximate methods of analysis based on the physical pictures of the phenomena, so that these may be used in the later, more difficult problems.

SIMPLE CIRCUITS AS EXAMPLES OF OSCILLATING SYSTEMS

1.02   Free Oscillations in an Ideal Simple Circuit

Let us start with the simplest possible circuit for electrical oscillations, an ideal capacitor connected across an ideal inductance. Consider first free oscillations, assuming that an amount of energy was supplied to the combination at some instant (for example, by placing a charge on the capacitor) and that from that time on there is no connection to the outside. Energy may be stored in the system in two forms:

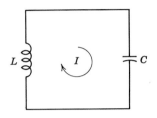

Fig. 1.02

1. Magnetic energy in the inductance. This may be considered analogous to kinetic energy in mechanics and has the value

$$U_L = \tfrac{1}{2}LI^2 \qquad (1)$$

where I is the current flowing through the inductance L.

2. Electric energy in the capacitance. This may be considered analogous to potential energy in mechanics and has the value

$$U_C = \tfrac{1}{2}CV^2 \qquad (2)$$

where V is the voltage across the capacitor C.

The presence of energy in the capacitor implies a voltage across the capacitor, and a consequent rate of change of current and stored magnetic energy in the inductance. Similarly, the presence of magnetic energy requires a current flowing in the inductance, and a consequent rate of change of voltage and stored electric energy in the capacitor. We are led then to expect oscillations, since the presence of energy in one form requires a rate of change of energy in the other. It is also necessary that the total energy in the system be a constant, the same at all instants, since there is no connection to the outside and ideal dissipationless conditions are assumed.

Before going further with purely physical reasoning, let us write an equation for the instantaneous current in the circuit. By Kirchhoff's laws, the sum of the induction voltage $L \, dI/dt$ and the capacitor voltage q/C must be zero:

$$L\frac{dI}{dt} + \frac{1}{C}\int I \, dt = 0. \qquad (3)$$

If this equation is differentiated with respect to time, it becomes a true differential equation.

$$L \frac{d^2I}{dt^2} + \frac{I}{C} = 0$$

or

$$\frac{d^2I}{dt^2} = -\frac{I}{LC}. \tag{4}$$

The differential equation (4) is called the simple harmonic motion equation. It is one of the most familiar of differential equations, and will be used in the next article as the mechanism for reviewing simple techniques of solution for such equations.

1.03 Simple Methods for Solution of the Simple Harmonic Motion Equation

The differential equation 1.02(4) is of second order and is linear in that a sum of solutions of the equation is also a solution. This is true since only the first power of I and its derivatives appear in the equations. The equation is also homogeneous in that all terms contain the dependent variable I or its derivatives. It is an equation with constant coefficients since the multipliers of I and its derivatives are not functions of the independent variable t. The methods to be illustrated are those which will be employed in less familiar equations later, and start with the assumption of a functional form for the solution, verifying and evaluating constants by substitution in the equation. Such methods are often called *heuristic* methods of solution of the equation.

Solution by Assumed Series. Let us first assume that 1.02(4) will have a solution in the form of a power series in t,

$$I = a_0 + a_1 t + a_2 t^2 + a_3 t^3 + a_4 t^4 + \cdots. \tag{1}$$

Differentiating,

$$\frac{dI}{dt} = a_1 + 2a_2 t + 3a_3 t^2 + 4a_4 t^3 + \cdots$$

$$\frac{d^2I}{dt^2} = 2 \cdot 1 a_2 + 3 \cdot 2 a_3 t + 4 \cdot 3 a_4 t^2 + \cdots.$$

These series forms may be substituted in Eq. 1.02(4) to determine the requirements on the coefficients in order that the series may satisfy that equation:

$$2 \cdot 1a_2 + 3 \cdot 2a_3 t + 4 \cdot 3a_4 t^2 + 5 \cdot 4a_5 t^3 + 6 \cdot 5a_6 t^4 + \cdots$$
$$= -\frac{1}{LC}(a_0 + a_1 t + a_2 t^2 + a_3 t^3 + a_4 t^4 + \cdots).$$

A little study shows that, if the foregoing equation is to be true for all values of t, coefficients of like powers of t must be equal on the two sides of the equation. That is,

$$a_2 = -\frac{a_0}{2 \cdot 1 LC}$$

$$a_3 = -\frac{a_1}{3 \cdot 2 LC}$$

$$a_4 = -\frac{a_2}{4 \cdot 3 LC} = \frac{a_0}{4! \, (LC)^2}$$

$$a_5 = -\frac{a_3}{5 \cdot 4 LC} = \frac{a_1}{5! \, (LC)^2}$$

and, generalizing,

$$a_{2n} = -\frac{a_{2n-2}}{(2n)(2n-1)LC} = \frac{(-1)^n a_0}{(2n)! \, (LC)^n}$$

$$a_{2n+1} = -\frac{a_{2n-1}}{(2n+1)(2n)LC} = \frac{(-1)^n a_1}{(2n+1)! \, (LC)^n}.$$

Notice that the requirements placed on the constants of the series by substituting in the differential equation have related all constants either to a_0 or to a_1, but there is nothing relating these two. This then yields the two independent solutions required for a second-order differential equation. Let us now write the assumed series (1), using the following constants:

$$I = a_0 \left[1 - \frac{t^2}{2! \, LC} + \frac{t^4}{4! \, (LC)^2} - \frac{t^6}{6! \, (LC)^3} + \cdots \right] + (a_1 \sqrt{LC})$$

$$\times \left[\frac{t}{(LC)^{1/2}} - \frac{t^3}{3! \, (LC)^{3/2}} + \frac{t^5}{5! \, (LC)^{5/2}} - \frac{t^7}{7! \, (LC)^{7/2}} + \cdots \right]. \quad (2)$$

Comparison with tables of series shows that the first quantity in brackets has the form of the series expansion for a cosine function and the second for a sine. That is,

$$I = a_0 \cos\left(\frac{t}{\sqrt{LC}}\right) + a_1 \sqrt{LC} \, \sin\left(\frac{t}{\sqrt{LC}}\right).$$

Since a_1 is arbitrary, the entire quantity $a_1\sqrt{LC}$ may be replaced by C_2 to stress the point that it is an arbitrary constant. Let us at the same time replace a_0 by C_1 and define

$$\omega_0 = \frac{1}{\sqrt{LC}}. \tag{3}$$

Then
$$I = C_1 \cos \omega_0 t + C_2 \sin \omega_0 t. \tag{4}$$

This expression (4), which is a solution to the differential equation, has two independent functions and two arbitrary constants. These constants cannot be determined until more information is given about the manner of starting oscillations in the circuit (the initial conditions).

Solution by Assumed Sinusoids. With some physical feeling for the probable result as an oscillating solution, we might have written the form (4) as a possible solution in the beginning. It would be known that the sine and cosine are linearly independent, and thus would be candidates for the two independent solutions required. Differentiation of (4) and substitution in Eq. 1.02(4) would verify that the assumed form is a solution and also give the value (3) for the oscillation frequency ω_0, as can be quickly verified.

Solution by Assumed Exponentials. Closely related to the foregoing, and most important in its extensions to the complex form for representation of sinusoids, is the assumption of a solution in terms of exponentials, which is a standard method for homogeneous, linear differential equations with constant coefficients. Suppose we try

$$I = A_1 e^{pt} + A_2 e^{-pt} \tag{5}$$

then
$$\frac{d^2 I}{dt^2} = p^2(A_1 e^{pt} + A_2 e^{-pt}).$$

Substitute these in Eq. 1.02(4):

$$p^2(A_1 e^{pt} + A_2 e^{-pt}) = -\frac{1}{LC}(A_1 e^{pt} + A_2 e^{-pt})$$

or
$$p^2 = -\frac{1}{LC}$$

$$p = j\sqrt{\frac{1}{LC}} = j\omega_0$$

where $j \equiv \sqrt{-1}$.

This substitution indicates that (5) is a solution of the simple harmonic motion equation, provided that $p = j\omega_0$:

$$I = A_1 e^{j\omega_0 t} + A_2 e^{-j\omega_0 t}. \tag{6}$$

Next let us remind ourselves of the identities

$$e^{jx} = \cos x + j \sin x \tag{7}$$

$$e^{-jx} = \cos x - j \sin x. \tag{8}$$

If identities (7) and (8) are substituted in (6),

$$I = (A_1 + A_2) \cos \omega_0 t + j(A_1 - A_2) \sin \omega_0 t. \tag{9}$$

Since A_1 and A_2 are both arbitrary, this may be written exactly in the earlier form (4). For many purposes it will be convenient to use the solution in the form of (6) instead of changing to (4). This use of exponentials to replace sinusoids will be the subject of later discussion.

Problems

1.03a Show that an alternative expression equivalent to Eq. 1.03(4) is

$$I = A \cos (\omega_0 t + \phi).$$

Relate A and ϕ to C_1 and C_2.

1.03b Obtain one power series solution for the equation

$$\frac{d^2 y}{dx^2} - \frac{1}{x} \frac{dy}{dx} + \beta^2 y = 0.$$

(The second solution of this second-order equation has singularities and is not obtainable by this method.)

1.03c Repeat b for the equation

$$\frac{d^2 y}{dx^2} - \frac{1}{x} \frac{dy}{dx} + \left(\beta^2 + \frac{1}{x^2} \right) y = 0.$$

1.03d The equations for a loss-free coupled circuit with input values L_1, C_1, output values L_2 and C_2, and mutual inductance M are

$$L_1 \frac{dI_1}{dt} + M \frac{dI_2}{dt} + \frac{1}{C_1} \int I_1 \, dt = 0$$

$$L_2 \frac{dI_2}{dt} + M \frac{dI_1}{dt} + \frac{1}{C_2} \int I_2 \, dt = 0.$$

Assuming sinusoidal forms for I_1 and I_2, find values for the natural frequency ω_0.

1.03e Solve the equations for the coupled circuit, Prob. d, using assumed exponentials.

1.04 Natural Oscillations With Losses—Approximate Method

The circuit analyzed previously was ideal. Suppose we now wish to consider the effect of the finite losses which must of necessity be present in the circuit. As will be shown in the next article, it is a simple matter to include these in the circuit equations rigorously; yet let us first use physical knowledge to develop an approximate method which will give the first-order effect of the losses, provided that losses are small. The point of view will be extremely useful in later analyses of cavity resonators and waveguides.

If losses are small, physical intuition tells us that the natural period of oscillation will be changed little, and over a short period of time the solution will be very nearly that for the ideal circuit. The major correction will be a long-time decrease in the amplitude of oscillation because of energy lost.

It is common experience to find exponential changes for a physical quantity which decreases (or increases) at a rate proportional to the amount of that quantity present. The power loss, or rate of energy decrease, for this example, is proportional to the amount of energy in the system. It would consequently be reasonable to expect an exponential damping factor to appear in the expressions for currents and voltages. As a first-order correction, the expression for current obtained previously (Prob. 1.03a) might be assumed to be multiplied by some negative exponential:

$$I = Ae^{-\alpha t}\cos(\omega_0 t + \phi). \tag{1}$$

The energy in the circuit may be calculated at an instant when it is all in the inductance:

$$U = \tfrac{1}{2}L(I_{max})^2 = \frac{LA^2}{2}e^{-2\alpha t}. \tag{2}$$

Within the limits of the assumption of relatively small losses, the negative rate of change of this stored energy averaged over several cycles is merely the average power loss:

$$-\frac{dU}{dt} = W_L. \tag{3}$$

From (2),
$$\frac{dU}{dt} = -2\alpha\frac{LA^2}{2}e^{-2\alpha t} = -2\alpha U. \tag{4}$$

So, by combining (3) and (4),

$$\alpha = \frac{W_L}{2U}. \tag{5}$$

Define the quality factor or Q of the circuit as the quantity

$$Q = \frac{\omega_0(\text{energy stored in circuit})}{\text{average power loss}} = \frac{\omega_0 U}{W_L} \tag{6}$$

$$Q = \frac{\pi(\text{energy stored in circuit})}{\text{energy lost per half cycle}} . \tag{7}$$

Then (5) may be written

$$\alpha = \frac{\omega_0}{2Q} . \tag{8}$$

The exponential decay is thus expressible in terms of the quantity Q.

Finally, let us interpret these results for a circuit with losses distributed as in Fig. 1.04. The current flow through the series combination of R and L is expressed by

$$I = A \cos (\omega_0 t + \phi)$$

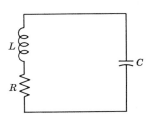

(neglecting any exponential damping for a few cycles). The energy stored in the circuit is the maximum energy in the inductance,

$$U = \frac{L}{2} A^2,$$

Fig. 1.04

and the average power loss in resistance R is

$$W_R = \tfrac{1}{2}R(I_{\text{max}})^2 = \frac{RA^2}{2} .$$

So Q, defined by (6), is

$$Q_L = \frac{\omega_0(LA^2)}{RA^2} = \frac{\omega_0 L}{R} . \tag{9}$$

This is the familiar expression for Q used to describe the excellence of an inductance, $\omega L/R$, calculated at resonance. It may be used in (8) to give the decay constant.

Problems

1.04a If losses are present owing to a conductance $G = 1/R_1$ shunted across the capacitor instead of a series resistance in the inductance, show that the Q to use in the general expression Eq. 1.04(8) is

$$Q_C = \frac{\omega_0 C}{G} = \frac{R_1}{\omega_0 L} .$$

1.04b If losses arise from both series resistance in L and shunt conductance across C, demonstrate that the Q to use in the general expressions may be found from the individual Q's defined previously.

$$\frac{1}{Q} = \frac{1}{Q_L} + \frac{1}{Q_C}$$

1.04c Damping in a lossy system is sometimes described through use of a logarithmic decrement, which is the relative amount amplitude decreases in one period,

$$\delta = 1 - \frac{I(t + T)}{I(t)},$$

where $T = 2\pi/\omega_0$. Show that $\delta = \pi/Q$ for small losses. Also find the time constant (or e-folding time) at which amplitude drops to $1/e$ its initial value.

1.05   Exact Solution of Circuit Equation with Losses

The exact solution to the circuit of Fig. 1.04 will now be obtained to check the approximate results of the previous article.

$$L\frac{dI}{dt} + RI + \frac{1}{C}\int I \, dt = 0$$

is the exact equation of the circuit. Differentiating,

$$L\frac{d^2I}{dt^2} + R\frac{dI}{dt} + \frac{I}{C} = 0. \tag{1}$$

Following the third method of Art. 1.03, assume a solution of exponential form,

$$I = Ae^{pt}. \tag{2}$$

If this is substituted in (1) and the resulting equation is solved for p, it is found that

$$p = -\frac{R}{2L} \pm \sqrt{\left(\frac{R}{2L}\right)^2 - \frac{1}{LC}}. \tag{3}$$

Since for low-loss circuits $(R/2L)^2$ will be less than $1/LC$, it will be convenient to write (3) as

$$p = -\frac{R}{2L} \pm \frac{j}{\sqrt{LC}}\sqrt{1 - \frac{R^2C}{4L}} = -\alpha \pm j\omega_0', \tag{4}$$

where

$$\alpha = \frac{R}{2L} = \frac{\omega_0}{2Q}, \tag{5}$$

$$\omega_0' = \frac{1}{\sqrt{LC}}\sqrt{1 - \frac{R^2C}{4L}} = \omega_0\sqrt{1 - \left(\frac{1}{2Q}\right)^2}, \tag{6}$$

Q denotes $\omega_0 L/R$ as in Eq. 1.04(9), and ω_0 is $1/\sqrt{LC}$.

The two possible values of p from (4) supply the two independent solutions needed for the second-order differential equation. Substitute these in (2):

$$I = A_1 e^{(-\alpha + j\omega_0')t} + A_2 e^{(-\alpha - j\omega_0')t}$$
$$= e^{-\alpha t}[A_1 e^{j\omega_0' t} + A_2 e^{-j\omega_0' t}].$$

By substitutions similar to those of Art. 1.03, an alternative expression is

$$I = e^{-\alpha t}[C_1 \cos \omega_0' t + C_2 \sin \omega_0' t]. \tag{7}$$

A comparison with the approximate analysis of Art. 1.04 shows that the same damping coefficient (5) is obtained. The natural frequency is different from ω_0 by (6), but this difference is small for low-loss (high-Q) circuits.

Problem

1.05 Obtain exact results for the cases solved approximately in Probs. 1.04*a* and 1.04*b*, showing for these also that Q may be used as an indication of the usefulness of the approximate results.

1.06 Forced Oscillations in an Ideal L-C Circuit

In previous examples, it was assumed that oscillations in the simple resonant circuit were free oscillations caused only by an initial deposit of energy in the circuit. In many practical cases, however, the circuit is continuously excited by a source of sinusoidal voltage. As the first example of such forced oscillations, consider the loss-free parallel L-C circuit excited by a sinusoidal voltage of constant magnitude (Fig. 1.06). The total current flow from the source is the sum of currents in the two impedances. The equations for these two currents are

$$L\frac{dI_1}{dt} = V \sin \omega t \tag{1}$$

$$\frac{1}{C}\int I_2 \, dt = V \sin \omega t. \tag{2}$$

Current may be obtained from (1) by integrating directly and from (2) by differentiating:

$$LI_1 = -\frac{V}{\omega} \cos \omega t + C_1 \tag{3}$$

$$\frac{I_2}{C} = \omega V \cos \omega t. \tag{4}$$

The constant term in (3) merely represents a possible constant d-c term flowing through the inductance, which is of no interest to the a-c problem so long as constant elements (linear systems) are assumed. Thus the total current

$$I = I_1 + I_2 = V\left(\omega C - \frac{1}{\omega L}\right) \cos \omega t. \qquad (5)$$

The foregoing relations, of course, check the well-known behavior of simple circuits. The current in the inductance has a phase lag of 90° with

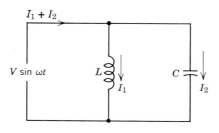

$I_1 + I_2$

$V \sin \omega t$ L I_1 C I_2

Fig. 1.06

respect to its voltage, whereas the current in the capacitance has a 90° phase lead with respect to the voltage. The total current is leading (the total circuit acts as a capacitance) if $\omega C > 1/\omega L$, and is lagging (total circuit acts as an inductance) if $1/\omega L > \omega C$. If $\omega C = 1/\omega L$, there is no current to be supplied by the source; under this condition the current flow to the inductance is at every instant exactly equal and opposite to the current flow to the capacitance. The frequency for which this condition occurs is the natural frequency found previously,

$$\omega C = \frac{1}{\omega L} \quad \text{or} \quad \omega = \frac{1}{\sqrt{LC}} = \omega_0. \qquad (6)$$

At this natural frequency the energy inside the system is a constant and merely passes back and forth from inductance to capacitance, and no energy need be supplied by the source at any instant of time. For a frequency lower than this resonant frequency, the maximum energy stored in the inductance is greater than the maximum energy stored in the capacitance, so that this excess energy must be supplied from the source during one part of the cycle, but will be delivered back to it unharmed during another part. This excess reactive energy from the inductance makes the circuit appear as an inductive load to the source. Similarly, for frequencies greater than the resonant frequency, the maximum energy in the capacitance is greater than the maximum energy in the inductance, and the excess reactive energy that must be supplied to the capacitance causes the circuit to appear as a capacitive load to the source.

At the resonant frequency the energy stored in the circuit is the maximum energy of the capacitance, or the maximum energy stored in the inductance, since both are equal:

$$U = \tfrac{1}{2}CV^2 = \frac{V^2}{2\omega_0}\sqrt{\frac{C}{L}}. \tag{7}$$

Problem

1.06 A series circuit of L and C is driven by a current generator $I\cos\omega t$. Find an expression for voltage across the circuit as a function of time, and study the behavior of the resonant frequency of this circuit.

1.07 Approximate Input Impedance at and Near Resonance

If the parallel circuit has losses in the coil or capacitor, these may be taken into account from physical consideration of the energy relations, before an exact analysis by the circuit equations is attempted.

At resonance the energy stored in the tuned circuit is given by Eq. 1.06(7). From the definition of Q given in Eq. 1.04(6), the power loss at resonance is

$$W_L = \frac{\omega_0 U}{Q} = \frac{V^2}{2Q}\sqrt{\frac{C}{L}}. \tag{1}$$

The source must supply to the circuit this amount of power. The circuit then looks like a high resistance R_i of value such that

$$W = \frac{V^2}{2R_i}. \tag{2}$$

By comparing with (1),

$$R_i = Q\sqrt{\frac{L}{C}}. \tag{3}$$

The approximations of reasonably low losses will be recognized in the foregoing reasoning, for we have taken the expression for energy stored as that developed from the loss-free case. In this picture, the major part of the energy is stored in the circuit and passes back and forth from the inductance to the capacitance. Only the small amount of power lost in the process need be supplied by the source. The resulting current flow to supply this loss component causes the circuit to have a high but finite input impedance in place of the infinite input impedance found previously.

For a small departure from resonance, it may be concluded that the major change will appear as a reactive component added to the admittance as the capacitive and inductive reactive currents no longer cancel. To a first approximation, the input power supplied will be constant, so that the conductive portion of the admittance may be considered constant and equal to that calculated from (3). Although loss power does change with frequency, this is a uniform change, not comparable with the change in the differences of large quantities which affects the reactive current. The susceptance portion of the admittance is approximately that calculated without losses. We will use here the complex notation under the assumption that it has been utilized by the reader elsewhere, but will review the base for its usefulness in the next article. The admittance may then be written

$$Y = G + jB \approx \frac{1}{Q}\sqrt{\frac{C}{L}} + j\left(\omega C - \frac{1}{\omega L}\right). \tag{4}$$

Let $\omega = \omega_0(1 + \delta)$, and make use of the approximation for small δ,

$$(1 + \delta)^{-1} \approx 1 - \delta$$

Then (4) becomes

$$Y \approx \sqrt{\frac{C}{L}}\left[\frac{1}{Q} + j2\delta\right] = G[1 + j2\delta Q]. \tag{5}$$

From (5), the frequency shift for which susceptance becomes equal to conductance, a common measure of circuit "sharpness," is

$$\delta_1 = \frac{1}{2Q}. \tag{6}$$

Problems

1.07a Discuss the significance of (3) in designing a resonant circuit for maximum R_i and a given resonant frequency if loss is predominantly in inductance and available inductances of comparable values have comparable Q's. Similarly, discuss the case of loss predominantly in C, all C's of different value having comparable Q's.

1.07b Write Eq. 1.07(3) in terms of: a series resistance in L, a shunt resistance across C, both series and shunt losses. For the first two cases, show that the resonant circuit can be considered an ideal transformer between the input terminals and the resistance R, and give the turns ratio n of the transformer for the two cases.

1.07c Plot the reactive part of (4), normalized to $\omega_0 C$, and note over what range the result (5) is a reasonable approximation.

USE OF COMPLEX EXPONENTIALS

1.08 Complex Exponentials in the Circuit Equation

The approximate results of the previous articles for the circuit relations when dissipation is included will now be verified by direct solution of the differential equation of the circuit. If a voltage $V \cos \omega t$ is applied to a circuit containing R, L, and C in series, the equation to be solved is

$$L \frac{dI}{dt} + RI + \frac{1}{C} \int I \, dt = V_m \cos \omega t. \tag{1}$$

But [see Eqs. 1.03(7), (8)]

$$\cos \omega t = \frac{e^{j\omega t} + e^{-j\omega t}}{2}. \tag{2}$$

If we assume that the current has the steady state solution

$$I = Ae^{j\omega t} + Be^{-j\omega t}, \tag{3}$$

the result of substituting in (1) is

$$j\omega L(Ae^{j\omega t} - Be^{-j\omega t}) + R(Ae^{j\omega t} + Be^{-j\omega t}) + \frac{1}{j\omega C}(Ae^{j\omega t} - Be^{-j\omega t})$$

$$= \frac{V}{2}(e^{j\omega t} + e^{-j\omega t}). \tag{4}$$

Following previous reasoning, this equation can be true for all values of time only if coefficients of $e^{j\omega t}$ are the same on both sides of the equation, and similarly for $e^{-j\omega t}$.

$$A\left[R + j\left(\omega L - \frac{1}{\omega C}\right)\right] = \frac{V_m}{2}. \tag{5a}$$

$$B\left[R - j\left(\omega L - \frac{1}{\omega C}\right)\right] = \frac{V_m}{2}. \tag{5b}$$

The complex quantity in the bracket of (5a) may be called Z and written in its equivalent form

$$Z = R + j\left(\omega L - \frac{1}{\omega C}\right) = |Z| e^{j\gamma}$$

where
$$|Z| = \sqrt{R^2 + \left(\omega L - \frac{1}{\omega C}\right)^2} \tag{6}$$

and
$$\psi = \tan^{-1}\frac{\left(\omega L - \dfrac{1}{\omega C}\right)}{R}. \tag{7}$$

Similarly,
$$R - j\left(\omega L - \frac{1}{\omega C}\right) = |Z|\, e^{-j\psi}.$$

Then
$$A = \frac{V_m}{2\,|Z|}\, e^{-j\psi},$$

$$B = \frac{V_m}{2\,|Z|}\, e^{j\psi}.$$

(A and B are conjugates: they have the same real parts and equal and opposite imaginary parts.) Substituting in (3),

$$I = \frac{V_m}{|Z|}\left[\frac{e^{j(\omega t - \psi)} + e^{-j(\omega t - \psi)}}{2}\right]. \tag{8}$$

By comparing with (2),

$$I = \frac{V_m}{|Z|}\cos{(\omega t - \psi)}. \tag{9}$$

This final result gives the desired magnitude and phase angle of the current with respect to the applied voltage. That information is contained in either constant A or constant B, and no information is given in one which is not in the other. Constant B is of necessity the conjugate of A, since this is the only way in which the two may add up to a real current, and the final exact answer for current must be real. It follows that half of the work was unnecessary. We could have started only with $V_m e^{j\omega t}$ in place of the two-term expression which is exactly equivalent to $V_m \cos \omega t$. For current, there would then be only

$$I = \frac{V_m}{|Z|}\, e^{j(\omega t - \psi)}. \tag{10}$$

Although this cannot actually be the expression for current, since it is a complex and not a real quantity, it contains all the information we wish to know: magnitude of current, $V/|Z|$, and its phase with respect to applied voltage, ψ. This procedure may be made exact by writing

$$V(t) = \mathrm{Re}\,[V_m e^{j\omega t}] \tag{11}$$

$$I(t) = \mathrm{Re}\left[\frac{V_m}{|Z|}\, e^{j(\omega t - \psi)}\right], \tag{12}$$

where Re denotes "the real part of." Because of the inconvenience of this notation, it is usually not written explicitly but is understood. That is, *if any single frequency sinusoid f(t) is expressed by its magnitude and phase, $Me^{j\theta}$, or by its real (in-phase) and imaginary (out-of-phase) parts $A + jB$, the instantaneous expression may be found by multiplying by $e^{j\omega t}$ and taking the real part:*

$$f(t) = \text{Re } [Me^{j(\omega t+\theta)}] = \text{Re } [(A + jB)e^{j\omega t}]. \qquad (13)$$

Problem

1.08 Utilizing the exact method of solution of this article, determine conditions for which the approximate solution of Art. 1.07 is a good approximation.

1.09   Use of Complex Exponentials in Power Calculations

The preceding article demonstrated the basis for the use of complex exponentials in the solution of problems involving steady-state sinusoids. The consequent simplification of all linear problems in the steady state will be apparent throughout the book. More care must be exercised for nonlinear expressions, the most common of which arises in the calculation of instantaneous power, requiring a product of terms.

Given a sinusoidal voltage across an impedance,

$$V(t) = V_m \cos (\omega t + \phi_1), \qquad (1)$$

and a sinusoidal current flow through the impedance,

$$I(t) = I_m \cos (\omega t + \phi_2), \qquad (2)$$

the expression for instantaneous power is given by multiplying (1) and (2):

$$W(t) = V_m I_m \cos (\omega t + \phi_1) \cos (\omega t + \phi_2).$$

But $\cos A \cos B = \frac{1}{2}[\cos (A - B) + \cos (A + B)].$

so $W(t) = \dfrac{V_m I_m}{2} \cos (\phi_1 - \phi_2) + \dfrac{V_m I_m}{2} \cos (2\omega t + \phi_1 + \phi_2). \qquad (3)$

This has an average part given by one-half the product of the peak amplitudes and the cosine of the difference in phase angles, and it has a double-frequency sinusoidal a-c part given by the last term in (3).

An expression identical with (3) is of course obtained if one utilizes the complex notation in the complete form of Eq. 1.08(13), since these are exact equivalents:

$$W(t) = \{\text{Re } [V_m e^{j(\omega t+\phi_1)}]\}\{\text{Re } [I_m e^{j(\omega t+\phi_2)}]\}. \qquad (4)$$

The exact expression for instantaneous power, (4), may also be written in complex notation. For this, note

$$\text{Re } A = \tfrac{1}{2}(A + A^*) \tag{5}$$

where the asterisk denotes the conjugate. So

$$(\text{Re } A)(\text{Re } B) = \tfrac{1}{4}(A + A^*)(B + B^*)$$
$$= \tfrac{1}{4}(A^*B + AB^*) + \tfrac{1}{4}(AB + A^*B^*)$$
$$(\text{Re } A)(\text{Re } B) = \tfrac{1}{2} \text{Re } [AB^* + AB]. \tag{6}$$

Thus if V and I are now considered the complex multipliers of $e^{j\omega t}$, (4) may be written

$$W = \tfrac{1}{2} \text{Re } [VI^* + VIe^{2j\omega t}]. \tag{7}$$

Most important is the average part of this,

$$W_{\text{av}} = \tfrac{1}{2} \text{Re } [VI^*]. \tag{8}$$

Problems

1.09a An a-c voltage of 100 volts at frequency 1 Mc/sec is applied across a parallel connection of 10 ohms resistance and a capacitance of 0.01 microfarad. Find the instantaneous power, utilizing (7), and check by first finding instantaneous expressions for voltage and current. Take phase of voltage as zero.

1.09b Show that the correct expression for instantaneous power is not obtained by first multiplying the complex representations $V_m e^{j(\omega t+\phi_1)}$ and $I_m e^{j(\omega t+\phi_2)}$ and then taking the real part. Why not?

FOURIER SERIES

1.10 Fourier Coefficients for Periodic Functions

All forced oscillations studied so far have consisted of sinusoids. Consider a more general oscillation which is periodic, returning once each cycle to any selected reference, or, stated mathematically,

$$f(t) = f(t - T).$$

This might be of any arbitrary form, such as is indicated by Fig. 1.10. Such a wave shape of voltage, if applied to a circuit, will act to that circuit as a superposition of a group of pure sinusoidal voltages. The wave may be replaced by a fundamental and its harmonics. The method of finding the amplitudes of these is the classic method of Fourier analysis, and the theorem that proves the truth of the foregoing statements is the Fourier theorem, which it is assumed the reader has agreed with in another study. What follows here is not a proof of the validity of a Fourier series expansion for a general periodic function, but merely a demonstration which shows the manner of obtaining the coefficients. This will be extremely useful when we later add up series to represent known functions along boundaries in field problems.

Fig. 1.10   Periodic wave of arbitrary shape.

We shall write the periodic function $f(t)$ as a series of sinusoids consisting of a fundamental and its harmonics:

$$f(t) = a_0 + a_1 \cos \omega t + a_2 \cos 2\omega t + a_3 \cos 3\omega t + \cdots$$
$$+ b_1 \sin \omega t + b_2 \sin 2\omega t + b_3 \sin 3\omega t + \cdots. \quad (1)$$

At the moment, the coefficients have not been determined. The manner of finding them is based on the so-called orthogonality property of sinusoids. This property indicates that the integral of the product of any two sinusoids of different frequencies, over an interval in which they are commensurate (for example, from $-\pi$ to π, or 0 to 2π) shall be zero. That is,

$$\int_0^{2\pi} \cos mx \cos nx \, dx = 0, \qquad m \neq n$$

$$\int_0^{2\pi} \sin mx \sin nx \, dx = 0, \qquad m \neq n \qquad (2)$$

$$\int_0^{2\pi} \sin mx \cos nx \, dx = 0, \qquad m \neq n \text{ or } m = n.$$

However, $\qquad \displaystyle\int_0^{2\pi} \cos^2 mx \, dx = \int_0^{2\pi} \sin^2 mx \, dx = \pi. \qquad (3)$

Thus, if each term in (1) is multiplied by $\cos n\omega t$, and integrated from

0 to 2π, every term on the right will be zero except that term containing a_n. That is,

$$\int_0^{2\pi} f(t) \cos n\omega t \, d(\omega t) = \int_0^{2\pi} a_n \cos^2 n\omega t \, d(\omega t).$$

By (3), the integral on the right has the value $a_n \pi$, or

$$a_n = \frac{1}{\pi} \int_0^{2\pi} f(t) \cos n(\omega t) \, d(\omega t). \tag{4}$$

Similarly, to obtain b_n, each term in (1) is multiplied by $\sin n\omega t$ and integrated from 0 to 2π. Then

$$b_n = \frac{1}{\pi} \int_0^{2\pi} f(t) \sin n(\omega t) \, d(\omega t). \tag{5}$$

Finally, to obtain the constant term a_0, every term is integrated directly over a period, and all terms on the right disappear, except that containing a_0:

$$\int_0^{2\pi} f(t) \, d(\omega t) = \int_0^{2\pi} a_0 \, d(\omega t) = 2\pi a_0$$

or

$$a_0 = \frac{1}{2\pi} \int_0^{2\pi} f(t) \, d(\omega t). \tag{6}$$

This merely states that a_0 is the average of the function $f(t)$.

It is sometimes convenient to write (1) in an alternate form as a sum of complex exponentials

$$f(t) = \cdots + c_{-3}e^{j3\omega t} + c_{-2}e^{j2\omega t} + c_{-1}e^{j\omega t} + c_0 + c_1 e^{-j\omega t}$$
$$+ c_2 e^{-j2\omega t} + c_3 e^{-j3\omega t} + \cdots = \sum_{n=-\infty}^{\infty} c_n e^{-jn\omega t}. \tag{7}$$

Multiplying both sides by $e^{jm\omega t}$ and integrating over one period, we have

$$\int_0^{2\pi} f(t)e^{jm\omega t} \, d(\omega t) = \sum_{n=-\infty}^{\infty} c_n \int_0^{2\pi} e^{j(m-n)\omega t} \, d(\omega t). \tag{8}$$

The integral on the right side has a value of zero if $n \neq m$ and 2π if $n = m$. Thus

$$c_n = \frac{1}{2\pi} \int_0^{2\pi} f(t)e^{jn\omega t} \, d(\omega t). \tag{9}$$

Though each term on the right side of (7) contains a complex exponential, the left side of (7) is real by virtue of the complex conjugate nature of the coefficients

$$c_{-n} = c_n{}^*. \tag{10}$$

Problems

1.10a Simplify the general expressions for Fourier coefficients found in Art. 1.10 for:

    (*a*) Even functions of *t*.
    (*b*) Odd functions of *t*.
    (*c*) Functions of a variable *x*, in terms of a period *l*.

1.10b Expand (7) into series of sines and cosines and find the relation between the coefficients c_{-n} and c_n and a_n and b_n. Verify by expanding (9).

1.11 Fourier Analysis of a Square Wave Voltage

Let us find by Fourier analysis the coefficients of the frequency components in the square wave shape of Fig. 1.11. Voltage is *V* over half

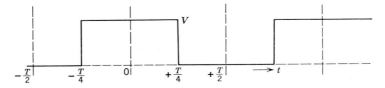

Fig. 1.11   Periodic wave of rectangular shape.

the period *T*, and zero over the remaining half. The origin will be selected arbitrarily in the center of the constant portion as shown, in order to make the function even. Voltage then drops to zero at $t = T/4$, or $\omega t = \pi/2$. The integral 1.10(6) shows that the constant term, a_0, is

$$a_0 = \frac{1}{2\pi} \int_{-\pi}^{+\pi} f(t)\, d(\omega t) = \frac{1}{2\pi} \int_{-\pi/2}^{+\pi/2} V\, d(\omega t) = \frac{V}{2}. \qquad (1)$$

This is clearly the average value of the wave. The integral 1.10(5) gives the coefficient b_n as:

$$b_n = \frac{1}{\pi} \int_{-\pi}^{+\pi} f(t) \sin n(\omega t)\, d(\omega t) = \frac{1}{\pi} \int_{-\pi/2}^{+\pi/2} V \sin n(\omega t)\, d(\omega t) = 0. \qquad (2)$$

Thus all coefficients of the sine terms are zero, as would be expected since sines are odd functions, and we have selected the origin to make $f(t)$ even.

Finally, the a_n terms, by Eq. 1.10(4), are

$$a_n = \frac{1}{\pi} \int_{-\pi}^{+\pi} f(t) \cos n\omega t \, d(\omega t) = \frac{1}{\pi} \int_{-\pi/2}^{+\pi/2} V \cos n\omega t \, d(\omega t)$$

$$a_n = \frac{V}{n\pi} [\sin n(\omega t)]_{-\pi/2}^{+\pi/2} . \tag{3}$$

The value of (3) is zero if n is even, is $+(2V/n\pi)$ if n is 1, 5, 9, etc., and is $-(2V/n\pi)$ if n is 3, 7, 11, etc. Thus the series expansion in sinusoids of the square wave voltage of Fig. 1.11 may be written

$$f(t) = \frac{V}{2} + \frac{2V}{\pi} \left[\cos \omega t - \frac{\cos 3\omega t}{3} + \frac{\cos 5\omega t}{5} - \frac{\cos 7\omega t}{7} + \cdots \right]. \tag{4}$$

The current that flows when such a voltage is applied to a linear circuit is found by determining the currents using the individual terms of (4) and superposing these. There will be, in general, a component of current of a frequency corresponding to each frequency component of the Fourier expansion. These, when added, give the wave shape of current. Such a procedure is straightforward and will not be carried further here.

Notice that an infinite number of terms are required to represent truly the square wave shape of voltage. Often a high degree of approximation to the desired wave shape is obtained when only a finite number of terms is used. For functions with sharp discontinuities, however, many terms may be required near the sharp corners, and the theory of Fourier series shows that the series may not converge to the function in the neighborhood of the discontinuity (Gibbs phenomenon). The derivative of the series may not always converge to the derivative of the function, but the integral of the series does always converge to that of the function.

Problems

1.11a Obtain Fourier series in sines and cosines for the following periodic functions:

(a) A triangular wave defined by $f(t) = V_0[1 - (2t/T)]$ from 0 to $T/2$, and $V_0[(2t/T) - 1]$ from $T/2$ to T.

(b) A saw-tooth wave defined by $f(t) = V_0 t/T$ for $0 < t < T$.

(c) A sinusoidal pulse given by $f(t) = (V_m \cos \omega t - V_0)$ for $-\alpha < \omega t < \alpha$, $f(t) = 0$ for $-\pi < \omega t < -\alpha$ and also for $\alpha < \omega t < \pi$.

1.11b Repeat Prob. a using complex exponential series and check that the relations found in Prob. 1.10b are satisfied.

1.12   Fourier Series to Represent a Function over an Interval

If a function $f(x)$ is defined over a finite interval $0 < x < l$, a Fourier series may be written for this even though it is not periodic. The point of view is that the interval of length l may be considered a period (or more commonly a half-period), and a periodic function defined to agree with the given function over the given interval, repeating itself outside that interval. A Fourier series may then be written for this periodic function which will give desired values in the interval, and, although it also gives values outside the interval, that is of no consequence since the original function is not defined there.

The interval is most commonly selected as a half-period since the function extended outside the interval may then be made either even or odd, and the corresponding Fourier series will then have respectively either cosine terms alone or sine terms alone. Thus a cosine series written to represent a function $f(x)$ over the interval $0 < x < l$ is

$$f(x) = a_0 + \sum_{n=1}^{\infty} a_n \cos \frac{n\pi x}{l}, \qquad 0 < x < l \tag{1}$$

$$a_0 = \frac{1}{l} \int_0^l f(x)\, dx \tag{2}$$

$$a_n = \frac{2}{l} \int_0^l f(x) \cos \frac{n\pi x}{l}\, dx. \tag{3}$$

Or a sine series written to represent $f(x)$ over the interval $0 < x < l$ is

$$f(x) = \sum_{n=1}^{\infty} b_n \sin \frac{n\pi x}{l}, \qquad 0 < x < l \tag{4}$$

$$b_n = \frac{2}{l} \int_0^l f(x) \sin \frac{n\pi x}{l}\, dx. \tag{5}$$

As an example, to represent the simple function $f(x) = C$ over the interval $0 < x < l$ in a series of sines, (5) yields

$$b_n = \frac{2}{l} \int_0^l C \sin \frac{n\pi x}{l}\, dx = \frac{2C}{n\pi} \left[-\cos \frac{n\pi x}{l} \right]_0^l \tag{6}$$

$$f(x) = \frac{2C}{\pi} \left[2 \sin \frac{\pi x}{l} + \frac{2}{3} \sin \frac{3\pi x}{l} + \frac{2}{5} \sin \frac{5\pi x}{l} + \cdots \right] \quad 0 < x < l. \tag{7}$$

The series (7) actually represents a repeating square wave much like that in Fig. 1.11 (except for the constant term and the choice of origin), but properly agrees with the given function over the required interval.

Problems

1.12a Suppose that a function is given over the interval 0 to l as $f(x) = \sin \pi x/l$. What do the cosine and sine representations yield? Explain how this single sine term can be represented in terms of cosines.

1.12b Find sine and cosine representations for the function e^{kx} defined over the interval $0 < x < l$.

TRANSMISSION LINES AS EXAMPLES OF WAVE SYSTEMS

1.13 The Ideal Transmission Line

To illustrate waves, we shall consider the uniform transmission line. The results developed are of importance themselves, since transmission lines are used in all modern high-frequency applications. Results will also be used for later comparison with more general electromagnetic wave phenomena. The approach used in this chapter is the conventional one, starting from distributed inductance and capacitance along the line. It is true that this in a sense is jumping ahead of the story, for in a later chapter on guided waves the transmission line differential equations will be derived from rigorous considerations of electromagnetic theory, with the conditions for applicability shown. Nevertheless, the approach to be used here is easy to visualize and is satisfactory for many purposes.

A transmission line may be made up of parallel wires, of parallel plates, of coaxial conductors, or in general of any two conductors separated by a dielectric material. In conventional analyses, we think in terms of a current flowing in the conductors, equal and opposite in the two conductors if measured at any given transverse plane, and a voltage difference existing between the conductors. The current flow is affected by a distributed series inductance representing the back induced voltage effects of magnetic flux surrounding the conductors; the voltage between conductors acts across a distributed shunt capacitance. There are also loss terms which will be neglected for this first analysis of the ideal case. Incidentally, this does not relegate the results to a position of only academic interest, for many high-frequency transmission line problems have loss terms which are truly negligible.

Consider a differential length of line dz, including only the distributed inductance, L per unit length, and the distributed capacitance, C per unit length. The length dz then has inductance $L\,dz$ and capacitance $C\,dz$

(Fig. 1.13). The voltage drop or negative change in voltage across this length is then equal to the product of this inductance and the time rate of change of current. For such a differential length the voltage change along it at any instant may be written as the length multiplied by the rate of change of voltage with respect to length. Then

$$\text{voltage change} = \frac{\partial V}{\partial z}\, dz = -(L\ dz)\frac{\partial I}{\partial t}. \qquad (1)$$

Note that time and space derivatives are written as partial derivatives, since the reference point may be changed in space or time, in completely independent fashion.

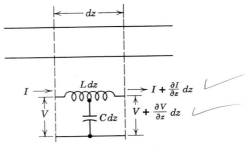

Fig. 1.13

Lossless Case ie no copper or Dielectric Loss

Similarly, the decrease in current across the element at any instant is merely the current that is shunted across the distributed capacity. The rate of decrease of current with distance is given by the capacity multiplied by time rate of change of voltage. Partial derivatives are again called for:

$$\text{current change} = \frac{\partial I}{\partial z}\, dz = -(C\ dz)\frac{\partial V}{\partial t}. \qquad (2)$$

The length dz may be canceled in (1) and (2):

$$\frac{\partial V}{\partial z} = -L\frac{\partial I}{\partial t} \qquad (3)$$

$$\frac{\partial I}{\partial z} = -C\frac{\partial V}{\partial t}. \qquad (4)$$

Equations (3) and (4) are the fundamental differential equations for the analysis of the ideal transmission line. They may be combined to give equations containing voltage alone or current alone. To accomplish this, differentiate (3) partially with respect to distance, (4) with respect to time:

$$\frac{\partial^2 V}{\partial z^2} = -L \frac{\partial^2 I}{\partial z\, \partial t} \tag{5}$$

$$\frac{\partial^2 I}{\partial t\, \partial z} = -C \frac{\partial^2 V}{\partial t^2}. \tag{6}$$

Since partial derivatives are the same taken in either order, (6) may be substituted directly in (5):

$$\frac{\partial^2 V}{\partial z^2} = LC \frac{\partial^2 V}{\partial t^2}. \tag{7}$$

Equations (3) and (4) are known as the telegraphist's equations, and the differential equation (7) is the one-dimensional wave equation. An exactly similar equation may be obtained in terms of current by differentiating (4) with respect to z, (3) with respect to t, and combining the results:

$$\frac{\partial^2 I}{\partial z^2} = LC \frac{\partial^2 I}{\partial t^2}. \tag{8}$$

Go To Maxwell's Equations P ?

1.14 Solutions of the Wave Equation

The differential equation to be solved, Eq. 1.13(7), may be written

$$\frac{\partial^2 V}{\partial z^2} = \frac{1}{v^2} \frac{\partial^2 V}{\partial t^2}, \tag{1}$$

where

$$v = \frac{1}{\sqrt{LC}}. \tag{2}$$

Unlike the previous differential equations in this chapter, this is a partial differential equation. A direct attack on the equation to yield a general solution is not easy, but a simple check shows that any function whatever in the variable $t - (z/v)$ is a solution. That is,

$$V = F\left(t - \frac{z}{v}\right) \tag{3}$$

is a solution to (1). This may be verified by differentiating:

$$\frac{\partial V}{\partial t} = F'\left(t - \frac{z}{v}\right) \quad \text{and} \quad \frac{\partial V}{\partial z} = -\frac{1}{v} F'\left(t - \frac{z}{v}\right)$$

$$\frac{\partial^2 V}{\partial t^2} = F''\left(t - \frac{z}{v}\right) \quad \text{and} \quad \frac{\partial^2 V}{\partial z^2} = \frac{1}{v^2} F''\left(t - \frac{z}{v}\right). \tag{4}$$

∇^2 *operator*

In the foregoing, the primes denote derivatives with respect to the entire variable, $t - (z/v)$. By comparing the two equations (4), (1) is verified.

It is necessary to show next what is meant by the statement that solution (3) represents a wave. This may be done by recognizing that we may stay on a particular reference value of the function (i.e., keep V constant) by keeping the argument, $t - (z/v)$, a constant. This is accomplished by moving in the positive z direction with velocity v as time increases. That is,

$$t - \frac{z}{v} = K$$

if

$$z = vt - Kv. \tag{5}$$

Only one solution of the second-order differential equation has been given. A second solution may be written as any function of $t + (z/v)$ and checked by methods exactly similar to those used for the first solution. This is identified as a wave traveling in the negative z direction with velocity v. A complete solution to (1) is then

$$V = F_1\left(t - \frac{z}{v}\right) + F_2\left(t + \frac{z}{v}\right) \tag{6}$$

where v is given by (2).

Problems

1.14a Differentiate the functions $\cos \omega[t - (z/v)]$, $e^{j\omega[t-(z/v)]}$, and $[t + (z/v)]^3$ to show that each satisfies (1).

1.14b Sketch the function $\cos \omega[t - (z/v)]$ versus $\omega z/v$ for values of $\omega t = 0$, $\pi/4$, $\pi/2$, $3\pi/4$, π. Note how this demonstrates the interpretation as a propagating wave. Repeat for $\cos \omega[t + (z/v)]$.

1.15   Relation Between Voltage and Current in the Ideal Line

If the expression for voltage given by Eq. 1.14(6) is substituted in the transmission line equation, 1.13(3),

$$-L\frac{\partial I}{\partial t} = -\frac{1}{v}F_1'\left(t - \frac{z}{v}\right) + \frac{1}{v}F_2'\left(t + \frac{z}{v}\right). \tag{1}$$

This expression may be integrated partially with respect to t:

$$I = \frac{1}{Lv}\left[F_1\left(t - \frac{z}{v}\right) - F_2\left(t + \frac{z}{v}\right)\right] + f(z). \tag{2}$$

If this result were substituted in the other transmission line equation, 1.13(4), it would be found that the function of integration, $f(z)$, could only be a constant. But we are not interested in possible superposed d-c solutions in studying the wave solution, so this will be ignored. Equation (2) may then be written

$$I = \frac{1}{Z_0}\left[F_1\left(t - \frac{z}{v}\right) - F_2\left(t + \frac{z}{v}\right)\right] \qquad (3)$$

where

$$Z_0 = Lv = \sqrt{\frac{L}{C}}. \qquad (4)$$

The constant Z_0 as defined by (4) is called the *characteristic impedance* of the line, and is seen from (3) to be the ratio of voltage to current for a single one of the traveling waves at any given point and given instant. The negative sign for the negatively traveling wave would of course be expected since the wave propagates to the left, and by our convention current is positive if flowing to the right.

1.16   Reflection and Transmission at a Discontinuity

Most transmission line problems are concerned with junctions between a given uniform line and a line of different characteristic impedance, a load resistance, or some other element that introduces a discontinuity. By Kirchhoff's laws, total voltage and current must be continuous across the discontinuity. The total voltage in the line may be regarded as the sum of voltage in a positively traveling wave, equal to V_+ at the point of discontinuity, and a voltage in a reflected or negatively traveling wave, equal to V_- at the discontinuity. The sum of V_+ and V_- must be V_L, the voltage appearing across the load resistance R_L:

$$V_+ + V_- = V_L. \qquad (1)$$

Similarly, the sum of currents in the positively and negatively traveling waves of the line, at the point of discontinuity, must be equal to the current flowing into R_L:

$$I_+ + I_- = I_L. \qquad (2)$$

By utilizing the relations between voltage and current for the two traveling waves as found in the preceding article, (2) becomes

$$\frac{V_+}{Z_0} - \frac{V_-}{Z_0} = \frac{V_L}{R_L}. \qquad (3)$$

By eliminating between (1) and (3), the ratio of voltage in the reflected

9/27/66

wave to that in the incident wave (reflection coefficient) and the ratio of the voltage in the load to that in the incident wave (transmission coefficient) may be found:

$$\rho = \frac{V_-}{V_+} = \frac{R_L - Z_0}{R_L + Z_0} \qquad (4)$$

$$\tau = \frac{V_L}{V_+} = \frac{2R_L}{R_L + Z_0}. \qquad (5)$$

The most interesting, and perhaps the most obvious, conclusion from the foregoing relations is this: there is no reflected wave if the terminating resistance is exactly equal to the characteristic impedance of the line. All energy of the incident wave is then transferred to the load, which cannot be distinguished from a line of infinite length and characteristic impedance $Z_0 = R_L$.

Problems

1.16a For arbitrary time functions, assuming R_L a pure resistance, find the fraction of the incident power reflected, and the fraction of the incident power transmitted to R_L.

1.16b Calculate the reflection coefficient, transmission coefficient, and the power quantities of Prob. a for $R_L = 0, \frac{1}{2}Z_0, Z_0, 2Z_0,$ and ∞.

1.17 Some Simple Problems on Traveling Waves

A. D-C Voltage Applied to an Infinite Line. Consider the case of a d-c voltage V_0, suddenly applied to an ideal line of infinite length (Fig. 1.17a). The line starts to charge to voltage V_0, the wave front traveling with the velocity $v = 1/\sqrt{LC}$. Since there is never any discontinuity, there is no reflected wave, and the only current is that flowing in the positive wave, V_0/Z_0. This then is a d-c current flowing to the charges which appear on the line as voltage moves along. At any time t after the voltage is impressed, there is voltage V_0 and current V_0/Z_0 in the line up to the point $z = vt$, and no voltage or current beyond.

B. D-C Voltage Applied to a Shorted Line. Suppose that the d-c voltage is applied to a line which is not infinite in length, but is shorted at some point, $z = l$ (Fig. 1.17b). We know that finally infinite current will flow if V is maintained. The mechanism of current build-up is interesting, however. After voltage is applied to the line, everything proceeds as in A until the time that the wave reaches the short circuit. At the time the incident wave with voltage V_0 appears across the short circuit, which demands zero voltage, a reflected or negatively traveling wave of voltage $-V_0$ is sent back so that the sum of voltages in the two waves is indeed zero. Since current in the negative traveling wave is the negative of voltage divided by Z_0, this is $-(-V_0/Z_0)$ or $+V_0/Z_0$ and so adds directly to the current in the positive traveling wave. This reflected wave then moves to the left, leaving a wake of zero voltage and a current equal to $2V_0/Z_0$

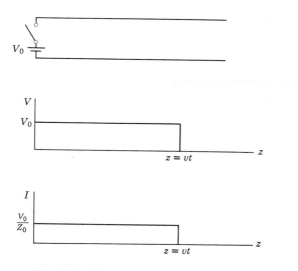

Fig. 1.17a   Constant voltage suddenly applied to an infinite line.

behind it. As soon as the reflected wave has traveled back to the source, it brings the zero voltage condition back to this point so that the d-c voltage must send out a new wave of voltage V_0 down the line, with associated current V_0/Z_0, making a total current in the line $3V_0/Z_0$ at this time. Current then builds up to infinity in the step manner indicated by Fig. 1.17b. T is the time l/v required for a wave to travel one way down the line.

C. Charged Line Connected to a Resistor. Consider an ideal line of length l initially charged to a d-c potential V_0, with a resistance R connected across the input at time $t = 0$.

The voltage across the resistance is the sum of the d-c voltage of the line and the voltage in the positive wave, V_+:

$$V_R = V_0 + V_+. \qquad (1)$$

9/27/66

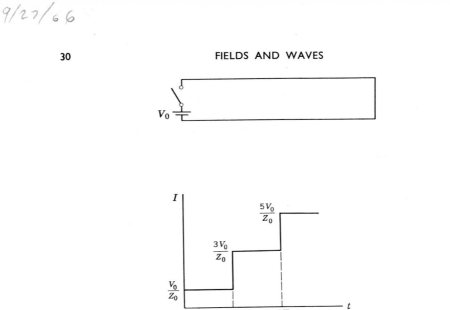

Fig. 1.17*b*   Constant voltage suddenly applied to a shorted line.

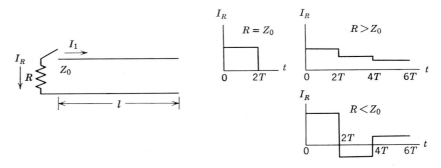

Fig. 1.17*c*   Charged line of length *l* suddenly connected to a resistor.

The current flowing into the resistor is merely the negative of current for the positively traveling wave:

$$I_R = -I_+$$

or
$$\frac{V_R}{R} = -\frac{V_+}{Z_0}.$$

(2)

By combining (1) and (2),

$$V_R = V_0\left(\frac{R}{R + Z_0}\right) = -V_+\frac{R}{Z_0}.$$

(3)

For example, if $R = Z_0$, the voltage appearing across the resistance at the first instant is half the d-c voltage of the line, as is the voltage appearing in the traveling wave. When this wave reaches the open end, there must then be started a reflected wave such that total current is zero, so current in the reflected wave must be $-I_+$ or $V_0/2R$. Because current in the reflected wave is the negative of voltage divided by Z_0, this will require a voltage $-V_0/2$ for the reflected wave. Thus in the case of $R = Z_0$, the original wave wipes out half the voltage, and the corresponding current, $-V_0/2Z_0$, is that which flows through R. The reflected wave wipes out the remaining half of the voltage and, of course, reduces current to zero. When this wave reaches $R = Z_0$ there is no further reflection, so all is still. Current wave shape is shown in Fig. 1.17c. Also shown are currents for $R > Z_0$ and $R < Z_0$.

Problems

1.17a An ideal line of length l is charged to d-c voltage V and shorted at its input at time $t = 0$. Sketch the current wave shape through the short as a function of time.

1.17b An ideal open-circuited line of length l, initially uncharged, has a d-c voltage V suddenly applied at its input at time $t = 0$. Sketch the current flow through the input source as a function of time.

1.17c A charged cable is connected suddenly to a resistor equal to its 50-ohm characteristic impedance. If its length is 3 meters and its phase velocity is one-half the velocity of light, how long is the pulse? Sketch the waveform assuming the cable is initially charged to 100 volts and the load is 25 ohms instead of 50.

1.17d Suppose a lossless transmission line is terminated by a pure capacitance. For arbitrary functions of time, state the boundary conditions which apply for determination of the reflected wave. Sketch the reflected wave resulting from a step-function incident wave, assuming that the load capacitance is initially uncharged.

1.18 Ideal Line with Applied Sinusoidal Voltages

Much of the preceding discussion has involved little restriction on the type of variation with time of the voltages applied to the transmission lines. Most practical problems are concerned entirely or at least partially with sinusoidal time variations. If a voltage which is sinusoidal in time is applied at $z = 0$, it may be represented by the exponential (see Art. 1.08):

$$V\big|_{z=0} = V(0, t) = Ve^{j\omega t}. \tag{1}$$

Then the corresponding positively traveling wave is written,

$$V_+e^{j\omega[t-(z/v)]}. \qquad = C_{os} \ \omega t$$

9/27/66

Similarly, a negatively traveling wave is written,

$$V_- e^{j\omega[t+(z/v)]}.$$

Or the total solution, made up of positive and negative traveling waves, is

$$V = e^{j\omega t}[V_+ e^{-j(\omega z/v)} + V_- e^{j(\omega z/v)}]. \qquad (2)$$

The corresponding current, from Art. 1.15, is

$$I = \frac{e^{j\omega t}}{Z_0}[V_+ e^{-j(\omega z/v)} - V_- e^{j(\omega z/v)}]. \qquad (3)$$

For problems in which we shall be concerned throughout with sinusoidal quantities, it is not necessary to write the factor $e^{j\omega t}$ explicitly each time, since it will always be understood that all terms are multiplied by this factor; we rewrite (2) and (3), omitting it:

$$V = V_+ e^{-j\beta z} + V_- e^{j\beta z} \qquad (4)$$

$$I = \frac{1}{Z_0}[V_+ e^{-j\beta z} - V_- e^{j\beta z}] \qquad (5)$$

where

$$\beta = \frac{\omega}{v}. \qquad (6)$$

The quantity β is called the phase constant of the line since βz measures the instantaneous phase at a point z with respect to $z = 0$. Moreover, if voltage and current are observed at any point z, they will be found exactly the same at points such that βz differs from that of the first point by multiples of 2π. The distance between points of like current and voltage is called a wavelength λ. By the foregoing reasoning,

$$\beta\lambda = 2\pi$$

or

$$\beta = \frac{2\pi}{\lambda}. \qquad (7)$$

The transformation of impedances by the ideal line is easily found from (4) and (5). Let us assume that the line is of length l and that the load impedance is Z_L. For convenience we take the origin $z = 0$ at the load, and the input then lies at $z = -l$. The ratio of (4) to (5) at $z = 0$ may be set equal to Z_L, and solved for the ratio V_-/V_+. The result is in agreement with that already given in Eq. 1.16(4) but generalized to a complex load impedance,

$$\rho = \frac{V_-}{V_+} = \frac{Z_L - Z_0}{Z_L + Z_0}. \qquad (8)$$

The input impedance may be found by dividing (4) by (5) for $z = -l$:

$$Z_i = Z_0 \left[\frac{e^{j\beta l} + \rho e^{-j\beta l}}{e^{j\beta l} - \rho e^{-j\beta l}} \right]. \tag{9}$$

Or, substituting the result of (8),

$$Z_i = Z_0 \left[\frac{Z_L \cos \beta l + jZ_0 \sin \beta l}{Z_0 \cos \beta l + jZ_L \sin \beta l} \right]. \tag{10}$$

By defining admittances $Y_i = 1/Z_i$, $Y_L = 1/Z_L$, and $Y_0 = 1/Z_0$, we can find an exactly similar expression,

$$Y_i = Y_0 \left[\frac{Y_L \cos \beta l + jY_0 \sin \beta l}{Y_0 \cos \beta l + jY_L \sin \beta l} \right]. \tag{11}$$

Problems

1.18a Find the special cases of (10) for a shorted line; an open line; a half-wave line with impedance Z_L; a quarter-wave line with impedance Z_L.

1.18b When two transmission lines are to be connected in cascade, a reflection of the wave to be transmitted from one to the other will occur if they do not have the same characteristic impedances. Show that a quarter-wave-length inserted between the cascaded lines will cause the first line to see its characteristic impedance Z_{01} as a termination and thus eliminate reflection in transfer if $\beta l_2 = \pi/2$ and $Z_{02} = \sqrt{Z_{01}Z_{03}}$ where Z_{02} and Z_{03} are the characteristic impedances of the quarter-wave section and the final line, respectively.

1.18c A television receiving line of negligible loss is one-third of a wavelength long and has characteristic impedance of 100 ohms. The detuned receiver acts as a load of $100 + j100$ ohms. Find the input impedance. Sketch phasor diagrams showing the values of V_+, V_-, I_+, and I_- at both the load and input, and check the calculated results for impedance from this diagram.

1.19 Standing-Wave Ratio   10/4/66

Of the two traveling-wave terms in the voltage equation, 1.18(4), the first becomes increasingly negative in phase as z increases, and the second becomes increasingly positive. There must consequently be some value of z for which the two terms are of the same phase. Their amplitudes then add directly, and at this point there is a maximum amplitude of voltage:

$$V_{max} = |V_+| + |V_-|. \tag{1}$$

A quarter wavelength from the position just discussed (say in a positive

z direction), the first term will have decreased in phase by $\pi/2$, and the second will have increased by $\pi/2$, so that the two are then π apart in phase; they subtract and give a minimum amplitude of voltage:

$$V_{min} = |V_+| - |V_-|. \tag{2}$$

The *standing-wave ratio* is then defined as the ratio of the maximum voltage amplitude to the minimum voltage amplitude,

$$S = \frac{V_{max}}{V_{min}}. \tag{3}$$

By substituting (1), (2), and the definition of reflection coefficient Eq. 1.18(8),

$$S = \frac{|V_+| + |V_-|}{|V_+| - |V_-|} = \frac{1 + |\rho|}{1 - |\rho|}. \tag{4}$$

It is seen that standing-wave ratio is directly related to the magnitude of reflection coefficient ρ, giving the same information as this quantity. The inverse relation is

$$|\rho| = \frac{S - 1}{S + 1}. \tag{5}$$

Because of the negative sign appearing in the current equation, 1.18(5), it is evident that, at the position where the two traveling-wave terms add in the voltage relation, they subtract in the current relation, and vice versa. The maximum voltage position is then a minimum current position:

$$I_{min} = \frac{|V_+| - |V_-|}{Z_0}.$$

At this position impedance is purely resistive and has the maximum value it will have at any point along the line:

$$Z_{max} = Z_0 \left[\frac{|V_+| + |V_-|}{|V_+| - |V_-|} \right] = Z_0 S. \tag{6}$$

At the position of the voltage minimum, current is a maximum, and impedance is a minimum and real:

$$I_{max} = \frac{|V_+| + |V_-|}{Z_0} \tag{7}$$

$$Z_{min} = Z_0 \left[\frac{|V_+| - |V_-|}{|V_+| + |V_-|} \right] = \frac{Z_0}{S}. \tag{8}$$

Problems

1.19a An impedance of $100 + j100$ ohms is placed as a load on a transmission line of characteristic impedance 50 ohms. Find the reflection coefficient in magnitude and phase and the standing-wave ratio for the line.

1.19b Suppose that reflection coefficient is given in magnitude and phase as $|\rho|e^{j\phi}$ at the load $z = 0$. Find the value of (negative) z for which voltage is a maximum. Show that current is in phase with voltage at this position, so that impedance there is real, as stated. Calculate the position of maximum voltage for the numerical values of Prob. *a*.

1.19c Give two designs for a power splitter consisting of one 50-ohm input line *T*-connected to two 50-ohm lines with matched terminations, using quarter-wave transformers as necessary to insure unity standing-wave ratio at the input at the design frequency and an equal power split. Plot power reflected in the input line as a function of frequency.

1.20 The Smith Transmission Line Chart

Many graphical aids for transmission line computations have been devised. Of these, the most generally useful has been one presented by P. H. Smith,[1] which consists of loci of constant resistance and reactance plotted on a polar diagram in which radius corresponds to magnitude of reflection coefficient, and angle corresponds to phase of reflection coefficient referred to a general point along the line. The chart enables one to find simply how impedances are transformed along the line, or to relate impedance to reflection coefficient or to standing-wave ratio and position of a voltage minimum. By combinations of operations, it enables one to understand the behavior of complex impedance-matching techniques and to devise new ones.

The discussion of the chart will begin with Eq. 1.18(9), which gives impedance in terms of reflection coefficient. If we define a normalized impedance

$$\zeta(l) = (r + jx) = \frac{Z_i}{Z_0} \tag{1}$$

and a complex variable w equal to the reflection coefficient at the end of the line, shifted in phase to correspond to the input position l,

$$w = u + jv = \rho e^{-2j\beta l}. \tag{2}$$

[1] P. H. Smith, "Transmission-Line Calculator," *Electronics*, **12**, 29–31 (Jan. 1939); "An Improved Transmission-Line Calculator," *Electronics*, **17**, 130 (Jan. 1944).

Equation 1.18(9) may then be written

$$\zeta(l) = \frac{1+w}{1-w} \tag{3}$$

or

$$r + jx = \frac{1 + (u + jv)}{1 - (u + jv)}. \tag{4}$$

This equation may be separated into real and imaginary parts as follows:

$$r = \frac{1 - (u^2 + v^2)}{(1 - u)^2 + v^2} \tag{5}$$

$$x = \frac{2v}{(1 - u)^2 + v^2} \tag{6}$$

or

$$\left(u - \frac{r}{1 + r}\right)^2 + v^2 = \frac{1}{(1 + r)^2} \tag{7}$$

$$(u - 1)^2 + \left(v - \frac{1}{x}\right)^2 = \frac{1}{x^2}. \tag{8}$$

If we then wish to plot the loci of constant resistance r on the w plane (u and v serving as rectangular coordinates), (7) shows that they are circles with centers on the u axis at $[r/(1 + r), 0]$ and with radii $1/(1 + r)$. The curves for $r = 0, \frac{1}{2}, 1, 2, \infty$ are sketched on Fig. 1.20a. From (8), the curves of constant x plotted on the w plane are also circles with centers at $(1, 1/x)$ and with radii $1/|x|$. Circles for $x = 0, \pm\frac{1}{2}, \pm1, \pm2, \infty$ are sketched on Fig. 1.20a. Any point on a given transmission line will have some impedance with positive resistance part, and will then correspond to a particular point on the inside of the unit circle of the w plane. Several uses of the chart will follow. Many extensions and combinations of the ones to be cited will be obvious to the student. A chart with more divisions is given in Fig. 1.20b.

To Find Reflection Coefficient Given Impedance, and Conversely. The point within the unit circle of the Smith chart corresponding to a particular position on a transmission line may of course be located at once if the normalized impedance corresponding to that position is known. This is done within a reasonable degree of accuracy by utilizing the orthogonal families of circles giving resistance and reactance as described above. Thus the point A of Fig. 1.20a is the intersection of the circles $r = 1$ and $x = 1$, and corresponds to a position with normalized impedance $1 + j1$. The magnitude of reflection coefficient is the radius of that point from the origin (as a ratio of the radius of the unit circle), by the definition of the w variable in (2). The phase of reflection coefficient referred to that particular position (that is, the phase of the reflected wave voltage with respect to the incident wave voltage at that position) is the angle measured counterclockwise from the right-hand u axis, by the definition of w. Thus, for a normalized load impedance of $1 + j1$, the reflection coefficient in magnitude and phase referred to that position is found from the polar coordinates of A to be $0.45e^{j1.11}$. Of course, the reversal of this procedure to give impedance if ρ is known is obvious.

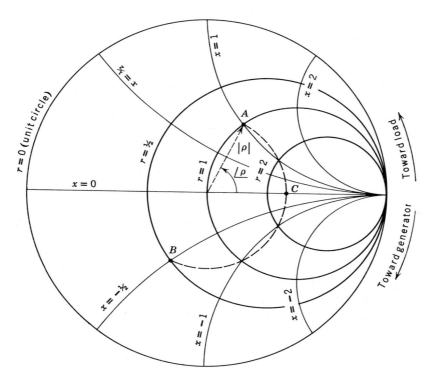

Fig. 1.20a   Polar transmission line chart.

To Transfer Impedances along the Line. If one moves along an ideal line between points of discontinuity, the magnitude of reflection coefficient must remain constant since incident and reflected waves shift in phase but do not change amplitude. On the chart, one then follows a circle with center at the origin of the w plane. The angle through which one moves is proportional to the length of the line, and by (2) is just twice the electrical length of the line βl. (Most charts have a scale around the outside calibrated in fractions of a wavelength, so that the angle need not be computed explicitly. See Fig. 1.20*b*.) Finally, the direction in which one moves is also defined by (2). If one moves toward the generator (increasing *l*), the angle of *w* becomes increasingly negative, which corresponds to clockwise motion about the chart. Motion toward the load corresponds to decreasing *l* in (2) and thus corresponds to counterclockwise motion about the chart. These directions are denoted by arrows on the chart.

As an example, if we are given a normalized load impedance of $1 + j1$, we have seen that this corresponds to point *A* of Fig. 1.20*a*. If the line is a quarter-wave long (90 electrical degrees), we move through an angle of 180° at constant radius on the chart toward the generator (clockwise) to point *B*. The normalized input impedance is then read as $0.5 - j0.5$ for point *B*. If input impedance is given and load impedance desired, the reverse of this procedure is obvious.

To Find Standing-Wave Ratio and Position of Voltage Maximum from a Given Impedance, and Conversely. If we wish the standing-wave ratio of an ideal transmission line terminated in a known load impedance, we make use of the information found in the last article (that the maximum impedance point along the line—which is also the voltage maximum and current minimum—is a pure resistance point, and this resistance is the standing-wave ratio times the characteristic impedance). That is, the normalized resistance of this point is exactly the standing-wave ratio. Thus, in following about the circle on the chart determined by the given impedance, we note its crossing of the right-hand *u* axis of the *w* plane. The value of the normalized resistance of this point is then the standing-wave ratio; the angle moved through to this position from the known impedance fixes the position of the voltage maximum.

As an example, for the given load impedance $1 + j1$ indicated by point *A* of Fig. 1.20*a*, one moves to the pure resistance point *C* by going 0.088 wavelength (31.7 electrical degrees) toward the generator from the load. The value of maximum normalized resistance, which is the standing-wave ratio, is read as 2.6. The reversal of this procedure to determine the load impedance, if standing-wave ratio and position of a voltage maximum are given, is straightforward, as is the extension to finding position of voltage minimum, or finding input impedance in place of load impedance.

Use as an Admittance Diagram. Since admittance transforms along the ideal line in exactly the same manner as impedance, Eq. 1.18(11), it is evident that exactly the same chart may be used for transformation of admittances with the same procedure as for impedances described in the above. Admittance is read for impedance, conductance for resistance, and susceptance for reactance. The differences to remember are: the right-hand *u* axis now represents an admittance maximum, and therefore a current maximum instead of a voltage maximum; the phase of reflection coefficient read directly corresponding to a given normalized admittance is that for current in the reflected wave compared with current in the incident wave and is therefore different by π from that based on voltages.

Problems

1.20a A 50-ohm line is terminated in a load impedance of $75 - j69$ ohms. The line is 3.5 meters long and is excited by a source of energy at 50 Mc/sec. Velocity of propagation along the line is 3×10^8 meters/sec. Find the input impedance, the reflection coefficient in magnitude and phase, the value of standing-wave ratio, and the position of a voltage minimum.

1.20b The standing-wave ratio on an ideal 70-ohm line is measured as 3.2, and a voltage minimum is observed 0.23 wavelength in front of the load. Find the load impedance.

1.20c Repeat Prob. b, using the chart to determine load admittance. Check to see if the result is consistent with the impedance found in b.

1.20d A 70-ohm line is teminated in an impedance of $50 + j10$ ohms. Find the position and value of a reactance that might be added in series with the line at some point to produce a perfect match for waves incident from the left.

1.20e Repeat Prob. d to determine the position and value of a shunt susceptance to be placed on the line for matching.

1.20f A 50-ohm transmission line is terminated with a load of $Z_L = 20 + j30$. A *double-stub tuner* consisting of a pair of shorted 50-ohm transmission lines connected in shunt to the main line at points spaced by 0.25λ is located with one stub at 0.2λ from the load. Find the lengths of the stubs to give unity standing-wave ratio at 0.45λ from the load.

1.20g A certain coaxial line has an alternating dielectric of vacuum and a material with $\epsilon = 4\epsilon_0$ and $\mu = \mu_0$ and is terminated at the end of a vacuum section by an impedance equal to the characteristic impedance of the vacuum regions. At frequency of f_0 the dielectric and vacuum regions are each $\lambda/2$ long (λ appropriate to each region). Show on a Smith chart the path of impedance variation along the line for operating frequencies f_0 and $2f_0$. Also plot the standing-wave ratio as a function of distance from the load.

1.21 Purely Standing Wave on an Ideal Line

Suppose that a transmission line, shorted at one end, is excited by sinusoidal voltage at the other. Let us select the position of the short as the reference, $z = 0$. The short imposes the condition that, at $z = 0$, voltage must always be zero. From Eq. 1.18(4),

$$V(0) = V_+ + V_-.$$

For this to be zero, V_- must be the negative of V_+. This result could be obtained as well from the general results for reflections at a discontinuity by setting $Z_L = 0$ in Eq. 1.18(8), or merely by physical reasoning which shows that no energy is absorbed by the short circuit, so all energy brought by the incident wave must appear in the reflected wave. The two waves of equal energy in the same line must have equal voltages. These must be in opposite directions at the short to add to the required zero voltage.

If $V_- = -V_+$ is substituted in Eqs. 1.18(4) and 1.18(5),

$$V = V_+[e^{-j\beta z} - e^{j\beta z}] = -2jV_+ \sin \beta z \qquad (1)$$

$$I = \frac{V_+}{Z_0}[e^{-j\beta z} + e^{j\beta z}] = 2\frac{V_+}{Z_0} \cos \beta z. \qquad (2)$$

These results, typical for standing waves, show the following.

1. Voltage is always zero not only at the short, but also at multiples of $\lambda/2$ to the left. That is,

$$V = 0 \text{ at } -\beta z = n\pi \qquad \text{or} \qquad z = -n\frac{\lambda}{2}.$$

2. Voltage is a maximum at all points for which βz is an odd multiple of $\pi/2$. These are at distances odd multiples of a quarter wavelength from the short circuit (Fig. 1.21).

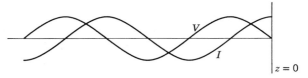

Fig. 1.21   Standing waves of voltage and current along shorted line.

3. Current is a maximum at the short circuit and at all points where voltage is zero; it is zero at all points where voltage is a maximum.

4. Current and voltage are not only displaced in their space patterns, but also are 90° out of time phase, as indicated by the j appearing in (1).

5. The ratio between the maximum current on the line and the maximum voltage is Z_0, the characteristic impedance of the line.

6. The total energy in any length of line a multiple of a quarter wavelength long is constant, merely interchanging between energy in the electric field of the voltages and energy in the magnetic field of the currents.

To check the energy relation just stated, let us calculate the magnetic energy of the currents at a time when the current pattern is a maximum and voltage is zero everywhere along the line. Current is given by (2). The energy is calculated for a quarter wavelength of the line.

$$U_M = \frac{L}{2} \int_{-\lambda/4}^{0} |I|^2 \, dz = \frac{L}{2} \int_{-\lambda/4}^{0} \frac{4V_+^2}{Z_0^2} \cos^2 \beta z \, dz$$

$$= \frac{2V_+^2 L}{Z_0^2} \left[\frac{z}{2} + \frac{1}{4\beta} \sin 2\beta z \right]_{-\lambda/4}^{0}.$$

Since $\beta = 2\pi/\lambda$ by 1.18(7), the foregoing is simply

$$U_M = \frac{V_+^2 L \lambda}{4Z_0^2}. \tag{3}$$

The maximum energy stored in the distributed capacity effect of the line is calculated for the quarter wavelength when the voltage pattern is a maximum and current is everywhere zero. Voltage is given by (1).

$$U_E = \frac{C}{2} \int_{-\lambda/4}^{0} |V|^2 \, dz = \frac{C}{2} \int_{-\lambda/4}^{0} 4V_+^2 \sin^2 \beta z \, dz$$

$$= 2CV_+^2 \left[\frac{z}{2} - \frac{1}{4\beta} \sin^2 \beta z \right]_{-\lambda/4}^{0} = \frac{CV_+^2 \lambda}{4}. \tag{4}$$

By the definition of Z_0, (3) may also be written

$$U_M = \frac{V_+^2 L \lambda}{4L/C} = \frac{V_+^2 C \lambda}{4} = U_E. \tag{5}$$

Thus the maximum energy stored in magnetic fields is exactly equal to that stored in electric fields 90° later in time. It could actually be shown that the sum of electric and magnetic energy at any other part of the cycle is equal to this same value.

Problem

1.21 Write the instantaneous expressions for voltage and current represented by the complex values (1) and (2). For a general instant of time, make the integration of total energy, electric plus magnetic, for a quarter wavelength of the line and show that it is constant.

1.22 Physical Approximations for Low-Loss Lines

In Art. 1.04 we saw that, by certain physical approximations amounting to a small perturbation of the ideal solution, we could arrive at the approximate behavior of a resonant circuit with small but finite losses.

We now wish to do the corresponding thing for transmission lines in order to arrive at approximate formulas for attenuation in a traveling wave, and impedance and quality factor of a standing wave. These techniques will be applied later in the book to the study of waveguides and cavity resonators.

If we take the formula for a traveling wave and assume that it is known that the major effect of small but finite losses in the line will be to produce an attenuating exponential multiplier,

$$V = V_m e^{-\alpha z} e^{j(\omega t - \beta z)} \tag{1}$$

$$I = I_m e^{-\alpha z} e^{j(\omega t - \beta z)}. \tag{2}$$

The average power transfer at any position is then

$$W_T = \tfrac{1}{2} V_m I_m e^{-2\alpha z}. \tag{3}$$

The factor $\frac{1}{2}$ in (3) comes from the time average of a $\sin^2$ term [or, if preferred, use Eq. 1.09(8)]. The rate of decrease of this average power with distance along the line must correspond to the average power loss in the line per unit length.

$$\frac{\partial W_T}{\partial z} = -W_L = -2\alpha(\tfrac{1}{2} V_m I_m e^{-2\alpha z}) = -2\alpha W_T$$

or

$$\alpha = \frac{W_L}{2W_T}. \tag{4}$$

This is a very important formula which, by the nature of the development, applies to the attenuation of a traveling wave along any uniform system.

To apply (4) to a transmission line with series resistance R and shunt conductance G, we first calculate the average power loss per unit length, part of which comes from the current flow through the resistance and another part from voltage appearing across the shunt conductance. The approximation comes in assuming Z_0 real for small losses, whereas it actually has a small reactive part as will be seen in Art. 1.23.

$$W_L = \frac{I_m^2 R}{2} + \frac{V_m^2 G}{2} = \frac{V_m^2}{2}\left[G + \frac{R}{Z_0^2}\right]. \tag{5}$$

The average power transferred by the wave is, using values at $z = 0$,

$$W_T = \tfrac{1}{2} V_m I_m = \frac{1}{2}\frac{V_m^2}{Z_0}. \tag{6}$$

So (4) gives the result

$$\alpha = \frac{1}{2}\left[GZ_0 + \frac{R}{Z_0}\right] \text{ nepers/meter.} \tag{7}$$

This formula will be obtained by a mathematical approximation in Art. 1.23.

We next want to ask about the effect of small losses on a quarter wave-length of the shorted line with standing waves, which has shown in Art. 1.21 to have the character of a resonant system. For the ideal line, the current a quarter wave in front of the short would be zero and voltage would be a maximum, so impedance would be infinite. When losses are present, there must be a high but finite resistance present representing energy dissipated in the losses of the line. To find these losses approximately, we shall use the expressions for voltage and current derived for the ideal line, Eqs. 1.21(1) and (2), assuming that they are not greatly changed by the small losses. The average power dissipated in the shunt conductance is then

$$W_G = \int_0^{\lambda/4} (2V_+ \sin \beta z)^2 \frac{G}{2} \, dz = \frac{4V_+^2 G}{4} \times \frac{\lambda}{4}, \tag{8}$$

and the average power dissipated in the series resistance is

$$W_R = \int_0^{\lambda/4} \left(\frac{2V_+ \cos \beta z}{Z_0}\right)^2 \frac{R}{2} \, dz = \frac{4V_+^2 R}{4Z_0^2} \times \frac{\lambda}{4}. \tag{9}$$

The input resistance (input at $\lambda/4$ from short) must be such that the voltage appearing across this resistance will produce losses equal to the sum of (8) and (9). The magnitude of voltage at $z = -\lambda/4$ is $2V_+$. Thus

$$\frac{1}{2} \frac{(2V_+)^2}{R_i} = \frac{V_+^2 \lambda}{4}\left(G + \frac{R}{Z_0^2}\right),$$

or

$$R_i = \frac{8Z_0}{\lambda[GZ_0 + (R/Z_0)]}. \tag{10}$$

The approximate Q of the device describing its excellence as an energy storage device may be found by using the definition stated in Eq. 1.04(6). The stored energy is taken as that for the ideal line, Eq. 1.21(5), and the power loss is given by the sum of (8) and (9). The result is

$$Q = \frac{\omega_0 U}{W_L} = \frac{4\omega_0 C V_+^2 \lambda}{4V_+^2 \lambda[G + (R/Z_0^2)]} = \frac{\omega_0 C Z_0}{GZ_0 + (R/Z_0)}. \tag{11}$$

Problem

1.22 Find the input resistance and Q of a half wavelength of the shorted line having small but finite R and G.

1.23   Transmission Lines with General Forms of Distributed Impedances

In the last article, we considered the possibility of adding series resistance and shunt conductance to the ideal transmission line of Fig. 1.13. For an exact analysis of this, and generalization to other forms of distributed impedances, let us take the line as shown in Fig. 1.23a with a distributed

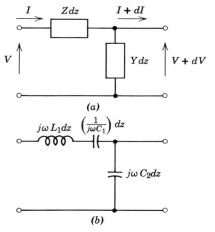

(a)

(b)

Fig. 1.23   (a) Differential length of general transmission line. (b) High-pass transmission line.

series impedance Z per unit length, and a distributed shunt admittance Y per unit length. For steady-state sinusoids, using complex notation, the differential equations for voltage and current variations with distance are then

$$\frac{dV}{dz} = -ZI \tag{1}$$

$$\frac{dI}{dz} = -YV. \tag{2}$$

Differentiation of (1) and substitution in (2) then yields

$$\frac{d^2V}{dz^2} = \gamma^2 V \tag{3}$$

where
$$\gamma = \sqrt{ZY}. \tag{4}$$

The solution to (3) may be written in terms of exponentials, as can be verified by substitution of the expression

$$V = Ae^{-\gamma z} + Be^{+\gamma z}. \tag{5}$$

From (1), the corresponding solution for current is

$$I = \frac{1}{Z_0}[Ae^{-\gamma z} - Be^{\gamma z}], \tag{6}$$

where

$$Z_0 = \frac{\gamma}{Z} = \sqrt{\frac{Z}{Y}} \text{ ohms}. \tag{7}$$

The characteristic impedance, Z_0, is in general complex, indicating that the voltage and current for a single traveling wave are not in phase. The quantity γ is called the propagation constant and is also generally complex,

$$\gamma = \alpha + j\beta = \sqrt{ZY} \tag{8}$$

so that if (5) is written in terms of α and β,

$$V = Ae^{-\alpha z}e^{-j\beta z} + Be^{\alpha z}e^{j\beta z}. \tag{9}$$

Thus α tells the rate of exponential attenuation of each wave and is correspondingly called the *attenuation constant*. The constant β tells the amount of phase shift per unit length for each wave and is called the *phase constant* as in the loss-free case.

The formula for reflection coefficient derived in Eq. 1.18(8) applies to this case also, remembering of course that Z_0 is complex. To find the input impedance at $z = -l$ in terms of a given reflection coefficient $\rho = B/A$ at $z = 0$, division of (5) by (6) yields

$$Z_i = Z_0\left[\frac{Ae^{\gamma l} + Be^{-\gamma l}}{Ae^{\gamma l} - Be^{-\gamma l}}\right] = Z_0\left[\frac{1 + \rho e^{-2\gamma l}}{1 - \rho e^{-2\gamma l}}\right]. \tag{10}$$

This may be put in terms of load impedance by substituting Eq. 1.18(8):

$$Z_i = Z_0\left[\frac{Z_L \cosh \gamma l + Z_0 \sinh \gamma l}{Z_0 \cosh \gamma l + Z_L \sinh \gamma l}\right]. \tag{11}$$

Transmission Line with Series and Shunt Losses. A very important case in practice is one in which losses must be considered in the transmission line. In general there may be distributed series resistance in the conductors of the line, and distributed shunt conductance because of leakage through the dielectric of the line. Distributed impedance and admittance are then

$$Z = R + j\omega L, \qquad Y = G + j\omega C. \tag{12}$$

TABLE 1.23

Quantity	General Line	Ideal Line	Approximate Results for Low-Loss Lines
Propagation constant $\gamma = \alpha + j\beta$	$\sqrt{(R+j\omega L)(G+j\omega C)}$	$j\omega\sqrt{LC}$	(See α and β below)
Phase constant β	$\mathrm{Im}(\gamma)$	$\omega\sqrt{LC} = \dfrac{\omega}{v} = \dfrac{2\pi}{\lambda}$	$\omega\sqrt{LC}\left[1 - \dfrac{RG}{4\omega^2 LC} + \dfrac{G^2}{8\omega^2 C^2} + \dfrac{R^2}{8\omega^2 L^2}\right]$
Attenuation constant α	$\mathrm{Re}(\gamma)$	0	$\dfrac{R}{2Z_0} + \dfrac{GZ_0}{2}$
Characteristic impedance Z_0	$\sqrt{\dfrac{R+j\omega L}{G+j\omega C}}$	$\sqrt{\dfrac{L}{C}}$	$\sqrt{\dfrac{L}{C}}\left[1 + j\left(\dfrac{G}{2\omega C} - \dfrac{R}{2\omega L}\right)\right]$
Input impedance Z_i	$Z_0\left[\dfrac{Z_L\cosh\gamma l + Z_0\sinh\gamma l}{Z_0\cosh\gamma l + Z_L\sinh\gamma l}\right]$	$Z_0\left[\dfrac{Z_L\cos\beta l + jZ_0\sin\beta l}{Z_0\cos\beta l + jZ_L\sin\beta l}\right]$	$Z_0\left[\dfrac{\alpha l\cos\beta l + j\sin\beta l}{\cos\beta l + j\alpha l\sin\beta l}\right]$
Impedance of shorted line	$Z_0\tanh\gamma l$	$jZ_0\tan\beta l$	$Z_0\left[\dfrac{\cos\beta l + j\alpha l\sin\beta l}{\alpha l\cos\beta l + j\sin\beta l}\right]$
Impedance of open line	$Z_0\coth\gamma l$	$-jZ_0\cot\beta l$	$Z_0\left[\dfrac{Z_0 + Z_L\alpha l}{Z_L + Z_0\alpha l}\right]$
Impedance of quarter-wave line	$Z_0\left[\dfrac{Z_L\sinh\alpha l + Z_0\cosh\alpha l}{Z_0\sinh\alpha l + Z_L\cosh\alpha l}\right]$	$\dfrac{Z_0^2}{Z_L}$	$Z_0\left[\dfrac{Z_L + Z_0\alpha l}{Z_0 + Z_L\alpha l}\right]$
Impedance of half-wave line	$Z_0\left[\dfrac{Z_L\cosh\alpha l + Z_0\sinh\alpha l}{Z_0\cosh\alpha l + Z_L\sinh\alpha l}\right]$	Z_L	$Z_0\left[\dfrac{Z_L + Z_0\alpha l}{Z_0 + Z_L\alpha l}\right]$
Voltage along line $V(z)$	$V_i\cosh\gamma z - I_i Z_0\sinh\gamma z$	$V_i\cos\beta z - jI_i Z_0\sin\beta z$	
Current along line $I(z)$	$I_i\cosh\gamma z - \dfrac{V_i}{Z_0}\sinh\gamma z$	$I_i\cos\beta z - j\dfrac{V_i}{Z_0}\sin\beta z$	
Reflection coefficient ρ	$\dfrac{Z_L - Z_0}{Z_L + Z_0}$	$\dfrac{Z_L - Z_0}{Z_L + Z_0}$	
Standing-wave ratio	$\dfrac{1+|\rho|}{1-|\rho|}$	$\dfrac{1+|\rho|}{1-|\rho|}$	

R, L, G, C Distributed resistance, inductance, conductance, capacitance per unit length.
l Length of line.
Subscript i denotes input end quantities.
Subscript L denotes load end quantities.

z Distance along line from input end.
λ Wavelength measured along line.
v Phase velocity of line equals velocity of light in dielectric of line for an ideal line.

These values may be used as the values of Z and Y in (4) and (7) to determine propagation constant and characteristic impedance. The formula (10) applies to impedance transformations, and the Smith transmission line chart may be utilized with a modification which recognizes that γ is complex. The procedure is as in Art. 1.20 except that, in moving along the line toward the generator, one moves not along a circle but along a spiral of radius decreasing according to the exponential $e^{-2\alpha l}$.

For many important problems, losses are finite but relatively small. If $R/\omega L \ll 1$ and $G/\omega C \ll 1$, the following approximations are obtained by retaining up to second-order terms in the binomial expansions of (4) and (7), with (12) substituted.

$$\alpha \approx \frac{R}{2\sqrt{L/C}} + \frac{G_0\sqrt{L/C}}{2} \tag{13}$$

$$\beta \approx \omega\sqrt{LC}\left[1 - \frac{RG}{4\omega^2 LC} + \frac{G^2}{8\omega^2 C^2} + \frac{R^2}{8\omega^2 L^2}\right] \tag{14}$$

$$Z_0 \approx \sqrt{\frac{L}{C}}\left[\left(1 + \frac{R^2}{8\omega^2 L^2} - \frac{3G^2}{8\omega^2 C^2} + \frac{RG}{4\omega^2 LC}\right) + j\left(\frac{G}{2\omega C} - \frac{R}{2\omega L}\right)\right] \tag{15}$$

In using the foregoing approximate formulas, it is often sufficient to retain only first-order correction terms, in which case β reduces to its ideal value of $2\pi/\lambda$, α is computed from (13), and Z_0 has a first-order reactive part, given by the last part of (15).

Several of the important formulas for loss-free, low-loss, and general lines are summarized in Table 1.23.

Filter-Type Distributed Circuits. Suppose the distributed series impedance of the general transmission line is formed by inductance and capacitance in series, as shown in Fig. 1.23b. Propagation constant γ is then

$$\gamma = \sqrt{j\omega C_2\left(j\omega L_1 + \frac{1}{j\omega C_1}\right)} = j\omega\sqrt{L_1 C_2\left(1 - \frac{\omega_c^2}{\omega^2}\right)}, \tag{16}$$

where

$$\omega_c = (L_1 C_1)^{-\frac{1}{2}}. \tag{17}$$

The interesting characteristic of this system is that for the lower range of frequencies, $\omega < \omega_c$, γ is purely real, representing an attenuation without losses in the system,

$$\gamma = \alpha = \omega\sqrt{L_1 C_2\left(\frac{\omega_c^2}{\omega^2} - 1\right)}, \qquad \omega < \omega_c. \tag{18}$$

The attenuation in this circuit occurs below the cutoff frequency defined by (17), so that the system is a distributed high-pass filter. The reactive attenuation which occurs arises essentially because of continuous reflections in the system, and is of the same nature as the attenuation in a loss-free, lumped-element filter in the attenuating band. Such behavior will be found in the very important waveguide systems to be studied later in the book.

For frequencies above ω_c, γ is purely imaginary, representing a propagation without attenuation. The phase velocity, v_p, is, however, a strong function of frequency for frequencies just above cutoff,

$$ v_p = \frac{\omega}{\beta} = \frac{1}{\sqrt{L_1 C_2}} \left[1 - \frac{\omega_c^2}{\omega^2} \right]^{-\frac{1}{2}} \tag{19} $$

Other velocities and the relation to energy transfer will be treated in following articles.

Problems

1.23a Show that (7), (8), and (11) reduce to previously derived forms for the ideal line with $Z = j\omega L$, $Y = j\omega C$.

1.23b For the filter-type circuit studied, find expressions for characteristic impedance Z_0. Show that this is real in the propagating region, and imaginary in the attenuating region. What does this signify with respect to power flow in a single propagating wave?

1.23c Use the formula for input impedance of a transmission line with losses to check Eq. 1.22(10), making approximations consistent with $R/\omega L \ll 1$ and $G/\omega C \ll 1$.

1.23d Suppose that frequency is varied by a small amount from the value giving resonance for the quarter-wave shorted line studied in Art. 1.22. For a line with $R/\omega L \ll 1$ and $G/\omega C \ll 1$, find the frequency shift for which impedance has decreased in magnitude to $1/\sqrt{2}$ its resonant value. How is this related to the Q defined by Eq. 1.22(11)?

1.24   Velocities of Wave Propagation

The velocity $v_p = \omega/\beta$ for a single-frequency sinusoid has been shown to represent the velocity with which one must travel to keep instantaneous phase constant, for in the factor

$$ e^{j(\omega t - \beta z)} = e^{j\omega[t - (z/v_p)]} $$

the instantaneous phase $(\omega t - \beta z)$ does remain constant if one travels with velocity v_p so that $z = v_p t + C$. This velocity is thus known as the *phase velocity*.

A function of time with arbitrary wave shape may be expressed as a sum of sinusoidal waves by Fourier analysis. If it happens that v_p is the same for each frequency component and there is no attenuation, the component waves will add in proper phase at each point along the line to reproduce the original wave shape exactly, but delayed by the time of propagation z/v_p. The velocity v_p in this case describes the rate at which the wave moves down the line and could be said to be *the* velocity of propagation. This case occurs, for example, in the ideal loss-free transmission line already studied for which v_p is a constant equal to $(LC)^{-1/2}$.

For transmission lines with losses and for other general electromagnetic wave guides, phase velocity may vary with frequency. In this case the individual sinusoidal components acting to make up a complex wave will shift in phase as they move down the line, the "faster" waves speeding ahead and the "slower" waves falling back. In this phenomenon, known as *dispersion*, the waves at some point down the line may add to produce a wave shape quite different in appearance from that which went in. It may then be very difficult to define any significant single velocity for this signal. When there is relatively little dispersion over the frequency band of interest, however, the group velocity, to be defined in the following paragraph, is a most useful additional concept.

The group velocity is most easily approached by considering the two-term combination representing sinusoids of slightly different frequency:

$$\sin(\omega_0 - d\omega)t + \sin(\omega_0 + d\omega)t. \tag{1}$$

If (1) represents the transmitted voltage, the voltage everywhere along the path (assuming no amplitude change) is

$$\sin[(\omega_0 - d\omega)t - (\beta_0 - d\beta)x] + \sin[(\omega_0 + d\omega)t - (\beta_0 + d\beta)x], \tag{2}$$

in which β is to be regarded as a function of frequency as indicated by the use of $d\beta$ to go with $d\omega$.

Expression (2) may be changed to

$$2\cos(d\omega t - d\beta x)\sin(\omega t - \beta x),$$

which shows that the resultant voltage on the line at any point may be pictured as a high-frequency wave whose amplitude varies at a low-frequency rate. The envelope of the wave, in other words, is

$$\cos(d\omega t - d\beta x). \tag{3}$$

It varies sinusoidally with both time and distance and thus may be regarded as a traveling wave. It is readily seen that the velocity of an imaginary observer who stays on the same point of the *envelope* is

$$v_g = \frac{d\omega}{d\beta}. \tag{4}$$

This is called the group velocity. Since the phase velocity is (ω/β) by Eq. 1.18(6), the group velocity may alternatively be written

$$v_g = \frac{v_p}{1 - \dfrac{\omega}{v_p}\dfrac{dv_p}{d\omega}}. \tag{5}$$

Similarly, for a signal made up of many sinusoidal components, so long as there is relatively small dispersion over the frequency band necessary to describe the signal, it may be shown that the group velocity v_g defined above expresses approximately the velocity of the composite envelope, and may thus be used as a "signal" velocity. For large dispersions, this may not be a good approximation, and in fact it may be impossible to give any single velocity describing the propagation of the wave since it changes shape so significantly as it goes. An excellent discussion of the several velocities of propagation is given by Stratton.[2]

Group velocity is often referred to as the "velocity of energy travel." This concept has validity for many important cases, but is not universally true. To illustrate the point, let us define here a separate velocity v_E based on energy flow so that power transfer is stored energy multiplied by this velocity. That is,

$$v_E = W_T/U_{av} \tag{6}$$

where W_T is average power flow in a single wave and U_{av} is average energy storage per unit length. Applying this to the ideal transmission line of Art. 1.18, we find for a single traveling wave

$$W_T = \tfrac{1}{2}Z_0 II^*$$

$$U_{av} = \frac{1}{2}\left(\frac{CVV^*}{2} + \frac{LII^*}{2}\right) = \frac{C}{4}\left(Z_0^2 + \frac{L}{C}\right)II^* = \frac{L}{2}II^*,$$

so
$$v_E = \frac{1}{L}\sqrt{\frac{L}{C}} = \frac{1}{\sqrt{LC}}. \tag{7}$$

This is equal to the group velocity, but of course in this dispersionless case

[2] J. A. Stratton, *Electromagnetic Theory*, McGraw-Hill, New York, 1941, pp. 330–340.

it is also equal to the phase velocity. More interesting is the case of the filter-type circuit of Fig. 1.23b, which is a case of normal dispersion $(dv_p/d\omega < 0)$. Here

$$W_T = \tfrac{1}{2}Z_0 II^* = \frac{II^*}{2}\left[\frac{L_1}{C_2}\left(1 - \frac{\omega_c^{\,2}}{\omega^2}\right)\right]^{1/2}$$

$$U_{\text{av}} = \frac{1}{2}\left(\frac{C_2 VV^*}{2} + \frac{L_1 II^*}{2} + \frac{C_1}{2}\frac{II^*}{\omega^2 C_1^{\,2}}\right)$$

$$= \frac{L_1}{4}\left(\frac{C_2 Z_0^{\,2}}{L_1} + 1 + \frac{\omega_c^{\,2}}{\omega^2}\right)II^* = \frac{L_1 II^*}{2}$$

so

$$v_E = (L_1 C_2)^{-1/2}\left[1 - \frac{\omega_c^{\,2}}{\omega^2}\right]^{1/2}. \tag{8}$$

This is equal to group velocity $d\omega/d\beta$, as can be found by differentiating Eq. 1.23(16), and is different from phase velocity. The identity of group velocity and energy velocity will also be shown to be true for the simple waveguides to be studied later, and it also applies to many other cases of normal dispersion. It does not usually apply to systems with anomalous dispersion $(dv_p/d\omega > 0)$, including the simple transmission line with losses.

Problems

1.24a Is phase or group velocity the larger for normal dispersion $(dv_p/d\omega < 0)$? For anomalous dispersion $(dv_p/d\omega > 0)$?

1.24b Find the phase and group velocities for a transmission line with small but finite losses.

1.24c Consider a transmission line with very high leakage conductance G per unit length so that series resistance R and shunt capacitance C are negligible. Find phase and group velocities.

1.24d For problems b and c, show that an energy velocity as defined by (6) is not equal to group velocity.

1.24e Certain water waves of large amplitude have phase velocities given by $v_p = g/\omega$ where g is acceleration due to gravity and ω is angular frequency. Determine the ratio of group velocity to phase velocity for such a wave.

1.25 Backward Waves and the ω-β Diagram

A wave in which phase velocity and group velocity have opposite signs is known as a *backward wave*. Conditions for these may seem unexpected or rare, but they are not. Consider for instance the distributed system of

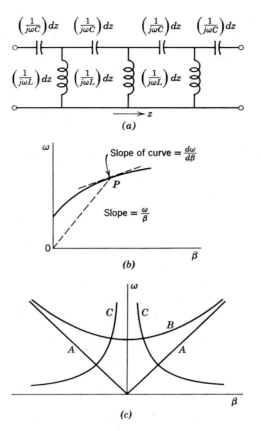

Fig. 1.25 (*a*) Backward-wave transmission line.
(*b*) ω-β diagram. (*c*) ω-β characteristics for:
ideal transmission line (*A*); filter line of Fig. 1.23*b*
(*B*); backward-wave line of Fig. 1.25*a* (*C*).

Fig. 1.25*a* in which there are series capacitances and shunt inductances—
the dual of the simple transmission line of Art. 1.13. From Art. 1.23,

$$\gamma = j\beta = \sqrt{ZY} = \sqrt{\left(\frac{1}{j\omega C}\right)\left(\frac{1}{j\omega L}\right)} = -\frac{j}{\omega\sqrt{LC}} \qquad (1)$$

so

$$v_p = \frac{\omega}{\beta} = -\omega^2\sqrt{LC} \qquad (2)$$

and

$$v_g = \frac{d\omega}{d\beta} = \omega^2\sqrt{LC}. \qquad (3)$$

So it is seen that this very simple transmission system satisfies the conditions for backward waves. The meaning of course is that if energy is made to flow in the positive z direction, group velocity will be in this direction, as this is a case where v_g does represent energy flow (see Prob. 1.25c). Phase will become increasingly negative or "lagging" in the direction of propagation, however, because of the C-L configuration, which yields the negative phase velocity. Thus there is seen to be no mystery or violation of principle in such waves.

Many filter-type lines similar to Fig. 1.23b will have backward waves, and it will be shown later in the text that all periodic circuits will have an equal number of forward and backward "space harmonics." A very useful diagram for both forward and backward waves is the plot of angular frequency ω versus phase constant β. It might seem more natural to consider ω as the independent variable and to plot β as ordinate, but the case for reversing axes is illustrated by Fig. 1.25b. With this selection, phase velocity ω/β is just the slope of the line from the origin to any point P under consideration, and group velocity $d\omega/d\beta$ is the slope of the curve at that point.

Figure 1.25c illustrates the ω-β plots for the ideal transmission line of Art. 1.13, the filter-type line of Fig. 1.23b, and the backward-wave line of Fig. 1.25a. Note that for a line with filter properties, the cutoff frequency ω_c is given by the condition of zero slope, which then gives zero group velocity and (where the concept is valid) the condition for zero energy transfer. Appendix IV gives some typical ω-β plots.

Problems

1.25a Plot the ω-β diagram for a distributed transmission system with series inductance L_1 per unit length, and a shunt admittance made up of L_2 in parallel with C_2 for a unit length of the system. Is this a backward or forward wave system? Show cutoff frequency and illustrate phase and group velocity on the plot.

1.25b Repeat for a system with the shunt admittance made up of L_2 and C_2 in series.

1.25c Calculate the velocity of energy propagation, as defined in Art. 1.24, for the backward-wave line of Fig. 1.25a. Show that it does correspond to group velocity for this line and discuss the concepts of normal and anomalous dispersion for backward waves.

1.26 Nonuniform Transmission Lines

For a transmission line with varying spacing or size of conductors, as illustrated in Fig. 1.26, a natural extension of the transmission line analysis would lead one to consider impedance and admittance as varying with distance in the transmission line equations. Actually, fields may be distorted so that the formulation is not this simple, but it is a good approximation in a number of important cases, and the methods discussed apply to some wave problems with spatial variations of the medium (i.e., inhomogeneous materials). The remainder of this article will consider cases where such nonuniform transmission line theory yields a good approximation.

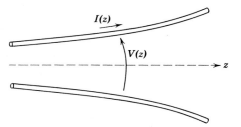

Fig. 1.26   Nonuniform transmission line.

If impedance and admittance per unit length vary with distance, the transmission line equations corresponding to Eqs. 1.23(1)–(2) are

$$\frac{dV(z)}{dz} = -Z(z)I(z) \tag{1}$$

$$\frac{dI(z)}{dz} = -Y(z)V(z). \tag{2}$$

Differentiate (1) with respect to z, denoting z differentiation by primes.

$$V'' = -[ZI' + Z'I]. \tag{3}$$

To obtain a differential equation in voltage alone, I may be substituted from (1) and I' from (2). The result is

$$V'' - \left(\frac{Z'}{Z}\right)V' - (ZY)V = 0. \tag{4}$$

Similar procedure, starting with differentiation of (2), yields a second-order differential equation in I:

$$I'' - \left(\frac{Y'}{Y}\right)I' - (ZY)I = 0. \tag{5}$$

If Z' and Y' are zero, the equations (4) and (5) reduce, as they should, to the equations for a uniform line (Art. 1.23). When these derivatives are finite, representing the nonuniform line discussed, the equations may be solved numerically or with analog equipment for arbitrary variations of Z and Y with distance. A few forms of the variation permit analytic solutions, including the "radial line," to be considered in Chapter 8, where either Z or Y are proportional to z, and their product is constant. Another important case is the "exponential line," which is taken as the example for this article.

Let us consider a loss-free exponential line with Z and Y varying as follows:

$$Z = j\omega L_0 e^{qz}; \qquad Y = j\omega C_0 e^{-qz}. \tag{6}$$

These variations yield constant values of ZY, Z'/Z, and Y'/Y so that the equations (4) and (5) become equations with constant coefficients,

$$V'' - qV' + \omega^2 L_0 C_0 V = 0 \tag{7}$$
$$I'' + qI' + \omega^2 L_0 C_0 I = 0. \tag{8}$$

These have solutions of the exponentially propagating form,

$$V = V_0 e^{-\gamma_1 z}; \qquad I = I_0 e^{-\gamma_2 z} \tag{9}$$

where
$$\gamma_1 = -\frac{q}{2} \pm \sqrt{\left(\frac{q}{2}\right)^2 - \omega^2 L_0 C_0} \tag{10}$$

$$\gamma_2 = +\frac{q}{2} \pm \sqrt{\left(\frac{q}{2}\right)^2 - \omega^2 L_0 C_0}. \tag{11}$$

We see the interesting property of "cutoff" again, for γ_1 and γ_2 are purely real for low frequencies $\omega < \omega_c$, where

$$\omega_c^2 L_0 C_0 = \left(\frac{q}{2}\right)^2. \tag{12}$$

The attenuation represented by these real values, like that for the loss-free filter-type lines, is reactive. This represents no power dissipation but only a continuous reflection of the wave. For $\omega > \omega_c$, however, the values of γ have both real and imaginary parts, which is a different behavior from that of the loss-free filters. Again the real parts represent no power dissipation (see Prob. 1.26b). The values of γ approach purely imaginary values representing phase change only for $\omega \gg \omega_c$.

The greatest use of this type of line is in matching between lines of different characteristic impedance. Unlike the resonant matching sections (Prob. 1.18b), this type of matching is insensitive to frequency. Note the ratio of V/I for a single wave direction at any at point z,

$$\frac{V(z)}{I(z)} = \frac{V_0 e^{-\gamma_1 z}}{I_0 e^{-\gamma_2 z}} = \frac{V_0}{I_0} e^{-(\gamma_1 - \gamma_2)z} = Z_0(0)e^{qz}. \tag{13}$$

Thus Z_0 can be changed by an appreciable factor if qz is large enough. The transmission line approximation will become poor, however, if there is too large a change of Z and Y in a wavelength, or in a distance comparable to conductor spacing.

Problems

1.26a Show that (9) with definitions (10) and (11) does give the solutions of (7) and (8) with the variations (6). Describe ways in which lines with the exponential variation of L and C might be designed, at least approximately.

1.26b Show that average power transfer is constant in the loss-free exponential line considered here for frequencies above cutoff, $\omega > \omega_c$.

1.26c There are two solutions of (10) and (11) representing positively and negatively traveling waves, as expected. Write the complete solutions for $V(z)$ and $I(z)$, showing both waves, using as constants the voltage amplitudes in positively and negatively traveling waves at $z = 0$. Note the interchange of behavior of positive and negative waves if the sign of q is changed, and explain physically.

1.26d Modify the analysis for the exponential line to include losses, retaining constancy of ZY, Z'/Z, and Y'/Y and interpret the effect on attenuation constant.

1.27 Energy Theorems for Transmission Lines

By physical reasoning, we can relate without much trouble the rate of change of power flow along a line to time rates of change of stored energy, and also account for losses if they are present. It will nevertheless be instructive to derive these equations formally for later comparison with a more general electromagnetic theorem concerning flow of power.

Let us start with the loss-free line, in time-varying form. From Art. 1.13,

$$\frac{\partial V}{\partial z} = -L\frac{\partial I}{\partial t}, \qquad \frac{\partial I}{\partial z} = -C\frac{\partial V}{\partial t}. \tag{1}$$

If the first part of (1) is multiplied by I, the second by V, and the results added, we obtain

$$\frac{\partial}{\partial z}(IV) + \frac{\partial}{\partial t}(\tfrac{1}{2}LI^2 + \tfrac{1}{2}CV^2) = 0, \tag{2}$$

which may be written

$$\frac{\partial}{\partial z}(\text{Power}) + \frac{\partial}{\partial t}(\text{Energy stored per unit length}) = 0. \tag{3}$$

The interpretation of (3) is that if power flow changes as we move along the line, it must be because there is a time rate of change in the stored energy at that location.

If losses are present because of series R and shunt G, (1) becomes

$$\frac{\partial V}{\partial z} = -RI - L\frac{\partial I}{\partial t}, \quad \frac{\partial I}{\partial z} = -GV - C\frac{\partial V}{\partial t}. \tag{4}$$

Repetition of the foregoing derivation now yields

$$\frac{\partial}{\partial z}(IV) + \frac{\partial}{\partial t}(\tfrac{1}{2}LI^2 + \tfrac{1}{2}CV^2) + (RI^2 + GV^2) = 0. \tag{5}$$

And the interpretation of this is as for (2) except that the last term shows that power may change along the line because of a loss in the line in addition to the changes from rates of change of stored energy.

Finally, if we utilize the complex form of Art. 1.23, writing $Z = R + jX$ and $Y = G + jB$, the transmission line equations are

$$\frac{dV}{dz} = -(R + jX)I, \quad \frac{dI}{dz} = -(G + jB)V. \tag{6}$$

Multiply the first of these by I^* and add to it the product of V and the conjugate of the second equation,

$$I^*\frac{dV}{dz} + \frac{dI^*}{dz}V + (RII^* + GVV^*) + j(XII^* - BVV^*) = 0 \tag{7}$$

or $$\frac{d}{dz}(\tfrac{1}{2}VI^*) + \tfrac{1}{2}(RII^* + GVV^*) + \frac{j}{2}(XII^* - BVV^*) = 0. \tag{8}$$

The real part of (8) gives the rate of change of average power flow with distance in terms of average power loss in resistance and conductance per unit length. The results (3), (5), and the real part of (8) are as expected from physical reasoning. Perhaps not quite so obvious, but useful in a number of instances, is the imaginary part of (8) which gives the rate of change of the "reactive" power by the last bracket of the equation.

Problem

1.27 Study and interpret equation (8) for a filter-type circuit in the propagating region where Z_0 is real and $\gamma = j\beta$; similarly study in the attenuating region where Z_0 is imaginary and $\gamma = \alpha$.

1.28   Analysis of Transmission Line in Terms of Natural Modes

In this article we shall demonstrate a technique which will be one of the most widely useful methods for solution of field and wave problems to come later. The method makes use of a summation or series of harmonic solutions to a wave problem to fit imposed boundary or initial conditions, just as in Art. 1.10 a series of sinusoids was used to fit any arbitrary periodic functions.

As the example, let us consider a problem quite similar to those solved by consideration of the traveling waves in Art. 1.17. For this problem, imagine the open-circuited transmission line, first charged to a d-c voltage V_0, and then shorted at both ends simultaneously at a specified instant of time. The voltage distribution at the instant of shorting is then known (zero at each end and a constant equal to V_0 at all other points). It is desired to find the current and voltage behavior at all later times.

In Art. 1.21 it was noted that natural sinusoidal oscillations for a line of length l, shorted at both ends, occur at all frequencies for which the line is a multiple of a half-wave long. From the results of that article one of these natural sinusoidal modes of oscillation may be written. For voltage,

$$V_m = A_m e^{j\omega_m t} \sin \frac{m\pi z}{l} \tag{1}$$

where

$$\omega_m = 2\pi f_m = \frac{m\pi v}{l} = \frac{m\pi}{\tau}, \tag{2}$$

τ is the time of travel of a wave down the line, l/v. The results of Art. 1.21 also reveal that the corresponding current for each natural frequency is 90° out of time and space phase with voltage and has the magnitude of voltage divided by Z_0. That is,

$$I_m = \frac{jA_m}{Z_0} e^{j\omega_m t} \cos \frac{m\pi z}{l}. \tag{3}$$

Now, let us form a solution to the transmission line equations from the sum of all solutions of the form of (1). The basis for this step may be traced to the fact that the sum of solutions to a linear differential equation is also a solution. The transmission line differential equations are linear, and (1) is a solution. Adding,

$$V = A_1 e^{j\omega_1 t} \sin \frac{\pi z}{l} + A_2 e^{j\omega_2 t} \sin \frac{2\pi z}{l} + A_3 e^{j\omega_3 t} \sin \frac{3\pi z}{l} + \cdots \tag{4}$$

and the corresponding sum of (3) for current,

$$I = \frac{j}{Z_0}\left(A_1 e^{j\omega_1 t}\cos\frac{\pi z}{l} + A_2 e^{j\omega_2 t}\cos\frac{2\pi z}{l} + A_3 e^{j\omega_3 t}\cos\frac{3\pi z}{l} + \cdots\right). \quad (5)$$

The amplitudes $A_1, A_2, \ldots, A_m$ are still arbitrary. They may be determined from the known initial condition by expanding the known initial voltage distribution with distance as a Fourier series.

At $t = 0$, the voltage is known to be a constant V_0 over the interval $0 < z < l$. Such a function has been expanded in a Fourier series of sines in Eq. 1.12(7).

$$V\Big|_{t=0} = \frac{4V_0}{\pi}\left(\sin\frac{\pi z}{l} + \tfrac{1}{3}\sin\frac{3\pi z}{l} + \tfrac{1}{5}\sin\frac{5\pi z}{l} + \cdots\right). \quad (6)$$

But, at $t = 0$, the series (4) reduces to

$$V\Big|_{t=0} = A_1 \sin\frac{\pi z}{l} + A_2 \sin\frac{2\pi z}{l} + A_3 \sin\frac{3\pi z}{l} + \cdots. \quad (7)$$

By a term-by-term comparison of (6) and (7) it is seen that all the even coefficients, A_2, A_4, etc., must be zero; for the odd coefficients,

$$A_1 = \frac{4V_0}{\pi} \quad A_3 = \frac{4V_0}{3\pi} \quad \cdots \quad A_n = \frac{4V_0}{n\pi}.$$

Now that the coefficients are determined, the complete series expressions for voltage and current at any time may be written

$$V = \frac{4V_0}{\pi}\left(e^{j(\pi t/\tau)}\sin\frac{\pi z}{l} + \frac{e^{j(3\pi t/\tau)}}{3}\sin\frac{3\pi z}{l} + \frac{e^{j(5\pi t/\tau)}}{5}\sin\frac{5\pi z}{l} + \cdots\right) \quad (8)$$

$$I = \frac{4jV_0}{Z_0\pi}\left(e^{j(\pi t/\tau)}\cos\frac{\pi z}{l} + \frac{e^{j(3\pi t/\tau)}}{3}\cos\frac{3\pi z}{l} + \frac{e^{j(5\pi t/\tau)}}{5}\cos\frac{5\pi z}{l} + \cdots\right). \quad (9)$$

It must be remembered that, to find instantaneous values, we must take the real part of the foregoing expressions (Art. 1.08), and voltage or current could then be calculated approximately at any point along the line for any time by retaining a number of terms from the above infinite series. It is especially interesting to note the current through the short circuit by letting $z = 0$.

$$I(0, t) = \mathrm{Re}\left\{\frac{4jV_0}{Z_0\pi}\left[e^{j(\pi t/\tau)} + \tfrac{1}{3}e^{j(3\pi t/\tau)} + \tfrac{1}{5}e^{j(5\pi t/\tau)} + \cdots\right]\right\}$$

$$= \frac{-4V_0}{Z_0\pi}\left[\sin\frac{\pi t}{\tau} + \tfrac{1}{3}\sin\frac{3\pi t}{\tau} + \tfrac{1}{5}\sin\frac{5\pi t}{\tau} + \cdots\right]. \quad (10)$$

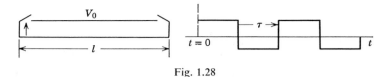

Fig. 1.28

This can be shown to be the Fourier series of a step function which changes from V_0/Z_0 to $-V_0/Z_0$ at intervals of τ, as sketched in Fig. 1.28. The same result would have been found by a traveling-wave analysis as in Art. 1.17.

Problem

1.28 Solve, by the method of this article, the problem of the charged line shorted at only one end.

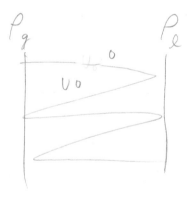

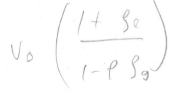

2 THE EQUATIONS OF STATIONARY ELECTRIC AND MAGNETIC FIELDS

2.01 Introduction

Following the introduction to oscillation and wave concepts in Chapter 1, this chapter begins the serious study of electric and magnetic fields. There are many ways of beginning such a study. A good case can be made for presenting at once the most general known form of the laws of concern to the subject, and then devoting the remainder of the text to understanding them by development of special cases. Another method follows the historical development of ideas leading to modern electromagnetic theory. The method to be followed is somewhat between these two courses, utilizing selected experimental laws from static electric and magnetic fields for the purpose of seeing how such laws are generalized, and for the presentation or review of the tools required for handling field concepts. It is hoped that the treatment of the general laws (Maxwell's equations) then will be much more meaningful when given in Chapter 4.

There is, of course, some risk in proceeding from the special case to the general. By concentrating on statics first, the student may become too strongly imbued with certain laws and concepts which are incomplete when time variations are important. An example is that of voltage defined along a path. This is equal to a potential difference between end points of the path in statics but not in electrodynamics in general. Yet the incorrect use of potential concepts for a-c fields is common among engineers. The answer is to remember that the next two chapters are special cases, and that additions will be necessary when time variations enter.

Even for static fields there is some choice of the laws that may be used as a starting point for the development. We shall use force laws because they have a strong tie to our physical feeling, and because they played an important early role in the development of the subject. Yet it should be remembered that these were set down as hypotheses by ingenious people after a certain set of real physical measurements (somewhat different from the idealizations to be described) were made to a certain degree of accuracy. Later measurements, either direct or designed to test other relations derived or generalized from these, define more clearly the accuracy and range of validity of the laws. Once the generalizations are verified, they are equally valid starting points and may indeed have a greater range of usefulness. The process of deriving and generalizing from a given starting point to provide a variety of useful forms is one of the important messages of this chapter.

Aside from the foregoing philosophical point, and the useful forms to be presented, the important tool of vector algebra will be introduced in this chapter. It will be presented along with the field laws to give the vector operations physical significance. It is hoped that this will help either for review or in learning to use this important tool for the first time.

Since the properties of materials directly affect electric and magnetic field laws, the last of the chapter will introduce some models for the interaction of fields and materials. The stress in this chapter will be on the dielectric and magnetic properties which affect static field distributions. The models will be extended in later chapters to include important dynamic effects.

STATIC ELECTRIC FIELDS

2.02   Force Between Electric Charges

The problem which must be solved in static electric field theory is that of obtaining relations which involve the geometrical configurations of conductors and dielectrics, the distribution of charges on the conductors and in the dielectric medium separating them, the potential differences between conductors, and the field distribution in the dielectric. Several or all of these factors will enter into the determination of capacitance between conductors, the maximum gradient in insulation, the amount of field between deflecting plates in an oscilloscope, the amount of shielding which a grid provides in a vacuum tube, the field acting on electrons and holes in a transistor, or the accelerating force on an electron in an electron gun.

Essentially, the problem is one of equilibrium. We require a knowledge of the forces that act on charges, thus making them move to eventual equilibrium positions, and we must know the manner in which conductors and dielectrics affect the charge distribution and the field distribution.

10/11/66

We shall thus take as our starting point for electrostatics the experimental law of Coulomb, which gives the force between two electric charges in an infinite medium, the characteristics of which are everywhere the same and do not depend on the locations of the charges, on their magnitudes, or on the orientation of the medium. The law includes the following information:

1. Like charges repel, opposites attract.
2. Force is proportional to the product of charge magnitudes.
3. Force is inversely proportional to the square of the distances between charges.
4. Force is dependent on the medium in which the charges are placed.
5. Force acts along the line joining the charges.

This information may be written as an equation:

$$f = k\frac{q_1 q_2}{\epsilon r^2}. \qquad (1)$$

In this equation, f is defined as the force of attraction acting on the line between charges, q_1 and q_2 represent the charges in magnitude and sign, r is the distance between charges, ϵ is a property of the medium which may be called the permittivity (dielectric constant in some systems of units), and k is a constant of proportionality which must be included for the present, since we have not as yet defined units.

The equation may be written so that the direction of the force is included:

$$\bar{f} = k\frac{q_1 q_2}{\epsilon r^2}\bar{a}_r. \qquad (2)$$

The bar above f denotes that force is a directed quantity, or vector; that is, it has both magnitude and direction. The direction of $\bar{f}$ is given by $\bar{a}_r$, a vector of unit length pointing from one charge directly away from the other, and the sign of $q_1 q_2$. Thus, if q_1 and q_2 have opposite signs, $q_1 q_2$ is negative and the force has the opposite direction to $\bar{a}_r$, or is from one charge toward the other. If q_1 and q_2 have the same signs, $\bar{f}$ has the same direction as $\bar{a}_r$ and is hence from one charge directly away from the other. This is merely the statement of opposite charges attracting, like charges repelling. Vectors such as $\bar{a}_r$ are known as unit vectors and will be useful throughout the study of fields, since they serve to indicate direction without interfering with magnitudes.

A simplified picture will show why the force may be expected to depend on the presence of matter. The electron clouds and the nuclei of the atoms experience oppositely directed forces as a result of the presence of the isolated charges. Thus the atoms are distorted or *polarized*. There is

10/11/66

shift of the center of symmetry of the electron cloud with respect to the nucleus in each atom as indicated schematically in Fig. 2.02. Similar distortions can occur in molecules, and an equivalent situation arises in some materials where naturally polarized molecules have a tendency to be aligned in the presence of free charges. The directions of the polarizations are such, for many materials, that the equivalent charge pairs in the atoms or molecules directly counteract the forces between the two isolated

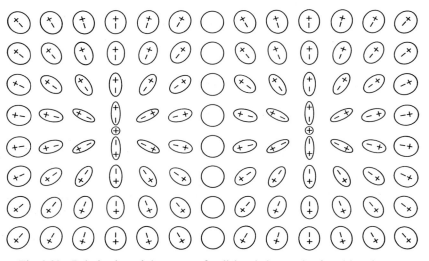

Fig. 2.02   Polarization of the atoms of a dielectric by a pair of positive charges

charges. The magnitude and the direction of the polarization depend on the nature of the material.

Because some materials (e.g., crystals) affect force in a more complicated manner than described by (2), this approach to electricity and magnetism has been criticized.[1] Although such criticism is valid, the present approach also has validity if it is remembered that we have purposely selected a simple starting point for generalization, as noted in the introduction.

2.03   Systems of Units

Equation 2.02(1) may be used to define systems of units. Originally, the most common system of units used for electric quantities in discussing the physical laws was a centimeter-gram-second system of units known as

[1] "The Teaching of Electricity and Magnetism at the College Level," Coulomb's Law Committee, 1950, *American Journal of Physics*, vol. 18, pp. 1–25.

10/4/66

the electrostatic system of units (esu). It is still used in much of the physics literature, and so will be defined briefly in this article. Since it is a cgs system, the unit of force appearing in Eq. 2.02(1) is the dyne, and the unit of distance is the centimeter. A unit charge is defined as that charge which repels an exactly similar charge with a force of 1 dyne when the two are placed 1 centimeter apart in vacuum, so that $k/\epsilon = 1$. In this system of units the permittivity of vacuum is further defined as unity, so that k is also unity. The unit of charge defined in this system is known as the stat-coulomb, and it is very nearly $\frac{1}{3} \times 10^{-9}$ of the practical unit of charge, the coulomb.

The system of units that has come to be used almost universally in applied electromagnetic theory is the system of units introduced by Giorgi[2] in 1901. It is an mks system, so that lengths are in meters, mass in kilograms, and time in seconds, but the significant advantage so far as its use in electricity and magnetism is concerned lies in the fact that the units of all primary electric quantities are those actually measured. Thus, current is in amperes, potential in volts, an impedance derived at any stage of the discussion is in ohms, power is in watts, etc. These and other advantages will become clearer as the various laws are introduced and studied.

The unit of force in any meter-kilogram system of units, defined as the product of mass and acceleration, has the units of kilogram-meters per (second)^2 and is known as a newton:

$$1 \text{ newton} = 1 \text{ kilogram-meter (second)}^{-2} = 10^5 \text{ dynes.} \qquad (1)$$

The unit of energy, the product of force and distance, is in newton-meters and is the well-known unit of physics and engineering called the joule:

$$1 \text{ joule} = 1 \text{ newton-meter} = 10^7 \text{ ergs.} \qquad (2)$$

For later purposes, it is also well to note that, from elementary circuit theory for a simple condenser, the energy in joules can be written in terms of charge in coulombs and capacitance in farads:

$$\text{energy in joules} = \frac{\frac{1}{2}(\text{charge in coulombs})^2}{(\text{capacitance in farads})}. \qquad (3)$$

The unit of charge appearing in Eq. 2.02(1) is selected as the practical unit, the coulomb. All dimensions in the basic force equation have now been selected except for the constant k and the permittivity ϵ. In this system the permittivity is allowed to absorb the conversion factors between units so that it has a value other than unity for free space, and definite dimensions. The remaining dimensionless factor k is selected

[2] Giorgi, *Elettricità* (Milan), **20**, 787–788 (Dec. 1901).

either as $1/4\pi$ or as unity, depending on whether a "rationalized" or an "unrationalized" system of units is desired. The relative advantages of these choices cannot be discussed intelligently until the entire set of electromagnetic equations has been presented, but, since the choice in the literature has been predominantly in favor of the rationalized system, that system will be used in this text. The constant k is therefore chosen as $1/4\pi$, and the force equation in rationalized mks units reads

$$\bar{f} = \frac{q_1 q_2}{4\pi \epsilon r^2}(\bar{a}_r). \tag{4}$$

The units of ϵ may now be found from (4) in conjunction with (2) and (3):

$$\epsilon = \frac{(\text{coulombs})^2}{\text{newtons (meter)}^2} = \frac{(\text{coulombs})^2}{\text{joules-meter}} = \frac{\text{farads}}{\text{meter}}.$$

To find the value of ϵ for free space, which will be denoted ϵ_0, we may refer to the known result from the force equation in esu: two charges of 1 statcoulomb each placed 1 centimeter apart in vacuum yield a force of 1 dyne. If these data are converted to the mks system and substituted in (4), the result is

$$\epsilon_0 = \frac{q_1 q_2}{4\pi r^2 f} = \frac{(\frac{1}{3} \times 10^{-9})^2}{4\pi (10^{-2})^2 10^{-5}} = \frac{1}{36\pi} \times 10^{-9} \text{ farads/meter.} \tag{5}$$

The use of the approximate conversion between statcoulombs and coulombs, as in (5), results in the easily remembered value shown. A more accurate value is 8.854×10^{-12} farads per meter. The permittivity of other materials may then be written as the product of ϵ_0 and the relative permittivity defined in the previous article:

$$\epsilon = \epsilon_r \epsilon_0. \tag{6}$$

The quantity ϵ_r is that commonly listed in tables for dielectric materials and is a measure of the polarization of the constituent atoms and molecules. The relative permittivity ϵ_r is frequently called the *dielectric constant* of a material.

Problems

2.03a Compute the force between two charges of 1 coulomb each placed 1 meter apart in vacuum. Use Coulomb's force law in both esu and mks units, and show that the results are equivalent.

2.03b Calculate the ratio of the electrostatic force of repulsion between two electrons to the gravitational force of attraction, assuming that Newton's law of gravitation holds. The electron's charge is 1.602×10^{-19} coulombs, its mass is 9.11×10^{-28} grams, and the gravitational constant K is 6.66×10^{-8} dyne cm^2 g^{-2}.

2.04   Characteristics of a Medium: Terminology

At various points throughout the book it will be desirable to specify the nature of the medium being considered. The method for the solution of a field problem usually depends strongly on whether the characteristics of the material in the space being considered vary with position, source strength, etc. There are certain standard terms used to describe the nature of the materials which apply to many physical characteristics, but we will use them for electric and magnetic properties.

1. If the characteristics of the material do not depend on position, the term "homogeneous" applies, otherwise the material is said to be "inhomogeneous." A practically important inhomogeneous medium is the atmosphere. This may have permittivity changes in space because of temperature and humidity variations, or ionization at the higher levels, producing a bending of radio waves.

2. If the behavior of the medium is the same regardless of the direction of any of the field vectors, it is called "isotropic." If the relations depend on field directions, the medium is "anisotropic." Many useful crystals are anisotropic, as are ionized gases and ferrites with applied magnetic fields.

3. A material is "linear" if the relations between the physical quantities in question do not depend on their magnitudes. For example, if the ratio of the force between charges to the product of the charge magnitudes does not depend on the values of charge, the medium is linear.

4. Materials may also have time-varying characteristics, as when the permittivity of a compressible medium is made to vary by applying a sound wave. The static problems of this chapter are of course concerned with time invariance of electric and magnetic properties.

Throughout this book, the media will be considered homogeneous, isotropic, linear, and time-invariant unless otherwise stated. From time to time, important exceptions will be noted, especially with respect to anisotropic or inhomogeneous materials.

2.05   Electric Field Intensity

Coulomb's force law gives the force that will be exerted on a charge when placed in the vicinity of another point charge. In the more general case, any charge placed in the vicinity of a system of charges experiences a force whose magnitude and direction are functions of the amounts and positions of all charges of the system. A region so influenced by charges is called a region of electric field. The force per unit charge on a positive test charge at a point is defined as the strength of electric field or electric intensity at the point, provided that the test charge is so small that it does not disturb the original charge distribution of the system. Since the force on the test charge has direction as well as magnitude, the electric intensity is a vector. The electric intensity or electric field vector is then defined by

$$\bar{E} = \frac{\bar{f}}{\Delta q},$$ (1)

where $\bar{f}$ is the force acting on the infinitesimal test charge Δq.

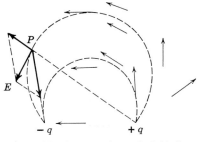

Fig. 2.05   Construction of field lines
about point charges.

The electric field arising from a point charge q in a homogeneous dielectric is then given by the force law, Eq. 2.03(4):

$$\bar{E} = \frac{q}{4\pi\epsilon r^2}(\bar{a}_r).$$ (2)

Since $\bar{a}_r$ is the unit vector directed from the point in a direction away from the charge, the electric field vector is seen to point away from positive charges and toward negative charges. The units of electric field in the mks system are in volts per meter, as may be found by substituting units in (2):

$$E = \frac{\text{coulombs meter}}{\text{farads (meter)}^2} = \frac{\text{volts}}{\text{meter}}.$$

For a system of point charges, the total electric field may be found by adding vectorially the forces from the individual charges, as is illustrated at point P of Fig. 2.05 for the charges q and $-q$ separated by distance d. In this manner the electric field vector could be found for any point in the vicinity of the two charges. An electric field line is defined as a line drawn tangent to the electric field vector at each point in space. If the vector is

10/11/66

constructed for enough points of the region, the electric field lines can be drawn in roughly by following the direction of the vectors as illustrated in the figure. Easier methods of constructing the electric field will be studied in later articles, but the present method, although laborious, demonstrates clearly the meaning of the electric field lines.

Problems

2.05a   Construct the electric field vector for several points in the x-y plane for like charges q at $(d/2, 0, 0)$ and $(-d/2, 0, 0)$, and draw in roughly a few electric field lines.

2.05b   Repeat Prob. *a* for charges of $2q$ and $-q$ at $(d/2, 0, 0)$ and $(-d/2, 0, 0)$, respectively.   Note any special points.

2.06 Electric Flux Density

Equation 2.05(2) shows that the electric intensity is dependent on the medium in which the charge is placed.

Let us define a new vector which is independent of the medium in regions of infinite extent having homogeneous, isotropic dielectric properties. Define the quantity $\bar{D}$ by

$$\bar{D} = \epsilon \bar{E}. \tag{1}$$

for isotropic materials. (The vector is also useful for anisotropic media as will be discussed in Art. 2.44.) This quantity for a point charge then becomes [Eq. 2.05(2)]

$$\bar{D} = \frac{q}{4\pi r^2}(\bar{a}_r). \tag{2}$$

The vector $\bar{D}$ at any point is thus a function of charge and position only, and is called an electric flux density. It is true that the justification for this name and the use of the concept of flux in connection with it cannot be appreciated fully at this stage but must gradually be built up over the next few articles. The name implies that each charge may be considered a source of flux or lines of flow in the medium, each charge giving rise to a certain amount of that flux. For example, if an imaginary spherical surface of radius r is chosen with center at the point charge of strength q, Eq. (2) shows that at each point on the surface of this sphere the vector which we have called electric flux density points radially outward and has strength $q/(4\pi r^2)$. If this is multiplied by the surface of the sphere, $4\pi r^2$, to obtain the total electric flux passing through the surface, it is found to be exactly

10/11/66

equal to the charge q, and is independent of the radius of the sphere chosen for the calculation. It will be demonstrated that this same result is obtained for any surface surrounding the charge, leading to the very important statement of Gauss's law.

For reasons which are largely historical, the vector $\bar{D}$ is also sometimes called the "displacement vector," and the flux associated with it is called "displacement flux." The terms electric flux density and electric flux give a better physical picture at this stage of the discussion. In (2), q has the dimensions of coulombs and r has the dimensions of meters, so D has the dimensions of coulombs per square meter in the mks system.

Problem

2.06 If (1) were used to define permittivity, with D in coulombs per meter^2 and E in volts per meter, show that ϵ has the units stated: farads per meter.

2.07 Gauss's Law

In Art. 2.06 it was shown that the electric flux passing through a spherical surface centered about a point charge q is exactly equal to the charge q. It is now desirable to generalize the demonstration to a surface of arbitrary

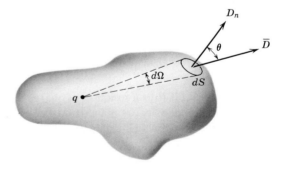

Fig. 2.07 Charge q and arbitrary surrounding surface.

shape containing any number of charges. If one of these point charges, q, is considered first (Fig. 2.07), the field intensity and electric flux density can be calculated for any point on the surface by equations of previous articles. Thus, at point P, D is $q/(4\pi r^2)$. (When a quantity normally a vector appears without the bar, it signifies that magnitude alone is being considered.) If we continue the interpretation of $\bar{D}$ as a flux or flow density vector, analogous to the flow vector for a fluid passing through a surface, it is the component of the vector normal to the surface at each point which determines the flow through the surface. Thus, if θ is the angle between $\bar{D}$ and the normal to the surface at some point, the amount of flux passing through an elemental surface dS is

$$d\psi = \frac{q}{4\pi r^2} dS \cos \theta;$$

$dS \cos \theta$ is the area dS', the component of dS normal to $\bar{D}$. But in solid geometry the element of solid angle $d\Omega$ is defined as the ratio of the surface subtended to the square of the radius:

$$d\Omega = \frac{dS'}{r^2} = \frac{dS \cos \theta}{r^2} .$$

Hence the amount of flux flowing through the elemental surface can be written as $qd\Omega/4\pi$. To obtain the total electric flux, this expression is integrated over all the surface, which amounts to integrating $d\Omega$. Since the total solid angle subtended by a closed surface is 4π steradians, the result is again simply q:

$$\oint_S D \cos \theta \, dS = q. \tag{1}$$

D is the magnitude of the electric flux density at any point on the surface, dS is an elemental area at that point, and θ is the angle between $\bar{D}$ and the normal to the surface. $\oint_S$ is used to denote the integral over a general surface, and the circle through the integral signifies that the surface is closed.

If there are a number of point charges inside the region considered, there will be an integration similar to the above for each of the charges and the flux will add linearly, since the total force on a test charge at any point will be the vector sum of the forces from the individual charges considered separately. Hence the q on the right side of Eq. (1) may be considered the total charge inside the surface under consideration.

The preceding is a statement of Gauss's law. In words, it is

flux out of a surface = charge enclosed.

It has been derived from Coulomb's force law by the introduction of new definitions and concepts, but without any further experimental information. It is more useful than the original law for much general thinking, and also for a variety of simple problems, some of which will be demonstrated in the next articles.

2.08   Examples of the Use of Gauss's Law

The simple but important examples to be discussed in this article demonstrate that Gauss's law enables one to obtain the field strength immediately in problems with certain kinds of symmetry. This symmetry allows one to tell the direction of the electric field by physical reasoning, and then allows one to write the flux as the product of area and flux density, since the flux density does not vary over the surface.

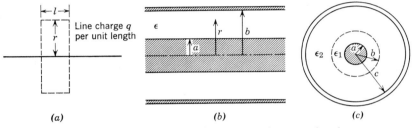

(a)   (b)   (c)

Fig. 2.08   Line charge, coaxial cylinders, and concentric spheres.

Field about a Line Charge or between Coaxial Cylinders. A line charge is defined as one for which the charge per unit length, q_l, is given along an axis, and its radial extent is assumed to be very small but is not otherwise specified. Unless stated, it is assumed to extend to infinity in each direction along the axis with uniform strength, and is hence the two-dimensional equivalent of the point charge. Practically, a long thin charged wire is a good approximation. The symmetry of this problem reveals that the force on a test charge, and hence the electric field, can only be radial. Moreover, this electric field will not vary with angle about the line charge, or with distance along it. If the strength of the radial electric field is desired at distance r from the line charge, Gauss's law may be applied to an imaginary cylindrical surface of radius r and any length l (Fig. 2.08a). Since the electric field (and hence the electric flux density $\bar{D}$) is radial, there is no normal component at the ends of the cylinder and hence no flux flow through them. However, $\bar{D}$ is exactly normal to the cylindrical part of the surface, and does not vary with either angle or distance along the axis, so that the flux out is the surface $2\pi rl$ multiplied by the electric flux density D_r. The charge enclosed is the length l multiplied by the charge per unit length, q_l. By Gauss's law, flux out equals the charge enclosed:

$$2\pi r l D_r = l q_l.$$

If the dielectric surrounding the wire has constant ϵ, D_r is ϵE_r, and

$$E_r = \frac{q_l}{2\pi\epsilon r}. \tag{1}$$

Hence the electric field about the line charge has been obtained by the use of Gauss's law and the special symmetry of the problem.

The same symmetry applies to the coaxial transmission line formed of two coaxial conducting cylinders of radii a and b with dielectric ϵ between them (Fig. 2.08b). Hence the result (1) applies for radius r between a and b. As a static problem, it is probably better to think of this as a cylindrical capacitor.

Field inside an Electron Beam. Next imagine a long cylindrical beam of electrons moving with velocity v_0 carrying a direct current I_0 in vacuum. Since the charges are in motion, it might appear that this is not a static problem, but, although the individual charges move through the beam, there is always the same total amount of charge (except for statistical fluctuations) in a given part of the beam. Again, because of the cylindrical symmetry, the imaginary surface for the application of Gauss's law is selected as a cylinder of length l and radius r. The electric field is radial, independent of angle and axial distance, and the flux out is again $2\pi r l \epsilon_0 E_r$. The charge per unit length to produce the current I_0 is I_0/v_0 coulombs per meter. If it is assumed here that this charge is distributed uniformly over the cross section, the total charge inside the cylinder of radius r and length l may be found and set equal to the outgoing flux by Gauss's law. For r taken inside the beam radius, a,

$$2\pi r l \epsilon_0 E_r = l \frac{r^2}{a^2} \frac{I_0}{v_0}$$

or

$$E_r = \frac{r I_0}{2\pi\epsilon_0 a^2 v_0} \qquad r < a. \tag{2}$$

If the field is desired outside the beam, the Gaussian surface is selected with radius greater than a, and the total charge per unit length for the beam is used:

$$2\pi r l \epsilon_0 E_r = \frac{l I_0}{v_0}$$

$$E_r = \frac{I_0}{2\pi\epsilon_0 r v_0} \qquad r > a. \tag{3}$$

Field in a Spherical Capacitor with Two Dielectrics. Figure 2.08c shows a capacitor formed of two conducting spheres of radii a and c, with one dielectric ϵ_1 extending from $r = a$ to $r = b$, and a second, ϵ_2, from $r = b$ to $r = c$. This problem has spherical symmetry about the center, which reveals that the electric field will be radial, and independent of the angular direction about the sphere. If the charge on the inner sphere is Q and that on the outer sphere is $-Q$, the charge enclosed by an imaginary spherical surface of radius r selected anywhere between the two conductors is only that charge Q on the inner sphere. The flux passing through it is the surface $4\pi r^2$ multiplied by the radial component of flux density, D_r. Hence, using Gauss's law,

$$D_r = \frac{Q}{4\pi r^2}. \qquad (4)$$

The form of the equation for the flux density is the same for either dielectric, since the flux passes from the positive charge on the center conductor continuously to the negative charge on the outer conductor. The electric field has a different form in the two regions, however, since in each dielectric D and E are related by the corresponding permittivity:

$$E_r = \frac{Q}{4\pi\epsilon_1 r^2} \qquad a < r < b \qquad (5)$$

$$E_r = \frac{Q}{4\pi\epsilon_2 r^2} \qquad b < r < c. \qquad (6)$$

The radial flux density is continuous at the dielectric discontinuity at $r = b$, but radial electric field is discontinuous there.

Problems

2.08a A coaxial transmission line has an inner conducting cylinder of radius a, and an outer conducting cylinder of radius c. Charge q_l per unit length is uniformly distributed over the inner conductor and $-q_l$ over the outer. If dielectric ϵ_1 extends from $r = a$ to $r = b$ and dielectric ϵ_2 from $r = b$ to $r = c$, find the electric field for $r < a$, for $a < r < b$, for $b < r < c$, and for $r > c$. Take the conducting cylinders as infinitesimally thin. Sketch the variation of $\bar{D}$ and $\bar{E}$ with radius.

2.08b In the electron beam example, find electric field in terms of total current and axial velocity for $r < a$ and for $r > a$ if the velocity as a function of radius is $v_z = v_0[1 - (r^2/a^2)]$ and the charge density is $\rho = \rho_0[1 + (r^2/a^2)]$ coulombs/meter^3 and sketch its variation with radius.

2.08c Imagine that a sphere of charge of radius a and uniform density ρ_0 coulombs/meter^3 can be considered static over a certain time interval. Find the electric field for $r < a$ and for $r > a$ and sketch its variation with radius.

2.08d   Derive the expression for the field about a line charge, Eq. 2.08(1), from the field of a point charge.

2.08e   Consider a sheet of charge of ρ_0 coulombs/meter^2 having infinite extent situated in free space. Find the field at a point d meters distant from the sheet. Notice the forms of variation of $\bar{E}$ with the point, line, and plane symmetries.

2.09   Surface and Volume Integrals; Gauss's Law in Vector Notation

The general notation for a surface integral used in the statement of Gauss's law in Eq. 2.07(1) is very useful, but frequently confusing to students on first introduction. Once the integral sign is sighted, it is felt that the process of integration should be performed as the next step. The actual evaluation of the integral cannot take place, however, until the particular surface and the particular way in which the flux density $\bar{D}$ varies over that surface are specified. Nevertheless, the general notation is of great usefulness in writing a general law such as Gauss's which says that, no matter what surface is selected, and no matter how the flux density varies over that surface, the net result of the integration, when performed, will always yield the charge enclosed. The actual evaluation of the surface integral will require a double integration in the general case.

The surface integral can also be written in a still more compact form if vector notation is employed. Define the unit vector normal to the surface under consideration, for any given point on the surface, as $\bar{a}_n$. Then replace $D \cos \theta$ by $\bar{D} \cdot \bar{a}_n$. This particular product of the two vectors $\bar{D}$ and $\bar{a}_n$ denoted by the dot between the two is known as the dot product of two vectors, or the scalar product, since it results by definition in a scalar quantity equal to the product of the two vector magnitudes and the cosine of the angle between them. Also the combination $\bar{a}_n \, dS$ is frequently abbreviated further by writing it $\overline{dS}$. Thus the elemental vector $\overline{dS}$, representing the element of surface in magnitude and orientation, has a magnitude equal to the magnitude of the element dS under consideration, and the direction of the outward normal to the surface at that point. The surface integral in Eq. 2.07(1) may then be written in any of the equivalent forms,

$$\oint_S D \cos \theta \, dS = \oint_S \bar{D} \cdot \bar{a}_n \, dS = \oint_S \bar{D} \cdot \overline{dS}. \tag{1}$$

All of these say that the normal component of the vector $\bar{D}$ is to be integrated over the general closed surface S.

If the charge inside the region is given as a density of charge per unit volume in coulombs per cubic meter for each point of the region, the total charge inside the region must be obtained by integrating this density over the volume of the region. This is of course exactly analogous to the process of finding the total mass inside a region when the variable mass density is given for each point of a region. This process may also be denoted by a general integral. The symbol $\int_V$ is used to denote this, and, as with the surface integral, the particular volume and the variation of density over that volume must be specified before the integration may be performed. Then, in the general case, it will have to be performed as a triple integral.

Gauss's law may then be written in this notation:

$$\oint_S \bar{D} \cdot \overline{dS} = \int_V \rho \, dV. \tag{2}$$

The notation is cryptic enough so that it may at first appear to conceal the physical meaning of the law rather completely, yet, after a bit of practice, the contrary will be found to be true. The left-hand side will reveal at once that the normal component of a vector $\bar{D}$ is to be integrated over a closed surface, yielding the flux out of the region, and the right side will show that the volume density ρ is to be integrated over the volume surrounded by that surface, yielding the total charge inside the region.

Problem

2.09 A point charge q is located at the origin of coordinates. Express the electric field vector in its rectangular coordinate components, and evaluate the surface integral for S chosen as the surface of a cube of sides $2a$ centered on the charge.

2.10 Scalar or Dot Product of Vectors

The vector operation defined in the last article is important since there is often occasion to multiply one vector by the projection of the other upon it. That is, if $\bar{A}$ and $\bar{B}$ are vectors (of magnitudes A and B) with an angle of θ between them, $AB \cos \theta$ is of interest. This has been written as $\bar{A} \cdot \bar{B}$. (Read A dot B.) This product may now be expressed in terms of the components of $\bar{A}$ and $\bar{B}$ along the coordinate axes, not only for the calculation of flux flow through a surface, as in preceding articles, but also in the computation of the work done by a vector force moving through a vector distance.

A unit vector has already been defined in the statement of Eq. 2.02(2).

If $\bar{a}_x$, $\bar{a}_y$, $\bar{a}_z$ are three such unit vectors having the directions of the three axes in rectangular coordinates, and if A_x, A_y, and A_z are the magnitudes of the components of $\bar{A}$ along these axes, $\bar{A}$ may be written

$$\bar{A} = A_x\bar{a}_x + A_y\bar{a}_y + A_z\bar{a}_z.$$

The addition of the three component vectors to obtain $\bar{A}$ is performed according to the definition of vector addition, which states that the beginning of one vector is placed in coincidence with the terminus of

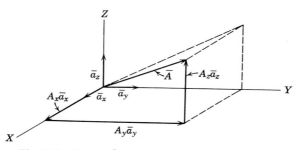

Fig. 2.10   Vector $\bar{A}$ and its rectangular components.

another, and the resultant drawn from the starting point to the final point (Fig. 2.10). The dot product is

$$\bar{A} \cdot \bar{B} = (A_x\bar{a}_x + A_y\bar{a}_y + A_z\bar{a}_z) \cdot (B_x\bar{a}_x + B_y\bar{a}_y + B_z\bar{a}_z).$$

If the multiplication is carried through term by term, with the dot product between component vectors retained,

$$\bar{A} \cdot \bar{B} = A_xB_x\bar{a}_x \cdot \bar{a}_x + A_xB_y\bar{a}_x \cdot \bar{a}_y, \text{ etc.}$$

The terms $\bar{a}_x \cdot \bar{a}_x$, $\bar{a}_y \cdot \bar{a}_y$, $\bar{a}_z \cdot \bar{a}_z$ are unity by definition of the unit vectors and the dot product. The terms $\bar{a}_x \cdot \bar{a}_y$, $\bar{a}_y \cdot \bar{a}_z$, etc., are zero since the angle between any of these unit vectors and either of the other two is 90°. The scalar product then reduces to

$$\bar{A} \cdot \bar{B} = A_xB_x + A_yB_y + A_zB_z. \tag{1}$$

Problems

2.10a   If $\bar{A}$, $\bar{B}$, and $\bar{C}$ are vectors, show

$$\bar{B} \cdot \bar{A} = \bar{A} \cdot \bar{B}$$
$$(\bar{A} + \bar{B}) + \bar{C} = \bar{A} + (\bar{B} + \bar{C})$$
$$\bar{A} \cdot (\bar{B} + \bar{C}) = \bar{A} \cdot \bar{B} + \bar{A} \cdot \bar{C}.$$

2.10b Vector $\bar{A}$ makes angles α_1, β_1, γ_1 with the x, y, and z axes respectively, and $\bar{B}$ makes angles α_2, β_2, γ_2 with the axes. If θ is the angle between the vectors, make use of the scalar product $\bar{A} \cdot \bar{B}$ to show that

$$\cos\theta = \cos\alpha_1 \cos\alpha_2 + \cos\beta_1 \cos\beta_2 + \cos\gamma_1 \cos\gamma_2.$$

2.11 Tubes of Flux

The concept of flux passing through an area does not have to be limited to electric phenomena. If $\bar{D}$ is any vector function of space, the product of the magnitude of $\bar{D}$ at any point by an element of area perpendicular to

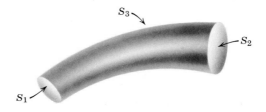

Fig. 2.11*a*   Tube of flux.

$\bar{D}$ at that point may be called the flux of $\bar{D}$ passing through that area. The total flux flowing through a surface is given by the surface integral

$$\psi = \int_S \bar{D} \cdot \overline{dS}. \tag{1}$$

Consider a surface (Fig. 2.11*a*), bounded by two planes, S_1 and S_2, perpendicular to the field vector at two points, and a surface S_3 always parallel to the direction of the field vector. If there is no charge enclosed, Gauss's law gives

$$\int_{S_1} \bar{D} \cdot \overline{dS} + \int_{S_2} \bar{D} \cdot \overline{dS} + \int_{S_3} \bar{D} \cdot \overline{dS} = 0. \tag{2}$$

Since S_3 is always parallel to $\bar{D}$, there is no flux flowing out through S_3. So

$$\int_{S_1} \bar{D} \cdot \overline{dS} = -\int_{S_2} \bar{D} \cdot \overline{dS}. \tag{3}$$

This equation states that the flux passing through the plane S_1 is that which comes out of the plane S_2, so that total flux across any cross section of the tube is a constant. Such a tubular region may be called a tube of flux. To study the field intensity distribution, it is sometimes helpful to draw out many of these tubes, the size of area being so selected that the flux through the area is one unit. Lines are often used to represent the tubes, and the tubes loosely called lines. Thus, the closer the spacing of these lines, the stronger is the flux density at that point.

The electrostatic tubes of flux emanate from positive charges, are continuous in regions without charge, and end on negative charges. The boundaries of the flux tubes, as have been shown, follow the direction of the flux density vector $\bar{D}$ and therefore the direction of the electric field $\bar{E}$. This fact is sometimes useful in drawing the electric field lines about

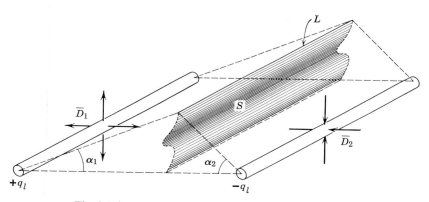

Fig. 2.11b   Construction of flux tubes about line charges.

charges. For example, consider two line charges, q_l at $x = -1$ and $-q_l$ at $x = 1$ (Fig. 2.11b). It is obvious from symmetry that the plane in which the two parallel lines lie will be a $\bar{D}$ line and hence can be the boundary of a tube of flux. The flux integral (1) or "flux function" can be arbitrarily assigned the value of zero on this plane. To find other flux tube boundaries, an expression will be derived for the flux passing between the line L parallel to the line charges and the plane where $\psi = 0$ across any arbitrary surface such as S in Fig. 2.11b. Then paths will be formed along which L may be moved while keeping the same flux between it and the $\psi = 0$ surface. Moving L along such a path therefore generates a surface which is the boundary of a flux tube of infinite length parallel to L. The flux may be divided into the part from the positive line charge and the part from the negative line charge, since the effects are superposable. The flux from the positive line goes out radially so that the amount (per unit length) crossing S is $q_l(\alpha_1/2\pi)$. The flux passing radially inward toward the negative line through S is in the same direction as that of the positive line and has the magnitude $q_l(\alpha_2/2\pi)$. The total flux crossing S is

$$\psi = \frac{q_l}{2\pi}(\alpha_1 + \alpha_2). \tag{4}$$

The surface generated by moving L in such a way as to keep ψ constant is a circular cylinder that passes through the lines $x = \pm 1$, with its axis in the plane normal to the $\psi = 0$ line midway between the line charges. Figure

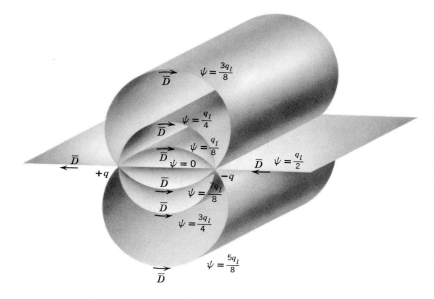

Fig. 2.11c   Tubes of flux between line charges.

2.11c shows several flux tubes with the values of the ψ indicating the amount of flux between the $\psi = 0$ surface and the one being considered, as α_2 is increased from zero to 2π. Note that, as a path is taken around one of the lines, the flux function goes from 0 to q_l; the total flux per unit length coming from a line charge is q_l. It is clear from this example that the flux function ψ is not single valued since it continues to increase as α_1 or α_2 increases; more flux lines are crossed as motion about the line charge continues. We must therefore limit α_1 and α_2 to the range 0 to 2π to insure unique values for ψ.

     In the next example, flux tubes about equal and opposite point charges, we choose a different surface for the reference $\psi = 0$. If q is located at $x = -1$ and $-q$ at $x = 1$, the flux from each of these point charges passes radially in or out from the charges in a spherical sense. The flux from the charge at A passing through a spherical cap bounded by a circle through P is $q\Omega_1/4\pi$, where Ω_1 is the solid angle subtended by the cap at the charge, and the flux due to the negative charge at B is $-q\Omega_2/4\pi$. The relation between solid angle subtended by a spherical cap centered about the axis

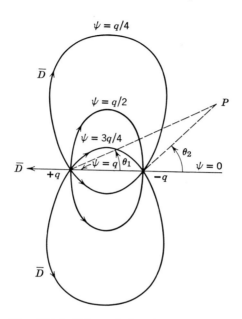

Fig. 2.11d Tubes of flux between point charges.

and the angle θ measured from the axis is

$$\Omega = 2\pi(1 - \cos\theta). \tag{5}$$

Hence the total flux for this problem may be written

$$\psi = \frac{q}{4\pi}(\Omega_1 - \Omega_2) = \frac{q}{2}(\cos\theta_2 - \cos\theta_1). \tag{6}$$

To plot field lines, the flux function may again be maintained constant as the angles θ_1 and θ_2 are varied. Figure 2.11d shows the results when the flux per tube is selected as $q/4$. In comparing Fig. 2.11 c and d, it should be remembered that the flux tubes in d are figures of revolution, whereas those in c are cylinders.

Problems

2.11a Plot the field from like charges q distance d apart (Prob. 2.05a) by making use of the flux function.

2.11b Plot the field of charges $2q$ and $-q$ distance d apart (Prob. 2.05b) by this method.

2.12   The Divergence of an Electrostatic Field

Gauss's law was derived from Coulomb's law, which was determined by experiment on systems of finite size. Let us extend it to an infinitesimally small system. Equation 2.09(2) may be divided by the volume element ΔV and the limit taken:

$$\lim_{\Delta V \to 0} \frac{\oint_S \bar{D} \cdot \overline{dS}}{\Delta V} = \lim_{\Delta V \to 0} \frac{\int_V \rho \, dV}{\Delta V}. \tag{1}$$

The right side is, by inspection, merely ρ. The left side is the amount of electric flux per unit volume flowing out of an infinitesimal volume. This will be defined as the divergence of flux density, abbreviated div $\bar{D}$. Then

$$\text{div } \bar{D} = \rho. \tag{2}$$

To make the picture clearer, consider the infinitesimal volume as a rectangular parallelepiped of dimensions Δx, Δy, Δz as shown in Fig. 2.12a. To compute the amount of flux leaving such a volume element as compared with that entering it, note that the flux passing through any face of the parallelepiped can differ from that which passes through the opposite face only if the flux density perpendicular to those faces varies from one

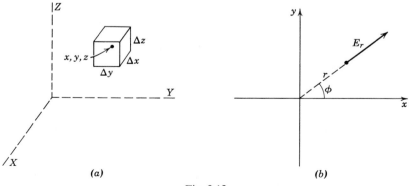

(a)   (b)

Fig. 2.12

face to the other. If the distance between the two faces is small, then to a first approximation the difference in any vector function on the two faces will simply be the rate of change of the function with distance times the distance between faces. According to the basis of calculus, this is exactly correct when we pass to the limit, since the higher order differentials are then zero.

If the vector at the center has components D_x, D_y, D_z,

$$D_x\left(x + \frac{\Delta x}{2}\right) = D_x(x) + \frac{\Delta x}{2}\frac{\partial D_x(x)}{\partial x}$$

$$D_x\left(x - \frac{\Delta x}{2}\right) = D_x(x) - \frac{\Delta x}{2}\frac{\partial D_x(x)}{\partial x}.$$

(3)

In this functional notation, the argument in parentheses show the points for evaluating the function D_x. When not included, the point (x, y, z) will be understood. The flux flowing out the front face is $\Delta y\, \Delta z\, D_x(x + \Delta x/2)$, and that flowing in the back face is $\Delta y\, \Delta z\, D_x(x - \Delta x/2)$, leaving a net flow out of $\Delta x\, \Delta y\, \Delta z(\partial D_x/\partial x)$, and similarly for the y and z directions, so that net flux flow out of all the parallelepiped is

$$\Delta x\, \Delta y\, \Delta z\, \frac{\partial D_x}{\partial x} + \Delta x\, \Delta y\, \Delta z\, \frac{\partial D_y}{\partial y} + \Delta x\, \Delta y\, \Delta z\, \frac{\partial D_z}{\partial z}.$$

By Gauss's law, this must be $\rho\, \Delta x\, \Delta y\, \Delta z$. So, in the limit,

$$\frac{\partial D_x}{\partial x} + \frac{\partial D_y}{\partial y} + \frac{\partial D_z}{\partial z} = \rho.$$

(4)

An expression for div $\bar{D}$ in rectangular coordinates is obtained by comparing (2) and (4):

$$\text{div } \bar{D} = \frac{\partial D_x}{\partial x} + \frac{\partial D_y}{\partial y} + \frac{\partial D_z}{\partial z}.$$

(5)

It will be convenient to define a vector operator ∇ (pronounced del) in rectangular coordinates as

$$\nabla = \bar{a}_x\frac{\partial}{\partial x} + \bar{a}_y\frac{\partial}{\partial y} + \bar{a}_z\frac{\partial}{\partial z}.$$

(6)

Consider the expansion for the dot or scalar product, Eq. 2.10(1), and the definition of ∇ above. Then (5) indicates that div $\bar{D}$ can correctly be written as $\nabla \cdot \bar{D}$. It should be remembered that ∇ is not a true vector but rather a vector operator. It has meaning only when it is operating on another quantity in a defined manner. The divergence represents the first of several of these operations to be defined:

$$\nabla \cdot \bar{D} = \frac{\partial D_x}{\partial x} + \frac{\partial D_y}{\partial y} + \frac{\partial D_z}{\partial z}. \qquad (7)$$

Finally
$$\nabla \cdot \bar{D} \equiv \text{div } \bar{D} = \rho. \qquad (8)$$

The divergence is made up of space derivatives of the field, so (8) is evidently a differential equation derived by generalizing from the previous laws for comparatively large systems. It will be so important that we should become accustomed to looking at it as an expression for Gauss's law generalized to a point in space. The physical significance of the divergence must be clear. It is, as defined, a description of the manner in which a field varies at a point. It is the amount of flux per unit volume emerging from an infinitesimal volume at a point. With this picture in mind, (8) seems a logical extension of Gauss's law.

As an example of the way in which this equation shows the relation between the charge density at a point and the way in which the field varies about that point, consider the cylindrical electron beam example of Art. 2.08. Since we have for the present an expression for divergence only in rectangular coordinates, let us convert the radial electric field inside the beam, Eq. 2.08(2), into rectangular coordinate components. By referring to the coordinate system of Fig. 2.12b,

$$D_x = \epsilon E_r \cos \phi = \epsilon \left(\frac{rI_0}{2\pi \epsilon a^2 v_0} \right) \frac{x}{r}.$$

$$D_y = \epsilon E_r \sin \phi = \epsilon \left(\frac{rI_0}{2\pi \epsilon a^2 v_0} \right) \frac{y}{r}.$$

If the divergence of $\bar{D}$ is taken according to Eq. (7), the result is

$$\nabla \cdot \bar{D} = \frac{\partial D_x}{\partial x} + \frac{\partial D_y}{\partial y} = \frac{I_0}{\pi a^2 v_0}.$$

This is exactly the charge density ρ, as it should be by (8). Similarly, the field components outside the beam may be found and the divergence computed. Here the result is zero, as it should be since the charge density is zero for each point outside the beam.

Problems

2.12a Evaluate the divergence of $\bar{D}$ in the remaining examples of Art. 2.08, and in the results of Probs. 2.08a, b, and c, comparing results with the known charge densities for those problems.

2.12b Evaluate $\nabla \cdot \bar{F}$, where $\bar{F} = \bar{a}_x x^3 + \bar{a}_y xyz + \bar{a}_z yz^2$.

2.12c Derive the expression for divergence in the circular cylindrical coordinate system.

2.13 Divergence Theorem

If Eq. 2.12(2) is integrated over any volume,

$$\int_V \text{div } \bar{D} \, dV = \int_V \rho \, dV. \tag{1}$$

Replace the last term by its equivalent from Gauss's law, Eq. 2.09(2):

$$\int_V \text{div } \bar{D} \, dV = \oint_S \bar{D} \cdot \overline{dS}. \tag{2}$$

Although this relation has been derived from a consideration of $\bar{D}$, a little thought will show that it is a direct consequence of the definition of divergence and so must hold for any vector field. For if divergence of any vector is considered a density of outward flux flow from a point for that vector, it seems that the total outward flux flow from a closed region must be obtained by integrating the divergence throughout the volume. If $\bar{F}$ is any vector,

$$\int_V \text{div } \bar{F} \, dV = \int_V \nabla \cdot \bar{F} \, dV = \oint_S \bar{F} \cdot \overline{dS}. \tag{3}$$

This relation is known as the divergence theorem or Gauss's theorem (as distinguished from Gauss's law of Art. 2.07) and will be useful later in manipulating vector equations in order to arrive at their most useful forms. Note that the theorem is true for any continuous vector function of space, regardless of the physical significance of that vector.

Problem

2.13 Given a vector $\bar{F} = \bar{a}_x x$. Evaluate $\oint_S \bar{F} \cdot \overline{dS}$ for S taken as the surface of a cube of sides $2a$ centered about the origin. Then evaluate the volume integral of $\nabla \cdot \bar{F}$ for this cube and show that the two results are equivalent, as they should be by the divergence theorem.

2.14 Conservative Property of Electrostatic Fields

Before proceeding very far in attempts to build up pictures and quantitative relations for electrostatic fields, we should pause to look into the very important matter of energy. The field may be checked with ideas of conservation of energy, to determine, for example, whether the energy of the electrostatic field is a function merely of its state at any given time, or whether it depends on the manner in which that state occurred. We no doubt already feel certain that the energy of an electrostatic field depends only on the amounts and positions of the charges, and not on how they grew; the inverse square law tells us that this must be so.

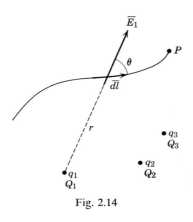

Fig. 2.14

The force on a small charge Δq moved from infinity to a point P in the vicinity of a system of charges: q_1 at Q_1, q_2 at Q_2, q_3 at Q_3, etc., may be calculated at any point along its path. This force would cause the particle to accelerate and move out of the region if unconstrained. We are interested, however, in applying a force the negative of that from surrounding charges in order to bring Δq from infinity to its final position.

Consider, then, the work integral arising from q_1. The differential work done on the system is the negative of the force component in the direction of the path, multiplied by differential path length:

$$dU = -\bar{F} \cdot \overline{dl}.$$

Or, using the definition of the scalar product, the angle θ as defined in Fig. 2.14, and the force as stated above,

$$U_1 = -\int \frac{\Delta q q_1 \cos \theta \, dl}{4\pi \epsilon r^2}.$$

But $dl \cos \theta$ is dr, so the integral is simply

$$U_1 = -\int_{\infty}^{PQ_1} \frac{\Delta q q_1 \, dr}{4\pi \epsilon r^2},$$

and similarly for contributions from other charges, so that the total work integral is

$$U = -\int_{\infty}^{PQ_1} \frac{\Delta q q_1}{4\pi \epsilon r^2} \, dr - \int_{\infty}^{PQ_2} \frac{\Delta q q_2}{4\pi \epsilon r^2} \, dr - \int_{\infty}^{PQ_3} \frac{\Delta q q_3}{4\pi \epsilon r^2} \, dr \cdots.$$

Integrating,

$$U = \frac{(\Delta q)q_1}{4\pi \epsilon PQ_1} + \frac{(\Delta q)q_2}{4\pi \epsilon PQ_2} + \frac{(\Delta q)q_3}{4\pi \epsilon PQ_3} + \cdots. \tag{1}$$

Equation (1) shows that the work done is only a function of final positions and not of the path of the charge. This conclusion leads to another: if a charge is taken around any closed path, no net work is done. Mathematically this is written

$$\oint \bar{E} \cdot \overline{dl} = 0. \tag{2}$$

This general integral signifies that the component of electric field in the direction of the path is to be multiplied by the element of distance along the path, and the sum taken by integration as one moves about the path. The circle through the integral sign signifies that a closed path is to be considered. As with the designation for a general surface or volume integral, the actual integration cannot be performed until there is a specification of a particular path and of the variation of $\bar{E}$ about that path.

In the study of magnetic fields and time-varying electric fields, we shall find corresponding line integrals which are not zero.

Problem

2.14 A point charge q is located at the origin of a system of rectangular coordinates. Evaluate $\int \bar{E} \cdot \overline{dl}$ in the x-y plane first along the x axis from $x = 1$ to $x = 2$, and next along a rectangular path as follows: along a straight line from the point $(1, 0)$ on the x axis to the point $(1, \frac{1}{2})$; along a straight line from $(1, \frac{1}{2})$ to $(2, \frac{1}{2})$; along a straight line from $(2, \frac{1}{2})$ to $(2, 0)$.

2.15 Electrostatic Potential

To solve the differential field equations, it is often convenient to introduce mathematical tools known as potential functions, which may aid materially during the solution but which need not appear in the final result. It is never necessary to give these mathematical tools physical significance, although it often may be desirable. We are already quite familiar with the potential function of electrostatics, and in this case it may easily have more significance for us than the fields, which were themselves only defined concepts to describe the situation in a region containing charges.

The common potential function in electrostatics is a scalar quantity defined so that the difference in this function between two points P and Q is given by the integral

$$\Phi_P - \Phi_Q = -\int_Q^P \bar{E} \cdot \overline{dl}. \tag{1}$$

The physical significance that may be attached to it is now apparent, for (1) is an expression for the work done on a unit charge in moving it from Q to P. The conclusion of the preceding article that the work in moving around any closed path is zero shows that the potential function defined is single valued; that is, corresponding to each point of the field there is only one value of potential, although the potential may, of course, vary from point to point.

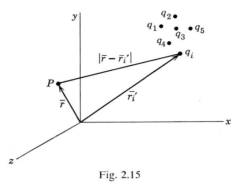

Fig. 2.15

Only a *difference* of potential has been defined. The potential of any point can be arbitrarily fixed, and then the potentials of all other points in the field can be found by application of the definition to give potential differences between all points and the base. This base is quite arbitrary since the potential differences alone have significance. For example, in certain cases it may be convenient to define the potential at infinity as zero and then find the corresponding potentials of all points in the field; for the determination of the field between two conductors, it will be more convenient to select the potential of one of these as zero.

If the potential at infinity is taken as zero, it is evident that the potential at the point P in the system of charges, Art. 2.14, is given by U of Eq. 2.14(1) divided by Δq, so

$$\Phi = \frac{q_1}{4\pi\epsilon PQ_1} + \frac{q_2}{4\pi\epsilon PQ_2} + \frac{q_3}{4\pi\epsilon PQ_3} + \cdots. \tag{2}$$

This may be written in a more versatile form as

$$\Phi(\bar{r}) = \sum_{i=1}^{n} \frac{q_i}{4\pi\epsilon \,|\bar{r} - \bar{r}_i'|}, \tag{3}$$

where $\bar{r}$ is a vector from an arbitrary origin to the point of observation and $\bar{r}_i'$ is a vector from the origin to the ith charge as shown in Fig. 2.15.

Therefore $|\vec{r} - \vec{r}'_i|$ is the magnitude of the separation of the ith charge from the point of observation,

$$|\vec{r} - \vec{r}'| = [(x - x')^2 + (y - y')^2 + (z - z')^2]^{1/2}. \tag{4}$$

Generalizing to the case of continuously varying charge density,

$$\Phi(\vec{r}) = \int_{V'} \frac{\rho(\vec{r})\, dV'}{4\pi\epsilon\, |\vec{r} - \vec{r}'|}. \tag{5}$$

The ρ is charge density, and the integral signifies that a summation should be made similar to that of (2) but continuous over all space. There are, of course, arbitrary added constants if the potential at infinity is not taken as zero.

At once there is evidence of the usefulness of the potential tool, for Φ is obtained by simple scalar addition; it would have been necessary to perform corresponding vector additions to obtain fields directly. Since the fields can be obtained simply from the potential, the work of obtaining electric fields from charges is simplified. We show in the next article how this may be done.

As an example of the relations between potential and electric field, consider first the problem of the line charge used as an example in Art. 2.08, with electric field given by Eq. 2.08(1). By (1) we integrate this from some radius r_0 chosen as the reference of zero potential to radius r:

$$\Phi = -\int_{r_0}^{r} E_r\, dr = -\int_{r_0}^{r} \frac{q_l\, dr}{2\pi\epsilon r} = -\frac{q_l}{2\pi\epsilon} \ln\left(\frac{r}{r_0}\right). \tag{6}$$

Or this expression for potential about a line charge may be written

$$\Phi = -\frac{q_l}{2\pi\epsilon} \ln r + C. \tag{7}$$

Note that it is not desirable to select infinity as the reference of zero potential for the line charge, for then by (6) the potential at any finite point would be infinite.

In a similar manner, the potential difference between the coaxial cylinders of Fig. 2.08b may be found:

$$\Phi_a - \Phi_b = -\int_b^a \frac{q_l\, dr}{2\pi\epsilon r} = \frac{q_l}{2\pi\epsilon} \ln\left(\frac{b}{a}\right).$$

The electrostatic capacitance of a two-conductor capacitor is defined as the charge on one conductor divided by the potential difference. So the capacitance per unit length for the coaxial cylindrical example is

$$C = \frac{q_l}{\Phi_a - \Phi_b} = \frac{2\pi\epsilon}{\ln(b/a)} \text{ farads/meter.} \tag{8}$$

Problems

2.15a Derive the expression for electrostatic capacitance of a spherical capacitor formed of concentric spherical conductors of radii a and b $(a < b)$, with dielectric ϵ between the spheres.

2.15b Find the expression for electrostatic capacitance of the spherical capacitor with two dielectrics used as an example in Art. 2.08.

2.15c A circular insulating disk of radius a is charged with a uniform surface density of charge ρ_s coulombs/meter^2. Find an expression for electrostatic potential Φ at a point on the axis distance z from the disk.

2.15d A charge of surface density ρ_s is spread uniformly over a spherical surface of radius a. Find the potential for $r < a$ and for $r > a$ by integrating contributions from the differential elements of charge. Check the results by making use of Gauss's law and the symmetry of the problem.

2.15e Check the result (6) or (7) for the potential about a line charge by integrating contributions from the differential elements of charge. Note that the problem is one of handling properly the infinite limits.

2.15f Assume a sheet of charge having infinite transverse extent, a finite thickness d, and charge density ρ_0 coulombs/meter^2. Using (1) and the results of Prob. 2.09d find the dependence of the potential difference across the sheet on the thickness d.

2.15g Consider two parallel sheets of charge having equal surface charge densities but with opposite sign. The sheets are both of infinite transverse dimension and are spaced by a distance d. Using the results of Prob. 2.09d, find the electric fields between and outside the sheets and find the dependence of potential difference across the pair of sheets on the spacing.

2.15h In a system of infinite transverse dimension, a sheet of charge of ρ_0 coulombs/meter^2 lies between, and parallel to, two conducting electrodes at zero potential spaced by distance d. Find the distribution of electric field and potential between the electrodes for arbitrary location of the charge sheet. Sketch the results for the cases where the sheet is (1) in the center and (2) at position $d/4$.

2.15i Three positive charges of equal magnitude q are located at the corners of an equilateral triangle. Find the potential at the center of the triangle and the force on one of the charges.

10/18/66   **2.16 Gradient**

If the definition of potential difference is applied to two points a distance dl apart,

$$d\Phi = -\bar{E} \cdot \overline{dl}, \tag{1}$$

$\overline{dl}$ may be written in terms of its components and the defined unit vectors (Art. 2.10):

$$\overline{dl} = dx\,\bar{a}_x + dy\,\bar{a}_y + dz\,\bar{a}_z. \tag{2}$$

Expand the dot product according to Eq. 2.10(1),

$$d\Phi = -(E_x\, dx + E_y\, dy + E_z\, dz).$$

Since Φ is a function of x, y, and z, the total differential may also be written

$$d\Phi = \frac{\partial \Phi}{\partial x}\, dx + \frac{\partial \Phi}{\partial y}\, dy + \frac{\partial \Phi}{\partial z}\, dz.$$

From a comparison of the two expressions,

$$E_x = -\frac{\partial \Phi}{\partial x}, \quad \text{etc.,} \tag{3}$$

$$\bar{E} = -\left(\bar{a}_x \frac{\partial \Phi}{\partial x} + \bar{a}_y \frac{\partial \Phi}{\partial y} + \bar{a}_z \frac{\partial \Phi}{\partial z}\right) \tag{4}$$

or

$$\bar{E} = -\operatorname{grad}\Phi, \tag{5}$$

where grad Φ, an abbreviation of the gradient of Φ, is a vector showing the direction and magnitude of the maximum space variation in the scalar function Φ, at any point in space. It is the maximum variation that is represented because the gradient is the vector sum of the variations in all three directions. That is, substituting back in (1), we have

$$d\Phi = (\operatorname{grad}\Phi) \cdot \overline{dl}.$$

Thus the change in Φ is given by the scalar product of the gradient and the vector $\overline{dl}$, so that, for a given element of length dl, the maximum value of $d\Phi$ is obtained when that element is oriented to coincide with the direction of the gradient vector.

The vector operator ∇ was defined by Eq. 2.12(6). Then grad Φ may be written as $\nabla\Phi$ if the operation is interpreted

$$\nabla\Phi = \bar{a}_x \frac{\partial \Phi}{\partial x} + \bar{a}_y \frac{\partial \Phi}{\partial y} + \bar{a}_z \frac{\partial \Phi}{\partial z} \tag{6}$$

and

$$\bar{E} = -\operatorname{grad}\Phi \equiv -\nabla\Phi. \tag{7}$$

Problems

2.16a   Given a scalar function $M = \sin \alpha x \cos \beta y \sinh \gamma z$; find the gradient of M.

2.16b   For two point charges q and $-q$ at $(d/2, 0, 0)$ and $(-d/2, 0, 0)$, respectively, find the potential for any point (x, y, z) and from this derive the electric field. Check the result by adding vectorially the electric field from the individual charges.

FIELDS AND WAVES

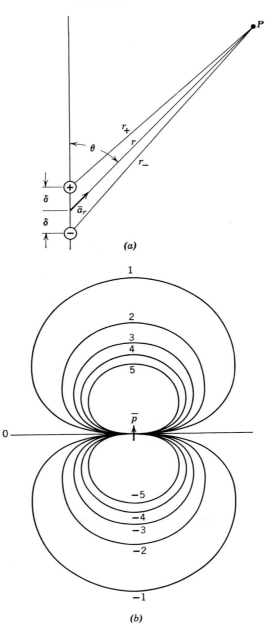

(a)

(b)

Fig. 2.17 (a) Electric dipole. (b) Equipotentials of
electric dipole.

2.16c For two line charges q_l and $-q_l$ at $(d/2, 0)$ and $(-d/2, 0)$, respectively, find the potential for any point (x, y) and from this derive the electric field.
2.16d Find the electric field along the axis for Prob. 2.15c.
2.16e Utilize the rectangular coordinate form to prove the vector equivalences

$$\nabla(\psi\Phi) = \psi\nabla\Phi + \Phi\nabla\psi$$

$$\nabla \cdot (\psi\bar{A}) = \psi\nabla \cdot \bar{A} + \bar{A} \cdot \nabla\psi$$

where ψ and Φ are any scalar functions and $\bar{A}$ is any vector function of space.

2.17 Equipotentials: Electric Dipole

All points of a field having the same potential may be thought of as connected by equipotential surfaces. The distribution and spacing of these equipotential surfaces can be used to describe the field. The electric field vector must be perpendicular to these surfaces at every point, for if there were the slightest component tangential to the surface, say E_t, then two points $d\xi$ apart would have a potential difference $E_t\,d\xi$ which would violate the condition for an equipotential surface. Since the flux tubes were shown in Art. 2.11 to have the same direction as the field lines, these also are at right angles to the equipotential surfaces.

If the potential were to vary in one direction only, say x, as in a potential difference applied between two infinite parallel conducting planes perpendicular to the x axis, the electric field, or negative gradient of potential, would be entirely in the x direction. The equipotential surfaces would be perpendicular to the x axis, or parallel to the conducting planes, as would be expected from symmetry. The equipotential surfaces about an isolated point charge would be spheres centered on the charge, and the equipotentials about an isolated line charge or between coaxial cylinders would be cylindrical surfaces of constant radius from the axis. In general, potential may be a function of all coordinates, the gradient will have components in all three component directions, and the equipotential surfaces will be more complex than those of the above simple examples.

To illustrate equipotentials, consider the useful example of an electric dipole. Assume two charges having opposite signs to be spaced by a distance 2δ as shown in Fig. 2.17a. The potential at some point a distance r from the origin displaced by an angle θ from the line passing from the negative to positive charges can be written as the sum of the potential of the individual charges as

$$\Phi = \frac{q}{4\pi\epsilon}\left(\frac{1}{r_+} - \frac{1}{r_-}\right). \tag{1}$$

Using the law of cosines, we have

$$r_+{}^2 = r^2 + \delta^2 - 2r\,\delta\cos\theta$$

and similarly for r_-. For $\delta \ll r$,

$$r_+ \approx r - \delta\cos\theta$$
$$r_- \approx r + \delta\cos\theta.$$

Substituting in (1) and again using the restriction $\delta \ll r$, one obtains

$$\Phi \approx \frac{2\,\delta q\cos\theta}{4\pi\epsilon r^2}. \qquad (2)$$

We define an *electric dipole moment* $\bar{p}$ of a pair of equal charges as the product of the charge and the separation. Direction of vector $\bar{p}$ is from the negative to the positive charge. Thus Eq. (2) may be written as

$$\Phi \approx \frac{\bar{p}\cdot\bar{a}_r}{4\pi\epsilon r^2}, \qquad (3)$$

where $\bar{a}_r$ is a unit vector directed outward toward the point of observation. It is seen that the dipole potential decreases as $1/r^2$ with increasing distance from the origin, whereas the potential of the single charge decreases only as the first power. The increased rate of decay of the potential is to be expected as a result of the cancellation of the potentials of opposite sign. Equipotential lines are shown plotted on a plane passing through the dipole in Fig. 2.17b. The values shown are relative. The electric field lines (lines of the gradient) are coincident with the lines of flux shown in Fig. 2.11d. Note that both the equipotentials and maximum gradient lines are actually surfaces of revolution generated by rotating the given figures about the dipole axis.

Problems

2.17a Show that the equipotential surfaces for the two line charges of Prob. 2.16c are cylinders whose traces in the x-y plane are circles.

2.17b A linear quadrupole is formed by two pairs of equal and opposite charges located along a line such that $+q$ lies at $+\delta$, $-2q$ at the origin, and $+q$ at $-\delta$. Find an approximate expression for the potential at large distances from the origin. Plot an equipotential line.

2.17c Show that the magnitude of the torque on a dipole in an electric field is the product of the magnitude of the dipole moment and the magnitude of the field component perpendicular to the dipole.

2.18   Boundary Conditions in Electrostatics

Many important problems of both static and time-varying fields have one material directly adjacent to another. The differential relations for each homogeneous medium, relating space derivatives of the field to sources at the point and to properties of the medium, may be applied separately to each region. The question is that of joining or matching the solutions across the surfaces of discontinuity. In this article the integral field equations are used to find the relations between electrostatic field vectors on two sides of a discontinuity. In solving problems, one finds solutions for the differential equations within regions of homogeneous characteristics. These solutions are joined across discontinuities by using the boundary conditions derived here.

Let us consider the relation between normal flux density components across an arbitrary boundary by using the integral form of Gauss's law. Consider an imaginary pillbox bisected as shown in Fig. 2.18 by the interface between regions 1 and 2. The thickness of the pillbox is considered to be small enough that the net flux out the sides vanishes in comparison with that out the flat faces. If we assume the existence of net surface charge ρ_s on the boundary, the total flux out of the box must equal $\rho_s \, \Delta S$. By Gauss's law,

$$D_{n1} \, \Delta S - D_{n2} \, \Delta S = \rho_s \, \Delta S$$

or

$$D_{n1} - D_{n2} = \rho_s, \tag{1}$$

where ΔS is small enough to consider D_n and ρ_s to be uniform.

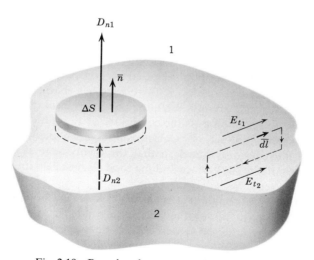

Fig. 2.18   Boundary between two different media.

A second relation may be found by taking a line integral about a closed path of length Δl on one side of the boundary and returning on the other side as indicated in Fig. 2.18. The sides normal to the boundary are considered to be small enough that their net contributions to the integral vanish in comparison with those of the sides parallel to the surface. By Eq. 2.14(2), any closed line integral of electrostatic field must be zero:

$$\oint \bar{E} \cdot \overline{dl} = E_{t1}\Delta l - E_{t2}\Delta l = 0$$

or
$$E_{t1} = E_{t2}. \tag{2}$$

The subscript t denotes components tangential to the surface. The length of the tangential sides of the loop are small enough to take E_t as a constant over the length. By integrating (2) along the boundary on both sides, it is seen that

$$\Phi_1 = \Phi_2 \tag{3}$$

across the boundary. Equations (1) and (2), or (1) and (3), form a complete set of boundary conditions to be used for solving electrostatic field problems.

Consider an interface between two dielectrics with no charge on the surface. From (1) and Eq. 2.06(1),

$$\epsilon_1 E_{n1} = \epsilon_2 E_{n2}.$$

It is clear that the normal component of $\bar{E}$ changes across the boundary, whereas the tangential components, according to (2) are unmodified. Therefore the direction of the resultant $\bar{E}$ must change across such a boundary except where either E_n or E_t are zero.

One very important special case has a perfect conductor in region 2. A perfect conductor is a material in which charges move freely when an electric field is applied. If charges are placed on or in the material, they will move about as long as there is the slightest force on them. They will move to an equilibrium position such that the forces are zero; all electric fields in the conductor are zero. If there were net charge in the body of the conductor, Gauss's law would require an electric field in the vicinity of this charge, so this is an impossible condition for the static case. All free charges in perfect conductors in electrostatics must then reside on the surface and must be distributed so that the component of electric field intensity tangential to the surface and the total electric field intensity inside the surface are zero.

Since the tangential component of electric field is zero along the perfectly conducting surface, it follows that the surface must be an equipotential surface. Moreover, since the field is zero inside the perfect conductor, the entire body will be at a constant potential in electrostatics.

As a simple example showing the relation between the field ending on a conductor and the charge which it induces there, let us find the charge induced on the anode of an idealized, parallel-plane, space-charge-limited diode if we take as given the fact that the potential varies as the $\frac{4}{3}$ power of distance across the diode:

$$\Phi = V_0 \left(\frac{x}{d}\right)^{\frac{4}{3}}, \tag{4}$$

where x is the distance from the cathode, d is the anode-cathode spacing, and V_0 is the anode potential with respect to the cathode. To find the electric field, we must take the gradient of Φ, which has an x component only

$$E_x = -\frac{\partial \Phi}{\partial x} = -\tfrac{4}{3}V_0 \frac{x^{\frac{1}{3}}}{d^{\frac{4}{3}}}. \tag{5}$$

The normal electric field at the anode, directed from the conductor into the field region, is $-E_x$ evaluated at $x = d$. Charge per unit area on the anode is then

$$\rho_s = -\epsilon_0 E_x \bigg|_{x=d} = \frac{4\epsilon_0}{3} \frac{V_0}{d} \text{ coulombs/meter}^2. \tag{6}$$

Problem

2.18   If the field vector makes an angle θ with the normal to the boundary in region 1, what angle does it have in region 2?

2.19   The Use of Images

A. Point Image in a Plane.   The method of images is useful when it is desired to find the field arising from point charges or line charges in the vicinity of conductors of certain simple shapes. The most simple case is that of a point charge near a grounded conducting plane (Fig. 2.19a). Boundary conditions require that the potential along the plane be zero. The requirement is met if in place of the conducting plane an equal and opposite image charge is placed at $x = -d$. Potential at any point P is then given by

$$\Phi = \frac{1}{4\pi\epsilon}\left(\frac{q}{r} - \frac{q}{r'}\right)$$

$$= \frac{q}{4\pi\epsilon}\{[(x-d)^2 + y^2 + z^2]^{-\frac{1}{2}} - [(x+d)^2 + y^2 + z^2]^{-\frac{1}{2}}\}. \tag{1}$$

This reduces to the required zero potential along the plane $x = 0$, so that (1) gives the potential for any point to the right of the plane. The expression of course does not apply for $x < 0$, for inside the conductor the potential must be everywhere zero.

If the plane is at a potential other than zero, the value of this constant potential is simply added to (1) to give the expression for potential at any point for $x > 0$.

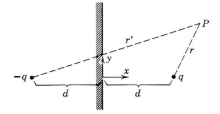

Fig. 2.19a   Image of a point charge in a plane.

B. Image of a Line Charge in a Plane. If there is a line charge of strength q_l coulombs per meter parallel to a conducting plane and distance d from it, we proceed as above, placing an image line charge of strength $-q_l$ at $x = -d$. The potential at any point $x > 0$ is then

$$\Phi = -\frac{q_l}{2\pi\epsilon} \ln\left(\frac{r}{r'}\right) = \frac{q_l}{4\pi\epsilon} \ln\left[\frac{(x+d)^2 + y^2}{(x-d)^2 + y^2}\right]. \tag{2}$$

C. Image of a Line Charge in a Cylinder. For a line charge of strength q_l parallel to the axis of a conducting circular cylinder, and at radius r from the axis, the image line charge of strength $-q_l$ is placed at radius $r' = a^2/r$, where a is the radius of the cylinder (Fig. 2.19b). The combination of the two line charges can be shown to produce a constant potential along the given cylinder of radius a. Potential outside the cylinder may be computed from the original line charge and its image. (Add q_l on axis if cylinder is uncharged.) If the original line charge is within a hollow cylinder a, the rule for finding the image is the same, and potential inside may be computed from the line charges.

D. Image of a Point Charge in a Sphere. For a point charge q placed distance r from the center of a conducting sphere of radius a, the image is a point charge of value $(-qa/r)$ placed at a distance (a^2/r) from the center (Fig. 2.19c). This combination gives the required zero potential along the spherical surface of radius a, and may be used to compute potential at any point P outside of radius a. (Or, it the original charge is inside, the image is outside, and the pair may be used to compute potential inside.)

E. Multiple Imagings. For a charge in the vicinity of the intersection of two conducting planes, as q in the region of AOB of Fig. 2.19d, there

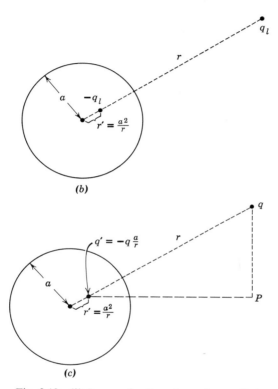

(b)

(c)

Fig. 2.19 (b) Image of a line charge in a cylinder.
(c) Image of a point charge in a sphere.

might be a temptation to use only one image in each plane, as 1 and 2 of Fig. 2.19d. Although $+q$ at Q and $-q$ at 1 alone would give constant potential as required along OA, and $+q$ at Q and $-q$ at 2 alone would give constant potential along OB, the three charges together would give constant potential along neither OA nor OB. It is necessary to image these images in turn repeating until further images coincide, or until all further images are too far distant from the region to influence potential.   It is

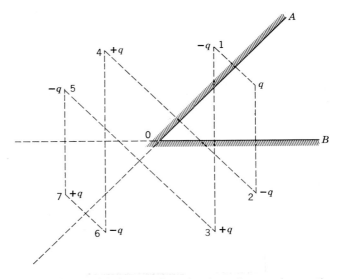

Fig. 2.19*d*   Multiple images of a point charge between intersecting planes.

possible to satisfy exactly the required conditions with a finite number of images only if the angle AOB is an exact submultiple of 180°, as in the 45° case illustrated by Fig. 2.19*d*.

Problems

2.19a Prove that the line charge and its image as described for a conducting cylinder of radius a will give constant potential along the cylinder of radius a.

2.19b Prove that the point charge and its image as described for the spherical conductor gives zero potential along the sphere of radius a.

2.19c A circularly cylindrical electron beam of radius a and uniform charge density ρ passes near a conducting plane that is parallel to the axis of the beam and distance s from it. Find the electric field acting to disperse the beam for the edge near the plane and for the edge farthest from the plane.

2.19d For a point charge q lying in a dielectric ϵ_1 distance $x = d$ from the plane boundary between ϵ_1 and a second dielectric ϵ_2, an image charge $q(\epsilon_1 - \epsilon_2)/(\epsilon_1 + \epsilon_2)$ placed at $x = -d$ in a homogeneous dielectric of permittivity ϵ_1 may be used to compute the potential for any point $x > 0$. To find the potential for a point $x < 0$, a single charge of value $2q\epsilon_2/(\epsilon_1 + \epsilon_2)$ is placed at the position of q in a homogeneous dielectric of permittivity ϵ_2. Show that these images satisfy the required continuity relations at a dielectric boundary.

2.19e Find and plot the surface charge density induced on the conducting plane as a function of y when the point charge q is at $x = d$. Repeat for a line charge at $x = d$.

2.19f Discuss the applicability of the image concept for the case of a line charge in the vicinity of the intersection of two conducting planes with an angle $AOB = 270°$ (see Fig. 2.19d).

2.20 Laplace's and Poisson's Equations

For many problems that do not have the simple geometrical configurations of the examples used up to now, it is most convenient to begin the solution from differential equations. In Art. 2.12 a differential equation relating the electric flux density $\bar{D}$ to charge density ρ was derived. It will often be more convenient to work directly with potentials instead of fields, since the specified boundary conditions on the problem will be more often given in terms of potentials. If the permittivity ϵ is constant throughout the region, the substitution of $\bar{E}$ from Eq. 2.16(7) in Eq. 2.12(2) yields

$$\operatorname{div}(\operatorname{grad}\Phi) \equiv \nabla \cdot \nabla \Phi = -\frac{\rho}{\epsilon}.$$

But, from the equations for divergence and gradient in rectangular coordinates [Eqs. 2.12(7) and 2.16(6)],

$$\nabla \cdot \nabla \Phi = \frac{\partial^2 \Phi}{\partial x^2} + \frac{\partial^2 \Phi}{\partial y^2} + \frac{\partial^2 \Phi}{\partial z^2} \tag{1}$$

so

$$\frac{\partial^2 \Phi}{\partial x^2} + \frac{\partial^2 \Phi}{\partial y^2} + \frac{\partial^2 \Phi}{\partial z^2} = -\frac{\rho}{\epsilon}. \tag{2}$$

This is a differential equation relating potential variation at any point to the charge density at that point, and is known as Poisson's equation. It is often written

$$\nabla^2 \Phi = -\frac{\rho}{\epsilon}, \tag{3}$$

where $\nabla^2 \Phi$ (del-squared of Φ) is known as the Laplacian of Φ.

$$\nabla^2 \Phi \equiv \nabla \cdot \nabla \Phi \equiv \operatorname{div}(\operatorname{grad}\Phi). \tag{4}$$

In the special case of a charge-free region, Poisson's equation reduces to

$$\frac{\partial^2 \Phi}{\partial x^2} + \frac{\partial^2 \Phi}{\partial y^2} + \frac{\partial^2 \Phi}{\partial z^2} = 0$$

or

$$\nabla^2 \Phi = 0, \tag{5}$$

which is known as Laplace's equation.

Any number of possible configurations of potential surfaces will satisfy the requirements of (3) and (5). All are called solutions to these equations. It is necessary to know the conditions existing around the boundary of the region in order to select the particular solution which applies to a given problem. It can be shown mathematically that, once ρ is given at every point in a region and Φ is given at every point on the surface surrounding the region, only one potential distribution is possible.

Equations exactly similar in form to (3) and (5) are found in many branches of physics. In fact, we shall discover later that they are true not only when the function is a static potential; for example, the function may be the static field strength vectors or certain of their components. Laplace's and Poisson's equations are of first importance in getting answers to all problems in which static electric and magnetic effects are involved. The ability to choose solutions of these equations is fundamental in arriving at the final solutions to the common problems discussed in Art. 2.02. For that reason the next chapter will be devoted almost entirely to a discussion of the techniques of building up solutions to these equations to fit boundary conditions that are likely to occur in practical problems.

Problems

2.20a Find the gradient and Laplacian of a scalar field varying as $1/r$ in two dimensions and in three dimensions.

2.20b Find the electric field and charge density as functions of x, y, and z if potential is expressed as

$$\Phi = C \sin \alpha x \sin \beta y \, e^{\gamma z} \qquad \gamma = \sqrt{\alpha^2 + \beta^2}$$

2.20c Find the electric field and charge density as a function of x for a space-charge-limited, parallel-plane diode with potential variation given by Eq. 2.18(4).

2.20d Argue from Laplace's equation that relative extrema of the electrostatic potential cannot exist and hence that a charge placed in an electrostatic field cannot be in stable equilibrium (Earnshaw's theorem).

2.21   Energy of an Electrostatic System

The work required to move a charge in the vicinity of a system of charges was discussed in the study of the electrostatic potential. The work done must appear as energy stored in the system, and consequently the potential energy of a system of charges may be computed from the magnitudes and positions of the charges. To do this, let us consider bringing the charges in from infinity to their positions in space. No force is required to bring the first charge in since no electric field acts on the charge. When the second charge q_2 is brought to a position separated from the location of q_1 by a distance r_{12}, an energy

$$U_{12} = \frac{q_1 q_2}{4\pi\epsilon r_{12}} \qquad (1)$$

is expended, as was shown in Art. 2.14. When the third charge is brought from infinity, it experiences the fields of q_1 and q_2, and an energy of

$$U_{13} + U_{23} = \frac{q_1 q_3}{4\pi\epsilon r_{13}} + \frac{q_2 q_3}{4\pi\epsilon r_{23}} \qquad (2)$$

is expended. The total energy expended to assemble these three charges is the sum of (1) and (2).

In summing this next over the three charges, we may write

$$U = \tfrac{1}{2}\sum_{i=1}^{3} q_i \sum_{j=1}^{3} \frac{q_j}{4\pi\epsilon r_{ij}}, \qquad i \neq j.$$

With the factor $\tfrac{1}{2}$, this yields the sum of (1) and (2), since by convention i and j are summed over all the particles, and each contribution to energy enters twice. In physical terms, the factor of two would result from assuming all other charges in position when finding the energy of the ith charge. The term $i = j$ has been excluded since the self energy of the point charge (i.e., the electron, ion, etc.) is not at issue here. For N charges, the direct extension gives

$$U_E = \tfrac{1}{2}\sum_{i=1}^{N} q_i \sum_{j=1}^{N} \frac{q_j}{4\pi\epsilon r_{ij}}, \qquad i \neq j \qquad (3)$$

where the subscript E indicates energy stored in electric charges and fields. By use of Eq. 2.15(3) for potential, this becomes

$$U_E = \tfrac{1}{2}\sum_{i=1}^{N} q_i \Phi_i. \qquad (4)$$

Extending (4) to a system with continuously varying charge density ρ per unit volume, we have

$$U_E = \tfrac{1}{2}\int_V \rho\Phi \, dV. \qquad (5)$$

The charge density ρ may be replaced by the divergence of $\bar{D}$ by Eq. 2.12(8):

$$U_E = \tfrac{1}{2}\int_V (\nabla \cdot \bar{D})\Phi \, dV.$$

Using the vector equivalence of Prob. 2.16e,

$$U_E = \tfrac{1}{2}\int_V \nabla \cdot (\Phi \bar{D})\, dV - \tfrac{1}{2}\int_V \bar{D} \cdot (\nabla \Phi)\, dV.$$

The first volume integral may be replaced by the surface integral of $\Phi \bar{D}$ over the closed surface surrounding the region, by the divergence theorem (Art. 2.13). But, if the region is to contain all fields, the surface should be taken at infinity. Since Φ dies off as $1/r$ at infinity, D as $1/r^2$, and area only increases as r^2, this surface integral approaches zero as the surface approaches infinity.

$$\int_V \nabla \cdot (\Phi \bar{D})\, dV = \oint_{S_\infty} \Phi \bar{D} \cdot \overline{dS} = 0.$$

Then there remains

$$U_E = -\tfrac{1}{2}\int_V \bar{D} \cdot (\nabla \Phi)\, dV = \tfrac{1}{2}\int_V \bar{D} \cdot \bar{E}\, dV. \qquad (6)$$

This result seems to say that the energy is actually in the electric field, each element of volume dV appearing to contain the amount of energy

$$dU_E = \tfrac{1}{2}\bar{D} \cdot \bar{E}\, dV. \qquad (7)$$

The right answer is obtained if this "energy density" picture is used. Actually, we know only that the total energy stored in the system will be correctly computed by the total integral in (6).

It is interesting to check these results against a familiar case. Consider a parallel plate capacitor of capacity C and a voltage between plates of V. The energy is known to be $\tfrac{1}{2}CV^2$, which is commonly obtained by integrating the product of instantaneous current and instantaneous voltage over the time of charging. The result may also be obtained by integrating the energy distribution in the field throughout the volume between plates according to (6). For plates of area A closely spaced so that the end effects may be neglected, the magnitude of field at every point in the dielectric is $E = V/d$ ($d = $ distance between plates).

Hence

$$D = \frac{\epsilon V}{d}.$$

$$\text{Stored energy} = \tfrac{1}{2}Ad\left(\frac{\epsilon V}{d}\right)\left(\frac{V}{d}\right)$$

$$= \frac{1}{2}\left(\frac{\epsilon A}{d}\right)V^2 = \tfrac{1}{2}CV^2. \qquad (8)$$

Problems

2.21a For a given potential difference V_0 between conductors of a coaxial capacitor, evaluate the stored energy in the electrostatic field per unit length. By equating this to $\frac{1}{2}CV^2$, evaluate the capacitance per unit length.

2.21b Evaluate the total energy stored in the space-charge-limited, parallel-plane diode of Prob. 2.20c when there is potential V_0 between the plates. Is there any meaning in equating this to $\frac{1}{2}CV^2$?

2.21c The energy required to increase the separation of a parallel plate capacitor by a distance dx is equal to the increase of energy stored. Find the force acting between the plates per unit cross-sectional area.

2.21d Discuss in more detail the exclusion of the self-energy term in (3), and explain why the problem disappeared in going to continuous distributions, as (5).

2.21e Show the equality of the energies found using (5) and (6) for a spherical shell of charge of radius r and surface charge density ρ_s coulombs/meter^2.

2.21f Find the energy stored in a system consisting of a point charge located a distance d from an infinite conducting plane.

STATIC MAGNETIC FIELDS

2.22 The Concept of a Magnetic Field

In the first part of this chapter the concept of the electric field has been developed starting from the experimental observation that a charge brought into the vicinity of other charges experiences a force. It can also be experimentally determined that a current element (e.g., a small loop carrying current) will be acted on by a force if it is brought in the vicinity of another current or system of currents. The region in which such forces exist is spoken of as a region of magnetic field. This concept may appear to exclude the well-known magnetic effects arising from permanent magnets, but these effects may be included conceptually if we think of them as arising from groups of atomic currents in the ferromagnetic material.

The force arising from two current elements depends on the magnitude of the currents, the medium, and the distance between currents in a similar manner to the force between electric charges already studied. However, current has direction and so it is a vector. The force law between the two currents will be more complicated than that for charges. Consequently, it is convenient to proceed by first defining the quantity which we will call the magnetic field, and then give in another section the law (Ampère's) that describes how currents contribute to that magnetic field. A vector field quantity $\bar{B}$, usually known as the magnetic flux density, is defined in terms of the force $\overline{df}$ produced on a small current element of length $\overline{dl}$ carrying current I, such that

$$df = I \, dl \, B \sin \theta, \qquad (1)$$

where θ is the angle between $\overline{dl}$ and $\bar{B}$. The direction relations of the vectors are so defined that the vector force $\overline{df}$ is along a perpendicular to the plane containing $\overline{dl}$ and $\bar{B}$, and has the sense determined by the advance of a right-hand screw if $\overline{dl}$ is rotated into $\bar{B}$ through the smaller angle. It is convenient to define a vector product which expresses this information in a more compact manner, and which will be useful in a manner similar to the dot or scalar product defined early in the chapter. If we define the vector product of two vectors (denoted by a cross) as a vector having a magnitude equal to the product of the magnitudes of the two vectors and the sine of the angle between them, a direction perpendicular to the plane containing the two vectors, and a sense given by the advance of a right-hand screw if the first is rotated into the second through the smaller angle, (1) may be written

$$\overline{df} = I \, \overline{dl} \times \bar{B}. \qquad (2)$$

The quantity known as the magnetic field vector or magnetic field intensity is denoted $\bar{H}$ and is related to the vector $\bar{B}$ defined by the force law (2) through a constant of the medium known as the permeability, μ:

$$\bar{B} = \mu\bar{H}, \qquad (3)$$

where μ has the various classifications discussed for ϵ in Art. 2.04. We will here consider it to be a scalar constant, but will consider nonlinear and anisotropic materials at the end of the chapter. The matter of units will be discussed in Art. 2.25.

Problem

2.22 Assuming that each electron constituting the current in a differential length of conductor is acted on by a force $\bar{v} \times \bar{B}$, show that the total force is equal to that given by Eq. 2.22(1).

2.23 Vector or Cross Product of Vectors

The relation between vectors met in the definition of the force law of Art. 2.22 will be met in many other types of situations, and has consequently been denoted by the convenient notation of the cross product.

In terms of two vectors $\bar{A}$ and $\bar{B}$ (Fig. 2.23a), the vector product or cross product $\bar{C} = \bar{A} \times \bar{B}$ is defined as a vector having a magnitude equal to the product of one by the normal component of the other,

$$C = AB \sin \theta. \tag{1}$$

The direction of $\bar{C}$ lies along the perpendicular to the plane containing $\bar{A}$ and $\bar{B}$, and the sense is that of a right-hand screw's sense of advance

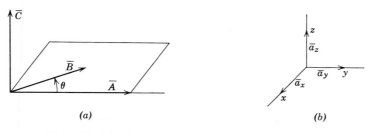

(a) (b)

Fig. 2.23 (a) Illustration of cross product, $\bar{C} = \bar{A} \times \bar{B}$.

if $\bar{A}$ is rotated into $\bar{B}$ through the smaller angle. From the sense definition, it is clear that

$$\bar{B} \times \bar{A} = -\bar{A} \times \bar{B}. \tag{2}$$

This vector product may be expressed in terms of the rectangular coordinate components as was the scalar product of Art. 2.10. For, if $\bar{A}$ and $\bar{B}$ are given in terms of the unit vectors and the components along the three coordinate axes,

$$\bar{A} \times \bar{B} = (A_x\bar{a}_x + A_y\bar{a}_y + A_z\bar{a}_z) \times (B_x\bar{a}_x + B_y\bar{a}_y + B_z\bar{a}_z). \tag{3}$$

From the definition of the vector product and a consideration of the coordinate system, Fig. 2.23b, it should be evident that

$$\bar{a}_x \times \bar{a}_y = \bar{a}_z = -\bar{a}_y \times \bar{a}_x$$

$$\bar{a}_y \times \bar{a}_z = \bar{a}_x = -\bar{a}_z \times \bar{a}_y$$

$$\bar{a}_z \times \bar{a}_x = \bar{a}_y = -\bar{a}_x \times \bar{a}_z$$

$$\bar{a}_x \times \bar{a}_x = 0 = \bar{a}_y \times \bar{a}_y = \bar{a}_z \times \bar{a}_z.$$

Notice that coordinates were purposely selected so that the sign of the unit vectors resulting from the product of one unit vector and the succeeding unit vector, in the order xyz, is positive. Such coordinate systems, known as right-handed systems, should always be selected to prevent confusion in signs. To check for a right-handed system, rotate one axis into the succeeding axis in order of writing; a right-hand screw given that motion should then progress in the positive direction along the third axis. Then

$$\bar{A} \times \bar{B} = \bar{a}_x(A_yB_z - A_zB_y) + \bar{a}_y(A_zB_x - A_xB_z) + \bar{a}_z(A_xB_y - A_yB_x). \quad (4)$$

Note that this quantity may also be written as the determinant:

$$\bar{A} \times \bar{B} = \begin{vmatrix} \bar{a}_x & \bar{a}_y & \bar{a}_z \\ A_x & A_y & A_z \\ B_x & B_y & B_z \end{vmatrix}. \quad (5)$$

Problems

2.23a Write the torque about an axis in terms of vector notation (suitably defining a vector to represent torque) when a force $\bar{F}$ acts at distance $\bar{r}$ from the axis.

2.23b Show the following:

$$\bar{A} \times (\bar{B} + \bar{C}) = \bar{A} \times \bar{B} + \bar{A} \times \bar{C}$$
$$\bar{A} \times (\bar{B} \times \bar{C}) = \bar{B}(\bar{A} \cdot \bar{C}) - \bar{C}(\bar{A} \cdot \bar{B})$$
$$\bar{A} \cdot (\bar{B} \times \bar{C}) = \bar{B} \cdot (\bar{C} \times \bar{A}) = \bar{C} \cdot (\bar{A} \times \bar{B}).$$

2.24 Ampère's Law: Field on the Axis of a Circular Loop

Ampère's law, deduced experimentally from a series of ingenious experiments,[3] describes how the magnetic field vector defined in Art. 2.22 is calculated from a system of direct currents. Consider an unbounded, homogeneous, isotropic medium with a small element dl' of current I' located at a point in space defined by a vector $\bar{r}'$ from an arbitrary origin. The magnitude of the magnetic field at some other point in space defined by a vector $\bar{r}$ from the same origin is

$$dH(\bar{r}) = \frac{I'(\bar{r}') \, dl' \sin \phi}{4\pi \, |\bar{r} - \bar{r}'|^2}.$$

It is seen from Fig. 2.24a that $|\bar{r} - \bar{r}'|$ is the distance between the current element producing the field and the point where the field is observed, ϕ is the angle between the direction of the current $\overline{dl'}$ and the vector $\bar{r} - \bar{r}'$ from the current to the point of observation. The direction of $d\bar{H}(\bar{r})$ is perpendicular to the plane containing $\overline{dl'}$ and $\bar{r} - \bar{r}'$, and the sense is determined by the sense of advance of a right-hand screw if $\overline{dl'}$ is rotated through the smallest angle into the vector $\bar{r} - \bar{r}'$. It is immediately recognized that the cross product may be used for writing this law:

$$d\bar{H}(\bar{r}) = \frac{I'(\bar{r}')\,\overline{dl'} \times (\bar{r} - \bar{r}')}{4\pi\,|\bar{r} - \bar{r}'|^3}. \tag{1}$$

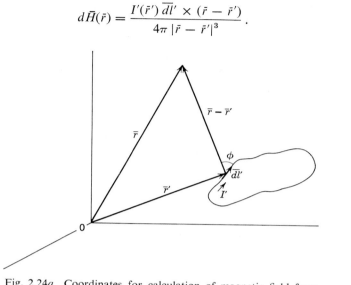

Fig. 2.24a Coordinates for calculation of magnetic field from current element.

To obtain the total magnetic field of the current elements along a current path, Eq. (1) is integrated over the path:

$$H(\bar{r}) = \int \frac{I'(\bar{r}')\,\overline{dl'} \times (\bar{r} - \bar{r}')}{4\pi\,|\bar{r} - \bar{r}'|^3}. \tag{2}$$

As an example of the application of the law, the magnetic field is computed for a point on the axis of a circular loop of wire carrying d-c

[3] For a description, see J. C. Maxwell, *A Treatise on Electricity and Magnetism*, Oxford, 3rd ed., 1892, Part IV, Chapter 2. The law is now more frequently named after Biot and Savart, but the assignment remains somewhat arbitrary. Following Oersted's announcement of the effect of currents on permanent magnets in 1820, Ampère immediately announced similar forces of currents on each other. Biot and Savart presented the first quantitative statement for the force of a current on a permanent magnet; Ampère later followed with his quantitative formulation for forces between currents. The form given here is a derived form borrowing from all that work. For more of the history see E. T. Whittaker, *A History of the Theories of the Aether and Electricity*, Philosophical Library, New York, 1952, or P. F. Mottelay *Bibliographical History of Electricity and Magnetism*, Charles Griffin & Co., London, 1922.

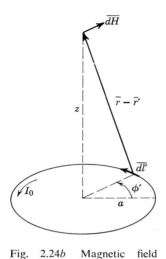

current I_0 (Fig. 2.24b). The element $\overline{dl}'$ has magnitude $a\,d\phi'$ and is always perpendicular to $\bar{r} - \bar{r}'$. Hence the contribution to dH from an element is

$$dH = \frac{I_0 a\,d\phi'}{4\pi(a^2 + z^2)}. \qquad (3)$$

As one integrates about the loop, the direction of $\bar{r} - \bar{r}'$ changes, and so the direction of $\overline{dH}$ changes, generating a conical surface as one moves about the loop. The radial components of the various contributions all cancel, and the axial components add directly:

$$dH_z = dH \sin\theta = \frac{dH a}{(a^2 + z^2)^{1/2}}.$$

Fig. 2.24b Magnetic field from element of a circular current loop.

So

$$H_z = \frac{I_0 a^2}{2(a^2 + z^2)^{3/2}}. \qquad (4)$$

Note that for a point at the center of the loop, $z = 0$,

$$H_z\bigg|_{z=0} = \frac{I_0}{2a}. \qquad (5)$$

Although the matter of units has not been mentioned in this article, the forms used are suitable for the rationalized mks system, which will be discussed in detail for magnetic quantities in the next article.

Problems

2.24a   Find from Ampère's law the magnetic field at a point distance r from an infinite straight wire carrying d-c current I_0.

2.24b   D-c current I_0 flows in a square loop of wire having sides $2a$. Find the magnetic field on the axis at a point z from the plane of the loop.

2.24c   Represent a solenoid of finite length d having n turns per meter by a continuous sheet of circumferential current. Integrate Eq. 2.24(4) to find the axial magnetic field at the center of the solenoid.

2.25   Units for Magnetic Field Quantities

In the rationalized mks system of units, current is chosen in the practical units of amperes, and distance is of course in meters. Hence magnetic field, which by Eq. 2.24(2) [or more clearly from the example, Eq. 2.24(5)] is seen to have the dimensions of a current divided by length, has dimensions of amperes per meter in this system.

The magnetic flux density B defined in Art. 2.22 is chosen in the mks system to have units of webers per square meter, where a magnetic flux of one weber is 10^8 maxwells or "lines." This choice is made for convenience in the study of time-varying fields, for a rate of change of magnetic flux of one weber per second will generate an emf of one volt. That is, a weber may also be written as a volt-second, and B could be said to have dimensions of volt-seconds per square meter.

With the units of B and H chosen by separate considerations, the permeability μ, simply the ratio of B to H for isotropic materials, will have definite units and a value other than unity for free space. As for the units,

$$\mu = \frac{B}{H} = \frac{\text{volt sec meter}^{-2}}{\text{amp meter}^{-1}} = \frac{\text{volt sec}}{\text{amp meter}} = \frac{\text{henry}}{\text{meter}}.$$

The equivalence utilized here between a henry and a volt-second per ampere may be checked from the well-known circuit equation for an inductance, $V = L\, dI/dt$. The value of μ for free space, denoted μ_0, may be shown to be

$$\mu_0 = 4\pi \times 10^{-7} \text{ henry/meter.} \tag{1}$$

Then, if μ_r is a relative permeability (the value of permeability commonly given in tables), the value of μ for any material may be written

$$\mu = \mu_r \mu_0. \tag{2}$$

The foregoing system may be compared with the electromagnetic system of units (emu), which is still much used by physicists. This is a cgs system, and is an unrationalized system, so that the factor of 4π is absent from the denominator of Ampère's law, Eq. 2.24(2). Unit magnetic field and unit current are then defined so that unit current (1 abampere) flowing in a loop of radius 1 centimeter produces a magnetic field of 2π oersteds at the center. Permeability of space is defined as unity, so that the numerical value of B is equal to that of H in vacuum. The units of B are maxwells per square centimeter, or gauss. Values of current in abamperes and flux density in gauss substituted in the force equation, 2.22(2), give force in dynes. One ampere is equal to 0.1 abampere, and a magnetic field of 1 ampere per meter is equal to $4\pi \times 10^{-3}$ oersteds.

Problem

2.25 Utilizing the preceding conversion factors, and the fact that B/H is unity for vacuum in the emu system, show that μ_0 is $4\pi \times 10^{-7}$ in the rationalized mks system as given in (1).

2.26 The Line Integral of Magnetic Field

Although Ampère's law describes how magnetic field may be computed from a given system of currents, other derived forms of the law may be more easily applied to certain types of problems. In this and the following articles, certain of these forms will be presented, with examples of their application. The sketch of the derivations of these forms, because they are more complex than for the corresponding electrostatic forms, will be postponed to Appendix II.

One of the most useful derived forms of the magnetic field laws is that which states that a line integral of static magnetic field taken about any given closed path must equal the current enclosed by that path. In the vector notation,

$$\oint \bar{H} \cdot \overline{dl} = \int_S \bar{i} \cdot \overline{dS} = I. \tag{1}$$

Obviously this law cannot be independent of Ampère's law, for, since the latter gives the magnetic field in the vicinity of the currents producing it, a line integral of that field could be taken about a closed path giving a result related to current in some way. That it actually does lead to the result (1) is shown later.

Although line integrals were met previously in the study of electric fields, a few additional comments may make the notation more meaningful. As with the general notations for surface and volume integrals, the actual integration cannot be performed until the path of integration is specified, and the variation of the vector over that path. Then, for each element of that path, the length of element dl is multiplied by the component of the vector in the direction of that element (as denoted by the dot product), and the results added by integration as one moves about the path. As a very simple example, consider the integral $\oint \bar{F} \cdot \overline{dl}$, where $\bar{F} = \bar{a}_x xy$, taken about a rectangular path from $(0, 1)$ to $(1, 1)$ to $(1, 2)$ to $(0, 2)$ back to $(0, 1)$. Along the vertical sides, $\bar{F}$ is perpendicular to $\overline{dl}$, so that there is no contribution to the dot product. Along the lower side, $\bar{F}$ and $\overline{dl}$ are in the same direction, so that a positive contribution will result, and along the upper side, in moving from $(1, 2)$ to $(0, 2)$, the direction of $\bar{F}$ and $\overline{dl}$ are opposite so that a negative contribution will result. Note that this negative relation may be taken care of by putting in the sign explicitly and integrating from the lower limit in x to the upper, or by letting the sign take care of itself by putting in limits in the order of moving about the path, but the two methods must not be confused. Then for this example

$$\oint \bar{F} \cdot \overline{dl} = \int_0^1 F_x(x, 1) \, dx + \int_1^0 F_x(x, 2) \, dx$$

$$= \int_0^1 F_x(x, 1) \, dx - \int_0^1 F_x(x, 2) \, dx$$

$$= \int_0^1 x \, dx - \int_0^1 2x \, dx = -\tfrac{1}{2}.$$

Note that the result of the line integration may give either a positive or a negative result. The sign convention for current on the right side of (1) is taken so that it is positive if it has the sense of advance of a right-hand screw rotated in the direction of circulation chosen for the line integration. This is simply a statement of the well-known right-hand rule relating direction of current and magnetic field.

Problems

2.26a   Evaluate $\oint \bar{F} \cdot \overline{dl}$ for a vector $\bar{F} = \bar{a}_x x + \bar{a}_y x^2 y^2$ for a path as described in the example in Art. 2.26. Also evaluate the integral for a triangular path from (0, 0) to (0, 1) to (1, 1) back to (0, 0).

2.26b   If $\bar{F}$ is derivable as the gradient of some scalar function $\bar{F} = -\nabla U$, show that $\oint \bar{F} \cdot \overline{dl}$ is always zero.

2.26c   An infinitely long solenoid has n turns/meter and carries current I. Given that the magnetic field is zero outside the solenoid and does not vary with distance along the axis, show that the magnetic field for any point inside the solenoid has a value

$$H_z = nI.$$

2.27   Field about a Line Current or between Coaxial Cylinders

The form of the law given in the preceding article is especially useful in problems with a symmetry such that the line integral may be written as a product of path length and magnetic field strength. An important example is that of a long line conductor carrying current I. If an integration is made about a circular path of radius r centered on the axis of the wire, the symmetry reveals that magnetic field will be circumferential and will not vary with angle as one moves about the path. Hence the line integral is just the product of circumference and the value of H_ϕ. This must equal the current enclosed:

$$\oint \bar{H} \cdot \overline{dl} = 2\pi r H_\phi = I$$

or
$$H_\phi = \frac{I}{2\pi r} \text{ ampere/meter.} \tag{1}$$

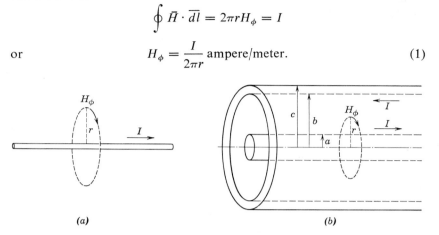

Fig. 2.27   Magnetic field about line current and between coaxial cylinders.

The sense relations are shown in Fig. 2.27a, agreeing with the sense convention described in the preceding article.

A coaxial line (Fig. 2.27b) carrying current I on the inner conductor, and $-I$ on the outer (the return current), has the same type of symmetry, and a path taken between the two conductors encloses just current I, so that the result (1) applies directly for the region between conductors:

$$\boxed{H_\phi = \frac{I}{2\pi r}} \quad a < r < b. \tag{2}$$

Outside the outer conductor, a circular path encloses both the going and return current, or a net current of zero. Hence the magnetic field outside is zero.

Problems

2.27a   For the coaxial line of Fig. 2.27b, find the magnetic field for $r < a$, and for $b < r < c$, assuming that current is distributed uniformly over the cross section of both conductors.

2.27b   Express the magnetic field about a long line current in rectangular coordinate components, taking the wire axis as the z axis, and evaluate $\oint \bar{H} \cdot \overline{dl}$ about a square path from $(-1, -1)$ to $(1, -1)$ to $(1, 1)$ to $(-1, 1)$ back to $(-1, -1)$. Also evaluate the integral about the path from $(-1, 1)$ to $(1, 1)$ to $(1, 2)$ to $(-1, 2)$ back to $(-1, 1)$. Comment on the two results.

2.27c   A long thin wire carries a current I_1 in the positive z direction along the axis of a cylindrical coordinate system. A thin rectangular loop of wire lies in a plane passing through the axis. The loop contains the region $0 \leqslant z \leqslant b$, $R - a/2 \leqslant r \leqslant R + a/2$ and carries a current I_2 which has the direction of I_1 on the side nearest the axis. Find the vector force on each side of the loop and the resulting force on the entire loop.

2.28   The Curl of a Vector Field

To write differential equation forms for laws having to do with line integrals, it will be necessary to define a new vector operation. This operation, called the curl, is defined in terms of a line integral taken around an infinitesimal path, divided by the area enclosed by that path. It is seen to have some similarities to the operation of divergence of Art. 2.12, which was defined as the surface integral taken about an infinitesimal surface divided by the volume enclosed by that surface. Unlike the divergence, however, the curl operation results in a vector because the orientation of the surface element about which the integral is taken must be described in some way. This is the only additional complication in the curl over the divergence, but it seems to be just enough to make it enormously more difficult for the beginning student to grasp. The student should attempt to obtain as much physical significance as possible from the definitions to be given, but at the same time should recognize that full appreciation of the operation will come only with practice in its use.

The curl of a vector field is defined as a vector function whose component at a point in a particular direction is found by orienting an infinitesimal area normal to the desired direction at that point, and finding the line integral per unit area:

$$[\text{Curl } \bar{F}]_i = \lim_{\Delta S_i \to 0} \frac{\oint \bar{F} \cdot \bar{dl}}{\Delta S_i}, \qquad (1)$$

where i denotes a particular direction, ΔS_i is normal to that direction, and the line integral is taken in the right-hand sense with respect to the positive i direction. In rectangular coordinates for example, to compute the z component of the curl the infinitesimal area is selected in the x-y plane in order to be normal to the z direction (Fig. 2.28). The right-hand sense of integration about the path with respect to the positive z direction is as shown by the arrows of the figure. The line integral is then

$$\oint \bar{F} \cdot \bar{dl} = dy\, F_y \bigg|_{x+dx} - dx\, F_x \bigg|_{y+dy} - dy\, F_y \bigg|_x + dx\, F_x \bigg|_y.$$

We have implied the limit of infinitesimals by writing the elements of length as dx and dy. Then

$$F_x\bigg|_{y+dy} = F_x\bigg|_y + dy\,\frac{\partial F_x}{\partial y}\bigg|_y\,; \qquad F_y\bigg|_{x+dx} = F_y\bigg|_x + dx\,\frac{\partial F_y}{\partial x}\bigg|_x$$

and
$$\oint F\cdot dl = \left(\frac{\partial F_y}{\partial x} - \frac{\partial F_x}{\partial y}\right) dx\,dy.$$

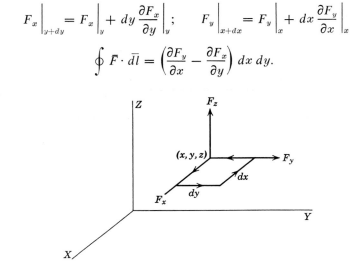

Fig. 2.28

Then, using the definition (1),

$$[\text{Curl }\bar F]_z = \frac{\oint \bar F\cdot \overline{dl}}{dx.dy} = \frac{\partial F_y}{\partial x} - \frac{\partial F_x}{\partial y}. \tag{2}$$

Similarly, by taking the elements of area in the y-z plane and x-z plane, respectively, we would find

$$[\text{Curl }\bar F]_x = \frac{\partial F_z}{\partial y} - \frac{\partial F_y}{\partial z} \tag{3}$$

$$[\text{Curl }\bar F]_y = \frac{\partial F_x}{\partial z} - \frac{\partial F_z}{\partial x}. \tag{4}$$

These components may be multiplied by the corresponding unit vectors and added to form the vector representing the curl:

$$\text{Curl }\bar F = \bar a_x\left[\frac{\partial F_z}{\partial y} - \frac{\partial F_y}{\partial z}\right] + \bar a_y\left[\frac{\partial F_x}{\partial z} - \frac{\partial F_z}{\partial x}\right] + \bar a_z\left[\frac{\partial F_y}{\partial x} - \frac{\partial F_x}{\partial y}\right]. \tag{5}$$

If this form is compared with the form of the cross product, Eq. 2.23(4) or (5), and the definition of the vector operator ∇, Eq. 2.12(6), it is noted that the above can logically be written as "del cross $\bar{F}$":

$$\text{Curl } \bar{F} \equiv \nabla \times \bar{F} = \begin{vmatrix} \bar{a}_x & \bar{a}_y & \bar{a}_z \\ \dfrac{\partial}{\partial x} & \dfrac{\partial}{\partial y} & \dfrac{\partial}{\partial z} \\ F_x & F_y & F_z \end{vmatrix}. \qquad (6)$$

This way of writing in terms of the del operator may be thought of as defining a new notation for the curl operation, and no other significance need be read into it. The name "curl" (or "rotation" as it has been called in the German literature) has some physical significance in the sense that a finite value for the line integral taken in the vicinity of a point is obtained if the curl is finite. The name should not be associated with the curvature of the field lines, however, for a field consisting of closed circles may have zero curl nearly everywhere, and a straight line field varying in certain ways may have a finite curl.

Finally, we want to write the line integral for magnetic field for a differential path, using this curl operation. It is clear that, if the line integral is made about an infinitesimal rectangle in the x-y plane, it should be equal to the current enclosed, by Art. 2.26. But this is just the current density (current per unit area) in the z direction, multiplied by the area $dx\, dy$. So

$$[\text{Curl } \bar{H}]_z = \frac{\oint \bar{H} \cdot \overline{dl}}{dx\, dy} = \frac{i_z\, dx\, dy}{dx\, dy} = i_z,$$

and similarly for the x and y components. If these component equations are multiplied by the corresponding unit vectors and added, we get the vector equation

$$\boxed{\text{Curl } \bar{H} \equiv \nabla \times \bar{H} = \bar{i}.} \qquad (7)$$

This is simply the equivalent of Eq. 2.26(1) for a differential path taken in the vicinity of a point. As a very simple example, if we wish to know the current distribution required to produce a magnetic field $\bar{H} = \bar{a}_z x^2$, from (7) and (5) the current density should be

$$\bar{i} = \nabla \times \bar{H} = -\bar{a}_y \frac{\partial H_z}{\partial x} = -2x\bar{a}_y. \qquad (8)$$

Problems

2.28a Find the curl of a vector field $\bar{F} = \bar{a}_x x^2 z^2 + \bar{a}_y y^2 z^2 + \bar{a}_z x^2 y^2$.

2.28b For the coaxial line of Fig. 2.27b, express the magnetic field found in Art. 2.27 and Prob. 2.27a in rectangular coordinates and find the curl in the four regions, $r < a$, $a < r < b$, $b < r < c$, $r > c$. Comment on the results.

2.28c By using the rectangular coordinate forms shown that

$$\nabla \times (\psi \bar{F}) = \psi \nabla \times \bar{F} - \bar{F} \times \nabla \psi,$$

where $\bar{F}$ is any vector function and ψ any scalar function.

2.28d Show that $\nabla \times \nabla \psi \equiv 0$.

2.28e Derive the expression for curl in the spherical coordinate system.

11/1/66

2.29 Stokes's Theorem

Just as the divergence should be thought of as a flux flow per unit volume, the curl should be thought of as a line integral per unit area, at a point in space. Just as the divergence theorem (Art. 2.13) states that the

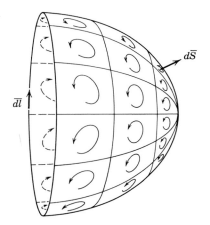

Fig. 2.29 Subdivision of arbitrary surface for proof of Stokes's theorem.

total flux flow out of any volume may be obtained by integration of the divergence throughout that volume, there is another theorem which states that the line integral around any surface may be obtained by integrating the normal components of the curl over that surface. If the surface is broken up into a large number of infinitesimal areas as shown in Fig. 2.29, it is known from the definition of curl that for each of these infinitesimal areas

$$\oint \bar{F} \cdot \overline{dl} = \text{curl } \bar{F} \cdot \overline{dS}. \tag{1}$$

If contributions from infinitesimal areas are summed over all the surface, the line integral must disappear for all internal areas, since a boundary is first traversed in one direction and then later in the opposite direction in determining the contribution from an adjacent area. The only places where these contributions do not disappear are along the outer boundary, so that the result of the summation is then the line integral of the vector around the boundary:

$$\oint \bar{F} \cdot \overline{dl} = \int_S \text{curl } \bar{F} \cdot \overline{dS} \equiv \int_S \nabla \times \bar{F} \cdot \overline{dS}. \tag{2}$$

This relation is known as Stokes's theorem, and, as with the divergence theorem, it holds for any continuous vector field.

This theorem may be used, for example, in going back from the differential form of the law, Eq. 2.28(7), to the integral form from which it was derived. Writing Stokes's theorem for magnetic field, we have

$$\oint \bar{H} \cdot \overline{dl} = \int_S (\nabla \times \bar{H}) \cdot \overline{dS}. \quad = I$$

But, by Eq. 2.28(7), the curl may be replaced by the current density:

$$\oint \bar{H} \cdot \overline{dl} = \int_S \bar{i} \cdot \overline{dS} \tag{3}$$

The right side represents the current flow through the surface of which the path for the line integration on the left is a boundary. Hence (3) is exactly equivalent to Eq. 2.26(1).

Problem

2.29   Prove the result of Problem 2.28d by integrating over an arbitrary surface and applying Stokes's theorem.

2.30 Vector Magnetic Potential: Field of a Parallel-Wire Line

It is shown in Appendix II that Ampère's law of Art. 2.24 may be broken into two steps by making use of certain vector equivalences. The result gives

$$\bar{B}(\bar{r}) = \nabla \times \bar{A}(\bar{r}), \tag{1}$$

where

$$\bar{A}(\bar{r}) = \int \frac{\mu I'(\bar{r}') \, dl'}{4\pi \, |\bar{r} - \bar{r}'|}. \tag{2}$$

Or, if the current is given as a vector density $\bar{i}$ in current per unit area spread over a volume V', the equivalent to (2) is

$$\bar{A}(\bar{r}) = \int_{V'} \frac{\mu \bar{i}(\bar{r}') \, dV'}{4\pi \, |\bar{r} - \bar{r}'|}. \tag{3}$$

In both (2) and (3), $|\bar{r} - \bar{r}'|$ is the distance from a current element of the integration to the point at which $\bar{A}$ is to be computed as in Fig. 2.24a.

Equations (1) and (2) together are equivalent to Eq. 2.24(2). The function $\bar{A}$, introduced as an intermediate step, is computed as an integral over the given currents from (2) or (3) and then differentiated in the manner

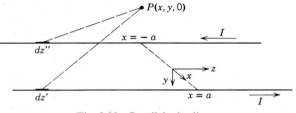

Fig. 2.30   Parallel-wire line.

defined by (1) to yield the magnetic field. Function $\bar{A}$ may be thought of as a potential in a way analogous to but different from the potential function of electrostatics which is found in terms of an integral over the charges and then differentiated in a certain way to yield the electric field. Unlike the potential of electrostatics, the vector magnetic potential does not have any very simple physical significance beyond that given by the definitions above. Some physical pictures can be developed, but the student should not worry about these until more familiarity with the function has been developed through certain examples.

The example to be given in this article will be that of a parallel-wire transmission line of infinite length carrying current I in one conductor and its return in the other distance $2a$ away. The coordinate system is set up as in Fig. 2.30. Since the field quantities will not vary with z, it will be convenient to calculate them in the plane $z = 0$. The line will first be taken as extending from $z = -L$ to $z = L$ to avoid indeterminacies in the integrals. Since current is only in the z direction, $\bar{A}$ by (2) will be in the z direction also. The contribution to A_z from both wires is

$$A_z = \int_{-L}^{L} \frac{\mu I \, dz'}{4\pi \sqrt{(x-a)^2 + y^2 + z'^2}} - \int_{-L}^{L} \frac{\mu I \, dz''}{4\pi \sqrt{(x+a)^2 + y^2 + z''^2}}$$

$$= \frac{2\mu}{4\pi} \left[\int_0^L \frac{I \, dz'}{\sqrt{(x-a)^2 + y^2 + z'^2}} - \int_0^L \frac{I \, dz''}{\sqrt{(x+a)^2 + y^2 + z''^2}} \right].$$

The integrals may be evaluated[4]

$$A_z = \frac{I\mu}{2\pi} \{\ln [z' + \sqrt{(x-a)^2 + y^2 + z'^2}]$$
$$- \ln [z'' + \sqrt{(x+a)^2 + y^2 + z''^2}]\}_0^L.$$

Now, as L is allowed to approach infinity, the upper limits of the two terms cancel. Hence

$$A_z = \frac{I\mu}{4\pi} \ln \left[\frac{(x+a)^2 + y^2}{(x-a)^2 + y^2}\right]. \tag{4}$$

If (1) is then applied, using the expression for curl in rectangular co-ordinates,

$$H_x = \frac{1}{\mu} \frac{\partial A_z}{\partial y} = \frac{I}{2\pi}\left[\frac{y}{(x+a)^2 + y^2} - \frac{y}{(x-a)^2 + y^2}\right] \tag{5}$$

$$H_y = -\frac{1}{\mu} \frac{\partial A_z}{\partial x} = \frac{I}{2\pi}\left[\frac{(x-a)}{(x-a)^2 + y^2} - \frac{(x+a)}{(x+a)^2 + y^2}\right]. \tag{6}$$

We have just seen that with special treatment of the integrals, it was possible to find an expression for the vector potential for the infinitely long pair of wires. If an infinite single-wire line of current is considered, the vector potential is infinite. However, the method may still be used. First, the vector potential for a wire of finite length is found. The magnetic flux density $\bar{B}$ is then calculated from $\bar{A}$ before letting the length of the line approach infinity. This procedure may be used in a variety of problems in which the vector potential approaches infinity with the magnetic field remaining finite.

Problems

2.30a Check the results (5) and (6) by adding vectorially the magnetic field from the individual wires, using the result of Art. 2.27.

2.30b A square loop of thin wire lies in the x-y plane extending from $(-a, -a)$ to $(a, -a)$ to (a, a) to $(-a, a)$ back to $(-a, -a)$ and carries current I in that sense of circulation. Find $\bar{A}$ and $\bar{H}$ for any point (x, y, z).

2.30c A circular loop of thin wire carries current I. Find $\bar{A}$ for a point distance z from the plane of the loop, and radius r from the axis, for $r/z \ll 1$. Use this to find the expression for magnetic field on the axis.

2.30d Show that $\bar{B}$ would also be given by $\nabla \times \bar{A}'$, where $\bar{A}'$ is obtained by adding to $\bar{A}$ the gradient of any scalar function,

$$\bar{A}' = \bar{A} + \nabla\psi.$$

[4] Integrals of this text will be found in H. B. Dwight, *Tables of Integrals*, 3rd ed, Macmillan, New York, 1961, unless otherwise noted.

2.30e A very long thin sheet of copper having a width b meters carries a direct current I in the direction of its length. Show that if the sheet is assumed to lie in the x-z plane with the z axis along its center line, the magnetic field about the strip will be given by

$$H_x = -\frac{I}{2\pi b}\left(\tan^{-1}\frac{b/2 + x}{y} + \tan^{-1}\frac{b/2 - x}{y}\right)$$

$$H_y = \frac{I}{4\pi b}\ln\left[\frac{(b/2 + x)^2 + y^2}{(b/2 - x)^2 + y^2}\right].$$

2.31 Distant Field of Current Loop: Magnetic Dipole

In Art. 2.24 the magnetic field on the axis of a loop of current was derived. Here we will find the magnetic vector potential at points not restricted to the axis but we limit consideration to points distant from the

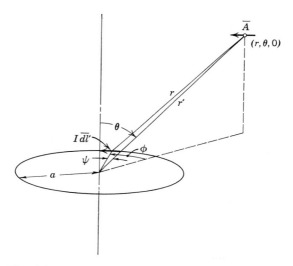

Fig. 2.31 Coordinates for calculation of magnetic-dipole fields.

loop. The arrangement to be analyzed is shown in Fig. 2.31. For any point (r, θ, ϕ) at which $\bar{A}$ is to be found, some current elements $I\,\overline{dl'}$ are oriented such that they produce components of $\bar{A}$ in directions other than the ϕ direction. However, by the symmetry of the loop, equal and opposite amounts of such components exist. As a result $\bar{A}$ is ϕ-directed and is independent of the value of ϕ at which it is to be found. For convenience, we choose to calculate $\bar{A}$ at the point $(r, \theta, 0)$. The ϕ-directed contribution of a differential element of current is

$$dA_\phi = \frac{\mu_0 \, dl' \cos \phi}{4\pi R} \tag{1}$$

where R is the distance $|\bar{r} - \bar{r}'|$ from the element dl' to $(r, \theta, 0)$. The total is found as the integral around the loop

$$A_\phi = \frac{\mu_0 I}{4\pi} \oint \frac{dl' \cos \phi}{R} = \frac{\mu_0 I a}{4\pi} \int_0^{2\pi} \frac{\cos \phi \, d\phi}{R} \tag{2}$$

where a is the radius of the loop. The distance R can be expressed in terms of the radius from the origin to $(r, \theta, 0)$ as

$$R^2 = r^2 + a^2 - 2ra \cos \psi. \tag{3}$$

To get $ra \cos \psi$ we note that $r \cos \psi$ is the projection of r onto the radius line to dl'. Therefore

$$ra \cos \psi = ra \sin \theta \cos \phi. \tag{4}$$

Substituting (4) into (3) and assuming $r \gg a$, we find

$$R \simeq r\left(1 - 2\frac{a}{r} \sin \theta \cos \phi\right)^{1/2}$$

or

$$R^{-1} \simeq r^{-1}\left(1 + \frac{a}{r} \sin \theta \cos \phi\right). \tag{5}$$

Replacing R^{-1} in (2) by (5), we find

$$A_\phi = \frac{\mu_0 I a}{4\pi r} \int_0^{2\pi} \left(\cos \phi + \frac{a}{r} \sin \theta \cos^2 \phi\right) d\phi$$

$$= \frac{\mu_0 I a}{4\pi r} \cdot \frac{a\pi \sin \theta}{r} = \frac{\mu_0 (I\pi a^2) \sin \theta}{4\pi r^2}. \tag{6}$$

As was noted at the outset, it was convenient to do the above derivation for the point $(r, \theta, 0)$, but by symmetry the result applies to any value of ϕ.

We may find the components of the magnetic flux density by applying Eq. 2.30(1),

$$\bar{B} = \nabla \times \bar{A}. \tag{7}$$

The components of $\bar{B}$ found by substituting (6) in (7) are

$$B_r = \frac{\mu_0 (I\pi a^2)}{2\pi r^3} \cos \theta \tag{8}$$

$$B_\theta = \frac{\mu_0 (I\pi a^2)}{4\pi r^3} \sin \theta \tag{9}$$

$$B_\phi = 0. \tag{10}$$

The group of terms $I\pi a^2$ can be given a special significance by comparison of (8) to (10) with the fields of an electric dipole. Let us take the gradient of Eq. 2.17(3) in spherical coordinates (see Appendix I). We find the components of electric field to be

$$E_r = \frac{p}{2\pi\epsilon r^3}\cos\theta \qquad (11)$$

$$E_\theta = \frac{p}{4\pi\epsilon r^3}\sin\theta \qquad (12)$$

$$E_\phi = 0. \qquad (13)$$

where p is the electric dipole moment. The identity of the functional form of the fields has led to defining magnitude of the magnetic dipole moment as

$$m = I\pi a^2. \qquad (14)$$

The dipole direction is along the $\theta = 0$ axis in Fig. 2.31 for the direction of I shown. The vector potential can be written in terms of the magnetic dipole moment $\bar{m}$ as

$$\bar{A} = \frac{-\mu_0}{4\pi}\bar{m}\times\nabla\left(\frac{1}{r}\right) \qquad (15)$$

where the partial derivatives in the gradient operation are with respect to the point of observation of $\bar{A}$.

Problem

2.31 Show that the torque on a small loop of current can be expressed as $\bar{\tau} = \bar{m}\times\bar{B}$.

2.32 Divergence of Magnetic Field   11/1/66

Magnetic flux density has been written as the curl of a vector, $\bar{A}$. Its divergence is then

$$\nabla\cdot\bar{B} = \nabla\cdot\nabla\times\bar{A}. \qquad (1)$$

The result, in rectangular coordinates, is

$$\nabla\cdot\bar{B} = \frac{\partial^2 A_z}{\partial x\,\partial y} - \frac{\partial^2 A_y}{\partial x\,\partial z} + \frac{\partial^2 A_x}{\partial y\,\partial z} - \frac{\partial^2 A_z}{\partial y\,\partial x} + \frac{\partial^2 A_y}{\partial z\,\partial x} - \frac{\partial^2 A_x}{\partial z\,\partial y} \qquad (2)$$

since partials may be taken in either order,

$$\nabla\cdot\bar{B} = 0. \qquad (3)$$

Notice that the evaluation of the divergence of the curl of $\bar{A}$ was independent of the value of $\bar{A}$, so then the divergence of the curl of any vector is identically zero.

A major difference between electric and magnetic fields is here apparent, for, unlike the electric field, the magnetic field must have zero divergence everywhere. That is, when the magnetic field is due to currents, there are no sources of magnetic flux which correspond to the electric charges as sources of electric flux. Fields with zero divergence such as these are consequently often called source-free fields.

Magnetic field concepts are often developed from an exact parallel with electric fields by considering the concept of isolated magnetic poles as sources of magnetic flux, corresponding to the charges of electrostatics. The result of zero divergence still seems entirely applicable, since such poles have never been isolated, but seem to appear in nature as equal and opposite pairs.

Problems

2.32a Express the magnetic field in rectangular coordinates for the coaxial line of Fig. 2.27b, and differentiate to form the divergence both for $r < a$ and for $a < r < b$.

2.32b If μ is a function of position and $\nabla \cdot \bar{B} = 0$, show that in general $\nabla \cdot \bar{H}$ will not be zero.

2.33 Differential Equation for Vector Magnetic Potential

The differential equation for magnetic field in terms of current density was developed in Art. 2.28:

$$\nabla \times \bar{H} = \bar{i}.$$

If the relation for $\bar{B}$ as the curl of vector potential $\bar{A}$ is substituted,

$$\nabla \times \nabla \times \bar{A} = \mu \bar{i}. \tag{1}$$

This may be considered a differential equation relating $\bar{A}$ to current density. It is more common to write it in a different form utilizing the Laplacian of a vector function defined in rectangular coordinates as the vector sum of the Laplacians of the three scalar components:

$$\nabla^2 \bar{A} = \bar{a}_x \nabla^2 A_x + \bar{a}_y \nabla^2 A_y + \bar{a}_z \nabla^2 A_z. \tag{2}$$

It may then be verified that, for rectangular coordinates,

$$\nabla \times \nabla \times \bar{A} = -\nabla^2 \bar{A} + \nabla(\nabla \cdot \bar{A}). \tag{3}$$

For other than rectangular coordinate systems, (3) may be taken as the definition of ∇^2 of a vector.

If $\bar{A}$ is defined by Eq. 2.30(3), it may be shown that its divergence is zero (Appendix II). Hence (1) may be written

$$\nabla^2 \bar{A} = -\mu\bar{\imath}. \tag{4}$$

This is a vector equivalent of the Poisson type of equation first met in Art. 2.20. It includes three component scalar equations which are exactly of the Poisson form.

For an example, take a case in which $\bar{A}$ has only a z component given by

$$A_z = -\frac{\mu i_0}{4}(x^2 + y^2). \tag{5}$$

From (4) and (2),

$$i_z = -\frac{1}{\mu}\nabla^2 A_z = -\frac{1}{\mu}\left(\frac{\partial^2 A_z}{\partial x^2} + \frac{\partial^2 A_z}{\partial y^2}\right) = i_0. \tag{6}$$

Going backwards, we can see that (5) is the appropriate form for vector potential in a cylindrical conductor carrying a current of constant density i_0. The corresponding magnetic field is

$$\bar{B} = \nabla \times \bar{A} = \frac{-\mu i_0}{2}(\bar{a}_x y - \bar{a}_y x). \tag{7}$$

The differential equation (4) is more useful in determining the vector potential $\bar{A}$ when the current density $\bar{\imath}$ is given. This requires solution of the differential equation; this phase of the subject will be reserved for the following chapter.

Problems

2.33a Deduce the appropriate form for vector potential outside a long straight wire carrying current I, and show that $\nabla^2\bar{A}$ is equal to zero there.

2.33b Use the rectangular coordinate forms to prove (3).

2.33c Show that the magnetic field given by (7) is circumferential and can be written

$$H_\phi = \frac{i_0 r}{2}.$$

Obtain this result also by the methods of Art. 2.27.

2.34 Scalar Magnetic Potential

In many problems it is desired to find the distribution of magnetic field in regions which contain no currents. As may be seen in Eq. 2.28(7), the curl of the magnetic intensity vector $\bar{H}$ is zero at any point where the current density is zero. Any vector with zero curl may be represented as the gradient of a scalar (see Problem 2.28d). Thus the magnetic intensity can be expressed for such points as

$$\bar{H} = -\nabla\Phi_m \tag{1}$$

where the minus sign is conventionally taken only to complete the analogy with electrostatic fields. Since the divergence of the magnetic flux density $\bar{B}$ is everywhere zero,

$$\nabla \cdot \mu\nabla\Phi_m = 0. \tag{2}$$

Thus, for a homogeneous medium, Φ_m satisfies Laplace's equation

$$\nabla^2\Phi_m = 0. \tag{3}$$

It will be observed from (1) that

$$\Phi_{m2} - \Phi_{m1} = -\int_1^2 \bar{H} \cdot d\bar{l}. \tag{4}$$

Thus, if the path of integration encircles a current, Φ_m does not have a unique value. For if 1 and 2 are the same point in space and the path of integration encloses a current I, two values of Φ_m, differing by I, will be assigned to the point. To make the scalar magnetic potential unique, we must restrict attention to regions which do not entirely encircle currents. Suitable regions are called "simply connected" because any two paths connecting a pair of points in the region form a loop which does not enclose any exterior points. An example of a simply connected region

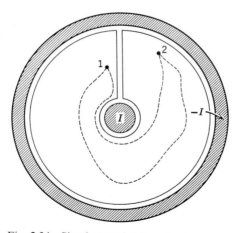

Fig. 2.34 Simply connected region between coaxial cylinders.

between coaxial conductors is shown in Fig. 2.34. The restriction to a
simply connected region is not an important drawback in many situations.

The importance of the scalar potential is that it satisfies Laplace's
equation for which exist numerous methods of solution. Some of these
are introduced in Chapter 3.

Problem

2.34 Show whether the following vector field can be obtained from a scalar
potential:

$$\bar{F} = \bar{a}_x 3y + \bar{a}_y 2x + \bar{a}_z 4.$$

2.35 Boundary Conditions for Static Magnetic Fields

The boundary conditions at an interface between two regions with
different permeabilities can be found in the same way as was done for
static electric fields in Art. 2.18. Consider a volume in the shape of a

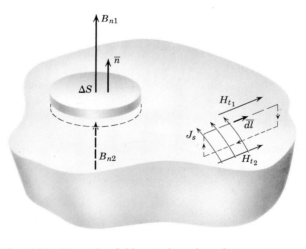

Fig. 2.35 Magnetic fields at boundary between two
different media.

pillbox enclosing the boundary between the two media as shown in Fig.
2.35. The surfaces ΔS of the volume are considered to be arbitrarily small
so the normal flux density B_n does not vary across the surface. The net
outward flux from the box is

$$B_{n1} \Delta S = B_{n2} \Delta S$$

or
$$B_{n1} = B_{n2} \tag{1}$$

where the directions of B_{n1} and B_{n2} are the same.

The relation between transverse magnetic fields may be found by integrating the magnetic intensity $\bar{H}$ along a line enclosing the interface plane as shown in Fig. 2.35:

$$\oint \bar{H} \cdot \overline{dl} = H_{t1}\,\Delta l - H_{t2}\,\Delta l = J_s \qquad (2)$$

where J_s is a surface current in amperes per meter width flowing in the direction shown. The lengths Δl of the sides are arbitrarily small so H_t may be considered uniform. The other legs of the integration path are reduced to zero length. From (2)

$$H_{t1} - H_{t2} = J_s \qquad (3)$$

There is a discontinuity of the tangential field at the boundary between two regions equal to any surface current which may exist on the boundary.

The scalar magnetic potential Φ_m is continuous across boundaries on which $J_s = 0$. Where surface currents exist, the components of the potential gradient which are tangential to the boundary must satisfy

$$(\nabla\Phi_{m2} - \nabla\Phi_{m1})_t = J_s \qquad (4)$$

as may be seen by combining (3) with the definition of Φ_m, Eq. 2.34(1).

Consider as an example, a boundary between free space and a superconductor, which is a material yielding zero resistance below some critical temperature. For certain classes of superconductors moved into a magnetic field, currents flow in such a way as to produce magnetic fields which just cancel the applied field within the body. Therefore, B_{n2} and H_{t2} are zero. From (1) the normal component of magnetic flux density B_{n1} is zero and from (3) the tangential magnetic intensity on the outside boundary of the superconductor equals the surface current density. It may be seen from Eq. 2.34(1) that the boundary of a superconductor is a surface with zero normal gradient of the scalar magnetic potential.

2.36 Energy of a Static Magnetic Field

In considering the energy of a magnetic field, it would appear by analogy with Art. 2.21 that we should consider the work done in bringing a group of current elements together from infinity. This point of view is correct in principle, but not only is it more difficult to carry out than for charges because of the vector nature of currents, but it also requires consideration of time-varying effects as shown in references deriving the relation from this point of view.[5] We will consequently set down the

[5] J. A. Stratton, *Electromagnetic Theory*, McGraw-Hill, New York, 1941, pp. 118–124.

result at this point, waiting for further discussion until we derive a most important general energy relationship in Chapter 4. The result is

$$U_H = \tfrac{1}{2} \int_V \bar{B} \cdot \bar{H} \, dV. \tag{1}$$

The analogy of this to Eq. 2.21(6) is apparent, and as there we interpret the energy of a system of sources as actually stored in the fields produced by those sources. The result is also consistent with the inductive circuit energy term, $\tfrac{1}{2} L I^2$, when circuit concepts hold, and this equality will be utilized in Chapter 5.

Problem

2.36 Find the energy stored per unit length between the conductors of a coaxial line carrying current I in the inner conductor and equal return current in the outer.

2.37 Completeness of Specification of $\bar{E}$ and $\bar{B}$

We have shown in this chapter how the important integral and differential equations for static fields can be deduced from the basic experimental evidence of Coulomb and Ampère. It is well to point out here that the field vectors $\bar{E}$ and $\bar{B}$ are completely specified by the expressions we have derived. There is a general theorem in vector analysis called the Helmholtz theorem[6] which states that a vector is completely determined by specification of its divergence and its curl. That a vector L is not uniquely determined by specifying only its divergence is clear since the relation

$$\nabla \cdot \bar{L} = \psi$$

is unmodified if L is replaced by a vector $\bar{L} + \nabla \times \bar{G}$. That is,

$$\nabla \cdot (\bar{L} + \nabla \times \bar{G}) = \nabla \cdot \bar{L} = \psi$$

since, as was shown in Art. 2.32, $\nabla \cdot \nabla \times \bar{G} \equiv 0$ for any vector $\bar{G}$. Therefore, as long as only the divergence is specified, a vector which is the curl of some other vector may be added to $\bar{L}$. That $\bar{L}$ is not uniquely determined by specifying only its curl is shown in the same way since

$$\nabla \times \bar{L} = \bar{F}$$

is unaffected if L is replaced by the vector $\bar{L} + \nabla \psi$. That is

$$\nabla \times (\bar{L} + \nabla \psi) = \nabla \times \bar{L}$$

since, as was seen in Prob. 2.28d, $\nabla \times \nabla \psi \equiv 0$ for any scalar ψ.

[6] H. B. Phillips, *Vector Analysis*, John Wiley and Sons, New York, 1933.

The proof of the Helmholtz theorem shows that the most general vector can be expressed as the sum of two vectors, one being the gradient of a scalar and the other being the curl of some other vector:

$$\bar{L} = \nabla\psi + \nabla \times \bar{G}.$$

The vector $\nabla\psi$ is called *irrotational* since its curl or rotation is identically zero and the vector $\nabla \times \bar{G}$ is called *solenoidal* since it is devoid of sources and sinks as indicated by the identity $\nabla \cdot \nabla \times \bar{G} \equiv 0$.

Thus for linear, homogeneous, isotropic materials, the specification of divergence of $\bar{D}$ by giving the charge sources throughout space also defines $\nabla \cdot \bar{E}$. With the curl of $\bar{E}$ known to be zero, the conditions for complete specification of $\bar{E}$ are then satisfied. Similarly, for such materials, the knowledge that $\nabla \cdot \bar{B} = 0$ gives $\nabla \cdot \bar{H} = 0$ and with $\nabla \times \bar{H} = \bar{\imath}$, $\bar{H}$ is uniquely specified. Some comments on uniqueness with more general materials are given in Chapter 4.

Problem

2.37 If μ is a function of position and $\nabla \cdot \bar{B} = 0$, show that in general $\nabla \cdot \bar{H}$ will not be zero.

DIELECTRIC AND MAGNETIC PROPERTIES OF MATTER

2.38 Concepts of Polarization and Magnetization

So far we have considered the effects of materials on electric and magnetic fields to be described by the quantities ϵ and μ relating $\bar{D}$ to $\bar{E}$ and $\bar{B}$ to $\bar{H}$, respectively. These are frequently referred to together as the *constitutive parameters* of the material. The simple picture of Art. 2.02 explained why one might expect the material to affect the electric force between charges or more generally the distribution of electric fields. It is now desirable to look more carefully at the behavior of the material from the microscopic point of view.[7] This is actually a very difficult matter, as whole books have been written on the subject, and certain aspects of the microscopic picture are not yet understood. Nevertheless, the subject is a most

---

[7] Although important, the discussion can be delayed for study along with the dynamic properties of matter to be treated in Chapters 6 and 9.

important one, so some simple models will be given which introduce the major concepts affecting classical electricity and magnetism. For fuller understanding of the nature of materials, one should begin with some of the introductory texts on solid-state physics.[8],[9],[10] Good survey articles[11],[12] and texts[13] are also available on dielectrics and magnetic materials.[14],[15] Several books on electromagnetic theory[16],[17] also contain introductions.

The point of view is that of Lorentz, in which electric flux density $\bar{D}$ is broken into two parts, the first related to the electric field by the free-space permittivity and the second called the *polarization* $\bar{P}$. That is,

$$\bar{D} = \epsilon_0 \bar{E} + \bar{P}. \tag{1}$$

$\bar{P}$ arises from a distribution of electric dipoles in the material, as illustrated by Fig. 2.02, although other mechanisms for producing dipole fields will be described briefly in this article. Similarly the magnetic flux density in material medium may be written

$$\bar{B} = \mu_0(\bar{H} + \bar{M}), \tag{2}$$

where $\bar{M}$ is a magnetic polarization, more commonly called *magnetization*, and arises from the magnetic dipoles of a material. As we have seen, magnetic dipoles may be thought of as arising from currents or magnetic charges; in this text we have stressed the concept of currents, and for materials they may be thought of as currents on the atomic scale, as will be illustrated in Art. 2.42.

For linear materials (Art. 2.04), $\bar{P}$ is directly proportional to $\bar{E}$ and $\bar{M}$ is proportional to $\bar{H}$, so that there is then no fundamental difference between this point of view and that of the constitutive parameters ϵ and μ in working electromagnetic problems. The point of view may nevertheless

[8] C. Kittel, *Introduction to Solid State Physics*, 2nd ed., John Wiley and Sons, New York, 1957.

[9] A. J. Dekker, *Solid-State Physics*, Prentice-Hall, Englewood Cliffs, N.J., 1957.

[10] M. Sachs, *Solid State Theory*, McGraw-Hill, New York, 1963.

[11] W. F. Brown, "Dielectrics", *Encyclopedia of Physics*, V. XVII, Springer-Verlag, Berlin, 1956.

[12] G. Wyllie, "Theory of Polarization and Absorption in Dielectrics," *Progress in Dielectrics*, vol. 2, John Wiley and Sons, New York, 1960.

[13] A. R. von Hippel, *Dielectrics and Waves*, John Wiley and Sons, New York, 1954.

[14] R. M. Bozorth, *Ferromagnetism*, Van Nostrand, Princeton, N.J., 1951.

[15] W. F. Brown, Jr., "Magnetic Materials," *Handbook of Physics*, E. U. Condon and H. Odishaw, eds., McGraw-Hill, New York, 1958; pp. 4–126 ff.

[16] R. M. Fano, L. J. Chu, R. B. Adler, *Electromagnetic Fields, Energy, and Forces*, John Wiley and Sons, New York, 1963, Chapt. 5.

[17] J. D. Jackson, *Classical Electrodynamics*, John Wiley and Sons, New York, 1962; Chapts. 4, 5.

be very useful in studying materials. Thus for linear materials,

$$\bar{P} = \epsilon_0 \chi_e \bar{E}, \qquad \bar{M} = \chi_m \bar{H} \tag{3}$$

where χ_e and χ_m are electric and magnetic *susceptibilities* respectively. Then

$$\epsilon = \epsilon_0 (1 + \chi_e), \qquad \mu = \mu_0 (1 + \chi_m). \tag{4}$$

For nonlinear materials, or those with permanently aligned dipoles, polarization and magnetization are almost essential tools. Such materials are becoming of increasing importance in communication devices.

Restricting consideration for the moment to electric polarization, let us note some of the phenomena which can produce dipoles in the dielectric. In addition to the elastic distortion of position for electrons of the atom pictured in Fig. 2.02, the applied field can cause an elastic separation of ions in the molecule, also producing effective dipoles. Many asymmetrical molecules may also have permanent dipoles in the absence of field because the constituent ions have different affinities for electrons. Such molecules are called *polar molecules*. In the absence of field, they are oriented at random, and their effect cancels out on the average. With an applied electric field, they tend to line up with the field, and would do so completely (at least in fluids) except for the thermal collisions which counter the applied torque. The result is a small but finite tendency for alignment, giving a net contribution to average dipole moment of the material. Similar but somewhat more subtle effects arise when electrons, subjected to an applied field, shift their population densities between two equal energy states separated by a potential barrier, as in the "site-jumping" phenomenon of certain solids.[9]

All of the foregoing phenomena are essentially nonlinear, but for many dielectrics at room temperature the effects are substantially linear for fields up to the breakdown level of the material. Polarization is proportional to field in the linear region, and can be written as free-space permittivity times the number of molecules per unit volume, N, multiplied by average *polarizability* per molecule, α_T and by the internal field acting upon the molecule $\bar{E}_i$.

$$\bar{P} = \epsilon_0 N \alpha_T \bar{E}_i. \tag{5}$$

It is also common to separate the several components contributing to polarizability as follows:

$$\alpha_T = \alpha_e + \alpha_i + \frac{p^2}{3kT}. \tag{6}$$

Here α_e is electronic polarizability (distortion of electron charge bond), α_i is ionic (separation of ions), and the last represents the alignment polarizability from permanent dipoles of strength p. The quantity T is absolute temperature in degrees Kelvin and k is Boltzmann's constant, 1.38×10^{-23} joules/°K. The separation between terms is somewhat arbitrary and important largely in dynamic matters to be studied later. The temperature dependence of the last term is significant, however, and serves to identify polar materials, and to give values of permanent dipole moment p. (The term of course breaks down near absolute zero, as the contribution does not become infinite there.)

With the definitions (1) and (5), permittivity for linear materials can now be related to the molecular polarizability. We must note however, that $\bar{E}_i$ of (5) is internal field, acting on a molecule, not the kind of average or *macroscopic* field appearing in field expressions earlier in the chapter. If the two quantities are related so that

$$\bar{E}_i/\bar{E} = g, \tag{7}$$

then

$$\epsilon = \epsilon_0(1 + gN\alpha_T). \tag{8}$$

For example, in a gas, the g factor is approximately $(\epsilon_r + 2)/3$ and (8) then becomes the useful Clausius-Mossotti relationship, as will be shown in more detail in Art. 2.41.

In the remaining articles, we wish to show that $\bar{P}$ as defined is in fact given by the density of dipoles, to show some examples of the use of the polarization concept in electromagnetic problems, and then look again at the form of permittivity in a simple dielectric. We will then consider similar matters for magnetic fields, and finally introduce the necessary generalizations for anisotropic materials.

Problems

2.38a For a gas, ϵ_r is near unity. From the approximation given in this article show the simplified form which results for $(\epsilon_r - 1)$. Utilizing the ideal gas law, $PV = NkT$, find the dependence of this quantity on pressure and temperature, assuming nonpolar molecules with $p = 0$. Interpret all results physically.

2.38b If a medium contains several kinds of molecules, argue that the generalization of (5) would yield

$$\bar{P} = \left(\sum_j N_j \alpha_{Tj}\right)\bar{E}_i.$$

2.38c Consider a pure polar liquid with $(\alpha_e + \alpha_i)$ negligible compared with the term from permanent dipoles. Show that, with the Clausius-Mossotti approximation for g given in this article, ϵ_r becomes infinite at some critical temperature T_c. This behavior does not generally occur, illustrating the inapplicability of the approximation to liquids in that temperature range.

2.38d Typical values of $(\alpha_e + \alpha_i)$ are 10^{-17} m^3 and of p for polar molecules are 10^{-13} m$^{3/2}$ joules$^{1/2}$. (cf C. P. Smyth, *Dielectric Behavior and Structure*, McGraw-Hill, New York, 1955, Chapt. 1.) Plot $(\epsilon_r - 1)$ vs. $1/T$ for a material of molecular weight 32. (Avogadro's number is 6.02×10^{23} molecules/gm molecular weight, and the volume of a mole at standard conditions is 22.4 liters.)

2.38e A simple model of an atom consists of a spherical volume of uniformly distributed charge surrounding a positive nucleus. Assume that the nucleus is displaced by a distance δ from the center of the electronic charge cloud by an applied field $\bar{E}_i$ and show that the polarizability of the atom is $\alpha_e = 4\pi a^3$. The displacement δ is less than the radius of the electronic charge a.

2.38f A plot of the relative permittivity of nitrobenzene shows that it is nearly constant at a value of about 4 up to a temperature of 278°K where there is a sudden jump of ϵ_r to about 35. Beyond this temperature there is a gradual decrease of the permittivity. Give a qualitative explanation.

2.39 Electric Polarization as Related to Dipole Density and Equivalent Charges

The preceding article introduced the polarization vector arising from equivalent dipoles of a material. We wish now to show that the definitions of Eqs. 2.38(1) and 2.38(5), adopted independently in that article, are consistent. Moreover, we will see that when dipole density changes with position, there is an equivalent "bound" charge in the material. This is understandable, for if dipole density is uniform, the positive charge of one dipole cancels the effect of the negative charge from an adjacent dipole. But when dipole density changes from point to point, this complete cancellation cannot occur. At a boundary especially, the ends of the dipoles leave an uncanceled charge on the surface, which is most important, as will be demonstrated in the examples of the following article. (Note for example Fig. 2.40d of the next article, showing both internal and external bound charges.)

Consider now the potential from a single dipole of strength $\bar{p}$ at a large distance r from it, as found in Art. 2.17.

$$\Phi = \frac{\bar{p} \cdot \bar{a}_r}{4\pi\epsilon_0 r^2}. \tag{1}$$

This can be written more generally as

$$\Phi(\bar{r}) = \frac{\bar{p} \cdot (\bar{r} - \bar{r}')}{4\pi\epsilon_0 |\bar{r} - \bar{r}'|^3}, \tag{2}$$

where $\bar{r}$ is a vector from an arbitrary origin of coordinates to the point where Φ is observed, and $\bar{r}'$ is a vector from the origin to the dipole (see

Fig. 2.15). Free space permittivity is used since we are replacing the electric effect of the matter by the molecular dipoles. We now take the definition Eq. 2.38(5) relating polarization to density of dipoles per unit volume,

$$\bar{P} = \lim_{\Delta V \to 0} \frac{\sum_i \bar{p}_i}{\Delta V}. \tag{3}$$

As usual in such definitions, ΔV is taken in the limit small compared with macroscopic dimensions, but large enough to contain many molecules of the material. Thus for a distribution of polarization, (3) is substituted in (2) and integrated over the region containing dipoles,

$$\Phi(\bar{r}) = \int_{V'} \frac{\bar{P}(\bar{r}') \cdot (\bar{r} - \bar{r}')}{4\pi\epsilon_0 |\bar{r} - \bar{r}'|^3} \, dV'. \tag{4}$$

By applying vector transformations similar to those used in Art. 2.21, (4) may be transformed to

$$\Phi(\bar{r}) = \int_{V'} \frac{(-\nabla \cdot \bar{P}) \, dV'}{4\pi\epsilon_0 |\bar{r} - \bar{r}'|} + \int_{S'} \frac{\bar{P} \cdot \bar{n} \, dS'}{4\pi\epsilon_0 |\bar{r} - \bar{r}'|}, \tag{5}$$

where S' is the surface surrounding the volume over which integration is taken, and $\bar{n}$ is a unit vector normal to that surface. By comparison of (5) with the expression for potential in free space resulting from volume and surface distribution of free charge,

$$\Phi(\bar{r}) = \int_{V'} \frac{\rho \, dV'}{4\pi\epsilon_0 |\bar{r} - \bar{r}'|} + \int_{S'} \frac{\rho_s \, dS'}{4\pi\epsilon_0 |\bar{r} - \bar{r}'|}, \tag{6}$$

we see that $\bar{P} \cdot \bar{n}$ has the effect of a surface charge density insofar as computation of potential is concerned, and $-\nabla \cdot \bar{P}$ has the effect of a volume charge density. We may therefore write

$$\rho_b = -\nabla \cdot \bar{P}, \qquad \rho_{sb} = \bar{P} \cdot \bar{n}. \tag{7}$$

These are denoted *bound* charges for obvious reasons, and are those predicted qualitatively in the reasoning of the first paragraph of this article. Their use in electromagnetic problems will be illustrated in the following article.

To show finally that all this is consistent with the definition Eq. 2.38(1) with which we started, note that within the material we can consider the bound charges as added to any free charges. The permittivity will be that of free space since, as already noted, the effect of the material is here being represented by these charges. Thus the divergence law can be written

$$\nabla \cdot \epsilon_0 \bar{E} = \rho + \rho_b. \tag{8}$$

Substitute ρ_b from (7) and rearrange,

$$\nabla \cdot (\epsilon_0 \bar{E} + \bar{P}) = \rho. \tag{9}$$

Comparison with Gauss's law yields Eq. 2.38(1) as desired.

Problems

2.39a Show that the bound volume charge ρ_b is zero within a linear, homogeneous, isotropic dielectric if the density of excess free charge is zero at the same point. Discuss the corresponding question for inhomogeneous dielectrics.

2.39b Show that Eq. 2.39(5) follows from Eq. 2.39(4).

2.40   Examples of the Use of Polarization and Equivalent Charges

We will consider here several problems using the polarization concept and the equivalent bound charges introduced in the preceding article. The first is an example with linear materials that can be handled adequately, and more simply, by treatments as in the first of this chapter where materials were described through their permittivity ϵ. This example serves to present an alternate point of view, and shows the identity of results from the two treatments. The second example is one with residual dipoles, where the polarization concept is nearly essential for treatment. The last examples are important ones in the study of materials; one aspect of this is demonstrated in the next article.

A. Planar Capacitor with Linear Dielectric. Consider the infinite parallel-plate capacitor shown in Fig. 2.40a. The dielectrics will be considered isotropic, homogeneous, and linear. If a voltage is applied between conducting plates, the simple picture of the polarization phenomenon would show that in any internal region dipoles are created in the direction of the field. There is a net bound surface charge at the plane boundary of each dielectric as shown in Fig. 2.40b, along with the surface charges on the conducting plates, ρ_s and $-\rho_s$. With no free charges in the dielectric, $\nabla \cdot \bar{P} = \rho_b = 0$ (see Prob. 2.39a.) The polarization vector is in the direction of electric field. Thus for medium 1, from the relations of Art. 2.38,

$$P_{1x} = (\epsilon_1 - \epsilon_0)E_{1x} \tag{1}$$

so that the total surface charge at $x = 0$ is

$$\rho_{s0} = \rho_s + \bar{n} \cdot \bar{P} = \rho_s - (\epsilon_1 - \epsilon_0)E_{1x}. \tag{2}$$

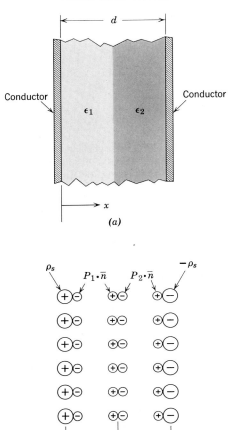

(a)

(b)

Fig. 2.40 (a) Capacitor with two different dielectrics. (b) Dielectrics replaced by polarization charges.

The total surface charge at $x = d/2$ is

$$\rho_{s1} = (\epsilon_1 - \epsilon_0)E_{1x} - (\epsilon_2 - \epsilon_0)E_{2x} \qquad (3)$$

and that at $x = d$ is

$$\rho_{s2} = -\rho_s + (\epsilon_2 - \epsilon_0)E_{2x} \qquad (4)$$

Thus we have the above sheet charges, considered as in free space. The field outside is zero and it is easy to find electric field between charge sheets. For medium 1, by Gauss's law

$$E_{1x} = \frac{\rho_{s0}}{\epsilon_0} = \frac{\rho_s}{\epsilon_0} - \frac{(\epsilon_1 - \epsilon_0)}{\epsilon_0} E_{1x}$$

or

$$E_{1x} = \frac{\rho_s}{\epsilon_1} \tag{5}$$

and similarly for medium 2. These results are just those that would be found using Gauss's law with the constitutive parameters ϵ_1 and ϵ_2 with only the surface charges on conductors. Thus the two points of view are equivalent, and the use of polarization would be the harder way of solving this problem as it generally is for linear problems.

B. Rod with Residual Polarization. Consider a material which can retain net polarization upon removal of the applied electric field. In this case there exists a non-linear relation between polarization and electric field; an equivalent permittivity cannot be defined. Consider a rod of such a material, having a residual polarization $\bar{P}$ as shown in Fig. 2.40c. From Eq. 2.39(7) we see that the equivalent set of charges is a surface charge density of $\rho_{sb} = \pm P$ at the end surfaces and zero volume charges. The equivalent charge system is shown in Fig. 2.40c. For distances from the rod which are large compared with the dimensions of the rod, the fields may be calculated by treating it as a dipole having charges

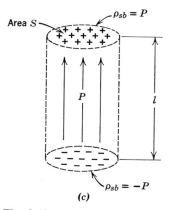

(c)

Fig. 2.40c Polarization charges on polarized dielectric rod.

$\pm SP$, where S is the end area, separated by the length l of the rod. Thus, the potentials are given by Eq. 2.39(1), which may be written as

$$\Phi(x, y, z) = \frac{SPl(\bar{a}_n \cdot \bar{a}_r)}{4\pi\epsilon_0 r^2} \tag{6}$$

where $\bar{a}_n$ is an outward normal to the end surface with positive charge.

C. Small Spherical Cavity in a Dielectric. Consider a spherical cavity in a dielectric, as illustrated in Fig. 2.40d. Like that of example (A), it could be handled adequately by considering differences in permittivity for the two regions, as will be shown in Chapter 3. We give this treatment because of its use in the theory of dielectrics, as will be demonstrated in Art. 2.41. If the cavity is small enough, the macroscopic field may be considered constant throughout the volume, but as indicated in the figure,

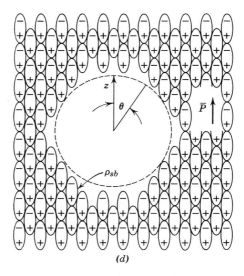

(d)

Fig. 2.40*d* Dipoles remaining after removal of spherical volume.

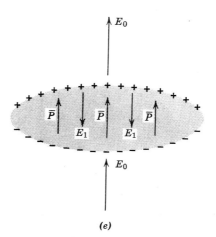

(e)

Fig. 2.40*e* Dielectric spheroid in uniform electric field.

bound charges will exist on the inside surface of the cavity. For constant $\bar{P}$, and the coordinates shown in Fig. 2.40d, Eq. 2.39(7) gives these as

$$\rho_{sb} = P \cos \theta. \tag{7}$$

The z component of electric field at the center resulting from charge on the surface is

$$E_P = \int_0^{2\pi} \int_0^{\pi} \frac{P \sin \theta \cos^2 \theta \, d\theta \, d\phi}{4\pi\epsilon_0}, \tag{8}$$

and the other components are zero by symmetry. Integration yields

$$\bar{E}_P = \frac{\bar{P}}{3\epsilon_0}. \tag{9}$$

D. Depolarization Factors of Spheroidal Bodies. A problem closely related to the cavity problem of C is that of the bound surface charges on the exterior of a material body placed in an electric field. Consider the spheroid pictured in Fig. 2.40e with an applied external field E_0. The polarization $\bar{P}$ in the body will leave bound surface charges on the exterior, as in the other examples. The figure shows that these surface charges will produce a field $\bar{E}_1$ on the interior, called the *depolarization field* since it is in the opposite direction to $\bar{P}$. It is the characteristic of the spheroidal shape that the field produced is uniform. A *depolarization factor* is defined as

$$N_d = \frac{\epsilon_0 E_1}{P}. \tag{10}$$

Some limiting forms for this factor are:[8]

Shape	Axis	N_d
Sphere	Any	$\frac{1}{3}$
Thin slab	Normal	1
Thin slab	In plane	0
Long circular cylinder	Longitudinal	0
Long circular cylinder	Transverse	$\frac{1}{2}$

The corresponding factors in magnetic problems are called *demagnetization factors.*[14] Note that these problems also can be solved by treating as a boundary-value problem with discontinuities in ϵ or μ, but the specific consideration of the bound charges as replacing the material can be very useful in the study of materials.

Problems

2.40a   Find the system of charges equivalent to the polarization of the dielectrics in the coaxial-line problem 2.08a.

2.40b   Discuss the application of the treatment of example D to spheroidal cavities in a material, as in the special case of example C. What does this reveal about the internal field in cavities of "pillbox" shape? For cavities of "needle" shape?

2.41   Simple Model of a Dielectric

We are now in a position to combine points from the preceding three articles to obtain a simple model for dielectric behavior. To find the approximate internal field acting on a molecule, we remove a spherical volume of molecules centered on the one under consideration, leaving a spherical cavity such as that studied in Fig. 2.40d. The size of the sphere is chosen to be sufficiently large that the molecules on the inside surface of the resulting cavity are far enough away from the center for the dipole approximation of Eq. 2.39(1) to be valid. On the other hand, the sphere is small enough that the macroscopic field can be considered constant throughout the volume. The result of Eq. 2.40(9) gives the internal field from the bound charges of the spherical cavity as

$$\bar{E}_{Pi} = \frac{\bar{P}}{3\epsilon_0}. \tag{1}$$

But what about the effect of the molecules removed? For the simple dielectrics covered by this model, the field from these sums to zero at the sphere's center. This is a good approximation, for example, in crystals with cubic symmetry, or as a statistical average of the effects in a gas or liquid. Total internal field is then the sum of (1) and the macroscopic field,

$$\bar{E}_i = \bar{E} + \frac{\bar{P}}{3\epsilon_0}. \tag{2}$$

The polarization $\bar{P}$ in (2), from the relations of Art. 2.38, may be expressed as

$$\bar{P} = (\epsilon - \epsilon_0)\bar{E}, \tag{3}$$

so that the ratio of internal to macroscopic field is

$$\frac{\bar{E}_i}{\bar{E}} = \frac{1}{3}\left(2 + \frac{\epsilon}{\epsilon_0}\right) = \frac{2 + \epsilon_r}{3}. \tag{4}$$

Substitution of this ratio in Eq. 2.38(8) gives

$$\frac{\epsilon_r - 1}{\epsilon_r + 2} = \frac{N\alpha_T}{3} \tag{5}$$

This is the Clausius-Mossotti relationship which applies fairly well to gases up to moderate pressures, but for denser media, one or more of the approximations made may break down. Attempts to extend the formula are well described in the literature.[11,12] It should be stressed, however, that the degree of approximation in the Clausius-Mossotti relationship or its various extensions does not limit the rigorous nature of the concept of polarization, and the related dipoles and bound charges, as presented in the preceding three articles.

2.42 Some Properties of Magnetic Polarization

Magnetic polarization or magnetization was defined in Art. 2.38 along with electric polarization. The use of this concept, and its relationship to density of magnetic dipoles, can be developed in a fashion exactly parallel to that given for electric quantities in Arts. 2.38 to 2.41. This does require acceptance of the concept of magnetic charges in the parallel to Art. 2.39. Since this is a model of an atomic process, it is valid to the extent that predicted results are valid. Nevertheless, we have stressed in this book the magnetic fields as arising from currents, so the alternate development[18] showing the current sources for magnetization is given in Appendix III. In this picture, bound volume currents arise when there is a non-zero curl of magnetization, and bound surface currents arise when there is a component of magnetization lying in the surface of the magnetic medium. The currents are thought of as arising from electron motions in the atoms, or from electron spins within the atom. Full understanding of these processes, however, requires very basic study of the physical base including quantum effects.

Although there is appreciable parallelism, there are some important practical differences between magnetic and electric properties. The simple contribution to magnetization from changes of electron orbits in the atom gives a negative magnetic susceptibility, and this effect is known as *diamagnetism*. Diamagnetic effects produce only small deviations from the free-space permeability, typically fractional changes of -10^{-8} to -10^{-5}.

---

[18] For a still closer comparison of the two methods of treatment, see Sec. 5.3 of Fano, Chu, and Adler, ref. 16.

The diamagnetic effect is usually obscured in materials with atoms having natural net magnetic moments. To have a net magnetic moment, an atom must have an incomplete outer electron shell. The net moments of the atoms tend to align with the magnetic field but are deflected from complete alignment by their thermal activity. The fields resulting from the partially aligned dipoles add to the applied field—an effect called *paramagnetism*. The magnitude of the magnetization can be expressed in terms of the magnetic field $\bar{H}_i$ acting on the atomic dipoles and the absolute temperature T by

$$M = Nm_0\left(\coth\frac{m_0\mu_0 H_i}{kT} - \frac{kT}{m_0\mu_0 H_i}\right) \tag{1}$$

where N is the number of dipoles per unit volume, m_0 is the natural dipole moment, and k is Boltzmann's constant. Equation (1) is derived from considerations of the statistical distribution of the dipole orientations.[19] The direction of $\bar{M}$ is parallel with $\bar{H}_i$ in materials of this type and the molecular field $\bar{H}_i$ is negligibly different from the applied field. For magnetic fields which are not too strong and temperatures not too low, the bracket in (1) may be approximated by the first term in its series expansion. Thus, using Eq. 2.38(4), we may write that the paramagnetic susceptibility is approximately

$$\chi_m \cong \frac{N\mu_0 m_0{}^2}{3kT}. \tag{2}$$

In a variety of materials at room temperature χ_m has values of the order of 10^{-5}.

Some of the most important of magnetic properties are those that involve coupling effects between atomic magnetic moments, but these are discussed together with the corresponding electric effects in the following article.

Problems

2.42a Consider a cylindrical permanent magnet having uniform magnetization $\bar{M}$ parallel to the magnet axis. Using the expressions for equivalent currents developed in Appendix III, find an expression for the field at a distance r which is much larger than either the radius a or the length L of the magnet.
2.42b Verify the approximate form for paramagnetic susceptibility, Eq. 2.42(2).

---

[19] This functional form, first derived by Langevin, applies also to permanent electric dipole moments in polar materials, although we discussed in Art. 2.38 only the important linear approximation. See for example Kittel, ref. 8.

2.43 Materials with Residual Magnetic and Electric Polarization

If the temperature of a paramagnetic substance is reduced below a certain value, which depends on the material, the magnetization $\bar{M}$ may be sufficient to produce the field necessary to hold the dipoles aligned even when the external field is not present. From Eq. AIII(10) we see that the molecular field produced by the magnetization is then

$$\bar{H}_i = \kappa \bar{M} \tag{1}$$

But from Eq. 2.42(1) it is seen that a second relation between $\bar{H}_i$ and $\bar{M}$ exists. Equating M of the two expressions, the conditions for *spontaneous magnetization* are obtained. The temperature below which a material exhibits spontaneous magnetization is called its *Curie temperature*. From experimental knowledge of the Curie temperatures for various materials it has been found that κ, the factor measuring the interaction of neighboring dipoles, must be of the order of 1000. On the basis of purely magnetic interactions, it would be expected to be about $\frac{1}{3}$, as was the corresponding factor in Eq. 2.41(2) for electric dipoles. The high values are explained using quantum-mechanical considerations on the basis of electric interaction between molecules resulting from distortions of the charge distributions in the molecules. In some materials it is energetically favorable for dipoles to align parallel to their neighbors; these are called *ferromagnetic* substances. In some materials it is energetically favorable for neighboring dipoles to assume an antiparallel orientation as indicated in Fig. 2.43a; these are called *antiferromagnetic* substances. In *ferrimagnetic* materials, also called *ferrites*, the neighboring dipoles are aligned in an antiparallel arrangement but different types of atoms are present and the dipoles do not cancel. This is illustrated schematically in Fig. 2.43b.

From the foregoing discussion one would expect that a piece of either ferromagnetic or ferrimagnetic material as found in nature would act as a magnet. However, the natural tendency of a physical system to minimize its stored energy leads to subdivision of the material into small regions called *domains* within each of which a complete alignment of the dipoles is maintained, but between which are various relative dipole orientations. When a magnetic field is applied, the walls of the domains move in such a way as to enlarge the domains having components of their dipole vectors in the direction of the magnetic field. If the magnetic field intensity is further increased, the dipole direction for each domain as a whole rotates toward the direction of the applied magnetic field. This process is nonlinear in that the magnetization and hence the flux density $\bar{B}$ is not simply proportional to the applied field. The magnetization tends to lag the field intensity with the result that the relation between $\bar{B}$ and $\bar{H}$ has the pattern shown in Fig. 2.43c which is called a *hysteresis loop*. The linear parts of the loop at high values of magnetic field correspond to the condition in which all of the dipole moments are aligned, and $\bar{B}$ and $\bar{H}$ are therefore related by μ_0 (neglecting diamagnetic effects).

The processes of wall movement and rotation of the domains require the expenditure of energy. The energy required for the traversal of the loop by

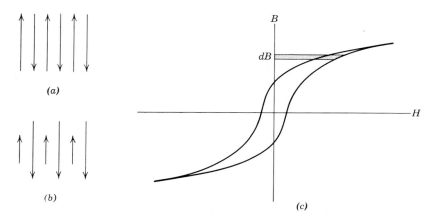

(a)

(b)

(c)

Fig. 2.43   (a) Anti-parallel arrangement of neighboring dipoles in antiferromagnetic materials. (b) Unbalanced anti-parallel dipoles in ferrites. (c) Hysteresis loop.

varying $\bar{H}$ from a large negative value to a large positive value and back again can be found by consideration of the expression for the stored magnetic energy, Eq. 2.36(1). If this is differentiated with respect to $\bar{B}$, the energy required to change $\bar{B}$ a differential amount is seen to be

$$dW = \int_V \bar{H} \cdot d\bar{B} \, dV$$

where the integration is over the volume of the material. This differential energy is shown as a shaded bar on the hysteresis loop in Fig. 2.43c. When the field is decreased, a portion of the energy indicated by the part of the bar outside the loop is returned to the field. The result of integrating around the loop is that the total expended energy per unit volume is equal to the area of the loop.

An effect similar to that discussed for magnetic polarization is found for electric polarization in some materials (for example, barium titanate).

These materials, called *ferroelectric* by analogy, exhibit a hysteresis loop in the relation between the electric flux density $\bar{D}$ and the electric field intensity $\bar{E}$. As in ferromagnetic materials, a domain structure occurs in ferroelectrics. The details of the interaction between neighboring dipoles are discussed in texts on solid state physics.[8,9,10]

It is clear from the shape of the hysteresis loop in Fig. 2.43c that it is meaningless to relate $\bar{B}$ to $\bar{H}$ by a permeability μ for materials with residual polarization. The permittivity ϵ also loses significance for ferroelectric materials. It is true, in fact, that for most materials subjected to sufficiently high fields, ϵ and μ cannot be considered constants. For most purposes, however, the materials without residual polarization can be represented by constant permittivity and permeability. In solving field problems, one is frequently concerned with small variations of a field about some larger average value. If the variations are small enough, any part of the hysteresis loop can be considered a straight line, the slope of which depends on the point on the loop. The slope of the loop at that point is called the *incremental permeability* in that it relates $\bar{B}$ and $\bar{H}$ for incremental changes of $\bar{H}$.

Problems

2.43a Spontaneous magnetization can occur only if there is some value of H_i for which Eqs. 2.42(1) and 2.43(1) can be simultaneously satisfied. For any given value of κ there is a maximum temperature, the Curie temperature T_c, for spontaneous magnetization. By noting the condition on the initial slope of $M = f(H_i)$ in Eq. 2.42(1) required for a simultaneous solution, write a relation between κ and T_c.

2.43b Find κ for iron using the result of Prob. *a* and Curie temperature of $1043°K$. There are 8.6×10^{22} atoms/cm³. Assume that the magnetic moment of the iron atom is 2.22 Bohr magnetons, where a Bohr magneton is $eh/4\pi m$. Here e is the electronic charge, h is Planck's constant (6.63×10^{-34} joule-sec), and m is the mass of an electron.

2.43c Estimate the maximum incremental permeability for the material having the B-H relation shown in Fig. 2.43c.

2.43d Assume that the material having the B-H relation shown in Fig. 2.43c saturates at $B = 1000$ gauss and estimate graphically the energy per unit volume for one complete traversal of the hysteresis loop.

2.44 Anisotropic Dielectric and Magnetic Properties

In our discussion of material properties up to this point, we have assumed that the polarization is parallel with the applied fields and is independent of the direction of the fields. We must modify this view for anisotropic materials. A helpful analogy is afforded by the strain in a solid body resulting from applied forces. Consider a rectangular solid having unequal edge lengths with a coordinate system oriented at an arbitrary angle as shown in Fig. 2.44. If a force is applied along any one coordinate, strains result in all three directions with different magnitudes in each direction.

In the same way, an electric field applied to an anisotropic material along an axis of an arbitrarily oriented coordinate system leads to polarization which has components in all coordinate directions. We assume

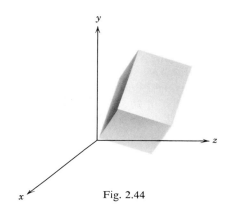

Fig. 2.44

here materials with no spontaneous polarization. If $\bar{E} = \bar{a}_x E_x$, then

$$\bar{P} = \epsilon_0(\bar{a}_x \chi_{e11} E_x + \bar{a}_y \chi_{e12} E_x + \bar{a}_z \chi_{e13} E_x),$$

where χ_e is electric susceptibility and the added subscripts refer to x, y, and z components of $\bar{P}$ and $\bar{E}$, respectively. Then if $\bar{E}$ has all three components

$$P_x = \epsilon_0(\chi_{e11} E_x + \chi_{e12} E_y + \chi_{e13} E_z)$$
$$P_y = \epsilon_0(\chi_{e21} E_x + \chi_{e22} E_y + \chi_{e23} E_z) \tag{1}$$
$$P_z = \epsilon_0(\chi_{e31} E_x + \chi_{e32} E_y + \chi_{e33} E_z)$$

If we use the relation between $\bar{D}$ and $\bar{P}$, Eq. 2.38(1), we may obtain from (1),

$$D_x = \epsilon_{11} E_x + \epsilon_{12} E_y + \epsilon_{13} E_z$$
$$D_y = \epsilon_{21} E_x + \epsilon_{22} E_y + \epsilon_{23} E_z \tag{2}$$
$$D_z = \epsilon_{31} E_x + \epsilon_{32} E_y + \epsilon_{33} E_z$$

where $\epsilon_{11} = \epsilon_0(1 + \chi_{e11}), \qquad \epsilon_{12} = \epsilon_0 \chi_{e12}$, etc. $\tag{3}$

Similar relations apply among $\bar{B}$, $\bar{H}$, and χ_m.

In crystals, coordinates can be selected along *principal axes* of the crystal so that off-diagonal terms are zero, leaving

$$D_x = \epsilon_{11}E_x, \quad D_y = \epsilon_{22}E_y, \quad D_z = \epsilon_{33}E_z. \tag{4}$$

Table 2.44 gives an example of observed differences for a few crystals.[20]

TABLE 2.44

Material	ϵ_{11}	ϵ_{22}	ϵ_{33}
Sodium chloride	←————5.6————→		
Quartz	←——4.5——→		4.6
Rutile	←——89——→		173
Gypsum	9.9	5.1	5.0

Anisotropic properties can affect static field distributions, but are of primary concern to wave problems. Thus further considerations will be delayed to Chapter 9 where effects on wave propagation will be studied.

[20] J. P. Nye, *Physical Properties of Crystals*, Oxford (Clarendon Press), New York, 1960.

3 SOLUTIONS TO STATIC FIELD PROBLEMS

BASIC CONSIDERATIONS IN SOLVING FIELD PROBLEMS BY DIFFERENTIAL EQUATIONS

3.01 Introduction

Chapter 2 presented the laws of electricity and magnetism for systems with no time variations, and the concepts of such static systems. It was noted at the beginning of that chapter that it is often necessary to solve problems involving the laws of static systems, not alone for cases involving d-c potentials and direct currents but also for the cases to be discussed later when the results of static solutions may be applied directly to high-frequency problems.

If the problem is the solution of a static system, the desired result may be the actual distribution of fields or potentials, as for instance when the maximum gradient is desired for purposes of calculating breakdown voltage between a given set of electrodes. If the static solution is to be used in studying motion of electrons, it will be desired to find the field strength at a given point in space so that forces exerted on the electrons may be calculated at that point. If it is desired to use static solutions for the calculation of inductances and capacitances, or the impedance of a transmission line, it is often necessary to find the field distribution around the desired configuration as a first step. Thus the calculation of the field or potential distribution in the vicinity of an electrode system, a transmission line, or a circuit element is usually the first step in the analysis of each system. This will be the major goal of this chapter.

The distribution of fields may be desired in regions containing charges, in regions containing currents, or in regions free from both charges and currents. We will defer consideration of regions containing currents since they are of principal interest for a-c problems where it is desired to calculate the impedance of a circuit element or the processes in an electron stream or a plasma. Regions containing charges are frequently of interest, so some methods of solving Poisson's equation [Eq. 2.20(3)] will be examined. Principal emphasis, however, will be on Laplace's equation, which governs the distribution of fields in charge- and current-free regions. The very extensive applicability of Laplace's equation throughout applied physics has motivated the development of many mathematical and computational methods for its solution. Despite the importance of this problem, it is impossible to attempt completeness here in considering these methods. A few of the most useful computational techniques suitable for arbitrary electrode shapes will be introduced. We shall also study here solutions applicable to certain simple and very useful geometrical configurations, stressing the physical pictures which follow, and those methods of solution which will best provide background for similar types of solutions in wave problems to follow.

3.02 Fields Governed by the Laplace and Poisson Equations

In Chapter 2, Poisson's equation appeared first to relate the derivatives of the electrostatic scalar potential Φ to each other and to the charge density at any point in a homogeneous, isotropic medium:

$$\nabla^2\Phi = -\frac{\rho}{\epsilon}. \tag{1}$$

A solution to this equation which satisfies the boundary conditions of the specified electrode configurations and applied potentials will be an equation giving the potential as a function of the space coordinates. For charge-free regions the potential satisfies Laplace's equation

$$\nabla^2\Phi = 0.$$

But not only potential satisfies Laplace's equation in such a region. It is easily seen from the basic relations of Chapter 2 that certain components of the electric field vector $\bar{E}$ also are distributed in space in accordance with this relation. It is easily seen from Stokes's theorem, Eq. 2.29(2), and the conservative property of electrostatic fields, Eq. 2.14(2), that

$$\nabla \times \bar{E} = 0.$$

If the curl of this equation is taken

$$\nabla \times \nabla \times \bar{E} = 0$$

or, by a vector equivalence (see inside cover),

$$\nabla(\nabla \cdot \bar{E}) - \nabla^2 \bar{E} = 0.$$

For a charge-free, homogeneous dielectric, Eq. 2.12(8) yields

$$\nabla \cdot \bar{E} = 0$$

so that

$$\nabla^2 \bar{E} = 0. \tag{2}$$

The last expression is a vector equation which in general may not be simple in form. In rectangular coordinates, however,

$$\nabla^2 \bar{E} = \bar{a}_x \nabla^2 E_x + \bar{a}_y \nabla^2 E_y + \bar{a}_z \nabla^2 E_z \tag{3}$$

so that

$$\nabla^2 E_x = 0, \qquad \nabla^2 E_y = 0, \qquad \nabla^2 E_z = 0. \tag{4}$$

Thus, for a charge-free region, each of the three components of electric field intensity in rectangular coordinates satisfies Laplace's equation. Expansion of $\nabla^2 \bar{E}$ in cylindrical coordinates shows that the axial component of $\bar{E}$ also satisfies Laplace's equation. That is, in cylindrical coordinates

$$\nabla^2 E_z = 0 \tag{5}$$

(but this is not true of E_r and E_ϕ). It may often be more convenient to use these components of field directly in Laplace's equation than to use the potential.

Similar arguments show that the magnetic field $\bar{H}$ or the magnetic vector potential $\bar{A}$ or magnetic scalar potential Φ_m satisfies Laplace's

TABLE 3.02

Application of Laplace's Equation

Condition	Quantity	Rectangular Coordinates	Cylindrical Coordinates	Spherical Coordinates
Charge-free region (static case)	Electrostatic scalar potential	Φ	Φ	Φ
	Electric field intensity	E_x, E_y, E_z	E_z	
Current-free region (static case)	Vector magnetic potential	A_x, A_y, A_z	A_z	
	Magnetic field intensity	H_x, H_y, H_z	H_z	
	Magnetic scalar potential	Φ_m	Φ_m	Φ_m
Static currents	Current density	i_x, i_y, i_z	i_z	

equation for a current-free region, and the d-c current density $\bar{\imath}$ satisfies it in a homogeneous conducting region. All this is summarized in Table 3.02.

Problems

3.02a Find the form of differential equation satisfied by E_r in cylindrical coordinates for a charge-free, homogeneous dielectric region. Repeat for E_ϕ.

3.02b Show that none of the components of electric field in spherical coordinates satisfies Laplace's equation.

3.02c Derive Laplace's equation for $\bar{H}$, $\bar{A}$, and Φ_m in a current-free region and for d-c current density $\bar{\imath}$ in a homogeneous conductor.

3.03 Uniqueness of a Solution

Many possible means of obtaining solutions to the equations of Laplace and Poisson will be presented in the following articles. It is important to realize that, when a solution to the equation within a region is obtained, it is the only possible solution if it satisfies the boundary conditions on that region.

It can be shown that the potentials governed either by the Laplace or Poisson equations in regions with given potentials on the boundaries are unique. With normal derivatives of potential specified on the boundaries (or equivalently, charges), the potential is unique to within an additive constant. Here we will prove the theorem for a charge-free region with potential specified on the boundary. The proofs of the other parts of the theorem are left as problems.

The usual way to demonstrate uniqueness of a quantity is first to assume the contrary and then show this assumption to be false. Imagine two possible solutions, Φ_1 and Φ_2. Since they must both reduce to the given potential along the boundary,

$$\Phi_1 - \Phi_2 = 0 \tag{1}$$

along the boundary surface. Since they are both solutions to Laplace's equation,

$$\nabla^2\Phi_1 = 0 \qquad \text{and} \qquad \nabla^2\Phi_2 = 0$$

or

$$\nabla^2(\Phi_1 - \Phi_2) = 0 \tag{2}$$

throughout the entire region.

In the divergence theorem, Eq. 2.13(3), $\bar{F}$ may be any continuous vector quantity. In particular, let it be the quantity

$$(\Phi_1 - \Phi_2)\nabla(\Phi_1 - \Phi_2).$$

Then

$$\int_V \nabla \cdot [(\Phi_1 - \Phi_2)\nabla(\Phi_1 - \Phi_2)] \, dV = \oint_S [(\Phi_1 - \Phi_2)\nabla(\Phi_1 - \Phi_2)] \cdot \overline{dS}$$

From the vector identity

$$\text{div } (\psi \bar{A}) = \psi \text{ div } \bar{A} + \bar{A} \cdot \text{grad } \psi$$

the equation may be expanded to

$$\int_V (\Phi_1 - \Phi_2)\nabla^2(\Phi_1 - \Phi_2) \, dV + \int_V [\nabla(\Phi_1 - \Phi_2)]^2 \, dV$$
$$= \oint_S (\Phi_1 - \Phi_2)\nabla(\Phi_1 - \Phi_2) \cdot \overline{dS}.$$

The first integral must be zero by (2); the last integral must be zero, since (1) holds over the boundary surface. There remains

$$\int_V [\nabla(\Phi_1 - \Phi_2)]^2 \, dV = 0. \tag{3}$$

The gradient of a real scalar is real. Thus its square can only be positive or zero. If its integral is to be zero, it can only be zero:

$$\nabla(\Phi_1 - \Phi_2) = 0 \tag{4}$$

or $$(\Phi_1 - \Phi_2) = \text{constant.} \tag{5}$$

This constant must apply even to the boundary, where we know that (1) is true. The constant is then zero, and $\Phi_1 - \Phi_2$ is everywhere zero, which means that Φ_1 and Φ_2 are identical potential distributions. Hence the proof of uniqueness: Laplace's equation can have only one solution which satisfies the boundary conditions of the given region. If by any sort of conniving we find a solution to a field problem that fits all boundary conditions and satisfies Laplace's equation, we may be sure it is the only one.

Problems

3.03a Prove that, if charge density ρ is given throughout a volume, any solution of Poisson's equation 2.20(3), must be the only possible solution provided that it satisfies the boundary conditions around the region.

3.03b Show that the potential in a charge-free region is uniquely determined, except for an arbitrary additive constant, by specification of the normal derivatives of potential on the bounding surfaces.

3.04 Superposition

It is frequently possible to divide a given field problem into two or more simpler problems, the solutions of which can be combined to obtain the desired answer. The validity of this procedure is based on the linearity of the Laplace and Poisson equations. That is,

$$\nabla^2(\Phi_1 + \Phi_2) = \nabla^2\Phi_1 + \nabla^2\Phi_2$$

and
$$\nabla^2(k\Phi_1) = k\nabla^2\Phi_1.$$

The utility of the superposition concept depends on finding the simpler problems with boundary conditions which add to give the original boundary conditions.

Consider, for example, the problem of finding the potentials inside a box when potentials are specified on more than one side and a given

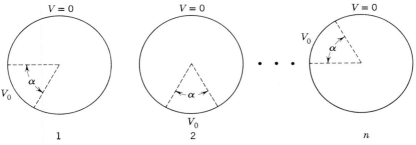

Fig. 3.04   Series of circular cylinders with sectors of angle α at the potential V_0 oriented at multiples of α with respect to each other.

distribution of charge is enclosed. The correct solution must satisfy Poisson's equation and the stated boundary conditions. As we will see later in the chapter, it is possible to find a potential which satisfies Laplace's equation and a specified non-zero potential on one side of the box, with all other sides at zero potential. It is not easy to satisfy all the non-zero boundary voltages in one step. However, we can find the desired potential as the superposition of the potentials $\Phi_1, \ldots \Phi_n$, each of which satisfies Laplace's equation and one of the non-zero boundary specifications. It is also possible to find a potential Φ_ρ which satisfies Poisson's equation and is zero on all boundaries. Because of the linearity of $\nabla^2\Phi$, the sum

$$\Phi_T = \Phi_1 + \Phi_2 + \cdots + \Phi_n + \Phi_\rho$$

satisfies Poisson's equation and has the required potentials at all boundaries.

An interesting example of the use of superposition is the solution for the potential at the center of some symmetrical structure. For example, consider a charge-free circular system as shown in Fig. 3.04, when a potential V_0 is applied over a portion of the boundary subtending the angle α. Suppose that $\alpha = 2\pi/n$. If the potential at the center were found for n different sets of boundary conditions as shown in Fig. 3.04, where the only difference between these is that the section of the boundary to be at potential V_0 is rotated by the angle $k\alpha$, with k an integer, the sum of the n solutions would be the potential at the center of a cylinder with V_0 over the entire boundary. This potential at the center of such an infinite cylinder is just V_0. Since every problem is identical except for a rotation by α, which would not affect the potential at the center, the potential at the center for the original problem must be V_0/n. This same technique could be applied to find the potential at the center point of a square, cube, equilateral polygon, sphere, etc., with one portion at a given potential.

Problems

3.04a A spherical surface is at zero potential except for a strip in the region $0 < \phi < \pi/3$, $0 < \theta < \pi/2$. Find the potential at the center of the sphere.

3.04b A sphere of radius a of uniform charge density contains a spherical hole of radius b offset from the center. Find the potential and field for $r > a$.

3.04c Discuss the validity of superposition for the field equations given in Chapter 2, other than the Laplace and Poisson equations.

3.04d Consider an infinite cylindrical conductor of circular cross section with a round cylindrical hole offset from the axis of the conductor. Find the magnetic field in the hole resulting from a current I flowing in the conductor.

3.05 Simple Example: Field between Coaxial Cylinders with Two Dielectrics

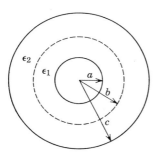

Fig. 3.05 Coaxial cylinders with two dielectrics.

As the first step in the study of problems in which Laplace's equation is used to obtain field and potential distributions, we will take an example with simple boundaries. The problem is one of finding the potential distribution between two coaxial conducting cylinders of radii a and c (Fig. 3.05), with a dielectric of constant ϵ_1 filling the region between a and b, and a second dielectric of constant ϵ_2 filling the region between b and c. The inner conductor is at potential zero, and the outer at potential V_0. Because of the symmetry of the problem, the solution could be readily obtained by using Gauss's law as in the example of Art. 2.08, but the primary purpose here is to demonstrate several processes in the solution by means of differential equations.

The geometrical form suggests that the Laplacian, $\nabla^2\Phi$, be expressed in cylindrical coordinates (see inside back cover), giving for Laplace's equation

$$\nabla^2\Phi = \frac{1}{r}\frac{\partial}{\partial r}\left(r\frac{\partial\Phi}{\partial r}\right) + \frac{1}{r^2}\frac{\partial^2\Phi}{\partial\phi^2} + \frac{\partial^2\Phi}{\partial z^2} = 0. \tag{1}$$

It will be assumed that there is no variation in the axial (z) direction, and the cylindrical symmetry eliminates variations with angle ϕ. Equation (1) then reduces to

$$\frac{1}{r}\frac{d}{dr}\left(r\frac{d\Phi}{dr}\right) = 0. \tag{2}$$

Note that, in (2), the derivative is written as a total derivative, since there is now only one variable remaining in the problem. Equation (2) may be integrated directly:

$$r\frac{d\Phi}{dr} = C_1. \tag{3}$$

Integrating again, we have

$$\Phi_1 = C_1 \ln r + C_2. \tag{4}$$

This has been labeled Φ_1 because we will consider that the result of (4) is applicable to the first dielectric region ($a < r < b$). The same differential equation with the same symmetry applies to the second dielectric region, so the same form of solution applies there also, but the arbitrary constants may be different. So, for the potential in region 2 ($b < r < c$), let us write

$$\Phi_2 = C_3 \ln r + C_4. \tag{5}$$

The boundary conditions at the two conductors are:

(a) $\qquad\qquad \Phi_1 = 0 \qquad$ at $\quad r = a$
(b) $\qquad\qquad \Phi_2 = V_0 \qquad$ at $\quad r = c$.

In addition, there are continuity conditions at the boundary between the two dielectric media. The potential and the normal component of electric flux density must be continuous across this charge-free boundary (Art. 2.18):

(c) $\qquad \Phi_1 = \Phi_2 \quad$ at $\quad r = b$
(d) $\qquad D_{r_1} = D_{r_2} \quad$ at $\quad r = b, \quad$ or $\quad \epsilon_1\frac{d\Phi_1}{dr} = \epsilon_2\frac{d\Phi_2}{dr}$ there.

The application of condition (a) to (4) yields

$$C_2 = -C_1 \ln a. \tag{6}$$

The application of (b) to (5) yields

$$C_4 = V_0 - C_3 \ln c. \tag{7}$$

Condition (c), applied to (4) and (5), gives

$$C_1 \ln b + C_2 = C_3 \ln b + C_4. \tag{8}$$

And condition (d), applied to (4) and (5), gives

$$\epsilon_1 C_1 = \epsilon_2 C_3. \tag{9}$$

Any one of the constants, as C_1, may be obtained by eliminating between the four equations, (6) to (9):

$$C_1 = \frac{V_0}{\ln(b/a) - (\epsilon_1/\epsilon_2)\ln(b/c)}. \tag{10}$$

The remaining constants, C_2, C_3, and C_4, may be obtained from (6), (9), and (7), respectively. The results are substituted in (4) and (5) to give the potential distribution in the two dielectric regions:

$$\Phi_1 = \frac{V_0 \ln(r/a)}{\ln(b/a) + (\epsilon_1/\epsilon_2)\ln(c/b)} \qquad a < r < b \tag{11}$$

$$\Phi_2 = V_0 \left[1 - \frac{(\epsilon_1/\epsilon_2)\ln(c/r)}{\ln(b/a) + (\epsilon_1/\epsilon_2)\ln(c/b)} \right] \qquad b < r < c. \tag{12}$$

It can be checked that these distributions do satisfy Laplace's equation and the boundary and continuity conditions of the problem. Only in such simple problems as this will it be possible to obtain solutions of the differential equation by direct integration, but the method of applying boundary and continuity conditions to the solutions, however obtained, is well demonstrated by the example.

Problems

3.05a Obtain by means of Laplace's equation the potential distribution between two concentric spherical conductors separated by a single dielectric. The inner conductor of radius a is at potential V_0, and the outer conductor of radius b is at potential zero.

3.05b Obtain by means of Laplace's equation the potential distribution between two concentric spherical conductors with two dielectrics filling the region. The inner conductor of radius a is at potential zero, and the outer conductor of radius c is at potential V_0. Dielectric of constant ϵ_1 extends from a to b, and one of constant ϵ_2 extends from b to c.

3.05c Two coaxial cylindrical conductors of radii a and b are at potentials zero and V_0, respectively. There are two dielectrics between the conductors, but this time the plane through the axis is the dividing surface. That is, dielectric ϵ_1 extends from $\phi = 0$ to $\phi = \pi$, and ϵ_2 extends from $\phi = \pi$ to $\phi = 2\pi$. Obtain the potential distribution from Laplace's equation.

3.05d Obtain the electrostatic capacitances for the two conductor systems described in the example of Art. 3.05, and in Probs. a, b, and c.

GRAPHICAL, NUMERICAL, AND ANALOG METHODS

3.06 Principles of Graphical Field Mapping

By a two-dimensional problem, we mean here one in which the fields do not vary in one linear direction, so that the field distribution need be given in only one cross-sectional plane since it is the same in all cross-sectional planes. We wish to describe first a graphical method for obtaining the potential and field distribution for such two-dimensional problems. It may seem that such a discussion is out of place now that we have set down the principles for the mathematical solution of Laplace's equation, but, since the method offers one of the best aids for visualizing the distribution problem, the physical pictures which it gives will be invaluable as we go on to the next subject, the method of conformal transformations. This graphical method is also a very useful engineering tool, since the configurations of electrodes in vacuum tubes, electron guns, transmission lines, and other practical problems are often not simple mathematical surfaces, so that purely mathematical solutions of the problem may be impractical.

In the method, the known potential difference between electrodes of the boundary is divided into a number of smaller potential divisions, and the equipotential lines (traces of the equipotential surfaces in the cross-sectional plane) are sketched by guess throughout the plot. The electric field lines are also sketched by guess, and these guesses are improved by means of certain properties of the field already studied in Chapter 2. As it was shown there that equipotentials and electric field lines intersect at right angles, a correct field map must have this property. Moreover, if the difference of potential between adjacent equipotentials, and the amount of electric flux between adjacent field lines, are made to be constant throughout the plot, the side ratios for all the little "curvilinear rectangles" formed by the intersection of the equipotentials and the orthogonal field lines must be the same throughout the plot, as will be shown in the following. For convenience in estimating by eye how well this property is satisfied, the side ratio is usually chosen as unity, so that the plot is divided into small "curvilinear squares." This property is demonstrated by the simple plot of the field between coaxial cylinders (Fig. 3.06a). In this, the field lines are radial and the equipotentials are circles with the spacing between adjacent equipotentials proportional to radius.

To demonstrate the side ratio property, consider one of the curvilinear rectangles from a general plot, as in Fig. 3.06b. If Δn is the distance between two adjacent equipotentials, and Δs the distance between two adjacent field lines, the magnitude of electric field, assuming a small square, is approximately $\Delta\Phi/\Delta n$. The electric flux flowing along a flux tube bounded by the two adjacent field lines, for a unit length, is then

$$\Delta\psi = \epsilon\,|E|\,\Delta s = \frac{\epsilon\,\Delta\Phi\Delta s}{\Delta n}$$

or $$\frac{\Delta s}{\Delta n} = \frac{\Delta\psi}{\epsilon\,\Delta\Phi}\,. \qquad (1)$$

So, if the flux per tube $\Delta\psi$, the potential difference per division $\Delta\Phi$, and

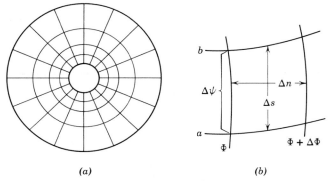

(a)   (b)

Fig. 3.06   (a) Map of field between coaxial conducting cylinders.
(b) Curvilinear rectangle for graphical field mapping.

the permittivity ϵ are constant throughout the plot, the side ratio $\Delta s/\Delta n$ must also be constant throughout the plot as stated above.

3.07   The Technique of Graphical Field Mapping

In applying the principles of the last article to the sketching of fields, each person will soon develop his own rules of procedure. In beginning the process, some schedule such as the following will be helpful.

1. Plan on making a number of rough sketches, taking only a minute or so apiece, before starting any plot to be made with care. The use of transparent paper over the basic boundary will speed up this preliminary sketching.

2. Divide the known potential difference between electrodes into an equal number of divisions, say four or eight to begin with.

3. Begin the sketch of equipotentials in the region where the field is known best, as for example in some region where it approaches a uniform

field. Extend the equipotentials according to your best guess throughout the plot. Note that they should tend to hug acute angles of the conducting boundary, and be spread out in the vicinity of obtuse angles of the boundary.

4. Draw in the orthogonal set of field lines. As these are started, they should form curvilinear squares, but, as they are extended, the condition of orthogonality should be kept paramount, even though this will result in some rectangles with ratios other than unity.

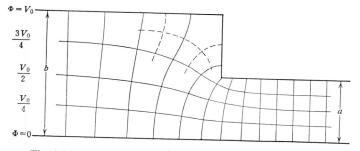

Fig. 3.07a   Map of fields between a plane and stepped conductor.

5. Look at the regions with poor side ratios, and try to see what was wrong with the first guess of equipotentials. Correct them and repeat the procedure until reasonable curvilinear squares exist throughout the plot.

6. In regions of low field intensity, there will be large figures, often of five or six sides. To judge the correctness of the plot in this region, these large units should be subdivided. The subdivisions should be started back a way, and, each time a flux tube is divided in half, the potential divisions in this region must be divided by the same factor.

There is little more that can be said in words except that the technique can be learned only by the study of some given plots, and by trying the technique on some examples. Some plots are given in Figs. 3.07a and 3.07b. Figure 3.07a shows the field between a plane conductor at potential zero, and a stepped plane at potential V_0, with a step ratio of $\frac{1}{2}$. Figure 3.07b shows a plot that was made to show the field about a particular two-conductor transmission line whose conductors were so shaped as to make difficult an exact mathematical solution. Many of the calculated maps from the method of conformal transformations to follow, especially those for the regions near conducting corners, will also help in forming the physical pictures necessary for this method.

The technique can be extended to some more complicated situations, but it should be pointed out that it becomes enormously more difficult

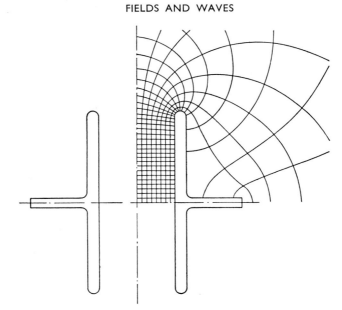

Fig. 3.07*b*   Map of fields between transmission line conductors of
special shape.

to apply for some of these, and that it is impractical except for very
important problems. Some of these extensions are:

    1. to a region with more than one dielectric;
    2. to the magnetic fields within a current-carrying region;
    3. to axially symmetric regions having variations in r and z. Some of
these techniques are discussed in the references.[1]

Problems

3.07a Map fields between an infinite plane conductor at potential zero and a
second conductor at potential V_0, as in Fig. 3.07*a*, but for step ratios a/b of
$\frac{1}{4}$ and $\frac{3}{4}$.

3.07b Map fields between an infinite flat plane and a cylindrical conductor
parallel to the plane. The conductor has diameter d, and its axis is at height h
above the plane. Take $d/h = 1, \frac{1}{4}$.

3.07c The outer conductor of a two-conductor transmission line is a rectangular tube of sides $3a$ and $5a$. The inner conductor is a circular cylinder of

---

[1] H. Poritsky, "Graphical Field Mapping Methods in Engineering," *Trans. A.I.E.E.*
57, 727–732 (1938). See also S. S. Attwood, *Electric and Magnetic Fields*, John Wiley
and Sons, New York, 3rd ed., 1949; and L. V. Bewley, *Two-Dimensional Fields in
Electrical Engineering*, Macmillan, New York, 1948.

radius a, with axis coincident with the central axis of the rectangular cylinder. Sketch equipotentials and field lines for the region between conductors, assuming a potential difference V_0 between conductors.

3.07d Two infinite parallel conducting planes defined by $y = a$ and $y = -a$ are at potential zero. A semi-infinite conducting plane lying halfway between ($y = 0$) and extending from $x = 0$ to $x = \infty$ is at potential V_0. Sketch a graphical field map for the region between conductors.

3.08 Information Obtained from Field Maps

Field maps are made to give not only a general idea of the field distribution for a given problem, but also more specific quantitative information. For example, the magnitude of electric field may be desired in a problem in which dielectric breakdown is in question. For a problem in which the motion of an electron through a field is to be computed, both magnitude and direction of field at each point of the path are required. The direction of the field is given by the direction of the electric field lines at each point, by definition. The magnitude is approximately the value $\Delta\Phi/\Delta n$, where $\Delta\Phi$ is the difference of potential per division, and Δn the distance between equipotentials.

The electrostatic capacitance per unit length can also be computed readily from a field plot. By Gauss's law, the charge induced on a conductor is equal to the flux ending there. This is the number of flux tubes N_f multiplied by the flux per tube. The potential difference between conductors is the number of potential divisions N_p multiplied by the potential difference per division. So, for a two-conductor system, the capacitance per unit length is

$$C = \frac{Q}{\Phi_2 - \Phi_1} = \frac{N_f \Delta\psi}{N_p \Delta\Phi} .$$

The ratio $\Delta\psi/\Delta\Phi$ can be obtained from Eq. 3.06(1):

$$C = \frac{N_f}{N_p}\left(\frac{\epsilon\,\Delta s}{\Delta n}\right). \tag{1}$$

And, for a small squares plot with $\Delta s/\Delta n$ equal to unity,

$$C = \epsilon \frac{N_f}{N_p} \text{ farads/meter.} \tag{2}$$

For example, in the transmission line plot of Fig. 3.07b, there are 16 potential divisions and 66 flux tubes, so the capacitance, assuming air dielectric, is

$$C = \frac{10^{-9}}{36\pi} \times \frac{66}{16} = 36.5 \times 10^{-12} \text{ farads/meter.} \tag{3}$$

Problems

3.08a Assume that Fig. 3.07a is full scale, and that V_0 is 1000 volts. Find the approximate direction of the minimum and maximum electric field strengths in the figure. Plot a curve of electric field magnitude along the bottom plane as a function of distance along this plane, and a curve showing surface charge density induced on this plane as a function of distance.

3.08b Calculate the capacitance per unit length from your plots for Probs. 3.07b and 3.07c.

3.08c Find the conductance per unit length of the transmission line of Prob. 3.07c assuming the medium between conductors to have a uniform conductivity σ.

3.09 Finite-Difference Solutions of Laplace and Poisson Equations

A large fraction of static field problems encountered in practice cannot be solved by analytic means. A graphical method for solving Laplace's equation in two dimensions with arbitrary boundary shapes has been described in the preceding sections. One of the most powerful methods for finding solutions of static field problems involves replacement of the Poisson or Laplace equation by a finite-difference approximation. The region to be studied is divided into a grid of mutually orthogonal lines having a finite number of intersections. We shall consider numerical methods for calculating the potentials at the intersections from a knowledge of the conditions on the boundary of the region. These methods are well adapted to digital computers and have grown to a position of special importance since high-speed machines have become available.

Let us derive the finite-difference equivalent of Poisson's equation assuming, for simplicity, no variations of potentials along the z coordinate. A convenient way to evaluate the second partial derivatives with respect to x and y is to expand the potential about the point (x, y) in a Taylor series:

$$\Phi(x + h, y) \cong \Phi(x, y) + h\frac{\partial \Phi(x, y)}{\partial x} + \frac{h^2}{2}\frac{\partial^2 \Phi(x, y)}{\partial x^2} \tag{1}$$

and

$$\Phi(x - h, y) \cong \Phi(x, y) - h\frac{\partial \Phi(x, y)}{\partial x} + \frac{h^2}{2}\frac{\partial^2 \Phi(x, y)}{\partial x^2}. \tag{2}$$

By adding (1) and (2) and rearranging, we have

$$\frac{\partial^2 \Phi(x, y)}{\partial x^2} = \frac{\Phi(x + h, y) - 2\Phi(x, y) + \Phi(x - h, y)}{h^2}. \tag{3}$$

The second partial derivative with respect to y can be obtained in the same way. Then Poisson's equation in two dimensions

$$\frac{\partial^2 \Phi}{\partial x^2} + \frac{\partial^2 \Phi}{\partial y^2} = -\frac{\rho}{\epsilon}$$

can be expressed in the approximate form

$$\Phi(x+h, y) + \Phi(x-h, y) + \Phi(x, y+h)$$
$$+ \Phi(x, y-h) - 4\Phi(x, y) = -\frac{\rho h^2}{\epsilon}, \quad (4)$$

where the distance increment h is taken, for simplicity, to be equal in the two directions. It is of interest to note that, if space charge is zero, the potential is the average of the potentials at the surrounding points.

An equation of the form of (4) can be written for each intersection in the grid yielding a set of n linear equations in n unknowns. In principle this set of equations can be inverted to give the potentials at the n intersections. The direct inversion is prohibitive, however, if n is a large number, as it usually is. The solution is obtained instead by successive adjustment of the potentials until (4) is satisfied to some specified degree of accuracy.

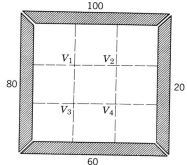

Fig. 3.09 Cylinder of square cross section and grid for difference equation solution.

Consider the problem illustrated in Fig. 3.09. This is an infinite cylinder of square cross section with the potential specified on the entire boundary. We will assume zero space charge. The broken lines represent the grid to be used to approximate the region for the finite-difference solution. The coarse grid was chosen to simplify the example; a finer grid would be used in most practical problems. The four unknown potentials designated V_1 to V_4 are assumed initially zero. The first calculation is to find V_1 as the average of the four surrounding potentials (80, 100, $V_2 = 0$, $V_3 = 0$). Therefore, in the column labeled Step 1 in Table 3.09, V_1 is given the value 45. Then V_2 is found as the average of 100, 20, 45, and 0, and this value is put in the table in Step 1. The procedure is repeated for V_3 and V_4. Then Step 2 proceeds in the same way. It is seen that after several steps the potentials converge to definite values. Since (4) is approximate and the grid coarse, the potentials have converged to approximate answers. The correct potentials for the four points are listed in the table.

TABLE 3.09

	STEP					Correct Potentials
	1	2	3	4	5	
V_1	45.0	66.9	74.9	76.9	77.4	75.2
V_2	41.3	57.2	61.2	62.2	62.4	60.5
V_3	46.2	62.2	66.2	67.2	67.4	65.4
V_4	41.9	49.9	51.9	52.3	52.4	50.7

Problems

3.09a Subdivide the region shown in Fig. 3.07a into a mesh of squares of sides $a/2$. Terminate the region on the right at a distance a from the corner and on the left at a distance $3b/4$ from the corner. Assume uniform distribution of potential on left and right edges to find boundary values. Find the potentials at the mesh nodes as in Art. 3.09, assuming zero space charge.

3.09b Set up the difference equation for a three-dimensional potential distribution.

3.09c Find the potential at the center of a cube having one side at potential V_0, an adjacent side at $V_0/2$, and the remaining sides at zero potential. Use the coarsest possible grid and assume zero space charge. Check by using the method of Art. 3.04.

3.09d Determine how the number of calculations increases for calculation of potential in a volume of fixed size and given mesh size as the dimensionality of the potential variation increases from one to three. That is, first assume that x and y variations are negligible, then that x variations can be taken as zero, and finally that there are significant variations in all three directions.

3.10 Relaxation Methods for Difference Equations

The method of successive approximation used in the preceding article to find the solution of the system of linear difference equations can be improved by a method which purposely leaves a small error at each point during the calculations. We define the difference from the exact satisfaction of Eq. 3.09(4) as a *residue* which is given by

$$R = \Phi(x + h, y) + \Phi(x - h, y) + \Phi(x, y + h)$$
$$+ \Phi(x, y - h) - 4\Phi(x, y) + \frac{\rho h^2}{\epsilon}. \quad (1)$$

At each step in a calculation, the potential and residue are listed for each point of the grid which is not on the boundary. When all residues approach zero, Eq. 3.09(4) is satisfied and the final solution is reached. If the potential at a point at step k is raised by a value equal to one-fourth of the residue at that time

$$\Phi^{k+1} = \Phi^k + \frac{R^k}{4} \qquad (2)$$

the new residue R^{k+1} is exactly zero. However, the residues at the neighboring points are changed. It is more advantageous to modify (2) so that the residue is not completely eliminated. That is, use

$$\Phi^{k+1} = \Phi^k + \beta \frac{R^k}{4} \qquad (3)$$

where β is a parameter determined as discussed below. Southwell[2] has given several rules for speeding the convergence. Some of the simpler ones are as follows:

1. At each step of the calculation adjust the potential of the point with the largest residue.

2. If most of the residues in the immediate neighborhood are of the same sign, let β be greater than unity. That is, *over-relax* the potential.

3. If the sign of the largest neighboring residue is opposite from that at the point being considered, the potential should be *under-relaxed* ($\beta < 1$).

We see that if the residue at a point not adjacent to a boundary is reduced by four units, the residues at four neighboring points are increased by one unit each and the net residue is unchanged. If, however, the point in question is adjacent to a boundary, a net change is made. If the total of the residue in a region differs from zero, it is as though there were undesired charges in the space. Shifting some of the excess to the boundary points corresponds to removing these charges from the space.

The storage capacities of modern digital computers have been developed to the point where it is profitable to solve field problems by finite difference methods. Grids with scores of divisions may be used to get solutions with high precision. The methods used are often similar to those described above. The rules given by Southwell, however, are not advantageous for a digital computer, since too much time is required for searching. Instead, the potentials are relaxed systematically starting from one boundary and working, step by step, across the grid using (3). In this process it is found that the optimum convergence is obtained if $1 < \beta < 2$ for all points. The exact value depends on the particular problem. As we have

[2] V. R. Southwell, *Relaxation Methods in Theoretical Physics*, Oxford University Press, New York, 1946.

seen above, the potentials are said to be *over-relaxed* when $\beta > 1$. Thus, this calculation procedure is called *successive over-relaxation*.

The methods just described are more complicated when the given boundaries do not lie along intersections of the grid. Special difference equations are written for these *irregular boundary* points. Also, if the normal derivative of the potential is specified rather than potential itself, the treatment is somewhat more complicated. For details on these more complex boundaries and other questions such as the effect of the grid size, determination of β, and stability, the literature on finite difference methods should be consulted.[3]

Problems

3.10a Calculate the potentials in the example of Art. 3.09 by using the method of successive over-relaxation with $\beta = 1.4$. Calculate residue and new potential at each point before moving to next point.

3.10b Repeat the calculation of Prob. 3.09a using the method of relaxation with Southwell's rules as stated in Art. 3.10.

3.11   Resistive Field Analogs

Whereas direct measurement of the potential distribution in free space surrounding a set of electrodes is precluded by the effect of the measurement apparatus on the fields, it is possible to establish an analog of the system to be studied in which potential measurements may be easily made. An *analog* system is one in which some quantity of importance varies in the same way as does the corresponding quantity in the given problem. In particular, it will be seen that the distribution of electric potential in a conducting medium is the same as in a dielectric when the boundaries are the same in both cases.

Continuous-Medium Analogs. The form of the relation of flux density to the field intensity in a dielectric system is the same as the relation of the current density to the field intensity in a conducting medium

$$\bar{D} = \epsilon \bar{E} \tag{1}$$

$$\bar{i} = \sigma \bar{E}. \tag{2}$$

By setting $\bar{E} = -\nabla\Phi$ in (1) and (2) and taking the divergence of each, we see that Laplace's equation is satisfied by the potential in each case if it is assumed that both media are homogeneous and that there are no free

---

[3] See for example: G. E. Forsythe and W. R. Wasow, *Finite Difference Methods for Partial Differential Equations*, John Wiley and Sons, New York, 1960.

charges in the dielectric and no current sources in the conductor. Then, if the same set of boundaries is used in both cases, the solutions are identical, in accordance with the uniqueness theorem. The resistance analog is also useful for finding the potential distribution in a system with free charges present. For example, analog methods have been used extensively in the design of electron guns where it is necessary to take

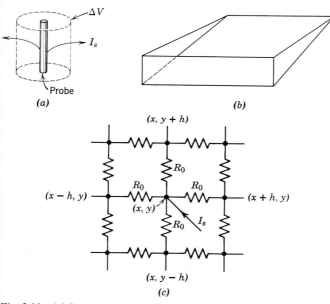

Fig. 3.11 (a) Space-charge simulation probe. (b) Electrolytic tank for axially symmetric problems. (c) Resistance network for problems with rectangular symmetry.

account of the effect of the electrons in the beam on the distribution of fields. Combining (1) and (2) we find

$$\bar{\imath} = \frac{\sigma}{\epsilon} \bar{D}. \tag{3}$$

Then, assuming homogeneity and taking the surface integral bounding some small volume ΔV in the analog, we find

$$\oint_S \bar{\imath} \cdot \overline{dS} = \frac{\sigma}{\epsilon} \oint_S \bar{D} \cdot \overline{dS} = \frac{\sigma}{\epsilon} \int_V \nabla \cdot \bar{D} \, dV. \tag{4}$$

The left side of (4) is the total current flowing out of the region ΔV and thus equals the current I_s supplied to the resistive medium by a probe inside ΔV as illustrated in Fig. 3.11a. Since $\nabla \cdot \bar{D} = \rho$, the integral on the right side of (4) gives the total free charge Q in ΔV in the dielectric system. Hence

$$I_s = \frac{\sigma}{\epsilon} Q. \tag{5}$$

Various methods are used to insert the current into the medium depending on the type of analog; the results are only approximations to the correct distribution of charge. Equation (5) must be modified if the analog is of different size or has different applied voltage from the dielectric system (see Problem 3.11a).

Various conducting media may be used.[4] Resistance paper is very simple to use for two-dimensional problems but is of limited accuracy. Some recent work has been done to produce other suitable solid media in which, as with resistance paper, direct currents may be used. These are isotropic and may be used for axially symmetric problems as well as for two-dimensional fields. Open tanks containing a liquid electrolyte (usually water) called *electrolytic tanks* may be used for either two- or three-dimensional problems, but accurate results may be obtained only if there exists a symmetry which allows measurements to be made at the surface of the electrolyte. A rectangular tank with an insulating floor is suitable for electrode systems with symmetry or periodicity in one rectangular coordinate such that the normal electric field at the upper and lower surfaces of the electrolyte are zero. The tank shown in Fig. 3.11b may be used for electrodes with uniformity or periodicity about the axis. Alternating current must be used with the electrolytic tank to avoid inaccuracies resulting from surface impedances on the electrodes.

Discrete Resistance Networks. If a grid of resistances similar to the grid of imaginary lines used for the numerical methods is considered, it may be shown that the potentials approximately satisfy the Laplace or Poisson equations. We assume here, for simplicity, a two-dimensional problem in rectangular coordinates. The appropriate resistor network is illustrated in Fig. 3.11c. Let us assume that each resistor represents a distance h, the step size used in the difference equations of Arts. 3.09 and 3.10. It is then clear that the current I_s flowing *into* a junction of the resistors from an outside source equals the current flowing out through the four resistors connected to the junction:

$$I_s = \frac{V(x, y) - V(x + h, y)}{R_0} + \frac{V(x, y) - V(x - h, y)}{R_0}$$

$$+ \frac{V(x, y) - V(x, y + h)}{R_0} + \frac{V(x, y) - V(x, y - h)}{R_0}$$

[4] G. Liebmann, *Brit. J. Appl. Phys.*, **4** (July 1953) 193–200.

or

$$V(x + h, y) + V(x - h, y) + V(x, y + h)$$
$$+ V(x, y - h) - 4V(x, y) = -I_s R_0. \quad (6)$$

For rectangular coordinates all resistors are the same, as assumed, but for other coordinate systems the values of the resistors depend on position.

If we now compare (6) with Eq. 3.09(4), we see that the voltages on the board can be identified with potentials in the corresponding problem. In addition the current I_s to be supplied by an external source is related to the charge density by

$$I_s = \frac{h^2}{R_0 \epsilon} \rho. \quad (7)$$

If we identify ρh^2 as the charge per unit length q_l contained in a cylinder of square cross section of area h^2 centered on the junction, (7) becomes

$$I_s = \frac{q_l}{R_0 \epsilon}. \quad (8)$$

By comparison with (5) it is seen that R_0 plays the role of a resistivity.

The use of the resistance network for finding solutions of Laplace's equation is especially simple and useful since no source currents I_s are required. After the boundary potentials are applied to the appropriate points in the network, potentials are easily measured.

The grading of resistors to calculate fields in axially symmetric regions and adjustment of the resistors along boundaries where the electrodes do not lie on intersection points of the grid are discussed in the literature.[5] Potentials may be found more accurately in the discrete-resistance network than in the continuous-medium analogs, but the discreteness is sometimes a disadvantage.

Problems

3.11a It is usually desirable to use analogs different both in size and in level of applied voltage from the dielectric system. Introduce scale factors relating lengths and voltages in the two systems and use these to find the form corresponding to Eq. 3.11(5) for the probe current in a scaled continuous analog.

3.11b Discuss the effect of the five insulating boundaries on the wedge-shaped tank of Fig. 3.11b. Why is this shape appropriate to axially symmetric configurations or problems with certain classes of periodicity?

3.11c By use of symmetry arguments and analyses of images in the insulating boundaries of an analog, it is frequently possible to devise models of structures wherein only a fraction of the structure is simulated. Use the fact that ϵ and

[5] J. R. Hechtel and J. A. Seeger, *Proc. IRE*, **49** (May 1961) 933–940.

σ are analogous quantities along with the discussion of images in Prob. 2.19*d* to devise a model to be used in an electrolytic tank for finding the potential distribution along the center lines of the rectangular openings of an infinite screen placed between and parallel to the plates of an infinitely broad capacitor. The potentials are to be measured only on the surface of the electrolyte.

3.11*d* Devise an analog method for finding the grid-to-cathode capacitance of a cylindrical electron tube structure. (Refer to Fig. 5.29*a* for the configuration.) Treat this as a two-dimensional problem. Use only two meters for the measurement and take just one reading on each.

3.11*e* A sheet of charge between parallel conducting plates is to be simulated on a resistance network. The sheet has uniform charge density ρ, a thickness of $h/4$ and is to be centered on a row of nodes of the resistance network. The field intensity at any point between nodes is taken to be the difference of potentials at the surrounding nodes divided by spacing h. Discuss the validity of the simulation for fields within and outside the sheet.

METHOD OF CONFORMAL TRANSFORMATIONS

3.12 Introduction to Complex Function Theory

A very general mathematical attack for the two-dimensional field distribution problem utilizes the theory of functions of a complex variable. The method is in principle the most general for two-dimensional problems, and the work can be carried out to yield actual solutions for a wide variety of practical problems. For these reasons, the general method with some examples will be presented in this and the following articles.

In the theory of complex variables, the complex notation introduced in Chapter 1 is retained, the imaginary number $\sqrt{-1}$ being denoted by j. Thus any pure imaginary $\sqrt{-b^2}$ may be written as jb, where b is a pure real. The sum of a pure real and a pure imaginary, as $a + jb$, is called a complex number. The variable $Z = x + jy$, where both x and y are real variables, is known as a *complex* variable. Since Z is defined by a pair of quantities x and y, it is convenient to associate any given value of Z with a point in the x-y plane (Fig. 3.12*a*), and to call this plane the complex Z plane. Of course the coordinates may also be expressed in the polar form in terms of r and θ:

$$r = \sqrt{x^2 + y^2} \qquad \theta = \tan^{-1}\left(\frac{y}{x}\right).$$

Then
$$Z = x + jy = r(\cos\theta + j\sin\theta).$$

The combination in the parentheses is recognized as $e^{j\theta}$. So the polar form of a complex number, showing the magnitude and phase angle, is most conveniently written

$$Z = re^{j\theta}. \tag{1}$$

Suppose that there is now a different complex variable W, where

$$W = u + jv = \rho e^{j\phi}$$

such that W is some function of Z. This means that, for each assigned value of Z, there is a rule specifying a corresponding value of W. The

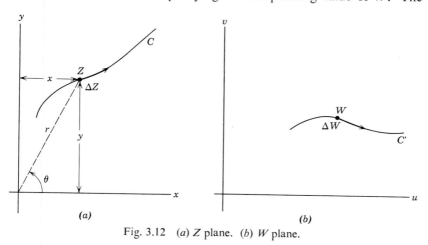

Fig. 3.12   (a) Z plane. (b) W plane.

functional relationship is written

$$W = f(Z). \tag{2}$$

If Z is made to vary continuously, the corresponding point in the complex Z plane moves about, tracing out some curve C. The values of W vary correspondingly, tracing out a curve C'. To avoid confusion, the values of W are usually shown on a separate sketch, called the complex W plane (Fig. 3.12b).

Next consider a small change in Z, ΔZ, and the corresponding change in W, ΔW. The derivative of the function will be defined as the usual limit of the ratio $\Delta W/\Delta Z$ as the element ΔZ becomes infinitesimal:

$$\frac{dW}{dZ} = \lim_{\Delta Z \to 0} \frac{\Delta W}{\Delta Z} = \lim_{\Delta Z \to 0} \frac{f(Z + \Delta Z) - f(Z)}{\Delta Z}. \tag{3}$$

A complex function is said to be analytic or regular whenever the derivative just defined exists and is unique. The derivative may fail to exist at certain isolated (singular) points where it may be infinite or undetermined, somewhat as in real function theory. But it would appear that there is another ambiguity in respect to complex variables, since ΔZ may be taken in any arbitrary direction in the Z plane from the original point. It would be expected that ΔW would correspondingly lie in different directions, and it is not obvious that the limit of the ratio $\Delta W/\Delta Z$ would turn out to be independent of this direction or phase of ΔZ. The definition requires that this independence be satisfied for analytic functions, since (3) is required to give a unique result for the point of interest.

If this independence of direction is to result, a necessary condition at least is that we obtain the same result if Z is changed in the x direction alone, or in the y direction alone. For $\Delta Z = \Delta x$,

$$\frac{dW}{dZ} = \frac{\partial W}{\partial x} = \frac{\partial}{\partial x}(u + jv) = \frac{\partial u}{\partial x} + j\frac{\partial v}{\partial x}. \tag{4}$$

For a change in the y direction, $\Delta Z = j\,\Delta y$,

$$\frac{dW}{dZ} = \frac{\partial W}{\partial(jy)} = \frac{1}{j}\frac{\partial}{\partial y}(u + jv) = \frac{\partial v}{\partial y} - j\frac{\partial u}{\partial y}. \tag{5}$$

Two complex quantities are equal if and only if their real and imaginary parts are separately equal. Hence (4) and (5) yield the same result if

$$\frac{\partial u}{\partial x} = \frac{\partial v}{\partial y} \tag{6}$$

$$\frac{\partial v}{\partial x} = -\frac{\partial u}{\partial y}. \tag{7}$$

These conditions, known as the Cauchy-Riemann equations, are then necessary conditions for dW/dZ to be unique at a point, and the function $f(Z)$ analytic there. It can be shown that, if they are satisfied, the same result for dW/dZ is obtained for any arbitrary direction of the change ΔZ, so they are also sufficient conditions.

As an example, from the function

$$W = Z^2 \tag{8}$$

$$u + jv = (x + jy)^2 = (x^2 - y^2) + j2xy$$

$$u = x^2 - y^2$$

$$v = 2xy.$$

A check of the Cauchy-Riemann equations yields

$$\frac{\partial u}{\partial x} = \frac{\partial v}{\partial y} = 2x$$

$$\frac{\partial u}{\partial y} = -\frac{\partial v}{\partial x} = -2y.$$

So they are satisfied everywhere in the finite Z plane, and the function is analytic everywhere there.

Actually, it is not necessary to apply the check when the functional relation is expressed explicitly between Z and W in terms of functions which possess a power series expansion about the origin, as e^Z, $\sin Z$, etc. The reason is that each term in the series, $C_n Z^n$, can be shown to satisfy the Cauchy-Riemann conditions, and consequently a series of such terms also satisfies them.

Problems

3.12a Check by the Cauchy-Riemann equations the analyticity of the general power term $W = C_n Z^n$, and a series of such terms,

$$W = \sum_{n=1}^{\infty} C_n Z^n.$$

3.12b Check the following functions by the Cauchy-Riemann equations to determine if they are analytic:

$$W = \sin Z$$
$$W = e^Z$$
$$W = Z^* = x - jy$$
$$W = ZZ^*.$$

3.12c Check the analyticity of the following, noting isolated points where the derivatives may not remain finite:

$$W = \ln Z$$
$$W = \tan Z.$$

3.12d Take the change ΔZ in any general direction $\Delta x + j\Delta y$. Show that, if the Cauchy-Riemann conditions are satisfied, Eq. (3) yields the same result for the derivative as when the change is in the x direction or the y direction alone.

3.12e If by following a path around some point in the Z plane, the variable W takes on different values when the same Z is reached, the point around which the path is taken is called a *branch point*. Evaluate $W = Z^{\frac{1}{2}}$ and $W = Z^{\frac{1}{3}}$ along a path of constant radius around the origin to show that $Z = 0$ is a branch point for these functions. Discuss the analyticity of these functions at the branch point.

3.13 Properties of Analytic Functions of Complex Variables

If Eq. 3.12(6) is differentiated with respect to x, Eq. 3.12(7) differentiated with respect to y, and the resulting equations added, there results

$$\frac{\partial^2 u}{\partial x^2} + \frac{\partial^2 u}{\partial y^2} = 0. \tag{1}$$

Similarly, if the order of differentiation is reversed, there results

$$\frac{\partial^2 v}{\partial x^2} + \frac{\partial^2 v}{\partial y^2} = 0. \tag{2}$$

These are recognized as the Laplace equations in two dimensions. Thus both the real and the imaginary parts of an analytic function of a complex variable satisfy Laplace's equation, and would thus be suitable for use as the potential functions for two-dimensional electrostatic problems. The manner in which these are used in specific problems, and the limitations on this usefulness, are demonstrated by examples in following articles.

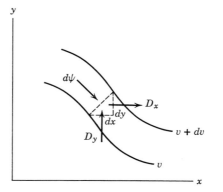

Fig. 3.13a   Coordinates for flux function.

For a problem in which one of the two parts, u or v, is chosen as the potential function, the other becomes proportional to the flux function. To show this, let us suppose that u is the potential function in volts for a particular problem. The electric field, obtained as the negative gradient of u, yields

$$E_x = -\frac{\partial u}{\partial x} \qquad E_y = -\frac{\partial u}{\partial y}. \tag{3}$$

By the equation for the total differential, the change in v corresponding to changes in the x and y coordinates of dx and dy is

$$dv = \frac{\partial v}{\partial x}\, dx + \frac{\partial v}{\partial y}\, dy.$$

But, from Cauchy-Riemann conditions, Eqs. 3.12(6) and 3.12(7),

$$-dv = \frac{\partial u}{\partial y}\, dx - \frac{\partial u}{\partial x}\, dy = -E_y\, dx + E_x\, dy$$

or

$$-\epsilon\, dv = -D_y\, dx + D_x\, dy. \tag{4}$$

By inspection of Fig. 3.13a, this is recognized to be just the electric flux $d\psi$ between the curves v and $v + dv$, with the positive direction as shown by the arrow. Then

$$-d\psi = \epsilon \, dv. \tag{5}$$

And, except for a constant which can be set equal to zero by choosing the reference for flux at $v = 0$,

$$-\psi = \epsilon v \text{ coulombs/meter.} \qquad \text{(6)}$$

Similarly, if v is chosen as the potential function in volts for some problem, ϵu is the flux function in coulombs per meter, with proper choice of the direction for positive flux.

We have seen that either u or v may be used as a potential function, and then the other may be used as the flux function, since both satisfy Laplace's equation. The utility of the concept, however, hinges on being able to find the analytic function $W = f(Z)$ such that u and v also satisfy the boundary conditions for the problem being considered.

As an example, suppose we desire the distribution of potentials in the Z plane where the given boundary condition is

$$V = x^{1/3}, \qquad y = 0. \tag{7}$$

If we let

$$W = Z^{1/3}, \tag{8}$$

it is clear that for $y = 0$, the real part of W is $u = x^{1/3}$. Furthermore, we see that dW/dZ exists and is unique except at $Z = 0$ (Prob. 3.13c.) Thus u is a suitable potential function for this problem; the real part of (8) gives the potential distribution. It is most convenient, for this particular function, to express Z in polar coordinates

$$W = u + jv = r^{1/3} e^{j\theta/3}. \tag{9}$$

Thus

$$u = r^{1/3} \cos \tfrac{4}{3}\theta \tag{10}$$

$$v = r^{1/3} \sin \tfrac{4}{3}\theta.$$

Equipotentials, found by setting u equal to a constant, are shown in Fig. 3.13b for $u = 0$ and 1. It is of interest to notice that the boundary function (7) has the same form as the potential in a plane diode, Eq. 2.18(4) with the cathode at $y = 0$. Using these ideas, a plane diode can be truncated and the correct potentials produced on the free edge by placing electrodes along the equipotential lines as shown in Fig. 3.13c. This

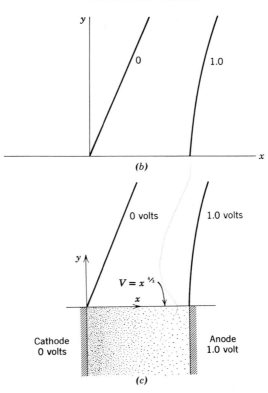

Fig. 3.13 (b) Equipotentials for four-thirds
potential distribution along x axis. (c) Focusing
for electron flow in a plane diode.

procedure is most important in designing electron guns with regular flow
and the result is known as the *Pierce gun*.[6]

Problems

3.13a   Plot the shape of the $u = \pm 0.5$ equipotentials for the $V = x^{4/3}$, $y = 0$
boundary condition used in Art. 3.13.

3.13b   Show that if u is the potential function, the field intensity E_y is equal to
the imaginary part of dW/dZ and E_x equals the negative of the real part.

3.13c   Use the results of Prob. *b* to find an expression for the slope of equipotential lines in terms of dW/dZ. Show that all equipotential lines except
$u = 0$ are normal to the beam edge. ($W = Z^{4/3}$ is not analytic at $Z = 0$ as
was shown in Prob. 3.12e, and the $u = 0$ line at $y = 0$ is a special case.)

[6] J. R. Pierce, *J. Appl. Phys.*, **11** (1940) 548–554.

3.14 Conformal Mapping

A somewhat different point of view toward the method in Art. 3.13 follows if we refer to the Z and W planes introduced in Art. 3.12. Since the functional relationship fixes a value of W corresponding to a given value of Z for a given function

$$W = f(Z),$$

any point (x, y) in the Z plane yields some point (u, v) in the W plane. As this point moves along some curve $x = F(y)$ in the Z plane, the corresponding point in the W plane traces out a curve $u = F_1(v)$. If it should move throughout a region in the Z plane, the corresponding W point would move throughout some region in the W plane. Thus, in general, a point in the Z plane transforms to a point in the W plane, a curve transforms to a curve, and a region to a region, and the function which accomplishes this is frequently spoken of as a particular *transformation* between the Z and W planes.

When the function $f(Z)$ is analytic, as we have seen, the derivative dW/dZ at a point is independent of the direction of the change dZ from the point. The derivative may be written in terms of magnitude and phase:

$$\frac{dW}{dZ} = Me^{j\alpha} \qquad (1)$$

or

$$dW = Me^{j\alpha}\,dZ. \qquad (2)$$

By the rule for the product of complex quantities, the magnitude of dW is M times the magnitude of dZ, and the angle of dW is α plus the angle of dZ. So the entire infinitesimal region in the vicinity of the point W is similar to the infinitesimal region in the vicinity of the point Z. It is magnified by a scale factor M and rotated by an angle α. It is then evident that, if two curves intersect at a given angle in the Z plane, their transformed curves in the W plane intersect at the same angle, since both are rotated through the angle α. A transformation with these properties is called a *conformal* transformation.

In particular, the lines $u = $ constant and the lines $v = $ constant in the W plane intersect at right angles, so their transformed curves in the Z plane must also be orthogonal (Fig. 3.14). We already know that this should be so, since the constant v lines have been shown to represent flux lines when the constant u lines are equipotentials, and vice versa. From this point of view, the conformal transformation may be thought of as one which takes a uniform field in the W plane (represented by the equispaced constant u and constant v lines) and transforms it so that it fits the given boundary conditions in the Z plane, always keeping the required properties of an electrostatic field.

Frequently the transformation is done in steps. That is, the uniform field is transformed first into some intermediate complex plane by $Z_1 = f(W)$, then perhaps into a second intermediate plane $Z_2 = g(Z_1)$, and then finally into a plane $Z_3 = h(Z_2)$ in which the boundary conditions are satisfied. In general, there can be any number of steps. Of course, these functions can be combined into a single transformation, the inverse of which can then be understood on the basis of finding a function with real or imaginary part satisfying the given boundary conditions as discussed in Art. 3.13.

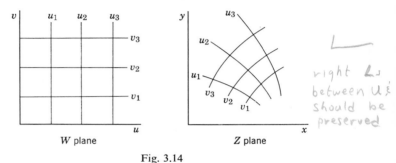

right $\angle s$
between u &
should be
preserved

Fig. 3.14

There are few circumstances in which knowledge of the required boundary conditions will lead directly to the transformation which gives the solution. It should be kept in mind that the potential distribution is the solution of a partial differential equation with given boundary conditions. As with solution of any differential equation, it is easier to work backward from the integrated form. For this purpose there are tables of conformal transformations[7] which show how one field maps into another. The mapping functions given in the tables may be used individually or combined in a series of steps to transform the uniform field into a field which fits the given problem. However, some examples of the simpler transformations will be given in following articles to illustrate the method.

3.15 The Power Function: Field Near a Conducting Corner

As a first example, consider W expressed as Z raised to some power:

$$W = Z^p. \qquad (1)$$

---

[7] For example, see H. Kober, *Dictionary of Conformal Representations*, Dover Publications, New York, 1952.

It is convenient to use the polar form for Z [Eq. 3.12(1)]:

$$W = (re^{j\theta})^p = r^p e^{j\,p\theta}$$

or
$$u = r^p \cos p\theta \qquad (2)$$

$$v = r^p \sin p\theta. \qquad (3)$$

From the conformal-mapping point of view, the field in the W plane is uniform. The parallel lines of equal potential (say, v equals constant) in the W plane can be mapped into the Z plane by setting v equals constant in (3). From the viewpoint of Art. 3.13 one does not take explicit consideration of the existence of the W plane but simply recognizes that v is a solution of Laplace's equation and tries to adjust constants such that v equals constant lines fit the equipotentials of the given problem. When only one step of transformation is required, the viewpoints are wholly equivalent.

If v is chosen as the potential function, the form of one curve of constant v (equipotential) is evident by inspection, for v is zero at $\theta = 0$, and also at $\theta = \pi/p$. Thus, if two semi-infinite conducting planes at potential zero intersect at angle α, where

$$p = \frac{\pi}{\alpha}, \qquad (4)$$

they coincide with this equipotential, and boundary conditions are satisfied. The form of the curves of constant u and of constant v within the angle then give the field configuration near a conducting corner, the sources presumably being far enough away so as not to disturb the field.

The equipotentials in the vicinity of the corner can be plotted by choosing given values of v, and plotting the polar equation of r versus θ from (3) with p given by (4). Similarly, the flux or field lines can be plotted by selecting several values of u and plotting the curves from (2). The form of the field, plotted in this manner, for corners with $\alpha = \pi/4$, $\pi/2$, and $3\pi/2$ are shown in Figs. 3.15a, b, and c, respectively. These plots are of considerable help in judging the correct form of the field in a graphical field map having one or more conducting boundaries.

This is one of the few examples in which the proper form of function to use for the problem might conceivably be arrived at if the boundaries were given as the starting point. For, if Z is raised to the power π/α, all angles are multiplied by this factor, and the conducting boundary is spread out to a straight line, $v = 0$ in the W plane. Thus v satisfies Laplace's equation in x and y (Art. 3.13) and the condition of potential on the boundary, so is the unique solution for potential inside, by the argument of Art. 3.03.

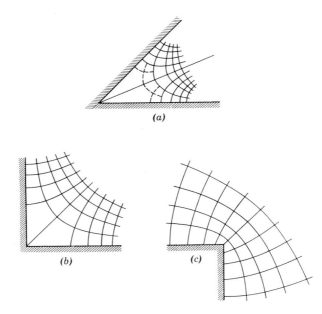

Fig. 3.15   Field near conducting corners of 45°, 90°, 270°.

Problem

3.15   Plot a few equipotentials and flux lines in the vicinity of conducting corners of angles $\alpha = \pi/3$ and $3\pi/4$.

3.16   The Logarithmic Transformation

Consider next the logarithmic function,

$$W = C_1 \ln Z + C_2. \tag{1}$$

The logarithm of a complex number is readily found if the number is in the polar form:

$$\ln Z = \ln (re^{j\theta}) = \ln r + j\theta. \tag{2}$$

So $$W = C_1(\ln r + j\theta) + C_2.$$

Take the constants C_1 and C_2 as real.   Then

$$u = C_1 \ln r + C_2 \tag{3}$$

$$v = C_1\theta. \tag{4}$$

If u is to be chosen as the potential function, we recognize the logarithmic potential forms found previously for potential about a line charge, a charged cylinder, or between coaxial cylinders. The flux function, $\psi = -\epsilon v$, is then proportional to angle θ, as it should be for a problem with radial electric field lines.

To evaluate the constants for a particular problem, take a coaxial line with an inner conductor of radius a at potential zero, and an outer conductor of radius b at potential V_0. Substituting in (3), we have

$$0 = C_1 \ln a + C_2$$
$$V_0 = C_1 \ln b + C_2.$$

Solving, we have

$$C_1 = \frac{V_0}{\ln (b/a)} \qquad C_2 = - \frac{V_0 \ln a}{\ln (b/a)}.$$

So (1) can be written

$$W = V_0 \left[\frac{\ln (Z/a)}{\ln (b/a)}\right] \tag{5}$$

or

$$\Phi = u = V_0 \left[\frac{\ln (r/a)}{\ln (b/a)}\right] \text{ volts} \tag{6}$$

$$\psi = -\epsilon v = \frac{-\epsilon V_0 \theta}{\ln (b/a)} \text{ coulombs/meter.} \tag{7}$$

In the foregoing, the reference for the flux function came out automatically at $\theta = 0$. If it is desired to use some other reference, the constant C_2 is taken as complex, and its imaginary part serves to fix the reference $\psi = 0$.

Problems

3.16a Evaluate the constant C_1 and C_2 in the logarithmic transformation so that u represents the potential function in volts about a line charge of strength q coulombs/meter. Take potential zero at $r = a$.

3.16b Show that, if v is taken as the potential function in the logarithmic transformation, it is applicable to the region between two semi-infinite conducting planes intersecting at an angle α, but separated by an infinitesimal gap at the origin so that the plane at $\theta = 0$ may be placed at potential zero, and the plane at $\theta = \alpha$ at potential V_0. Evaluate the constants C_1 and C_2, taking the reference for zero flux at $r = a$. Write the flux function in coulombs per meter.

3.16c In the example of Prob. 3.16b, take the gradient of potential v to give the electric field. From this, find the electric flux density vector. Integrate this from radius a to r to give the total flux function, and compare with the result of the above problem.

3.17   The Inverse Cosine Transformation

Consider the function

$$W = \cos^{-1} Z \tag{1}$$

or $x + jy = \cos(u + jv) = \cos u \cosh v - j \sin u \sinh v$

$$x = \cos u \cosh v$$

$$y = -\sin u \sinh v.$$

It then follows that

$$\frac{x^2}{\cosh^2 v} + \frac{y^2}{\sinh^2 v} = 1 \tag{2}$$

$$\frac{x^2}{\cos^2 u} - \frac{y^2}{\sin^2 u} = 1. \tag{3}$$

Equation (2) for constant v represents a set of confocal ellipses with foci at ± 1, and (3) for constant u represents a set of confocal hyperbolas orthogonal to the ellipses. These are plotted in Fig. 3.17a. With a proper

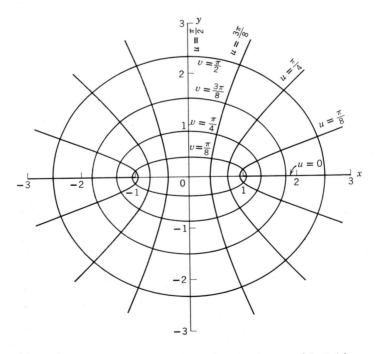

Fig. 3.17a   Plot of the transformation $u + jv = \cos^{-1}(x + jy)$.

choice of the region, and the function (either u or v) to serve as the potential function, the foregoing transformation could be made to give the solution to the following problems:

1. Field around a charged elliptic cylinder, including the limiting case of a flat strip.
2. Field between two confocal elliptic cylinders, or between an elliptic cylinder and a flat strip conductor extending between the foci.
3. Field between two confocal hyperbolic cylinders, or between a hyperbolic cylinder and a plane conductor extending from the focus to infinity.
4. Field between two semi-infinite conducting plates, coplanar and with a gap separating them. (This is a limiting case of 3.)
5. Field between an infinite conducting plane and a perpendicular semi-infinite plane separated from it by a gap.

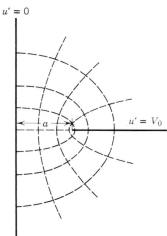

Fig. 3.17b Field between perpendicular planes with a finite gap.

To demonstrate how the result is obtained for a particular one of these, consider example 5, illustrated by Fig. 3.17b. The infinite plane is taken at potential zero, and the perpendicular semi-infinite plane at potential V_0. In using the results of the foregoing general transformation, we must now put in scale factors. To avoid confusion with the preceding, let us denote the variables for this specific problem by primes:

$$W' = C_1 \cos^{-1} kZ' + C_2. \qquad (4)$$

The constant C_1 is put in to fix the proper scale of potential, the constant k to fix the scale of size, and the additive constant C_2 to fix the reference for the potential. By comparing with (1),

$$Z = kZ'$$
$$W' = C_1 W + C_2.$$

The constants C_1 and C_2 may be taken as real for this problem. Then

$$u' = C_1 u + C_2. \qquad (5)$$

By comparing Figs. 3.17a and b, we want Z' to be a when Z is unity, so $k = 1/a$. Also, when $u = 0$, we want $u' = V_0$; and, when $u = \pi/2$,

$u' = 0$. Substitution of these values in (5) yields

$$C_1 = -\frac{2V_0}{\pi} \qquad C_2 = V_0.$$

So the transformation with proper scale factors for this problem is

$$W' = u' + jv' = V_0\left[1 - \frac{2}{\pi}\cos^{-1}\left(\frac{Z'}{a}\right)\right], \qquad (6)$$

where u' is the potential function in volts, and $\epsilon v'$ is the flux function in coulombs per meter. A few of the equipotential and flux lines with these scale factors applied are shown on Fig. 3.17b.

Problems

3.17a   Find the form of the curves of constant u and constant v for the functions $\sin^{-1} Z$, $\cosh^{-1} Z$, and $\sinh^{-1} Z$. Do these permit one to solve problems in addition to those from the function $\cos^{-1} Z$ of this article?

3.17b   Apply the results of the $\cos^{-1}$ transformation to example 4 of Art. 3.17. Take the right-hand semi-infinite plane extending from $x = a$ to $x = \infty$ at potential V_0. Take the left-hand semi-infinite plane extending from $x = -a$ to $x = -\infty$ at potential zero. Evaluate the scale factors and additive constant.

3.17c   Apply the results of the transformation to example 2 of Art. 3.17. Take the elliptic cylindrical conductor of semi-major axis a and semi-minor axis b at potential V_0. The inner conductor is a strip conductor extending between the foci, $x = \pm c$, where

$$c = \sqrt{a^2 - b^2}.$$

Evaluate all required scale factors and constants. Find the total charge per unit length induced upon the outer cylinder, and the electrostatic capacitance of this two-conductor system.

3.18 Parallel Conducting Cylinders

Consider next the function

$$W = C \ln\left(\frac{Z - a}{Z + a}\right). \qquad (1)$$

This may be written in the form

$$W = C[\ln(Z - a) - \ln(Z + a)].$$

By comparing with the logarithmic transformation of Art. 3.16 which, among other things, could represent the field about a single line charge, it follows that this expression can represent the field about two line charges, one at $Z = a$, and the other of equal strength but opposite sign at $Z = -a$. However, it is more interesting to show that this form can also yield the field about parallel cylinders of any radius.

Taking C as real,

$$u = \frac{C}{2} \ln \left[\frac{(x - a)^2 + y^2}{(x + a)^2 + y^2} \right] \tag{2}$$

$$v = C \left[\tan^{-1} \frac{y}{(x - a)} - \tan^{-1} \frac{y}{(x + a)} \right]. \tag{3}$$

Thus lines of constant u can be obtained from (2) by setting the argument

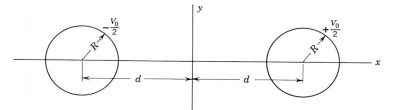

Fig. 3.18   Two parallel conducting cylinders.

of the logarithm equal to a constant:

$$\frac{(x - a)^2 + y^2}{(x + a)^2 + y^2} = K.$$

As this may be put in the form

$$\left[x - \frac{a(1 + K)}{1 - K} \right]^2 + y^2 = \frac{4a^2 K}{(1 - K)^2}, \tag{4}$$

the curves of constant u are circles with centers at

$$x = \frac{a(1 + K)}{1 - K}$$

and radii $(2a\sqrt{K})/(1 - K)$. If u is taken as the potential function, any one of the circles of constant u may be replaced by an equipotential conducting cylinder. Thus, if R is the radius of such a conductor with center at $x = d$ (Fig. 3.18), the values of a and the particular value of K (denoted K_0) may be obtained by setting

$$\frac{a(1 + K_0)}{1 - K_0} = d \qquad \frac{2a\sqrt{K_0}}{1 - K_0} = R.$$

Solving,
$$a = \sqrt{d^2 - R^2} \tag{5}$$

$$\sqrt{K_0} = \frac{d}{R} + \sqrt{\frac{d^2}{R^2} - 1}. \tag{6}$$

The constant C in the transformation depends upon the potential of the conducting cylinder. Let this be $V_0/2$. Then, by the definition of K,

$$\frac{V_0}{2} = C \ln \sqrt{K_0} = C \ln \left(\frac{d}{R} + \sqrt{\frac{d^2}{R^2} - 1} \right)$$

or
$$C = \frac{V_0}{2 \ln \left(\dfrac{d}{R} + \sqrt{\dfrac{d^2}{R^2} - 1} \right)} = \frac{V_0}{2 \cosh^{-1}\left(\dfrac{d}{R} \right)}. \tag{7}$$

Substituting in (2), the potential at any point (x, y) is

$$\Phi = u = \frac{V_0}{4 \cosh^{-1}(d/R)} \ln \left[\frac{(x - a)^2 + y^2}{(x + a)^2 + y^2} \right]. \tag{8}$$

And the flux function, ϵv, is

$$\psi = \epsilon v = \frac{\epsilon V_0}{2 \cosh^{-1}(d/R)} \left[\tan^{-1} \frac{y}{(x - a)} - \tan^{-1} \frac{y}{(x + a)} \right]. \tag{9}$$

Although we have not put in the left-hand conducting cylinder explicitly, the odd symmetry of the potential from (8) will cause this boundary condition to be satisfied also if the left-hand cylinder of radius R with center at $x = -d$ is at potential $-V_0/2$.

If we wish to use the result to obtain the capacitance per unit length of a parallel wire line, we obtain the charge on the right-hand conductor from Gauss's law by finding the total flux ending on it. In passing once around the conductor, the first term of (9) changes by 2π, and the second by zero. So

$$q = 2\pi \frac{\epsilon V_0}{2 \cosh^{-1}(d/R)} \text{ coulombs/meter}$$

or
$$C = \frac{q}{V_0} = \frac{\pi \epsilon}{\cosh^{-1}(d/R)} \text{ farads/meter.} \tag{10}$$

Problems

3.18a Modify the derivation in Art. 3.18 to apply to the problem of parallel cylinders of unequal radius. Take the left-hand cylinder of radius R_1 with center at $x = -d_1$, the right-hand cylinder of radius R_2 with center at $x = d_2$, and a total difference of potential V_0 between cylinders. Find the electrostatic capacitance per unit length in terms of R_1, R_2, and $(d_1 + d_2)$.

3.18b Show that the lines of constant v in the transformation of Art. 3.18 do represent a family of circles.

3.18c The important bilinear transformation is of the form

$$Z = \frac{aZ' + b}{cZ' + d}.$$

Take a, b, c, and d as real constants, and show that any circle in the Z' plane is transformed to a circle in the Z plane by this transformation. (Straight lines are considered circles of infinite radius.)

3.18d Consider the special case of Prob. c with $a = R$, $b = -R$, $c = 1$, and $d = 1$. Show that the imaginary axis of the Z' plane transforms to a circle of radius R, center at the origin, in the Z plane. Show that a line charge at $x' = d$ and its image at $x' = -d$ in the Z' plane transform to points in the Z plane at radii r_1 and r_2 with

$$r_1 r_2 = R^2.$$

Compare with the result for imaging line charges in a cylinder (Art. 2.19).

3.19   The Schwarz Transformation for General Polygons

In all the preceding examples, specific functions have been set down, and the electrostatic problems solvable by these deduced from a study of their properties. In a practical problem, the reverse procedure is usually required, for the specific equipotential conducting boundaries will be given and it will be desired to find the complex function useful in solving the problem. For some of the preceding examples, it is true that the function might have been arrived at if one were given the problem first, and used a good physical picture combined with a bit of ingenuity. The greatest limitation on this method of conformal transformations, however, is that, for general shaped boundaries, there is no straightforward procedure by which one can always arrive at the desired transformation if the two-dimensional physical problem is given. There is such a procedure, however, when the boundaries consist of straight line sides with angle intersections. We wish to describe it briefly.

Suppose that a polygon is given in the Z plane (Fig. 3.19a) with vertices at $P_1, P_2, \ldots, P_n$ and with corresponding interior angles $\alpha_1, \alpha_2, \ldots, \alpha_n$. Suppose that it is desired to transform this boundary into the straight line $y' = 0$ in some other Z' plane, with P_1 going into the point $Z' = x_1'$, P_2 into x_2', etc. The Schwarz transformation states that the proper function may be found by integrating the derivative:

$$\frac{dZ}{dZ'} = K(Z' - x_1')^{(\alpha_1/\pi)-1}(Z' - x_2')^{(\alpha_2/\pi)-1} \ldots (Z' - x_n')^{(\alpha_n/\pi)-1}. \tag{1}$$

note Z' (primed)

We do not wish to attempt to prove this,[8] but each factor in (1) may be thought of as straightening out the boundary at one of the vertices, as the transformation of Art. 3.15 did for the single corner. That is, if dZ' is changed always in the same direction along the line $y' = 0$, dZ remains of the same direction (phase) except when we pass through a point corresponding to one of the vertices, say x'_m. Here the factor $(Z' - x'_m)$ changes

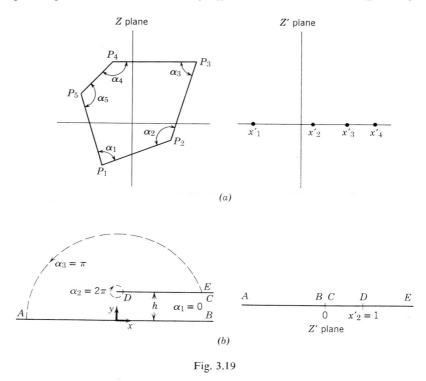

(a)

(b)

Fig. 3.19

phase by a factor π, and the factor $(Z' - x'_m)^{(\alpha_m/\pi)-1}$ changes phase by a factor $\alpha_m - \pi$, so the direction of dZ is changed by $\alpha_m - \pi$, and passes along the next side of the polygon.

Although we have spoken of the figure to be transformed as a polygon, in the practical application of the method, one or more of the vertices are often at infinity, and part of the boundary may be at a different potential from the remaining part. Then the line $y' = 0$ in the Z' plane consists of two parts at different potentials. If this latter electrostatic problem is

[8] For more details see R. V. Churchill, *Introduction to Complex Variables and Applications*, Second Edition, McGraw-Hill, New York, 1960, pp. 218–221.

solved, it may be considered a transformation from the Z to the W plane, and thus the transformation from the Z to the W plane is given with the Z' plane only as an intermediate step. Another sort of problem in which the method is useful is that in which a thin charged wire lies on the interior of a conducting polygon, parallel to the elements of the polygon. By the Schwarz transformation, the polygon boundary is transformed to the line $y' = 0$, and the wire will then correspond to some point in the upper half of the Z' plane. This electrostatic problem can be solved by the method of images, and so the original problem can be solved in this case also.

To clarify some of these general statements, let us consider one of the most simple standard examples for the Schwarz transformation. This is the problem of the edge effect for a parallel plate condenser, and is one of the first type described in the preceding paragraph. The problem is idealized by taking the infinite plane $y = 0$ at potential V_0, and a zero-potential parallel semi-infinite plane extending from $x = 0$, $y = h$ to $x = \infty$, $y = h$ (Fig. 3.19b). In this example, the vertices (two of which are at infinity) have angles $\alpha_1 = 0$, $\alpha_2 = 2\pi$, $\alpha_3 = \pi$. We choose to transform the first vertex to the origin of the Z' plane, with the gap separating the two conductors becoming an infinitesimal gap at the origin. The second vertex is transformed to $x_2' = 1$, and the third vertex to $x_3' = \infty$. The factor of Eq. (1) corresponding to a vertex transformed to infinity in the Z' plane is not included in the equation (Prob. 3.19a). Then

$$\frac{dZ}{dZ'} = K(Z' - 0)^{(0/\pi)-1}(Z' - 1)^{(2\pi/\pi)-1} = K\,\frac{(Z' - 1)}{Z'} \qquad (2)$$

or
$$Z = K \int \left(1 - \frac{1}{Z'}\right) dZ' = K(Z' - \ln Z') + C. \qquad (3)$$

To evaluate the constants K and C, note first that $Z = 0 + jh$ when $Z' = 1$.

$$jh = K + C$$

$$Z = K(Z' - 1 - \ln Z') + jh. \qquad (4)$$

A second, less direct, condition may be imposed by integrating between B and C, approaching infinity in the Z plane and zero in the Z' plane:

$$\int_B^C dZ = \int_B^C \frac{dZ}{dZ'}\, dZ'. \qquad (5)$$

But, from (2) for $Z' \to 0$,

$$\frac{dZ}{dZ'} \to -\frac{K}{Z'}.$$

If the right side of (5) is integrated about a circle of radius r',

$$dZ' = d(r'e^{j\theta'}) = jr'e^{j\theta'}\,d\theta' = jZ'\,d\theta'.$$

Then

$$\int_{\infty+j0}^{\infty+jh} dZ = \int_{\pi}^{0}\left(-\frac{K}{Z'}\right)jZ'\,d\theta'$$

or

$$jh = jK\pi$$

$$K = \frac{h}{\pi}.$$

And the transformation is

$$Z = \frac{h}{\pi}(Z' - 1 - \ln Z' + j\pi). \qquad (6)$$

It can be shown (compare with Prob. 3.16b) that the transformed problem in the Z' plane, which consists of the left half plane at potential V_0 and the right half at potential zero, may be solved by the function

$$W = u + jv = \frac{V_0}{\pi}\ln Z'$$

or

$$Z' = e^{\pi W/V_0}.$$

In the foregoing, v represents the potential function, and the reference for zero flux is taken at the point D $(r' = 1)$. Substituting in (6), we have

$$Z = \frac{h}{\pi}\left(e^{\pi W/V_0} - 1 - \frac{\pi W}{V_0} + j\pi\right). \qquad (7)$$

Equation (7) is the solution to the problem in that it gives the potential and flux functions as implicit functions of the coordinates x and y. Results for some other important problems which have been solved by the Schwarz technique are given in Table 3.19.

TABLE 3.19

$Z = x + jy$; $W = u + jv$, where u = Flux Function, v = Potential

check

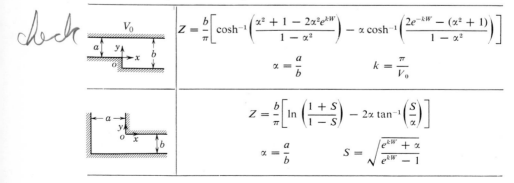

V_0, with a, b dimensions	$Z = \frac{b}{\pi}\left[\cosh^{-1}\left(\dfrac{\alpha^2 + 1 - 2\alpha^2 e^{kW}}{1 - \alpha^2}\right) - \alpha\cosh^{-1}\left(\dfrac{2e^{-kW} - (\alpha^2 + 1)}{1 - \alpha^2}\right)\right]$ $\alpha = \dfrac{a}{b}$ $\qquad$ $k = \dfrac{\pi}{V_0}$
a, b L-shaped region	$Z = \frac{b}{\pi}\left[\ln\left(\dfrac{1+S}{1-S}\right) - 2\alpha\tan^{-1}\left(\dfrac{S}{\alpha}\right)\right]$ $\alpha = \dfrac{a}{b}$ $\qquad$ $S = \sqrt{\dfrac{e^{kW} + \alpha}{e^{kW} - 1}}$

Problems

3.19a Explain why a factor in the Schwarz transformation is left out when it corresponds to a point transformed to infinity in the Z' plane, as for the third vertex in the example in Art. 3.19.

3.19b In the example of Art. 3.19, separate Z into real and imaginary parts. Show that the boundary condition for potential is satisfied along the two conductors. Obtain the asymptotic equations for large positive u and for large negative u, and interpret the results in terms of the type of field approached in these limits.

3.19c Work the example of Prob. 3.17b by the Schwarz technique and show that the same result is obtained. This is the problem of two coplanar semi-infinite plane conductors separated by a gap $2a$, with the right-hand conductor at potential zero and the left-hand conductor at potential V_0.

3.19d For the first example of Table 3.19, find the electrostatic capacitance in excess of what would be obtained if a uniform field existed in both of the parallel-plane regions.

3.19e Plot $V_0/4$, $V_0/2$, and $3V_0/4$ equipotentials for the example of Art. 3.19.

THE SEPARATION OF VARIABLES TECHNIQUE AND PRODUCT SOLUTIONS IN RECTANGULAR, CYLINDRICAL, AND SPHERICAL COORDINATES

3.20 The Product Solution Method

In spite of the great generality in principle of the transformation method for solving two-dimensional Laplace equation problems, we have seen that there are practical difficulties in using it to yield the solution for all two-dimensional problems. Moreover, there is no direct extension of the method to three-dimensional problems. We wish now to describe one of the standard methods for the solution of partial differential equations in any number of variables. In this method, the solution is expressed as a product of functions, each of which contains only one of the variables of the coordinate system used. For example, in a cylindrical coordinate system, the solution for potential may be expressed as a product of three functions, one in terms of radius r, one in terms of azimuthal angle ϕ, and one in terms of the axial distance z. Substitution in the partial differential equation allows us to separate it into ordinary differential equations in each of the variables, and these may be solved separately. The technique is known as the method of *product solutions* or of *separation of variables*.

It may seem that elimination at the outset of all solutions not of the product form represents a severe limitation, but it is not so severe, since a series of such solutions may be used when one alone will not permit a matching of boundary conditions. This is permissible by the linearity discussed in Art. 3.04. The amounts of the individual solutions to be added are determined by the boundary conditions in a manner somewhat analogous to that used to determine the amounts of the individual harmonics to add up to a complex wave shape in a Fourier analysis. (See Arts. 1.10 and 1.28.)

In the following articles we shall apply the product solutions technique to Laplace's equation in rectangular, cylindrical, and spherical coordinates. Since a solution of Laplace's equation continuous through the second derivative is called a *harmonic* function, the corresponding product solutions for the foregoing cases are often called *rectangular harmonics*, *cylindrical harmonics*, and *spherical harmonics*. Various series of these will be combined to fit, exactly or approximately, the boundary conditions for many shapes of electrodes. In addition to the importance of the method for these specific problems, it is of greatest importance to us since the same technique (and some of the same functions) will be used to obtain solutions of the wave equation for various time-varying problems in later chapters.

3.21   Rectangular Harmonics

As the simplest example of the method of separation of variables, let us first consider two-dimensional problems in the rectangular coordinates x and y, as we have in the transformation method of the past section. Laplace's equation in these coordinates is

$$\frac{\partial^2 \Phi}{\partial x^2} + \frac{\partial^2 \Phi}{\partial y^2} = 0. \tag{1}$$

We wish to study product solutions of the form

$$\Phi(x, y) = X(x)\,Y(y), \tag{2}$$

where we see that we have a function of x alone times a function of y alone. From this point on $X(x)$ will be replaced by X and $Y(y)$ by Y. Substituting in (1), we have

$$X''Y + XY'' = 0. \tag{3}$$

The double prime denotes differentiation (twice) with respect to the independent variable in the function. Now to separate into the sum of functions of one variable only, divide (3) by (2)

$$\frac{X''}{X} + \frac{Y''}{Y} = 0. \tag{4}$$

Next follows the key argument for this method. Equation (4) is to hold for all values of the variables x and y. Since the second term does not contain x, and so cannot vary with x, the first term cannot vary with x either. A function of x alone which does not vary with x is a constant. Similarly, the second term must be a constant. Let us denote the first as k_x^2 and the second as k_y^2. Then

$$k_x^2 + k_y^2 = 0 \tag{5}$$

and

$$X'' - k_x^2 X = 0$$

$$Y'' - k_y^2 Y = 0. \tag{6}$$

We recognize that these are in the standard form having real exponentials or hyperbolic functions as solutions. Let us write them in hyperbolic form and substitute in (2):

$$\Phi(x, y) = (A \cosh k_x x + B \sinh k_x x)(C \cosh k_y y + D \sinh k_y y). \tag{7}$$

It is clear from (5) that either k_x^2 or k_y^2 must be negative and therefore either k_x or k_y must be imaginary while the other is real. Furthermore, their magnitudes must be the same. For the two cases, (7) becomes

$$\Phi(x, y) = (A \cosh kx + B \sinh kx)(C' \cos ky + D' \sin ky) \tag{8}$$

and

$$\Phi(x, y) = (A' \cos kx + B' \sin kx)(C \cosh ky + D \sinh ky) \tag{9}$$

where, since $|k_x| = |k_y|$, we have used the single symbol k. The primes are used to indicate that the constants have changed. The choice between (8) and (9) is dictated by the nature of the boundary conditions. If the potential is required to have repeated zeros as a function of y, then (8) is used; if repeated zeros are specified for the x variation, (9) is chosen. If the boundaries extend to infinity in one direction, the hyperbolic functions are replaced by real exponentials. It may be noted from (6) that for $k_x = jk_y = 0$ the general solution has the form

$$\Phi(x, y) = (A_1 x + B_1)(C_1 y + D_1).$$

It is typical for product solutions that when the separation constants go to zero the functional forms of the solutions change. We will see in subsequent articles how the constants are evaluated using the boundary conditions.

For the three-dimensional case in rectangular coordinates, the procedure is simply extended. Laplace's equation is

$$\frac{\partial^2 \Phi}{\partial x^2} + \frac{\partial^2 \Phi}{\partial y^2} + \frac{\partial^2 \Phi}{\partial z^2} = 0. \tag{10}$$

Consider solutions of the form

$$\Phi(x, y, z) = X(x)\,Y(y)Z(z) \tag{11}$$

where each term on the right side is a function of just one of the independent space variables. Substituting (11) in (10), we have

$$X''YZ + XY''Z + XYZ'' = 0$$

and dividing by Φ, we see that

$$\frac{X''}{X} + \frac{Y''}{Y} + \frac{Z''}{Z} = 0. \tag{12}$$

We use the same argument as was used in the two-dimensional case. If the second two terms do not vary with x, neither can the first. Since it is a function of x alone and does not vary with x, it must be a constant. Similar arguments apply for the second and third terms. If we let the first term be $k_x{}^2$, the second $k_y{}^2$, and the third $k_z{}^2$, (12) becomes

$$k_x{}^2 + k_y{}^2 + k_z{}^2 = 0, \tag{13}$$

and differential equations of the form (6) apply for X, Y, and Z. So the general solution, written as the product of X, Y, and Z, becomes

$$\Phi(x, y, z) = [A \cosh k_x x + B \sinh k_x x][C \cosh k_y y + D \sinh k_y y]$$
$$\times\ [E \cosh k_z z + F \sinh k_z z]. \quad (14)$$

It is clear that at least one of $k_x{}^2$, $k_y{}^2$, or $k_z{}^2$ must be negative for (13) to hold. Therefore, at least one of $k_x, k_y,$ or k_z must be imaginary. If repeated potential zeros are required in the x and y directions, the functions of x and y must be trigonometric functions so k_x and k_y are imaginary. There are various other combinations which may be useful. In some cases it is advantageous to replace the hyperbolic functions by real exponentials as mentioned earlier for the two-dimensional solutions.

In (14) there appear to be nine constants to be evaluated using the six possible boundary conditions, two for each of the three coordinate directions. If, however, the first bracket is divided by B', the second by D', and the third by F and the entire expression is multiplied by a single constant $B'D'F$, it becomes clear that there are just four unknown multiplicative constants. From (13) we see that there are only two independent separation constants so the total number of unknowns equals the number of boundary conditions.

Problems

3.21a Check by differentiation to show that (14) does satisfy (10).
3.21b Find the basic forms [in the sense that (9) is different from (8)] of (14) obtained by allowing k_x, k_y, k_z and various combinations to become imaginary.
3.21c The so-called circular harmonics are the product solutions to Laplace's equation in the two circular cylindrical coordinates r and ϕ. Apply the basic separation of variables technique to Laplace's equation in these coordinates to yield two ordinary differential equations. Show that the r and ϕ equations are satisfied respectively by the functions R and F_ϕ where

$$R = C_1 r^n + C_2 r^{-n}$$

$$F_\phi = C_3 \cos n\phi + C_4 \sin n\phi.$$

3.22 Field Described by a Single Rectangular Harmonic

Let us see what boundaries would be required in order to have some one of the forms of Art. 3.21 as a solution. Take the special case of Eq. 3.21(8) with $A = 0$, $C' = 0$. The product of remaining constants, BD', may be denoted as a single constant C_1:

$$\Phi = C_1 \sinh kx \sin ky. \tag{1}$$

It is evident from (1) that potential is zero at $x = 0$ for all y. Hence one boundary can be a zero-potential conducting plane at $x = 0$. Similarly, potential is zero along the plane $y = 0$, and also at other parallel planes defined by $ky = n\pi$. Let us confine attention to the region $0 < ky < \pi$ and $0 < x < \infty$. The intersecting zero-potential planes of interest then form a rectangular conducting trough. Let its depth in the y direction be b. Then $kb = \pi$ or

$$k = \frac{\pi}{b}. \tag{2}$$

If there is to be a finite field in the region, there must be some electrode at a potential other than zero. Without knowing its shape for the moment, let us take the value of x at which it crosses the midplane $y = b/2$ as $x = a$, and the potential of the electrode as V_0. Then, from (1),

$$V_0 = C_1 \sinh \frac{\pi a}{b} \sin \frac{\pi}{2} = C_1 \sinh \frac{\pi a}{b}$$

or, substituting in (1), we have

$$\Phi = \frac{V_0 \sinh (\pi x/b)}{\sinh (\pi a/b)} \sin (\pi y/b). \tag{3}$$

The potential at any point x, y may be computed from (3). In particular, the form that the electrode at potential V_0 must take, can be found from (3) by setting $\Phi = V_0$, yielding

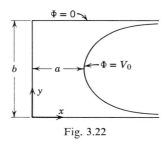

$$\sinh \frac{\pi x}{b} = \frac{\sinh (\pi a/b)}{\sin (\pi y/b)}. \tag{4}$$

Equation (4) can be plotted to show the form of the electrode. This is done for a value $a/b = \frac{1}{2}$ in Fig. 3.22. Actually, the electrodes should extend to infinity, but if they are extended a large but finite distance,

Fig. 3.22

the solution studied here will represent the potential very well everywhere except near edges.

Problems

3.22a Plot the form of equipotentials for $\Phi = \frac{1}{4}V_0, \frac{1}{2}V_0$, and $\frac{3}{4}V_0$ for Fig. 3.22.

3.22b Describe the electrode structure for which the single rectangular harmonic $C_1 \cosh kx \sin ky$ is a solution for potential. Take electrodes at potential V_0 passing through $|x| = a$ when $y = a/2$.

3.22c Describe the electrode structure and exciting potentials for which the single circular harmonic (Prob. 3.21c) $Cr^2 \cos 2\phi$ is a solution.

3.23 Series of Rectangular Harmonics: Two-Dimensional Field

As an example of a problem which cannot be solved by using a single one of the solutions of Art. 3.21, but can be by means of a series of these solutions, consider the two-dimensional region of Fig. 3.23 bounded by a zero-potential plane at $x = 0$, a zero-potential plane at $y = 0$, a parallel zero-potential plane at $y = b$, and a plane conducting lid of potential V_0 at $x = a$. In the ideal problem, the lid is separated from the remainder of the rectangular box by infinitesimal gaps. In a practical problem, it would only be expected that these gaps should be small compared with the rest of the box.

In selecting the proper forms from Art. 3.21, we will choose the form having sinusoidal solutions in y, since potential is zero at $y = 0$ and also at $y = b$, and sinusoids have repeated zeros. So the form of Eq. 3.21(8) is suitable. Moreover, $\Phi = 0$ at $x = 0$ for all y of interest, so the function of x must go to zero at $x = 0$, showing that $A = 0$. Similarly, since

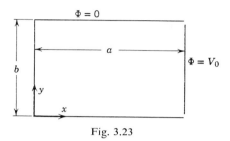

$$\Phi = 0$$
$$a$$
$$b$$
$$\Phi = V_0$$
$$y$$
$$x$$

Fig. 3.23

$\Phi = 0$ at $y = 0$ for all x of interest, $C' = 0$. Then Φ is again zero at $y = b$, so $kb = n\pi$, or

$$k = \frac{n\pi}{b}.$$

Denoting the product of the remaining constants BD' as C_n, we have

$$\Phi = C_n \sinh \frac{n\pi x}{b} \sin \frac{n\pi y}{b}.$$

This form satisfies the Laplace equation and the boundary conditions at $x = 0$, at $y = 0$, and at $y = b$, but a single term of this form cannot satisfy the boundary condition along the plane lid at $x = a$, as a study like that of Art. 3.22 would show. But a series of such solutions also satisfies Laplace's equation and the boundary conditions at $x = 0$, at $y = 0$, and at $y = b$:

$$\Phi = \sum_{n=1}^{\infty} C_n \sinh \frac{n\pi x}{b} \sin \frac{n\pi y}{b}. \tag{1}$$

For the sum (1) to give the required constant potential V_0 along the plane $x = a$ over the interval $0 < y < b$, we require

$$V_0 = \sum_{n=1}^{\infty} C_n \sinh \frac{n\pi a}{b} \sin \frac{n\pi y}{b}, \qquad 0 < y < b. \tag{2}$$

But this is recognized as a Fourier expansion in sines of the constant function V_0 over the interval $0 < y < b$. This expansion was carried out in Art. 1.12 to yield

$$f(y) = V_0 = \sum_{n=1}^{\infty} a_n \sin \frac{n\pi y}{b} \qquad (3)$$

$$a_n = \begin{cases} \dfrac{4V_0}{n\pi}, & n \text{ odd} \\[2mm] 0, & n \text{ even.} \end{cases} \qquad (4)$$

Comparison of (3) with (2) shows that

$$C_n \sinh \frac{n\pi a}{b} = a_n. \qquad (5)$$

Substitution of the results of (5) and (4) in (1) gives

$$\Phi = \sum_{n \text{ odd}} \frac{4V_0}{n\pi} \frac{\sinh (n\pi x/b)}{\sinh (n\pi a/b)} \sin \frac{n\pi y}{b}. \qquad (6)$$

This series is rapidly convergent except for values of x approaching a, so it can be used for reasonably convenient calculation of potential at any interior point x, y.

We note that the evaluation of the constants in the general solution depended on the fact that the boundary potentials were specified on surfaces in the coordinate system. Furthermore, non-zero conditions, potential or normal derivative of potential, must exist on some part of the boundary to yield a non-zero solution. As will be clarified in the problems, superposition may be used to solve problems where the boundary conditions involve several sides.

Problems

3.23a Obtain a series solution for the two-dimensional box problem in which sides at $y = 0$ and $y = b$ are at potential zero, and end planes at $x = a$ and $x = -a$ are at potential V_0. *Hint:* Utilize the symmetry of the problem in the evaluation of constants.

3.23b Find the potential distribution for the box of Prob. a with the same boundary conditions except that the potential on the side at $y = 0$ should be V_1 rather than zero.

3.23c In a two-dimensional problem, parallel planes at $y = 0$ and $y = b$ extend from $x = 0$ to $x = \infty$, and are at zero potential. The one end plane at $x = 0$ is at potential V_0. Obtain a series solution. *Hint:* Use the exponential form for the solution in x, and consider the condition at infinity.

3.23d Consider a two-dimensional rectangular conducting solid located in free space. Boundary potentials are specified as zero at $x = 0$ and $\Phi = ky$ at $x = a$. Apply appropriate boundary conditions on the sides at $y = 0$, b and find the potential distribution.

3.23e Using the circular harmonics of Prob. 3.21c, form a series for solution of potential inside an infinite split cylinder of radius a whose lower half $(-\pi < \phi < 0)$ is at potential $-V_0$ and whose upper half $(0 < \phi < \pi)$ is at potential V_0. Similarly, write a series solution valid for $r > a$.

3.23f Infinite parallel conducting plates are located at $y = 0$ and $y = a$. A conducting strip at $x = 0$, $a/2 \leq y \leq a$, $-\infty < z < \infty$ is connected to the plate at $y = a$, thus introducing additional capacitance between the plates. Assume a linear potential variation from $0 \leq y \leq a/2$ at $x = 0$, and use superposition of boundary conditions (see Art. 3.04) to find an expression for the capacity per meter in the z direction added by the strip at $x = 0$.

3.24 Series of Rectangular Harmonics: Three-Dimensional Field

The method used in Art. 3.23 to find the series of harmonics satisfying given two-dimensional boundary conditions can be extended to three dimensions. Consider the box shown in Fig. 3.24. The potential is zero on all sides and the bottom and is $V(x, y)$ on the top. We will find a summation of product solutions which satisfies Laplace's equation and meets the specified boundary conditions.

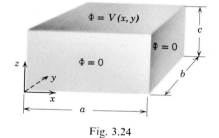

Fig. 3.24

Starting with the general form, Eq. 3.21(14), it is clear, first of all, that the repeated zeros in the x and y directions require k_x and k_y to be imaginary. The remaining constant k_z must be real. Then the general form may be written as

$$\Phi(x, y, z) = [A' \cos k_x'x + B' \sin k_x'x][C' \cos k_y'y + D' \sin k_y'y]$$
$$\times [E \cosh k_zz + F \sinh k_zz] \quad (1)$$

where k_x' is jk_x and $k_y' = jk_y$. Thus from Eq. 3.21(13),

$$k_z^2 - k_x'^2 - k_y'^2 = 0. \quad (2)$$

Since the potential is required to be zero at $x = 0$, $y = 0$, and $z = 0$, the coefficients of functions that do not vanish there must be zero. Therefore

$A' = C' = E = 0$. For the $\sin k'_x x$ to again reach zero at the other side of the box, it is necessary that

$$k'_x = \frac{m\pi}{a}, \tag{3}$$

as was discussed in Art. 3.23. Similarly,

$$k'_y = \frac{n\pi}{b} \tag{4}$$

and, therefore, from (2)

$$k_z = \sqrt{\left(\frac{m\pi}{a}\right)^2 + \left(\frac{n\pi}{b}\right)^2}. \tag{5}$$

The remaining coefficients B', D', and F will be combined in a single constant C_{mn} where the subscripts refer to the m and n in (3) and (4). So (1) becomes

$$\Phi_{mn} = C_{mn} \sin \frac{m\pi}{a} x \sin \frac{n\pi}{b} y \sinh \sqrt{\left(\frac{m\pi}{a}\right)^2 + \left(\frac{n\pi}{b}\right)^2} z. = V_o \tag{6}$$

The functional notation for Φ is dropped from this point on for simplicity. The one remaining constant will be evaluated using the second boundary condition on the variation in the z direction.

In order to have an arbitrary potential $V(x, y)$ at $z = c$ we must take a doubly infinite series of harmonics of the form of (6). Thus the potential at any point within the box has the form

$$\Phi = \sum_n \sum_m C_{mn} \sin \frac{m\pi}{a} x \sin \frac{n\pi}{b} y \sinh \sqrt{\left(\frac{m\pi}{a}\right)^2 + \left(\frac{n\pi}{b}\right)^2} z \tag{7}$$

which must equal $V(x, y)$ at $z = c$. We can write

$$V(x, y) = \sum_n \sum_m D_{mn} \sin \frac{m\pi}{a} x \sin \frac{n\pi}{b} y, \tag{8}$$

where

$$D_{mn} = C_{mn} \sinh \sqrt{\left(\frac{m\pi}{a}\right)^2 + \left(\frac{n\pi}{b}\right)^2} c. \tag{9}$$

Then we multiply both sides of (8) by $\sin (p\pi/a)x \sin (q\pi/b)y$ and integrate over the surface $0 < x < a$, $0 < y < b$. We find that, if either $p \neq m$ or $q \neq n$, the right side vanishes as a result of the orthogonality of sine functions discussed in Art. 1.10. If $p = m$ and $q = n$, the integral of the right side becomes

$$\int_0^b \int_0^a D_{mn} \sin^2 \frac{m\pi}{a} x \sin^2 \frac{n\pi}{b} y \, dx \, dy = \frac{ab}{4} D_{mn}. \tag{10}$$

Equating the integrals of both sides and multiplying by $4/ab$ we have

$$D_{mn} = \frac{4}{ab} \int_0^b \int_0^a V(x, y) \sin \frac{m\pi}{a} x \sin \frac{n\pi}{b} y \, dx \, dy. \qquad (11)$$

Then by combining (7), (9), and (11) we have an expression for the potential at any point in the box.

If we consider the special case of $V(x, y) = V_0$, a constant, we have from (11)

$$D_{mn} = \frac{16}{nm\pi^2}$$

and by using (9), (7) becomes

$$\Phi = \frac{16}{nm\pi^2} \sum_n \sum_m \frac{\sin (m\pi/a)x \sin (n\pi/b)y \sinh \sqrt{(m\pi/a)^2 + (n\pi/b)^2} \, z}{\sinh \sqrt{(m\pi/a)^2 + (n\pi/b)^2} \, c}.$$

Problems

3.24a For the box with dimensions given in Fig. 3.24 find the potential distribution if the box is filled with a homogeneous, isotropic dielectric in the bottom half of the box $0 \leqslant z \leqslant c/2$ and free space in the remainder. (Note that this problem requires a good deal of work.)

3.24b Consider a rectangular prism of width a in the x direction and b in the y direction with all four sides at zero potential extending from $z = 0$ to $z = \infty$. At $z = 0$ the cylinder has a cap with the following potential distribution:

$$V(x, y, 0) = \begin{cases} 0 & \text{for } 0 < x < a/2 \text{ all } y. \\ V_0 & \text{for } a/2 < x < a \text{ all } y. \end{cases}$$

Find the potentials within the prism.

3.25 Cylindrical Harmonics

In a large class of problems of major interest, the field distribution is desired for regions with boundaries lying along the surfaces of a cylindrical coordinate system. Examples are the familiar electrostatic electron lenses found in many cathode-ray tubes or certain coaxial transmission line problems for which static solutions are useful. As has been pointed out in Art. 3.23, the ability to evaluate the constants in product solutions depends on having boundaries on coordinate surfaces. Therefore, the fields for this type of problem are found by separating variables in cylindrical coordinates.

A variety of types of solution are found, depending on symmetries assumed. In general, Laplace's equation in cylindrical coordinates has the form

$$\frac{1}{r}\frac{\partial}{\partial r}\left(r\frac{\partial \Phi}{\partial r}\right) + \frac{1}{r^2}\frac{\partial^2 \Phi}{\partial \phi^2} + \frac{\partial^2 \Phi}{\partial z^2} = 0. \tag{1}$$

Axial Symmetry with Longitudinal Invariance. In Art. 3.05 we saw that for this case

$$\Phi(r) = C_1 \ln r + C_2. \tag{2}$$

Longitudinal Invariance. It was shown in Prob. 3.21c that the solutions for this case, called *circular harmonics*, are given by

$$\Phi(r, \phi) = (C_1 r^n + C_2 r^{-n})(C_3 \cos n\phi + C_4 \sin n\phi). \tag{3}$$

Note that, for $n = 0$, axial symmetry exists but (3) breaks down and the solution is given by (2).

Axial Symmetry. Since it is assumed that there are no variations with ϕ, Laplace's equation (1) becomes

$$\frac{\partial^2 \Phi}{\partial r^2} + \frac{1}{r}\frac{\partial \Phi}{\partial r} + \frac{\partial^2 \Phi}{\partial z^2} = 0. \tag{4}$$

To solve this equation, let us try to find solutions of the product form

$$\Phi(r, z) = R(r)Z(z). \tag{5}$$

Substituting in the differential equation (4), we have

$$R''Z + \frac{1}{r}R' + RZ'' = 0,$$

where R'' denotes d^2R/dr^2, Z'' denotes d^2Z/dz^2, etc. The variables are separated by dividing by (5)

$$\frac{Z''}{Z} = -\frac{R''}{R} + \frac{1}{r}\frac{R'}{R}.$$

By the standard argument for the method of separation of variables, the left side, which is a function of z alone, and the right side, which is a function of r alone, must be equal to each other for all values of the variables r and z. Both sides must then be equal to a constant. Let this constant be T^2. Two ordinary differential equations then result as follows:

$$\frac{1}{R}\frac{d^2R}{dr^2} + \frac{1}{rR}\frac{dR}{dr} = -T^2 \tag{6}$$

$$\frac{1}{Z}\frac{d^2Z}{dz^2} = T^2. \tag{7}$$

Equation (7) is the familiar differential equation of simple harmonic motion studied in Chapter 1. The solution is then in sinusoids if T^2 is negative, in hyperbolic functions (or exponentials) if T^2 is positive.

1. First consider T^2 positive so that the solution to (7) is in terms of hyperbolic functions. Equation (6) is then

$$\frac{d^2R}{dr^2} + \frac{1}{r}\frac{dR}{dr} + T^2R = 0. \qquad (8)$$

For those familiar with Bessel functions, (8) will be recognized as the simplest form of the Bessel equation. For those who are not, a sketch of the solution will be given. In Chapter 1, the familiar equation resulting in sinusoids was solved by assuming a solution in the form of a power series. Substitution in the differential equation told the form this series must have to be truly a solution of the equation. Similarly, to solve (8), the function R may also be assumed to be some series of powers of r:

$$R = a_0 + a_1 r + a_2 r^2 + a_3 r^3 + \cdots$$

or
$$R = \sum_{p=0}^{\infty} a_p r^p. \qquad (9)$$

Substitution of this function in (8) shows that it is a solution if the constants are as follows:

$$a_p = a_{2m} = C_1(-1)^m \frac{(T/2)^{2m}}{(m!)^2}.$$

(C_1 is any arbitrary constant.) That is,

$$R = C_1 \sum_{m=0}^{\infty} \frac{(-1)^m (Tr/2)^{2m}}{(m!)^2} = C_1\left[1 - \left(\frac{Tr}{2}\right)^2 + \frac{(Tr/2)^4}{(2!)^2} - \cdots\right] \qquad (10)$$

is a solution to the differential equation (8).

As with the series for sines and cosines in Chapter 1, it is easy to check and find that (10) is convergent, so that values may be calculated for any argument (Tr). Such calculations have been made over a wide range of values for the argument, the results tabulated, and the function defined by the series denoted by $J_0(Tr)$ and called a Bessel function (of first kind, zero order; the reason for such specific designation will be apparent later). Thus defined,

$$J_0(v) \equiv 1 - \left(\frac{v}{2}\right)^2 + \frac{(v/2)^4}{(2!)^2} - \cdots \equiv \sum_{m=0}^{\infty} \frac{(-1)^m (v/2)^{2m}}{(m!)^2}. \qquad (11)$$

The particular solution (10) may then be written simply as

$$R = C_1 J_0(Tr).$$

The differential equation (8) is of second order and so must have a second solution with a second arbitrary constant. (The sine and cosine constitute the two solutions for the simple harmonic motion equation.) This solution cannot be obtained by the power series method outlined above, since a general study of differential equations would show that at least one of the two independent solutions of (8) must have a singularity at $r = 0$. There are several methods for obtaining this second solution, all too detailed to be included here, and several different forms for the solution. One form for the second solution (any of which may be called Bessel functions of second kind, order zero) easily found in tables is

$$N_0(v) = \frac{2}{\pi} \ln \left(\frac{\gamma v}{2}\right) J_0(v) - \frac{2}{\pi} \sum_{m=1}^{\infty} \frac{(-1)^m (v/2)^{2m}}{(m!)^2} \left(1 + \frac{1}{2} + \frac{1}{3} + \cdots \frac{1}{m}\right). \quad (12)$$

The constant $\ln \gamma = 0.5772 \ldots$ is Euler's constant. In general, then,

$$R = C_1 J_0(Tr) + C_2 N_0(Tr) \quad (13)$$

is the solution to (8), with

$$Z = C_3 \sinh (Tz) + C_4 \cosh (Tz) \quad (14)$$

as the corresponding form for the solution to (7). It should be noted from (12) that $N_0(Tr)$, the second solution to R, becomes infinite at $r = 0$, so it cannot be present in any problem for which $r = 0$ is included in the region over which the solution applies.

2. If T^2 is negative, let $T^2 = -\tau^2$ or $T = j\tau$, where τ is real, and (8) may be written

$$\frac{d^2 R}{dr^2} + \frac{1}{r}\frac{dR}{dr} - \tau^2 R = 0. \quad (15)$$

The series (10) is still a solution, and T in (10) may be replaced by $j\tau$. Since all powers of the series are even, imaginaries disappear, and a new series is obtained which is real and also convergent. That is,

$$J_0(jv) = 1 + \left(\frac{v}{2}\right)^2 + \frac{(v/2)^4}{(2!)^2} + \frac{(v/2)^6}{(3!)^2} + \cdots . \quad (16)$$

Values of $J_0(jv)$ may be calculated for various values of v from such a series; these are also tabulated in the references. The defined function is denoted $I_0(v)$ in many of the references. Thus a solution to (15) is

$$R = C_1' J_0(j\tau r) \equiv C_1' I_0(\tau r). \quad (17)$$

There must also be a second solution in this case, and, since it is usually not taken simply as $N_0(j\tau r)$, the choice of this will be discussed in a later article (3.26). One of the forms for the second solution in this case is denoted $K_0(\tau r)$, so that the general solution to (15) may be written

$$R = C_1' I_0(\tau r) + C_2' K_0(\tau r). \quad (18)$$

The second solution K_0 becomes infinite at $r = 0$ just as does N_0, and so will not be required in the simple examples immediately following which include the axis $r = 0$ in the range over which the solution is to apply. The solution to the z equation (7) when $T^2 = -\tau^2$ is

$$Z = C_3' \sin \tau z + C_4' \cos \tau z. \tag{19}$$

Summarizing, either of the following forms satisfies Laplace's equation in the two cylindrical coordinates r and z:

$$\Phi(r, z) = [C_1 J_0(Tr) + C_2 N_0(Tr)][C_3 \sinh Tz + C_4 \cosh Tz] \tag{20}$$

$$\Phi(r, z) = [C_1' I_0(\tau r) + C_2' K_0(\tau r)][C_3' \sin \tau z + C_4' \cos \tau z]. \tag{21}$$

As was the case with the rectangular harmonics, the two forms are not really different since (20) includes (21) if T is allowed to become imaginary, but the two separate ways of writing the solution are useful, as will be demonstrated in following examples. The case with no assumed symmetries is discussed in Art. 3.26.

Problem

3.25 Demonstrate that the series (10) does satisfy the differential equation (8).

3.26 Bessel Functions

In Art. 3.25 an example of a Bessel Function was shown as a solution of the differential equation 3.25(8) which describes the radial variations in Laplace's equation for axially symmetric fields where a product solution is assumed. This is just one of a whole family of functions which are solutions of the general Bessel differential equation.

Bessel Functions with Real Arguments. For certain problems, as, for example, the solution for field between the two halves of a longitudinally split cylinder, it may be necessary to retain the ϕ variations in the equation. The solution may be assumed in product form again, RZF_ϕ, where R is a function of r alone, Z of z alone, and F_ϕ of ϕ alone. Z has solutions in exponentials or sinusoids as before, and F_ϕ may also be satisfied by sinusoids:

$$Z = Ce^{Tz} + De^{-Tz} \tag{1}$$

$$F_\phi = E \cos \nu\phi + F \sin \nu\phi. \tag{2}$$

The differential equation for R is then slightly different from the zero-order Bessel equation obtained previously:

$$\frac{d^2R}{dr^2} + \frac{1}{r}\frac{dR}{dr} + \left(T^2 - \frac{\nu^2}{r^2}\right)R = 0. \tag{3}$$

It is apparent at once that Eq. 3.25(8) is a special case of this more general equation, that is, $\nu = 0$. A series solution to the general equation carried through as in Art. 3.25 shows that the function defined by the series

$$J_\nu(Tr) = \sum_{m=0}^{\infty} \frac{(-1)^m (Tr/2)^{\nu+2m}}{m!\,\Gamma(\nu + m + 1)} \qquad (4)$$

is a solution to the equation.

$\Gamma(\nu + m + 1)$ is the gamma function of $(\nu + m + 1)$ and, for ν integral, is equivalent to the factorial of $(\nu + m)$. Also for ν non-integral, values of this gamma function are tabulated. If ν is an integer n,

$$J_n(Tr) = \sum_{m=0}^{\infty} \frac{(-1)^m (Tr/2)^{n+2m}}{m!\,(n + m)!}. \qquad (5)$$

A few of these functions are plotted in Fig. 3.26a. Similarly, a second independent solution[9] to the equation is

$$N_\nu(Tr) = \frac{\cos \nu\pi J_\nu(Tr) - J_{-\nu}(Tr)}{\sin \nu\pi}. \qquad (6)$$

As may be noted in Fig. 3.26b these are infinite at the origin. So a complete solution to (3) may be written,

$$R = AJ_\nu(Tr) + BN_\nu(Tr). \qquad (7)$$

The constant ν is known as the order of the equation. J_ν is then called a Bessel function of first kind, order ν; N_ν is a Bessel function of second kind, order ν. Of most interest for this chapter are cases in which $\nu = n$, an integer.

It is useful to keep in mind that, in the physical problem considered here, ν is the number of radians of the sinusoidal variation of the potential per radian of angle about the axis. For different applications of Bessel functions, ν has other significances.

The functions $J_\nu(v)$ and $N_\nu(v)$ are tabulated in the references.[10,11,12] Some care should be observed in using these references, for there is a wide variation in notation for the second solution, and not all the functions used are equivalent, since they differ in the values of arbitrary constants

[9] If ν is non-integral, $J_{-\nu}$ is not linearly related to J_ν, and it is then proper to use either $J_{-\nu}$ or N_ν as the second solution; for ν integral, N_ν must be used. Equation (6) is indeterminate for ν integral but is subject to evaluation by usual methods.
[10] E. Jahnke, F. Emde, and F. Lösch, *Tables of Higher Functions*, 6th ed. revised by F. Lösch, McGraw-Hill, New York, 1960.
[11] G. N. Watson, *Theory of Bessel Functions*, 2nd ed., Cambridge University Press, Macmillan, New York, 1944.
[12] N. W. McLACHLAN, *Bessel Functions for Engineers*, 2nd ed., Oxford Clarendon Press, New York, 1955.

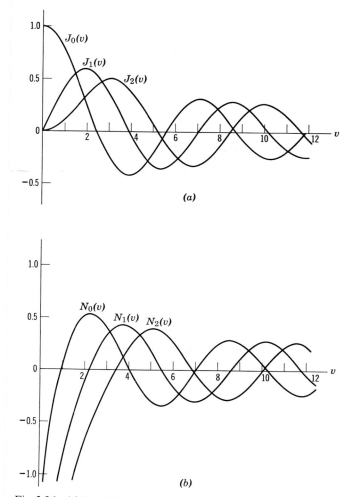

Fig. 3.26 (a) Bessel functions of the first kind. (b) Bessel functions of the second kind.

selected for the series. The $N_v(v)$ is chosen here because it is the form most common in current mathematical physics, and also the form most commonly tabulated. It is equivalent to the $Y_v(v)$ used by Watson and by McLachlan. Of course, it is quite proper to use any one of the second solutions throughout a given problem, since all the differences will be absorbed in the arbitrary constants of the problem, and the same final numerical result will always be obtained; but is is necessary to be consistent in the use of only one of these throughout any given analysis.

It is of interest to observe the similarity between (3) and the simple harmonic equation, the solutions of which are sinusoids. The difference between these two differential equations lies in the term $(1/r)(dR/dr)$ which produces its major effect as $r \to 0$. Note that for regions far removed from the axis as, for example, near the outer edge of Fig. 3.06a, the region bounded by surfaces of a cylindrical coordinate system approximate a cube. For these reasons, it may be expected that, away from the origin, the Bessel functions are similar to sinusoids. That this is true may be seen in Figs. 3.26a and b. For large values of the arguments, the Bessel functions approach sinusoids with magnitude decreasing as the square root of radius. For example,

$$J_\nu(Tr) \underset{Tr \to \infty}{=} \sqrt{\frac{2}{\pi T r}} \cos\left(Tr - \frac{\pi}{4} - \frac{\nu\pi}{2}\right)$$

and the second kind, $N_\nu(Tr)$ approaches a sine variation with the same argument.

Hankel Functions. It is sometimes convenient to take solutions to the simple harmonic equation in the form of complex exponentials rather than sinusoids. That is, the solution of

$$\frac{d^2Z}{dz^2} + K^2Z = 0 \tag{8}$$

can be written as

$$Z = Ae^{+jKz} + Be^{-jKz} \tag{9}$$

where

$$e^{\pm jKz} = \cos Kz \pm j \sin Kz. \tag{10}$$

Since the complex exponentials are linear combinations of cosine and sine functions, we may also write the general solution of (8) as

$$Z = A'e^{jKz} + B' \sin Kz$$

or other combinations.

Similarly, it is convenient to define new Bessel functions which are linear combinations of the $J_\nu(Tr)$ and $N_\nu(Tr)$ functions. By direct analogy with the definition (10) of the complex exponential, we write

$$H_\nu^{(1)}(Tr) = J_\nu(Tr) + jN_\nu(Tr) \tag{11}$$

$$H_\nu^{(2)}(Tr) = J_\nu(Tr) - jN_\nu(Tr). \tag{12}$$

These are called *Hankel functions* of the first and second kinds, respectively. Since they both contain the function $N_\nu(Tr)$, they are both singular at $r = 0$. For large values of the argument, these can be approximated by complex exponentials with magnitude decreasing as square root of radius. For example,

$$H_\nu^{(1)}(Tr) \underset{Tr \to \infty}{=} \sqrt{2/(\pi T r)}\, e^{j(Tr - \pi/4 - \nu\pi/2)}.$$

This asymptotic form suggests that Hankel functions may be useful in wave propagation problems, as the complex exponential was in wave propagation on transmission lines in Chapter 1. We shall see more of these functions applied to wave propagation problems in later chapters. It is also sometimes convenient to use Hankel functions as alternate independent solutions in static problems. Complete solutions of (3) may be written in a variety of ways using combinations of Bessel and Hankel functions.

Bessel and Hankel Functions of Imaginary Arguments. If T is imaginary, $T = j\tau$, as in Eq. 3.25(15), (3) becomes

$$\frac{d^2R}{dr^2} + \frac{1}{r}\frac{dR}{dr} - \left(\tau^2 + \frac{\nu^2}{r^2}\right)R = 0. \qquad (13)$$

The solution in (3) is valid here if T is replaced by $j\tau$ in the definitions of $J_\nu(Tr)$ and $N_\nu(Tr)$. In this case $N_\nu(j\tau r)$ is complex and so requires two numbers for each value of the argument whereas $j^{-\nu}J_\nu(j\tau r)$ is always a purely real number. It is convenient to replace $N_\nu(j\tau r)$ by a Hankel function. The quantity $j^{\nu-1}H_\nu^{(1)}(j\tau r)$ is also purely real and so requires tabulation of only one value for each value of the argument. If ν is not an integer, $j^\nu J_{-\nu}(j\tau r)$ is independent of $j^{-\nu}J_\nu(j\tau r)$ and may be used as a second solution. Thus, for nonintegral ν two possible complete solutions are

$$R = A_2 J_\nu(j\tau r) + B_2 J_{-\nu}(j\tau r) \qquad (14)$$

and
$$R = A_3 J_\nu(j\tau r) + B_3 H_\nu^{(1)}(j\tau r) \qquad (15)$$

where powers of j are included in the constants. For $\nu = n$, an integer, the two solutions in (14) are not independent but (15) is still a valid solution.

It is common practice to denote these solutions as

$$I_{\pm\nu}(v) = j^{\mp\nu}J_{\pm\nu}(jv) \qquad (16)$$

$$K_\nu(v) = \frac{\pi}{2} j^{\nu+1}H_\nu^{(1)}(jv), \qquad (17)$$

where $v = \tau r$.

As is noted in Art. 3.27 some of the formulas relating Bessel functions and Hankel functions must be changed for these *modified* Bessel functions. Special cases of these functions were seen as $I_0(\tau r)$ and $K_0(\tau r)$ in Art. 3.25 for the axially symmetric field. The forms of $I_\nu(\tau r)$ and $K_\nu(\tau r)$ for $\nu = 0, 1$ are shown in Fig. 3.26c. As is suggested by these curves, the asymptotic forms of the modified Bessel functions are related to growing and decaying real exponentials. For example,

$$K_\nu(\tau r) \underset{\tau r \to \infty}{\longrightarrow} \sqrt{\frac{\pi}{2\tau r}}\, e^{-\tau r}.$$

It is also clear from the figure that $K_\nu(\tau r)$ is singular at the origin.

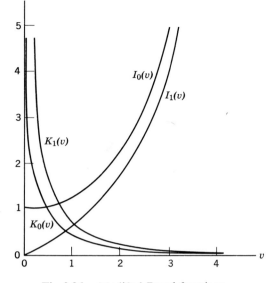

Fig. 3.26c   Modified Bessel functions.

3.27 Bessel Function Formulas

Asymptotic Forms.

$$J_\nu(v) \underset{v \to \infty}{\longrightarrow} \sqrt{\frac{2}{\pi v}} \cos\left(v - \frac{\pi}{4} - \frac{\nu\pi}{2}\right) \tag{1}$$

$$N_\nu(v) \underset{v \to \infty}{\longrightarrow} \sqrt{\frac{2}{\pi v}} \sin\left(v - \frac{\pi}{4} - \frac{\nu\pi}{2}\right) \tag{2}$$

$$H_\nu^{(1)}(v) \underset{v \to \infty}{\longrightarrow} \sqrt{\frac{2}{\pi v}} \, e^{j[v - (\pi/4) - (\nu\pi/2)]} \tag{3}$$

$$H_\nu^{(2)}(v) \underset{v \to \infty}{\longrightarrow} \sqrt{\frac{2}{\pi v}} \, e^{-j[v - (\pi/4) - (\nu\pi/2)]} \tag{4}$$

$$j^{-\nu} J_\nu(jv) = I_\nu(v) \underset{v \to \infty}{\longrightarrow} \sqrt{\frac{1}{2\pi v}} \, e^{v} \tag{5}$$

$$j^{\nu+1} H_\nu^{(1)}(jv) = \frac{2}{\pi} K_\nu(v) \underset{v \to \infty}{\longrightarrow} \sqrt{\frac{2}{\pi v}} \, e^{-v} \tag{6}$$

Derivatives. The following formulas which may be found by differentiating the appropriate series, term by term, are valid for any of the functions $J_\nu(v)$, $N_\nu(v)$, $H_\nu^{(1)}(v)$, $H_\nu^{(2)}(v)$. Let $R_\nu(v)$ denote any one of these, and R'_ν denote $(d/dv)[R_\nu(v)]$.

$$R'_0(v) = -R_1(v) \tag{7}$$

$$R'_1(v) = R_0(v) - \frac{1}{v}R_1(v) \tag{8}$$

$$vR'_\nu(v) = \nu R_\nu(v) - vR_{\nu+1}(v) \tag{9}$$

$$vR'_\nu(v) = -\nu R_\nu(v) + vR_{\nu-1}(v) \tag{10}$$

$$\frac{d}{dv}\,[v^{-\nu}R_\nu(v)] = -v^{-\nu}R_{\nu+1}(v) \tag{11}$$

$$\frac{d}{dv}\,[v^{\nu}R_\nu(v)] = v^{\nu}R_{\nu-1}(v) \tag{12}$$

Note that

$$R'_\nu(Tr) = \frac{d}{d(Tr)}\,[R_\nu(Tr)] = \frac{1}{T}\frac{d}{dr}\,[R_\nu(Tr)]. \tag{13}$$

For the I and K functions different forms for the foregoing derivatives must be used. They may be obtained from these formulas by substituting Eqs. 3.26(16) and 3.26(17) in the preceding expressions. Some of these are

$$vI'_\nu(v) = \nu I_\nu(v) + vI_{\nu+1}(v)$$
$$vI'_\nu(v) = -\nu I_\nu(v) + vI_{\nu-1}(v) \tag{14}$$

$$vK'_\nu(v) = \nu K_\nu(v) - vK_{\nu+1}(v)$$
$$vK'_\nu(v) = -\nu K_\nu(v) - vK_{\nu-1}(v) \tag{15}$$

Recurrence Formulas. By recurrence formulas, it is possible to obtain the value for Bessel functions of any order, when the values of functions for any two other orders, differing from the first by integers, are known. For example, subtract (10) from (9). The result may be written

$$\frac{2\nu}{v}R_\nu(v) = R_{\nu+1}(v) + R_{\nu-1}(v). \tag{16}$$

As before, R_ν may denote J_ν, N_ν, $H_\nu^{(1)}$, $H_\nu^{(2)}$, but not I_ν or K_ν. For these, the recurrence formulas are

$$\frac{2\nu}{v}I_\nu(v) = I_{\nu-1}(v) - I_{\nu+1}(v) \tag{17}$$

$$\frac{2\nu}{v}K_\nu(v) = K_{\nu+1}(v) - K_{\nu-1}(v). \tag{18}$$

Integrals. Integrals that will be useful in solving later problems are given below. R_ν denotes J_ν, N_ν, $H_\nu^{(1)}$, or $H_\nu^{(2)}$:

$$\int v^{-\nu} R_{\nu+1}(v)\, dv = -v^{-\nu} R_\nu(v) \qquad (19)$$

$$\int v^\nu R_{\nu-1}(v)\, dv = v^\nu R_\nu(v) \qquad (20)$$

$$\int v R_\nu(\alpha v) R_\nu(\beta v)\, dv$$

$$= \frac{v}{\alpha^2 - \beta^2} [\beta R_\nu(\alpha v) R_{\nu-1}(\beta v) - \alpha R_{\nu-1}(\alpha v) R_\nu(\beta v)], \qquad \alpha \neq \beta \quad (21)$$

$$\int v R_\nu{}^2(\alpha v)\, dv = \frac{v^2}{2} [R_\nu{}^2(\alpha v) - R_{\nu-1}(\alpha v) R_{\nu+1}(\alpha v)]$$

$$= \frac{v^2}{2} \left[R_\nu'^2(\alpha v) + \left(1 - \frac{v^2}{\alpha^2 v^2} \right) R_\nu{}^2(\alpha v) \right]. \qquad (22)$$

3.28 Expansion of a Function as a Series of Bessel Functions

In Chapter 1 a study was made of the familiar method of Fourier series by which a function may be expressed over a given region as a series of sines or cosines. It is possible to evaluate the coefficients in such a case because of the orthogonality property of sinusoids, expressed in Art. 1.10. A study of the integrals, Eqs. 3.27(21) and 3.27(22), shows that there are similar orthogonality expressions for Bessel functions. For example, these integrals may be written for zero-order Bessel functions, and, if α and β are taken as p_m/a and p_q/a, where p_m and p_q are the mth and qth roots of $J_0(v) = 0$, that is, $J_0(p_m) = 0$ and $J_0(p_q) = 0$, $p_m \neq p_q$, then Eq. 3.27(21) gives

$$\int_0^a r J_0\left(\frac{p_m r}{a}\right) J_0\left(\frac{p_q r}{a}\right) dr = 0. \qquad (1)$$

So, if a function $f(r)$ may be expressed as an infinite sum of zero-order Bessel functions,

$$f(r) = b_1 J_0\left(p_1 \frac{r}{a}\right) + b_2 J_0\left(p_2 \frac{r}{a}\right) + b_3 J_0\left(p_3 \frac{r}{a}\right) + \cdots$$

or

$$f(r) = \sum_{m=1}^{\infty} b_m J_0\left(\frac{p_m r}{a}\right). \qquad (2)$$

The coefficients b_m may be evaluated in a manner similar to that used for Fourier coefficients by multiplying each term of (2) by $r J_0(p_m r/a)$ and integrating from 0 to a. Then by (1) all terms on the right disappear except the mth term:

$$\int_0^a rf(r)J_0\left(\frac{p_m r}{a}\right) dr = \int_0^a b_m r \left[J_0\left(\frac{p_m r}{a}\right)\right]^2 dr.$$

From Eq. 3.27(22),

$$\int_0^a rJ_0^2\left(\frac{p_m r}{a}\right) dr = \frac{a^2}{2} J_1^2(p_m). \qquad (3)$$

So

$$\int_0^a rf(r)J_0\left(\frac{p_m r}{a}\right) dr = \frac{b_m a^2}{2} J_1^2(p_m)$$

or

$$b_m = \frac{2}{a^2 J_1^2(p_m)} \int_0^a rf(r)J_0\left(\frac{p_m r}{a}\right) dr. \qquad (4)$$

Thus a formula for the coefficients of the series (2) is derived. A mathematical study of the subject would be concerned with showing that the series thus formally derived actually does converge to the desired function over the range of interest. Such a discussion is outside the range of this text, but the results of such studies show that completeness and convergence requirements are met, so that such a series may be used to represent any piecewise continuous function over the range $0 < r < a$.

Problems

3.28a Write a function $f(r)$ in terms of nth order Bessel functions over the range 0 to a and determine the coefficients.

3.28b Determine coefficients for a function $f(r)$ expressed over the range 0 to a as a series of zero-order Bessel functions as follows:

$$f(r) = \sum_{m=1}^{\infty} c_m J_0\left(\frac{p_m' r}{a}\right)$$

where p_m' denotes the mth root of $J_0'(v) = 0$ [i.e., $J_1(v) = 0$].

3.29 Fields Described by Cylindrical Harmonics

We will consider here the two basic types of boundary value problems which exist in axially symmetric cylindrical systems. These can be understood by reference to Fig. 3.29a. In one type both Φ_1 and Φ_2, the potentials on the ends, are zero and a non-zero potential Φ_3 is applied to the cylindrical surface. In the second type $\Phi_3 = 0$ and either (or both) Φ_1 or Φ_2 are non-zero. The gaps between ends and side are considered negligibly

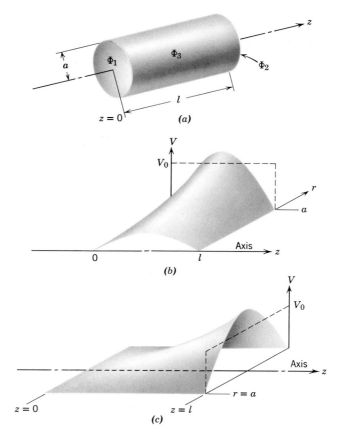

Fig. 3.29 (a) Cylinder with conducting boundaries. (b) One harmonic component for matching boundary conditions when non-zero potential is applied to cylindrical surface in (a). (c) One harmonic component for matching boundary conditions when non-zero potential is applied to end surface in (a).

small. For simplicity, the non-zero potentials will be taken to be independent of the coordinate along the surface. In the first type, a Fourier series of sinusoids is used to expand the boundary potentials as was done in the rectangular problems. In the second situation, a series of Bessel functions is used to expand the boundary potential along the radial coordinate.

Non-Zero Potential on Cylindrical Surface. Since the boundary potentials are axially symmetric, zero-order Bessel functions should be used. The repeated zeros along the z coordinate dictate the use of sinusoidal functions of z. The potential in Eq. 3.25(21) is the appropriate form.

Certain of the constants can be evaluated immediately. Since $K_0(\tau r)$ is singular on the axis, C_2' must be identically zero to give a finite potential there. The $\cos \tau z$ equals unity at $z = 0$ but the potential must be zero there so $C_4' = 0$. As in the problem discussed in Art. 3.22, the repeated zeros at $z = l$ requires that $\tau = m\pi/l$. Therefore the general harmonic which fits all boundary conditions except $\Phi = V_0$ at $r = a$ is

$$\Phi_m = A_m I_0\left(\frac{m\pi r}{l}\right) \sin\left(\frac{m\pi z}{l}\right).$$

Figure 3.29b shows a sketch of this harmonic for $m = 1$ and the boundary potential on the cylinder. It is clear that we have here the problem of expanding the boundary potential in sinusoids just as in the rectangular problem of Art. 3.23. Following the procedure used there we obtain

$$\Phi(r, z) = \sum_{m \text{ odd}} \frac{4V_0}{m\pi} \frac{I_0(m\pi r/l)}{I_0(m\pi a/l)} \sin \frac{m\pi z}{l}.$$

Non-Zero Potential on End. In this situation, if we refer to Fig. 3.29a, we see that $\Phi_1 = \Phi_3 = 0$ and $\Phi_2 = V_0$. In selecting the proper form for the solution from Art. 3.25, the boundary condition that $\Phi = 0$ at $r = a$ for all values of z indicates that the R function must become zero at $r = a$. Thus we select the J_0 functions since the I_0's do not ever become zero. (The corresponding second solution, N_0, does not appear since potential must remain finite on the axis.) The value of T in Eq. 3.25(20) is determined from the condition that $\Phi = 0$ at $r = a$ for all values of z. Thus, if p_m is the mth root of $J_0(v) = 0$, T must be p_m/a. The corresponding solution for Z is in hyperbolic functions, Eq. 3.25(20), but the coefficient of the hyperbolic cosine term must be zero since Φ is zero at $z = 0$ for all values of r. Thus a sum of all cylindrical harmonics with arbitrary amplitudes which satisfy the symmetry of the problem and the boundary conditions so far imposed may be written

$$\Phi = \sum_{m=1}^{\infty} B_m J_0\left(\frac{p_m r}{a}\right) \sinh\left(\frac{p_m z}{a}\right). \tag{1}$$

One of the harmonics and the required boundary potentials are shown in Fig. 3.29c.

The remaining condition is that, at $z = l$, $\Phi = 0$ at $r = a$, and $\Phi = V_0$ for all other r's. To use this condition it seems advisable to expand such a function over this plane in terms of Bessel functions as in Eq. 3.28(2). For the coefficients, Eq. 3.28(4) is used with $f(r) = 0$ at $r = a$ and $f(r) = V_0$ for $0 < r < a$. Then

$$b_m = \frac{2}{a^2 J_1^2(p_m)} \int_0^a r V_0 J_0\left(\frac{p_m r}{a}\right) dr = \frac{2V_0}{p_m J_1(p_m)}.$$

The above integral was evaluated by Eq. 3.27(20). So

$$f(r) = \Phi\big|_{z=l} = \sum_{m=1}^{\infty} \frac{2V_0}{p_m J_1(p_m)} J_0\left(\frac{p_m r}{a}\right). \tag{2}$$

But (1) at $z = l$ is

$$\Phi\big|_{z=l} = \sum_{m=1}^{\infty} B_m \sinh\left(\frac{p_m l}{a}\right) J_0\left(\frac{p_m r}{a}\right). \tag{3}$$

Equations (2) and (3) must be equivalent for all values of r. Consequently, coefficients of corresponding terms of $J_0(p_m r/a)$ must be equal. The constant B_m is now completely determined, and the potential at any point inside the region is

$$\Phi = \sum_{m=1}^{\infty} \frac{2V_0}{p_m J_1(p_m) \sinh(p_m l/a)} \sinh\left(\frac{p_m z}{a}\right) J_0\left(\frac{p_m r}{a}\right). \tag{4}$$

Problems

3.29a Find the series for potential inside the cylindrical region with end plates $z = 0$ and $z = l$ at potential zero, and the cylinder of radius a in two parts. From $z = 0$ to $z = l/2$, it is at potential V_0; from $z = l/2$ to $z = l$, it is at potential $-V_0$.

3.29b The problem is as in Prob. 3.29a except that the cylinder is divided in three parts with potential zero from $z = 0$ to $z = b$ and also from $z = l - b$ to $z = l$. Potential is V_0 from $z = b$ to $z = l - b$.

3.29c Write the general formula for obtaining potential inside a cylindrical region of radius a, with two zero-potential end plates at $z = 0$ and $z = l$, provided potential is given as $\Phi = f(z)$ at $r = a$.

3.29d Suppose that the end plate at $z = l$ of Fig. 3.29a is divided into insulated rings and connected to sources in such a way that the potential approximates a single J_0 function of radius. That is,

$$\Phi(r, l) = C J_0\left(\frac{p_1 r}{a}\right).$$

The end plate at $z = 0$ is at potential zero. Write the solution for $\Phi(r, z)$ at any point inside the cylindrical region.

3.29e Write the general formula for obtaining potential inside a cylinder of radius a which, with its plane base at $z = 0$, is at potential zero, provided that the potential is given across some plane surface at $z = l$, as

$$\Phi(r, l) = f(r).$$

3.30 Spherical Harmonics

Consider next Laplace's equation in spherical coordinates for regions with symmetry about the axis so that variations with azimuthal angle ϕ

may be neglected. Laplace's equation in the two remaining spherical coordinates r and θ then becomes (inside cover)

$$\frac{\partial^2(r\Phi)}{\partial r^2} + \frac{1}{r \sin \theta} \frac{\partial}{\partial \theta}\left(\sin \theta \frac{\partial \Phi}{\partial \theta}\right) = 0 \tag{1}$$

or

$$r\frac{\partial^2 \Phi}{\partial r^2} + 2\frac{\partial \Phi}{\partial r} + \frac{1}{r}\frac{\partial^2 \Phi}{\partial \theta^2} + \frac{1}{r \tan \theta}\frac{\partial \Phi}{\partial \theta} = 0. \tag{2}$$

Assume a product solution,

$$\Phi = R\Theta$$

where R is a function of r alone, Θ of θ alone,

$$rR''\Theta + 2R'\Theta + \frac{1}{r}R\Theta'' + \frac{1}{r \tan \theta}R\Theta' = 0$$

and

$$\frac{r^2 R''}{R} + \frac{2rR'}{R} = -\frac{\Theta''}{\Theta} - \frac{\Theta'}{\Theta \tan \theta}. \tag{3}$$

From the previous logic, if the two sides of the equations are to be equal to each other for all values of r and θ, both sides can be equal only to a constant. Since the constant may be expressed in any nonrestrictive way, let it be $m(m + 1)$. The two resulting ordinary differential equations are then

$$r^2\frac{d^2 R}{dr^2} + 2r\frac{dR}{dr} - m(m + 1)R = 0 \tag{4}$$

$$\frac{d^2\Theta}{d\theta^2} + \frac{1}{\tan \theta}\frac{d\Theta}{d\theta} + m(m + 1)\Theta = 0. \tag{5}$$

Equation (4) has a solution which is easily verified to be

$$R = C_1 r^m + C_2 r^{-(m+1)}. \tag{6}$$

A solution to (5) in terms of simple functions is not obvious, so, as with the Bessel equation, a series solution may be assumed. The coefficients of this series must be determined so that the differential equation (5) is satisfied and the resulting series made to define a new function. There is one departure here from an exact analogue with the Bessel functions, for it turns out that a proper selection of the arbitrary constants will make the series for the new function terminate in a finite number of terms if m is an integer. Thus, for any integer m, the polynomial defined by

$$P_m(\cos \theta) = \frac{1}{2^m m!}\left[\frac{d}{d(\cos \theta)}\right]^m(\cos^2 \theta - 1)^m \tag{7}$$

is a solution to the differential equation (5). The equation is known as Legendre's equation; the solutions are called Legendre polynomials of order m. Their forms for the first few values of m are tabulated below and are shown in Fig. 3.30. It is evident that, since they are polynomials

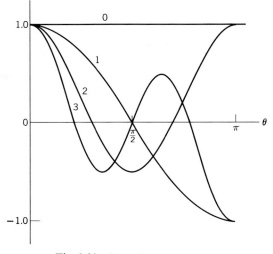

Fig. 3.30   Legendre polynomials

and not infinite series, their values can be calculated exactly if desired, but values of the polynomials are also tabulated in many references.

$$P_0(\cos \theta) = 1$$

$$P_1(\cos \theta) = \cos \theta$$

$$P_2(\cos \theta) = \tfrac{1}{2}(3 \cos^2 \theta - 1) \tag{8}$$

$$P_3(\cos \theta) = \tfrac{1}{2}(5 \cos^3 \theta - 3 \cos \theta)$$

$$P_4(\cos \theta) = \tfrac{1}{8}(35 \cos^4 \theta - 30 \cos^2 \theta + 3)$$

$$P_5(\cos \theta) = \tfrac{1}{8}(63 \cos^5 \theta - 70 \cos^3 \theta + 15 \cos \theta)$$

It is recognized that $\Theta = C_1 P_m(\cos \theta)$ is only one solution to the second-order differential equation (5). There must be a second independent solution, which may be obtained in a similar manner, but it turns out that this solution becomes infinite for $\theta = 0$. Consequently it will never be present for any case in which the axis of spherical coordinates is included in the region over which the solution applies. Several important situations require their use, however; when this occurs certain of the references[13] should be consulted.

An orthogonality relation for Legendre polynomials is quite similar to those for sinusoids and Bessel functions which led to the Fourier series and expansion in Bessel functions respectively.

$$\int_0^\pi P_m(\cos\theta)P_n(\cos\theta)\sin\theta\,d\theta = 0, \qquad m \neq n \qquad (9)$$

$$\int_0^\pi [P_m(\cos\theta)]^2 \sin\theta\,d\theta = \frac{2}{2m+1}. \qquad (10)$$

It follows that, if a function $f(\theta)$ defined between the limits of 0 to π is written as a series of Legendre polynomials,

$$f(\theta) = \sum_{m=0}^\infty \alpha_m P_m(\cos\theta), \qquad 0 < \theta < \pi \qquad (11)$$

the coefficients must be given by the formula

$$\alpha_m = \frac{2m+1}{2}\int_0^\pi f(\theta)P_m(\cos\theta)\sin\theta\,d\theta. \qquad (12)$$

Problem

3.30 Apply the separation of variables technique to Laplace's equation in the three spherical coordinates r, θ, and ϕ, obtaining the three resulting ordinary differential equations. Write solutions to the r equation and the ϕ equation. (Solutions to the θ equation are discussed in Chapter 10.)

3.31 Example of Use of Spherical Harmonics; High-Permeability Sphere in Uniform Field

We will examine the field distribution in and around a sphere of permeability $\mu \neq \mu_0$ when it is placed in an otherwise uniform magnetic field in free space. The uniform field is disturbed by the sphere as indicated in Fig. 3.31. The reason for choosing this example is threefold. It shows, first of all, an application of spherical harmonics. Second, it is an example of a situation in which the constants in series solutions for two regions are evaluated by matching across a boundary. Finally, it is an example of a magnetic boundary-value problem.

[13] E.g., W. R. Smythe, *Static and Dynamic Electricity*, Second Edition, McGraw-Hill, New York (1950), and E. W. Hobson, *Spherical and Ellipsoidal Harmonics*, Cambridge (1931).

Since there are no currents in the region to be studied, we may use the scalar magnetic potential introduced in Art. 2.34. The magnetic intensity is given by

$$\bar{H} = -\nabla\Phi_m. \tag{1}$$

As the problem is axially symmetric and the axis is included in the region

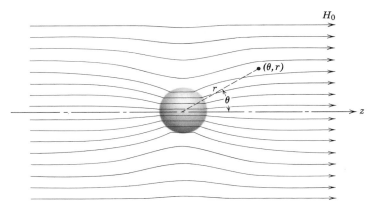

Fig. 3.31   Sphere of magnetic material in otherwise uniform magnetic field.

of interest, the solutions $P_m(\cos\theta)$ discussed in Art. 3.30 are applicable. The series solutions with these restrictions are

$$\Phi_m(r, \theta) = \sum_m P_m(\cos\theta)[C_{1m}r^m + C_{2m}r^{-(m+1)}]. \tag{2}$$

The procedure is to write general forms for the potential inside and outside the sphere and match these across the boundary. Since the potential must remain finite at $r = 0$, the coefficients of the negative powers of r must vanish. The series becomes, for the inside region,

$$\Phi_m = \sum_m A_m r^m P_m(\cos\theta). \tag{3}$$

Outside, the potential must be such that it gives a uniform magnetic field H_0 at infinity. The potential form which satisfies this condition is

$$\Phi_m = -H_0 r \cos\theta. \tag{4}$$

That this gives a uniform field may be seen by noting that $dz = dr\cos\theta$ so

$$H_z = -\frac{\partial\Phi_m}{\partial z} = \frac{1}{\cos\theta}\frac{\partial\Phi_m}{\partial r} = H_0.$$

Terms of the series (2) having negative powers of r may be added to (4), since they all vanish at infinity. Then the form of the solution outside the sphere is

$$\Phi_m = -H_0 r \cos \theta + \sum_m B_m P_m(\cos \theta) r^{-(m+1)}. \tag{5}$$

It was pointed out in Art. 2.35 that Φ_m is continuous across boundaries without surface currents. Therefore, the terms in (3) and (5) having the same form of θ dependence are equated, giving

$$A_0 = B_0 a^{-1} \qquad\qquad m = 0$$
$$A_1 a = B_1 a^{-2} - H_0 a \qquad m = 1$$
$$\vdots$$
$$\vdots \tag{6}$$
$$\vdots$$
$$A_m a^m = B_m a^{-(m+1)} \qquad m > 1.$$

Furthermore, the normal flux density is continuous at the boundary so

$$\mu_0 \frac{\partial \Phi_m}{\partial r}\bigg|_{r=a+} = \mu \frac{\partial \Phi_m}{\partial r}\bigg|_{r=a-}. \tag{7}$$

Substituting (3) and (5) in (7) and equating terms with the same θ dependence, we find

$$B_0 = 0 \qquad\qquad\qquad m = 0$$
$$\mu A_1 = -2\mu_0 B_1 a^{-3} - \mu_0 H_0 \qquad m = 1$$
$$\vdots$$
$$\vdots \tag{8}$$
$$\mu m A_m a^{m-1} = -\mu_0(m+1)B_m a^{-(m+2)} \qquad m > 1.$$

From (6) and (8) we see that $A_0 = B_0 = 0$, and that for $m > 1$, all coefficients must be zero to satisfy the two sets of conditions. The only remaining terms are those with $m = 1$. These two equations may be solved to give A_1 and B_1 in terms of H_0. Substituting the results in (5) gives

$$\Phi_m = \left[\left(\frac{\mu - \mu_0}{2\mu_0 + \mu} \right) r - 1 \right] H_0 r \cos \theta, \tag{9}$$

from which $\bar{H}$ can be found by using (1) for $r > a$. Substitution of A_1 and B_1 into (3) gives for $r < a$

$$\Phi_m = -\left(\frac{3\mu_0}{2\mu_0 + \mu} \right) H_0 r \cos \theta. \tag{10}$$

Applying (1), we find the field inside to be

$$\bar{H} = \bar{a}_z \left(\frac{3\mu_0}{2\mu_0 + \mu} \right) H_0. \tag{11}$$

It is of interest to observe that the field inside the homogeneous sphere is uniform. Finally, multiplication of (11) by μ gives the flux density

$$\bar{B} = \bar{a}_z \left(\frac{3}{2(\mu_0/\mu) + 1} \right) B_0. \tag{12}$$

From (12) we see that for $\mu \gg \mu_0$ the maximum possible value of the flux density is

$$\bar{B} = \bar{a}_z 3 B_0. \tag{13}$$

Problems

3.31a Assume a spherical surface split into two thin hemispherical shells with a small gap between them. Assume a potential V_0 on one hemisphere and zero on the other and find the potential distribution in the surrounding space.

3.31b Write the general formula for obtaining potential for $r < a$ and for $r > a$, when potential is given as a general function $f(\theta)$ over a thin spherical shell at $r = a$.

3.31c The result (11) of this article may be obtained using the demagnetization factor mentioned in Art. 2.40. Determine the demagnetization relation analogous to Eq. 2.40(10) which will lead to equation (11). Assume the values of N_d in the table of Art. 2.40 also apply to demagnetization factors N_m and choose directions of magnetic field components to correspond to the directions used in Fig. 2.40e.

3.32 Expansion in Spherical Harmonics when Field Is Given along an Axis

It is often relatively simple to obtain the field or potential along an axis of symmetry by direct application of fundamental laws, yet difficult to obtain it at any point off this axis by the same technique. Once field is found along an axis of symmetry, expansions in spherical harmonics give its value at any other point. Thus, if potential, or any component of field which satisfies Laplace's equation, is given for every point along an axis in such a form that it may be expanded in a power series in z, the distance along this axis,

$$\Phi\big|_{\text{axis}} = \sum_{m=0}^{\infty} b_m z^m, \qquad 0 < z < a. \tag{1}$$

If this axis is taken as the axis of spherical coordinates, $\theta = 0$, the potential off the axis may be written

$$\Phi(r, \theta) = \sum_{m=0}^{\infty} b_m r^m P_m(\cos \theta). \tag{2}$$

This is true since it is a solution of Laplace's equation (Art. 3.30) and does reduce to the given potential (1) for $\theta = 0$ where all $P_m(\cos \theta)$ are unity.

If potential is desired outside of this region, the potential along the axis must be expanded in a power series good for $a < z < \infty$.

$$\Phi|_{\theta=0} = \sum_{m=1}^{\infty} c_m z^{-(m+1)}, \qquad z > a. \tag{3}$$

Then Φ at any point outside is given by comparison with the second series of Eq. 3.31(2).

$$\Phi = \sum_{m=0}^{\infty} c_m P_m(\cos \theta) r^{-(m+1)}, \qquad r > a. \tag{4}$$

For example, the magnetic field H_z was found along the axis of a circular loop of wire carrying current I in Art. 2.24 as

$$H_z = \frac{a^2 I}{2(a^2 + z^2)^{3/2}} = \frac{I}{2a[1 + (z^2/a^2)]^{3/2}}. \tag{5}$$

The binomial expansion

$$(1 + u)^{-3/2} = 1 - \tfrac{3}{2}u + \tfrac{15}{8}u^2 - \tfrac{105}{48}u^3 + \cdots$$

is good for $0 < |u| < 1$. Applied to (5), this gives

$$H_z|_{\text{axis}} = \frac{I}{2a}\left[1 - \frac{3}{2}\left(\frac{z^2}{a^2}\right) + \frac{15}{8}\left(\frac{z^2}{a^2}\right)^2 - \frac{105}{48}\left(\frac{z^2}{a^2}\right)^3 + \cdots\right].$$

Since H_z, axial component of magnetic field, satisfies Laplace's equation (Art. 3.02), H_z at any point r, θ with $r < a$ is given by

$$H_z(r, \theta) = \frac{I}{2a}\left[1 - \frac{3}{2}\left(\frac{r^2}{a^2}\right)P_2(\cos \theta) + \frac{15}{8}\left(\frac{r^4}{a^4}\right)P_4(\cos \theta) + \cdots\right] \tag{6}$$

Problems

3.32a For the example given in this article, write the series for H_z at any point r, θ with $r > a$.

3.32b A Helmholtz coil is used to obtain very nearly uniform magnetic field over a region through the use of coils of large radius compared with coil cross sections. Consider two such coaxial coils, each of radius a, one lying in the plane $z = d$, and the other in the plane $z = -d$. Take the current for each coil (considered as a single turn) as I. Obtain the series for H_z applicable to a region containing the origin, writing specific forms for the first three coefficients. Show that, if $a = 2d$, the first non-zero coefficient (other than the constant term) is the coefficient of r^4.

TABLE 3.33

Method	Symmetries Required of Electrode System	Comments
1. Gauss' Law	Planar, spherical, or cylindrical	Charge distribution must have the symmetries of the electrodes.
2. Images	(a) Point charges—spherical planar (b) Line charges—cylindrical planar (c) Sheet charges—planar	Possible to treat combinations of electrode shapes not on surfaces of same coordinate system by multiple images.
3. Field mapping by trial-and-error sketching	Uniform in one rectangular coordinate. Cylindrical symmetry only with difficulty.	
4. Finite-difference equations	None	*
5. Continuous solid resistance analog	Uniform in one rectangular coordinate or axial symmetry.	
6. Electrolytic tank	None	*
7. Resistance network analog	None	*
8. Conformal transformations	Uniform in one rectangular coordinate.	Laplace's equation only.
9. Separation of variables (Product solutions)	Boundary potentials must be specified on coordinate planes of one of eleven coordinate systems.	Solution of Poisson's equation by super-position may involve integrals which must be evaluated numerically.

* These methods do not, in principle, require any special symmetries but are generally used only for problems with either axial symmetry or uniformity in one rectangular coordinate for practical reasons.

3.33 Review of Methods for Solving Static Field Problems

In all the methods listed in Table 3.33 it is possible, in principle, to obtain solutions for the fields including the effect of space charge by methods of superposition. In some, practical difficulties obviate application of the method for solutions of Poisson's equation as is indicated in the column of comments.

Other advanced techniques not treated in this text may be found, for example, in the following references:

Principles and Techniques of Applied Mathematics, B. Friedman, John Wiley and Sons, New York, 1956.

Static and Dynamic Electricity, W. R. Smythe, McGraw-Hill, New York, 1950.

Foundations of Potential Theory, O. D. Kellog, Dover, New York, 1953.

4 MAXWELL'S EQUATIONS

THE LAWS OF TIME-VARIABLE ELECTROMAGNETIC PHENOMENA

4.01 Introduction

When the subject material of Chapter 2 was introduced, the objective was stated to be the derivation of a group of equations which would contain a description of fields due to static charges and static currents. It was claimed that in the solution of problems it would be well to have several forms for the statement of fundamental laws so that the most convenient might be chosen for the problem at hand. A number of the techniques involved in this process of selection of equations and their subsequent solution were discussed in Chapters 2 and 3.

In a similar way, an attempt will now be made to present the more complex theory that underlies electric and magnetic effects that vary with time. Of course, some of this theory is only an extension of the static theory. But the additional effects brought in by the varying of charges and currents give rise to some entirely different physical phenomena, and may require different mathematical tools for treatment. In this chapter, a consistent set of equations describing varying electric and magnetic effects will be obtained and applied to some important examples. This material will serve as a basis for several subsequent chapters in which the equations will be applied to practical field and wave problems.

4.02 Voltages Induced by Changing Magnetic Fields

Faraday discovered experimentally that, when the magnetic flux linking a closed circuit is altered, a voltage is induced in that circuit proportional to the rate of change of flux linking the circuit. This law is an experimental law of electricity and magnetism that requires little generalization to be

widely useful. In the consideration of most circuits and electrical machinery
it is necessary only to write

$$V = n \frac{d\psi}{dt} \qquad (1)$$

where V is the voltage induced in a coil having n turns, and ψ is the
flux linking the coil. The equation may be used directly to find the
voltage induced by a generator coil moving in a magnetic field that
varies with space, or to calculate the impedance
presented by a coil to an alternating voltage. In
ordinary circuit and machine problems, Faraday's
law is ordinarily applied to circuits taken along conductors. One important generalization is to an
electromotive force about any closed path in space.
This is indicated by the fact that the resistance of
the path does not enter into the law, so that it seems
logical that the law could be extended to an infinite
resistance path. Perhaps the most graphic illustration of this fact comes
from the betatron,[1] which accelerates charged particles in vacuum by means
of an electric field induced by a changing magnetic field, as predicted by
Faraday's law.

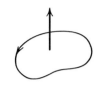

Fig. 4.02   Right-hand
sense   relation.

   If the electromotive force about any closed path, whether in space, in
dielectrics, along conductors, or any combination of these, is defined as the
line integral of electric field about that path,

$$\mathrm{emf} = \oint \bar{E} \cdot \overline{dl}$$

it is equal by Faraday's law to the (negative) time rate of change of magnetic
flux flowing through that path. The magnetic flux may be evaluated by
taking the integral of the normal component of magnetic flux density $\bar{B}$
over any surface which has the desired path as a boundary. Then

$$\oint \bar{E} \cdot \overline{dl} = -\frac{\partial}{\partial t} \int_s \bar{B} \cdot \overline{dS}. \qquad (2)$$

The negative sign is introduced so that the law is correct when the line
integral is taken in the usual positive sense of circulation about the path
with respect to the positive direction of flow through the surface. This is
obtainable by the usual right-hand rule, and is indicated in Fig. 4.02. The
partial derivative with time is used to distinguish it from variations in
space, indicating that the law as written refers to a fixed region in space.

[1] D. W. Kerst and R. Serber, "Electronic Orbits in the Induction Accelerator," *Phys. Rev.* **60**, 53 (1941).

To transform to the differential equation form, refer to Stokes's theorem, Art. 2.29. Applied to (2),

$$\oint \bar{E} \cdot \overline{dl} = \int_S (\nabla \times \bar{E}) \cdot \overline{dS} = -\frac{\partial}{\partial t} \int_S \bar{B} \cdot \overline{dS}.$$

If this equation is to be true for any surface, the integrands of the surface integrals must be equal, and we have the differential equation form of Faraday's law:

$$\nabla \times \bar{E} = -\frac{\partial \bar{B}}{\partial t}. \tag{3}$$

Since the line integral of electric field about a closed path need not be zero for a time-varying field, work may be done in taking a charge about a closed path in such a field. The principle of energy conservation is of course not violated, for the energy comes from that in the changing magnetic fields.

Problems

4.02a The betatron makes use of the electric field produced by a time-varying magnetic field in space to accelerate charged particles. Suppose that the magnetic field of a betatron has an axial component in cylindrical coordinates which is a function of r but not of ϕ:

$$H_z = f(r, t).$$

Find the induced electric field in magnitude and direction at radius r. Find the specific form for electric field when $f(r, t)$ is given over an interval of time by

$$f(r, t) = Ctr^{-n}.$$

4.02b In an air gap between magnet poles having parallel-plane faces of circular cross section, magnetic field builds up linearly with time. Find the maximum allowed rate of change of the field if breakdown in the air is to be avoided. The breakdown field in air at normal conditions is about 3×10^6 volt/meter, and the pole radii are 0.1 meter.

4.03 Continuity of Charge

Faraday's law is but one of the fundamental laws for changing fields. Let us assume for the moment that certain of the laws derived for static fields in Chapter 2 can be extended simply to time-varying fields. We will write the divergence of electric and magnetic fields in exactly the same form as in statics. For the curl of electric field we will take the result of Faraday's law, Eq. 4.02(3). For the curl of magnetic field, we will take for the time being the result from statics, Eq. 2.28(7).

$$\nabla \cdot \bar{D} = \rho \tag{1}$$

$$\nabla \cdot \bar{B} = 0 \tag{2}$$

$$\nabla \times \bar{E} = -\frac{\partial \bar{B}}{\partial t} \tag{3}$$

$$\nabla \times \bar{H} = \bar{i}. \tag{4}$$

An elimination between these equations can be made to give an equation relating charge and current. We would expect this to show that, however ρ may vary with space or time, total charge should be conserved. If current flows out of any volume, the amount of charge inside must decrease, and, if current flows in, charge inside increases. Considering a smaller and smaller volume, in the limit the outward flow of current per unit time and per unit volume (which is recognized as the divergence of current density) must give the negative of the time rate of change of charge per unit volume at that point:

$$\nabla \cdot \bar{i} = -\frac{\partial \rho}{\partial t}. \tag{5}$$

However, if we take the divergence of $\bar{i}$ from (4),

$$\nabla \cdot \bar{i} = \nabla \cdot (\nabla \times \bar{H}) \equiv 0$$

which does not agree with the continuity argument and equation (5). Maxwell, by reasoning similar to this, recognized that (4), borrowed from statics, was not complete for time-varying fields. He postulated an added term $\partial \bar{D}/\partial t$:

$$\nabla \times \bar{H} = \bar{i} + \frac{\partial \bar{D}}{\partial t}. \tag{6}$$

Continuity is now satisfied, as may be shown by taking the divergence of (6) and substituting from (1):

$$\nabla \cdot \bar{i} = -\frac{\partial}{\partial t}(\nabla \cdot \bar{D}) = -\frac{\partial \rho}{\partial t}.$$

4.04 The Concept of Displacement Current

The term added to form Eq. 4.03(6) contributes to the curl of magnetic field in the same way as an actual conduction current density (motion of charges in conductors), or convection current density (motion of charges in space). Because it arises from the displacement vector $\bar{D}$, it has been named the displacement current term. Thus Eq. 4.03(6) could be written

$$\nabla \times \bar{H} = \bar{i}_c + \bar{i}_d \tag{1}$$

where $\bar{i}_c$ = conduction or convection current density in amperes per square meter; $\bar{i}_d$ = displacement current density = $\partial \bar{D}/\partial t$ amperes per square meter.

The displacement current term disappears in the static case, but there is no violation of the continuity equation since, for this special case,

$$\nabla \cdot \bar{i} = -\frac{\partial \rho}{\partial t} = 0 .$$

The displacement current term is not of great importance in many low frequency problems, because it is much smaller than common current densities in conductors. For example, a field of 10^4 volts per meter would yield a displacement current density of 0.555 ampere per square meter if varying sinusoidally at a frequency of 10^6 cycles per second in air. Of course the term may be of importance even for low frequencies in such places as the region between condenser plates, as is explained in more detail in the next article. It becomes important, however, in more and more situations as the frequency is raised to the range of higher frequencies. As will be seen in following chapters, it is this term combined with the Faraday's law term for electric field induced by changing magnetic fields that permits the prediction of the phenomena of wave propagation, resonance, and radiation.

4.05 Physical Pictures of Displacement Current

The displacement current term enables one to explain certain things that would have proved inconsistent had only conduction current been included in the magnetic field laws. Consider, for example, the circuit including the a-c generator and the capacitor of Fig. 4.05a. Suppose that

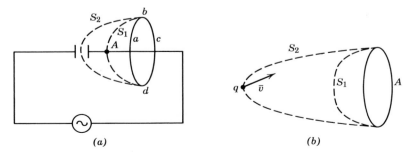

(a)   (b)

Fig. 4.05 (a) Evaluation of $\oint \bar{H} \cdot \overline{dl}$ for an a-c circuit with a condenser. (b) Evaluation of $\oint \bar{H} \cdot \overline{dl}$ for charge q moving toward loop A.

it is required to evaluate the line integral of magnetic field around the loop a-b-c-d-a. The law from statics states that the result obtained should be the current enclosed, that is, the current through any surface of which the loop is a boundary. Then it is true that, if we take as the arbitrary surface through which current is to be evaluated one which cuts the wire A, as S_1, a finite value is obtained for the line integral. But suppose that the surface selected is one which does not cut the wire, but instead passes between the plates of the capacitor, as S_2. If conduction current alone were included, the computation would have indicated no current passing through this surface and the result would be zero. The path around which the integral is evaluated is the same in each case, and it would be quite annoying to possess two different results. It is the displacement current term which appears at this point to preserve the continuity of current between the plates of the capacitor, giving the same answer in either case.

To show how this continuity is preserved, consider a parallel-plate capacitor of capacitance C, spacing d, area of plates A, and applied voltage $V_0 \sin \omega t$. From circuit theory the charging current

$$I_c = C \frac{dV}{dt} = \omega C V_0 \cos \omega t.$$

The field inside the capacitor has a magnitude $E = V/d$, so the displacement current density is

$$i_d = \epsilon \frac{\partial E}{\partial t} = \omega \epsilon \frac{V_0}{d} \cos \omega t.$$

Total displacement current flowing between the plates is the area of the plate multiplied by the density of displacement current:

$$I_d = A i_d = \omega \left(\frac{\epsilon A}{d} \right) V_0 \cos \omega t.$$

The factor in parentheses is recognized as the electrostatic capacitance for the ideal parallel-plate capacitor in mks units, so

$$I_d = \omega C V_0 \cos \omega t.$$

This value for total displacement current flowing between the capacitor plates is then exactly the same as the value of charging current flowing in the leads, calculated by the usual circuit methods above, so the displacement current does act to complete the circuit, and the same result would be obtained by the use of either S_1 or S_2 of Fig. 4.05a, as required.

Inclusion of displacement current is necessary for a valid discussion of another example in which a charge region q (Fig. 4.05b) moves with velocity $\bar{v}$. If the line integral of magnetic field is to be evaluated about some loop A at a given instant, it should be possible to set it equal to the current flow for that instant through any surface of which A is a boundary.

If the displacement current term were ignored, we could use any one of the infinite number of possible surfaces, as S_1, having no charge passing through it, and obtain the result zero. If one of the surfaces is selected, as S_2, through which charge is passing at that instant, however, there is a contribution from convection current, and a non-zero result. The apparent inconsistency is resolved when one notes that the electric field arising from the moving charge will be varying with time, and thus will actually give rise to a displacement current term through both of the surfaces S_1 and S_2. The sum of displacement and convection currents for the two surfaces is the same at the given instant.

Problems

4.05a For a coaxial cylindrical capacitor of radii a and b and length l, evaluate the total displacement current flowing across any cylindrical surface of radius r $(a < r < b)$, taking the voltage variation as sinusoidal in time, and the variation of electric field with radius the same as in statics. Show that the result is independent of radius and equal to the charging current for the capacitor.

4.05b Repeat Prob. a for the spherical surface of radius r lying between the concentric conductors of radii a and b of a spherical capacitor.

4.05c Starting from Eq. 4.04(1), prove that for a closed surface

$$\oint_S (\bar{i}_c + \bar{i}_d) \cdot \overline{dS} = 0.$$

From this, show that the sum of convection and displacement currents is the same for both of the surfaces S_1 and S_2 in Fig. 4.05b.

4.05d Calculate the displacement current density for a radio wave of 1 Mc/sec having a field of 1 microvolt/meter; for a 60-cycle field between power transmission-line conductors with a field of 100 kilovolts/meter; for a laser beam with field 3×10^4 volts/meter at frequency 10^{15} cps.

4.06 Maxwell's Equations in Differential Equation Form

Rewriting the group of equations of Art. 4.03 with the displacement current term added, we have

$$\nabla \cdot \bar{D} = \rho \qquad (1)$$

$$\nabla \cdot \bar{B} = 0 \qquad (2)$$

$$\nabla \times \bar{E} = -\frac{\partial \bar{B}}{\partial t} \qquad (3)$$

$$\nabla \times \bar{H} = \bar{i} + \frac{\partial \bar{D}}{\partial t}. \qquad (4)$$

This set of equations, together with certain auxiliary relations and definitions, is the basic set of equations of classical electricity and magnetism, governing all electromagnetic phenomena in the range of frequencies from zero through the highest-frequency radio waves (and many phenomena at light frequencies), and in the range of sizes above atomic size. The equations were first written (not in the above notation) by Maxwell in 1863, and are known as *Maxwell's equations*. The material in the sections preceding this should not be considered a derivation of the laws, for they cannot in any real sense be derived from less fundamental laws. Their ultimate justification comes, as with all experimental laws, in that they have predicted correctly, and continue to predict, all electromagnetic phenomena over a wide range of physical experience.

The foregoing set of equations is a set of differential equations, relating the time and space rates of change of the various field quantities at a point in space. The use of these will be demonstrated in many following chapters. Equivalent large-scale equations will be given in the following article.

The major definitions and auxiliary relations that must be added to complete the information are as follows:

1. *The Force Law.* This is, from one point of view, merely the definition of the electric and magnetic fields. For a charge q moving with velocity $\bar{v}$ through an electric field $\bar{E}$ and a magnetic field of flux density $\bar{B}$, the force is

$$\bar{f} = q[\bar{E} + \bar{v} \times \bar{B}] \text{ newtons.} \tag{5}$$

2. *The Definition of Conduction Current (Ohm's Law).* For a conductor,

$$\bar{i} = \sigma\bar{E} \text{ amp/meter}^2 \tag{6}$$

where σ is conductivity in mhos per meter.

3. *The Definition of Convection Current.* For a charge density ρ moving with velocity $\bar{v}_\rho$, the current density is

$$\bar{i} = \rho\bar{v}_\rho \text{ amp/meter}^2. \tag{7}$$

4. *Definition of Permittivity (Dielectric Constant).* The electric flux density $\bar{D}$ is related to the electric field intensity $\bar{E}$ by the relation

$$\bar{D} = \epsilon\bar{E} = \epsilon_r\epsilon_0\bar{E} \tag{8}$$

where ϵ_0 is the permittivity of space $\cong (1/36\pi) \times 10^{-9}$ farads per meter and ϵ_r characterizes the effect of the atomic and molecular dipoles in the material.

As with static fields (Art. 2.44) ϵ, or ϵ_r, is in general a tensor, and in Chapter 9 we will be concerned with anisotropic materials where this characterization must be used. Unless specifically noted, the text otherwise will be concerned with homogeneous, isotropic, linear, and time-invariant materials, and ϵ will be a scalar constant.

5. *Definition of Permeability.* The magnetic flux density $\bar{B}$ is related to the magnetic intensity $\bar{H}$ by

$$\bar{B} = \mu\bar{H} = \mu_r\mu_0\bar{H} \tag{9}$$

where μ_0 is the permeability of space $= 4\pi \times 10^{-7}$ henrys per meter and μ_r measures the effect of the magnetic dipole moments of the atoms comprising the medium. In general μ and μ_r are tensors, but unless otherwise noted they will be considered scalar constants, representing homogeneous, isotropic, linear, and time-invariant materials.

In addition, the major quantities appearing in Maxwell's equations have definitions and units as given below.

	Quantity	Units
$\bar{D}$	electric flux density vector	coulombs/meter^2
ρ	charge density	coulombs/meter^3
$\bar{B}$	magnetic flux density vector	webers/meter^2 = volt sec/meter^2
$\bar{E}$	electric field vector	volts/meter
$\bar{H}$	magnetic field vector	amp/meter
$\bar{i}$	conduction or convention current density	amp/meter^2

Problems

4.06a Check the dimensional consistency of equations (1) through (9) of this article.

4.06b Show that, in a charge-free, current-free dielectric, the two divergence equations, (1) and (2), may be derived from the two curl equations, (3) and (4), so far as time-varying parts of the field are concerned.

4.06c Show that, if the equation for continuity of charge is assumed, the two divergence equations, (1) and (2), may be derived from the curl equations, (3) and (4), so far as a-c components of the field are concerned, for regions with finite ρ and $\bar{i}$. This fact has made it quite common to refer to the two curl equations alone as Maxwell's equations.

4.06d Can a time-varying magnetic field of any form exist in space without a corresponding electric field? Can a time-varying electric field exist without the corresponding magnetic field?

4.07 Maxwell's Equations in Large-Scale Form

It is also convenient to have the information of Maxwell's equations in large-scale or integral form applicable to overall regions of space, to paths surrounding conductors, etc. This is of course the type of relation that we started with in the discussion of Faraday's law, Art. 4.02, when we derived the differential expression from it. The large-scale equivalents for Eqs. 4.06(1)–4.06(4) are

$$\oint_S \bar{D} \cdot \overline{dS} = \int_V \rho \, dV \tag{1}$$

$$\oint_S \bar{B} \cdot \overline{dS} = 0 \tag{2}$$

$$\oint \bar{E} \cdot \bar{dl} = -\frac{\partial}{\partial t} \int_S \bar{B} \cdot \overline{dS} \tag{3}$$

$$\oint \bar{H} \cdot \bar{dl} = \int_S \bar{i} \cdot \overline{dS} + \frac{\partial}{\partial t} \int_S \bar{D} \cdot \overline{dS}. \tag{4}$$

Equations (1) and (2) are obtained by integrating respectively Eqs. 4.06(1) and 4.06(2) over a volume and applying the divergence theorem. Equations (3) and (4) are obtained by integrating respectively Eqs. 4.06(3) and 4.06(4) over a surface and applying Stokes's theorem. For example, integrating Eq. 4.06(1),

$$\int_V \nabla \cdot \bar{D} \, dV = \int_V \rho \, dV$$

and applying the divergence theorem,

$$\oint_S \bar{D} \cdot \overline{dS} = \int_V \rho \, dV.$$

Equation (1) is seen to be the familiar form of Gauss's law utilized so much in Chapter 2. Now that we are concerned with fields which are a function of time, the interpretation is that the electric flux flowing out of any closed surface *at a given instant* is equal to the charge enclosed by the surface *at that instant*.

Equation (2) states that the surface integral of magnetic field or total magnetic flux flowing out of a closed surface is zero for all values of time, expressing the fact that magnetic charges have not been found in nature. Of course the law does not prove that such charges will never be found; if they are, a term on the right similar to the electric charge term in (1) will simply be added, and a corresponding magnetic current term will be added to (3).

Equation (3) is Faraday's law of induction, stating that the line integral of electric field about a closed path (electromotive force) is the negative of the time rate of change of magnetic flux flowing through the path. The law was discussed in some detail in Art. 4.02.

Equation (4) is the generalized Ampère's law including Maxwell's displacement current term, and it states that the line integral of magnetic field about a closed path (magnetomotive force) is equal to the current (conduction, convection, or displacement) flowing through the path. The physical significance of this complete law has been discussed in Arts. 4.04–4.05.

Problems

4.07a A conducting spherical balloon is charged with a constant charge Q, and its radius made to vary sinusoidally in some manner from a minimum value, r_{min}, to a maximum value, r_{max}. It might be supposed that this would produce a spherically symmetric, radially outward propagating electromagnetic wave. Show that this does not happen by finding the electric field at some radius $r > r_{max}$.

4.07b A capacitor formed by two circular parallel plates has an essentially uniform axial electric field produced by a voltage $V_0 \sin \omega t$ across the plates. Utilize the symmetry to find the magnetic field at radius r between the plates. Show that the axial electric field could not be exactly uniform under this time-varying condition.

4.07c Suppose that there were free magnetic charges of density ρ_m, and that a continuity relation similar to Eq. 4.04(5) applied to such charges. Find the magnetic current term that would have to be added to Maxwell's equations in such a case. Give the units of ρ_m and the magnetic current density.

4.08 Maxwell's Equations for the Time-Periodic Case

By far the most important time-varying case is that involving steady-state a-c fields varying sinusoidally in time. The reasons for this are that the majority of engineering applications utilize such fields (at least approximately), and also that transients or time variations of other forms, by the method of Fourier analysis, may be considered a superposition of such steady-state sinusoids of different frequency. The advantages of the use of the complex exponential form ($e^{j\omega t}$) described in Chapter 1 for circuit problems are perhaps even more important for the more intricate field problems. Formally, the set of equations 4.06(1)–4.06(4) are easily changed over by replacing $\partial/\partial t$ by $j\omega$:

$$\nabla \cdot \bar{D} = \rho \tag{1}$$

$$\nabla \cdot \bar{B} = 0 \tag{2}$$

$$\nabla \times \bar{E} = -j\omega\bar{B} \tag{3}$$

$$\nabla \times \bar{H} = \bar{i} + j\omega\bar{D}. \tag{4}$$

And the auxiliary relations, Eqs. 4.06(6)–4.06(9), remain

$$\bar{I} = \sigma\bar{E} \quad \text{for conductors} \tag{5}$$

$$\bar{D} = \epsilon\bar{E} = \epsilon_r\epsilon_0\bar{E} \tag{6}$$

$$\bar{B} = \mu\bar{H} = \mu_r\mu_0\bar{H}. \tag{7}$$

Equations 4.06(5) and 4.06(7) should be used with instantaneous values because of the nonlinear terms in the equations.

It must be recognized that the symbols in the equations of this article have a different meaning from the same symbols used in Art. 4.06. There they represented the instantaneous values of the indicated vector and scalar quantities. Here they represent the complex multipliers of $e^{j\omega t}$, giving the in-phase and out-of-phase parts with respect to the chosen reference. The complex scalar quantities are commonly referred to as *phasors*, and by analogy the complex vector multipliers of $e^{j\omega t}$ may be called *vector phasors*. It would seem less confusing to use a different notation for the two kinds of quantities, but one quickly runs out of symbols. The difference is normally clear from the context, and when there is danger of confusion, we will use functional notation to denote the time-varying quantities.

If we wish to obtain the instantaneous values of a given quantity from the complex value, as in Chapter 1, we insert the $e^{j\omega t}$ and take the real part. For example, for the scalar ρ suppose that the complex value of ρ is

$$\rho = \rho_r + j\rho_i \tag{8}$$

where ρ_r and ρ_i are real scalars. The instantaneous value of ρ is then

$$\rho(t) = \text{Re}\left[(\rho_r + j\rho_i)e^{j\omega t}\right] = \rho_r \cos \omega t - \rho_i \sin \omega t. \tag{9}$$

Or, alternatively, if ρ is given in magnitude and phase,

$$\rho = |\rho|\, e^{j\theta_\rho} \tag{10}$$

where

$$|\rho| = \sqrt{\rho_r^{\,2} + \rho_i^{\,2}}$$

$$\theta_\rho = \tan^{-1}\frac{\rho_i}{\rho_r},$$

the true time-varying form is

$$\rho(t) = \text{Re}\left[|\rho|\, e^{j(\omega t + \theta_\rho)}\right] = |\rho| \cos (\omega t + \theta_\rho). \tag{11}$$

For a vector quantity, such as $\bar{E}$, the complex value may be written

$$\bar{E} = \bar{E}_r + j\bar{E}_i \tag{12}$$

where $\bar{E}_r$ and $\bar{E}_i$ are real vectors. Then

$$\bar{E}(t) = \text{Re}\left[(\bar{E}_r + j\bar{E}_i)e^{j\omega t}\right] = \bar{E}_r \cos \omega t - \bar{E}_i \sin \omega t. \tag{13}$$

Note that $\bar{E}_r$ and $\bar{E}_i$ do not in general have the same direction in space. (This aspect of the subject is discussed more in Art. 6.03 under the heading of field polarization.) For the vector quantity, the information cannot in general be given by single values of magnitude and phase angle. Of course the magnitude and phase can be given for each of the three scalar components of the vector $\bar{E}$ to define the complete complex vector.

Problems

4.08a   Under what conditions can a complex vector quantity $\bar{E}$ be represented by a vector magnitude and phase angle,

$$\bar{E} = \bar{E}_0 e^{j\theta_E}$$

where $\bar{E}_0$ is a real vector and θ_E a real scalar?

4.08b   Consider a case in which the complex field vectors can be represented by single values of magnitude and phase,

$$\bar{E} = \bar{E}_0(x, y, z)e^{j\theta_1(x,y,z)}$$
$$\bar{H} = \bar{H}_0(x, y, z)e^{j\theta_2(x,y,z)}$$
$$\bar{i} = \bar{i}_0(x, y, z)e^{j\theta_3(x,y,z)}$$
$$\rho = \rho_0(x, y, z)e^{j\theta_4(x,y,z)}.$$

Substitute in Maxwell's equations in the complex form, and separate real and imaginary parts to obtain the set of differential equations relating $\bar{E}_0, \bar{H}_0, \ldots,$ θ_4. Check the result by using the corresponding instantaneous expressions,

$$\bar{E}_{\text{inst.}} = \text{Re} \ [\bar{E}_0 e^{j\theta_1} e^{j\omega t}] = \bar{E}_0(x, y, z) \cos \ [\omega t + \theta_1(x, y, z)], \text{ etc.}$$

substituting in Maxwell's equations for general time variations, eliminating the time variations, and again getting the set of equations relating $\bar{E}_0, \ldots, \theta_4$.

4.09   Other Systems of Units for Electromagnetic Quantities

Although the rationalized mks system of practical units is now almost uniformly used in the discussion of electromagnetic problems in engineering, the valuable literature still existing in the other systems of units requires some knowledge of these. Conversion factors are given in Table 4.09.

The Gaussian system of units, used most commonly before about 1930, utilized esu units for all electric quantities, and the emu system for all magnetic quantities. A conversion factor c (which turns out to be equal to the velocity of light) is then required in the electromagnetic equations relating the two kinds of quantities. Maxwell's equations in Gaussian units are then as follows:

$$\nabla \cdot \bar{D} = 4\pi\rho \tag{1}$$

$$\nabla \cdot \bar{B} = 0 \tag{2}$$

$$\nabla \times \bar{E} = -\frac{1}{c}\frac{\partial \bar{B}}{\partial t} \tag{3}$$

$$\nabla \times \bar{H} = \frac{4\pi}{c}\left(i + \frac{\partial \bar{D}}{\partial t}\right). \tag{4}$$

In the foregoing, ρ is charge density in statcoulombs per cubic centimeter, E is electric field in statvolts per centimeter, B is magnetic flux density in gauss, H is magnetic field in oersteds, and i is the current density in stat-amps per square centimeter.

TABLE 4.09

Multiply	by	To Obtain
1. Coulombs	$\frac{1}{10}$	abcoulombs
Coulombs	3×10^9	statcoulombs
2. Amperes	$\frac{1}{10}$	abamperes
Amperes	3×10^9	statamperes
3. Volts	10^8	abvolts
Volts	$\frac{1}{300}$	statvolts
4. Ohms	10^9	abohms
Ohms	$\frac{1}{9} \times 10^{-11}$	statohms
5. Farads	9×10^{11}	statfarads
6. Henrys	10^9	abhenrys
7. Watts (joules/second)	10^7	ergs/second
8. Volts/meter	$\frac{1}{3} \times 10^{-4}$	statvolts/centimeter
9. Webers	10^8	maxwells
10. Webers/meter^2	10^4	gauss
11. Amp/meter	$4\pi \times 10^{-3}$	oersted

The Heaviside-Lorentz system of rationalized units is the same as the Gaussian system except that the units of charge, current, and electric field have been modified by a factor of $\sqrt{4\pi}$ to eliminate the factors of 4π from Maxwell's equations. Note that this is a somewhat different way of eliminating the 4π from that employed in the rationalized mks system. Maxwell's equations in Heaviside-Lorentz units are then as (1)–(4) except for the absence of 4π.

Problem

4.09 *A rationalized system of cgs practical units* utilizing volts, amperes, coulombs, ohms, and watts for the electromagnetic quantities, as in the mks system, but centimeters, grams, and seconds for the units of length, mass, and

time, has also been used to some extent in the engineering literature. The form
of the equations appears exactly as in that given for the mks system (Arts.
4.06-4.08). Find the values of μ_0 and ϵ_0 for this system, and the required
modification of the force equation.

4.10 Poynting's Theorem for Energy Relations in an Electromagnetic Field

The simple transmission line waves studied in Chapter 1 were primarily of interest because of their ability to transfer energy from one point
to another. Energy transfer may also be accomplished through more
general types of electromagnetic waves, the amount of the energy depending on the magnitudes, distribution, and phases of the electric and
magnetic fields of the wave. This dependence will now be investigated in a
manner similar to that used in Art. 1.27 for transmission lines.

Let us take a region in which dielectric constant and permeability may
be functions of position but not of time. Maxwell's equations, written in
terms of the total fields, currents, and charges of a region, describe the
electromagnetic behavior of the region. The two curl equations are:

$$\nabla \times \bar{E} = -\frac{\partial \bar{B}}{\partial t}, \tag{1}$$

$$\nabla \times \bar{H} = \bar{\imath} + \frac{\partial \bar{D}}{\partial t}. \tag{2}$$

An equivalence of vector operations (inside cover) shows that

$$\bar{H} \cdot (\nabla \times \bar{E}) - \bar{E} \cdot (\nabla \times \bar{H}) = \nabla \cdot (\bar{E} \times \bar{H}). \tag{3}$$

If products in (1) and (2) are taken as indicated by this equivalence and
added,

$$-\bar{H} \cdot \frac{\partial \bar{B}}{\partial t} - \bar{E} \cdot \frac{\partial \bar{D}}{\partial t} - \bar{E} \cdot \bar{\imath} = \nabla \cdot (\bar{E} \times \bar{H}). \tag{4}$$

This may now be integrated over the volume of concern,

$$\int_V \left(\bar{H} \cdot \frac{\partial \bar{B}}{\partial t} + \bar{E} \cdot \frac{\partial \bar{D}}{\partial t} + \bar{E} \cdot \bar{\imath} \right) dV = -\int_V \nabla \cdot (\bar{E} \times \bar{H}) \, dV.$$

From the divergence theorem, Art. 2.13, the volume integral of div $(\bar{E} \times \bar{H})$
equals the surface integral of $\bar{E} \times \bar{H}$ over the boundary.

$$\int_V \left(\bar{H} \cdot \frac{\partial \bar{B}}{\partial t} + \bar{E} \cdot \frac{\partial \bar{D}}{\partial t} + \bar{E} \cdot \bar{\imath} \right) dV = -\oint_S (\bar{E} \times \bar{H}) \cdot \overline{dS}. \tag{5}$$

This form is valid for general media, but in the common case of linear, isotropic, time-invariant materials, ϵ is a scalar independent of time. Then

$$\frac{1}{2}\frac{\partial(\bar{D}\cdot\bar{E})}{\partial t} = \frac{1}{2}\frac{\partial(\epsilon\bar{E}^2)}{\partial t} = \bar{E}\cdot\frac{\partial\bar{D}}{\partial t}$$

$$\frac{1}{2}\frac{\partial(\bar{B}\cdot\bar{H})}{\partial t} = \bar{H}\cdot\frac{\partial\bar{B}}{\partial t}.$$

Equation (5) then becomes

$$\int_V\left[\frac{\partial}{\partial t}\left(\frac{\bar{B}\cdot\bar{H}}{2}\right) + \frac{\partial}{\partial t}\left(\frac{\bar{D}\cdot\bar{E}}{2}\right) + \bar{E}\cdot\bar{\imath}\right]dV = -\oint_S(\bar{E}\times\bar{H})\cdot\overline{dS}. \quad (6)$$

The term $\epsilon E^2/2$ was shown (Art. 2.21) to represent the energy storage per unit volume for an electrostatic field. If this interpretation is extended by definition to any electric field,[2] the second term of (6) represents the time rate of increase of the stored energy in the electric fields of the region. Similarly, if $\mu H^2/2$ is defined as the density of energy storage for any magnetic field, the first term represents the time rate of increase of the stored energy in the magnetic fields of the region. The third term is the usual ohmic term and so represents energy dissipated in heat per unit time. (Or, if $\bar{\imath}$ is made up of a motion of free charges, $\rho\bar{v}_\rho$, $\bar{E}\cdot\rho\bar{v}_\rho$ represents the energy of acceleration given these charges; and, if there are sources, $\bar{E}\cdot\bar{\imath}$ for these sources is of opposite sign and will represent energy added by them.) All the net energy term must have been supplied externally. Thus the term on the right represents the energy flow into the volume per unit time. Changing sign, the rate of energy flow out through the enclosing surface is

$$W = \oint_S\bar{P}\cdot\overline{dS}, \quad (7)$$

where

$$S = \bar{P} = \bar{E}\times\bar{H}$$

and is called the *Poynting vector*.

Although it is known from the proof only that total energy flow out of a region per unit time is given by the total surface integral (6), it is often convenient to think of the vector $\bar{P}$ defined by (7) as the vector giving direction and magnitude of energy flow at any point in space. Though this step does not follow strictly, it will not lead us into pitfalls for present applications.

[2] For an excellent discussion of the arbitrariness of these definitions, refer to J. A. Stratton, *Electromagnetic Theory*, McGraw-Hill, New York, 1941, p. 133.

To demonstrate the interpretation of the theorem, let us take the simple example of a round wire carrying direct current I_z (Fig. 4.10). If R is the

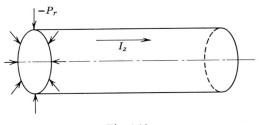

Fig. 4.10

resistance per unit length, the electric field in the wire is known from Ohm's law to be

$$E_z = I_z R. \tag{8}$$

The magnetic field at the surface, or at any radius r outside the wire, is

$$H_\phi = \frac{I_z}{2\pi r}. \tag{9}$$

The Poynting vector $\bar{P} = \bar{E} \times \bar{H}$ is everywhere radial, directed toward the axis:

$$P_r = -E_z H_\phi = -\frac{R I_z^{\,2}}{2\pi r}. \tag{10}$$

If we then make an integration over a cylindrical surface of unit length and radius equal to that of the wire, there is no flow through the ends of the cylinder since $\bar{P}$ has no component normal to the ends. All the flow is through the cylindrical surface, giving a power flow inward of amount

$$W = 2\pi r(-P_r) = I_z^2 R. \tag{11}$$

We know that this result does represent the correct power flow into the conductor, being dissipated in heat. If we accept the Poynting vector as giving the correct *density* of power flow at each point, we must then picture the battery or other source of energy as setting up the electric and magnetic fields, so that the energy flows through the field and into the wire through its surface. If one happens to like this interpretation, it is fine, but the Poynting theorem cannot be considered a proof of its correctness, for it says only that the *total* power balance for a given region will be computed correctly in this manner.

It is also instructive to consider the cases for which there will be no power flow through the electromagnetic field. Accepting the foregoing interpretation of the Poynting vector, we see that it will be zero when either $\bar{E}$ or $\bar{H}$ is zero, or when the two vectors are mutually parallel. Thus, for example, there is no power flow in the vicinity of a system of static charges which has electric field but no magnetic field. Another very important case is that of a perfect conductor, which by definition must have a zero tangential component of electric field at its surface. Then $\bar{P}$ can have no component normal to the conductor and there can be no power flow through the perfect conductor.

Finally, we shall give a useful form for the average power in steady-state a-c problems using the complex notation. If $\bar{E}$ and $\bar{H}$ are the complex vectors representing the electric and magnetic fields in the time-periodic case, the average Poynting vector is

$$\bar{P}_{av} = \tfrac{1}{2} \operatorname{Re} (\bar{E} \times \bar{H}*). \tag{12}$$

The construction of this is exactly similar to that for voltage and current in Art. 1.09.

Problems

4.10a Describe the Poynting vector and discuss its interpretation for the case of a static point charge Q located at the center of a small loop of wire carrying direct current I.

4.10b Show that, if $\bar{E}$ and $\bar{H}$ are the complex multipliers of $e^{j\omega t}$, the instantaneous Poynting vector may be found as follows:

$$\bar{P} = \tfrac{1}{2} \operatorname{Re} [(\bar{E} \times \bar{H}*) + (\bar{E}e^{j\omega t}) \times (\bar{H}e^{j\omega t})].$$

4.10c Assuming current density constant over the conductor cross-section in the example of Art. 4.10, find the Poynting vector within the wire and interpret this in terms of the distribution of dissipation.

4.10d Interpret the Poynting vector about a parallel-plate capacitor charged from zero to some final charge Q. Repeat for an inductor in which current builds up from zero to some final value. Repeat for each of these cases as charge and current is made to decay from a given value to zero.

4.11 Application of Maxwell's Equations: Wave Propagation

As the first example of the application of Maxwell's equations we shall study a simple but very important example of wave propagation. Let us consider a region in space containing no sources so there will be no charge or current terms in Maxwell's equations 4.06(1) to (4). Arbitrary time variations of the fields will be permitted and the medium is to be considered homogeneous, isotropic, linear, and with zero conductivity.

To attempt a solution of a group of simultaneous equations, it is usually a good plan to separate the various functions of position, such as $\bar{D}$ and $\bar{B}$, to arrive at equations that give the distributions of each.

First, taking the curl of Eq. 4.06(3), we see that

$$\nabla \times \nabla \times \bar{E} = -\mu \nabla \times \frac{\partial \bar{H}}{\partial t}. \qquad (1)$$

The left side may be expanded, using a vector identity, to give

$$\nabla(\nabla \cdot \bar{E}) - \nabla^2 \bar{E} = -\mu \nabla \times \frac{\partial \bar{H}}{\partial t}. \qquad (2)$$

A source-free region has been specified so $\nabla \cdot \bar{E} = 0$ and, since time and space partial derivatives may be taken in any order, (2) becomes

$$\nabla^2 \bar{E} = \mu \frac{\partial}{\partial t} \nabla \times \bar{H}. \qquad (3)$$

Substitution of Eq. 4.06(4) with $\bar{i}$ set to zero gives

$$\nabla^2 \bar{E} = \mu\epsilon \frac{\partial^2 \bar{E}}{\partial t^2}, \qquad (4)$$

which is the general form of the wave equation for the medium being considered. This form applies as well to the magnetic field, as may be seen by a similar derivation started by taking the curl of Eq. 4.06(4),

$$\nabla^2 \bar{H} = \mu\epsilon \frac{\partial^2 \bar{H}}{\partial t^2}. \qquad (5)$$

From this simple special case of space variation in one dimension only, many of the characteristics of electromagnetic waves can be found that will aid the study of more complex cases. Recalling that in rectangular coordinates the Laplacian of a vector can be separated into the vector sum of the Laplacian of the components, we have

$$\nabla^2 E_x = \mu\epsilon \frac{\partial^2 E_x}{\partial t^2}, \qquad (6)$$

and identical expressions for the y and z components. This reduces to

$$\frac{\partial^2 E_x}{\partial z^2} = \mu\epsilon \frac{\partial^2 E_x}{\partial t^2} \qquad (7)$$

for the case of variation in the z direction only. This is exactly the form of the one-dimensional wave equation studied in Chapter 1. It was shown there that the equation has a general solution in the form

$$E_x = f_1\left(t - \frac{z}{v}\right) + f_2\left(t + \frac{z}{v}\right), \qquad (8)$$

where $v = 1/\sqrt{\mu\epsilon}$, f_1 denotes a function of $(t - z/v)$, etc. The first term of (8) represents the wave or function f_1 traveling with velocity v and unchanging form in the positive z direction; the second term represents the wave or function f_2 traveling with velocity v and unchanging form in the negative z direction. These functions are called uniform plane waves. It will be helpful to anticipate later discussions by pointing out that the commonest radio waves at some distance from the antenna and the ground are approximately of this simple form with space variations in one direction only.

For more general cases involving variations in more than one direction, the solution of the wave equation is not quite so simple, yet the general idea of waves propagating with definite velocities can always be obtained from it. Many of these more complicated cases are treated later.

To make the foregoing concepts concrete, let us consider the important solution of the one-dimensional problem of (7) for a steady-state sinusoidal wave. It is assumed that this has been set up with no reflections, so that there is propagation in only one direction (say the positive z direction). If electric field is then given over one transverse plane, $z = 0$, as

$$\bar{E} = \bar{a}_x E_0 e^{j\omega t}. \tag{9}$$

The wave traveling in the positive z direction must be of the form of f_1 in (8) and must satisfy the boundary condition (9) at $z = 0$. The expression

$$E_x = E_0 e^{j\omega[t-(z/v)]} \tag{10}$$

satisfies these requirements. The instantaneous value of the wave

$$E_x(z, t) = \operatorname{Re}[E_x] = E_0 \cos \omega\left(t - \frac{z}{v}\right) \tag{11}$$

is shown in Fig. 4.11 for $t = 0$. The y component of Eq. 4.08(3), taking account of the relation between $\bar{B}$ and $\bar{H}$, may be written for the present example as

$$\frac{\partial E_x}{\partial z} = -j\omega\mu H_y, \tag{12}$$

since we have assumed that there are no variations with the x coordinate. It may also be seen from Eq. 4.08(3) that the x and z components of $\bar{H}$ are zero. By using the variation of E_x given by (10), (12) becomes

$$H_y = \frac{1}{\mu v} E_x = \sqrt{(\epsilon/\mu)} E_x. \tag{13}$$

We can calculate the power carried by a plane wave by using the Poynting theorem for complex vectors, Eq. 4.10(12). Thus

$$\bar{P}_{\text{av}} = \bar{a}_z P_z = \bar{a}_z \tfrac{1}{2} \operatorname{Re}[E_x H_y{}^*] = \bar{a}_z \tfrac{1}{2}\sqrt{(\epsilon/\mu)} E_x{}^2, \tag{14}$$

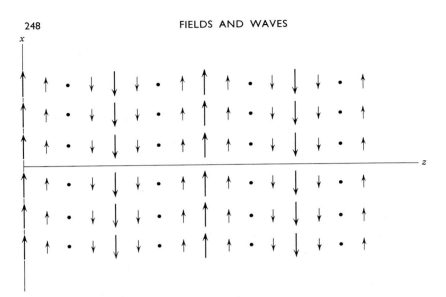

Fig. 4.11   Sinusoidal, uniform, plane wave filling the half space $0 \leqslant z \leqslant \infty$ shown
at one instant.   Vectors show magnitude and direction of E_x

where E_x is the peak value of the sinusoidal electric field vector. We see
that the time average power flow is in the direction of the travel of the
wave and is the same at all points. This is to be expected since no power
can be dissipated in a perfect dielectric.

Problems

4.11a   Derive the complex form of Eq. 4.11(7) starting from Maxwell's equations for complex quantities, Eqs. 4.08(1) through (4).

4.11b   Show that the wave equation may be written directly in terms of any of the components of $\bar{H}$, $\bar{E}$, or $\bar{A}$ in rectangular coordinates, or for the axial components of $\bar{H}$, $\bar{E}$, or $\bar{A}$ in any coordinate system, but not for other components, such as radial and tangential components in cylindrical coordinates, or any component in spherical coordinates. That is,

$$\nabla^2 E_x = \mu\epsilon \frac{\partial^2 E_x}{\partial t^2} \qquad \nabla^2 H_z = \mu\epsilon \frac{\partial^2 H_z}{\partial t^2} \text{ , etc.}$$

but
$$\nabla^2 E_r \neq \mu\epsilon \frac{\partial^2 E_r}{\partial t^2} \qquad \nabla^2 H_\phi \neq \mu\epsilon \frac{\partial^2 H_\phi}{\partial t^2} \text{ , etc.}$$

4.11c   Show that the power flow in the uniform plane wave Eq. 4.11(14) equals the product of the average energy density and the group velocity v of the wave.

4.11d A uniform plane wave is excited by a waveshape E_x rectangular in time. That is, $E_x = C$ for $mT < t < (m + \frac{1}{2})T, m = 0, 1, 2, 3,$ and zero otherwise.

Plot E_x and H_y versus distance z for $t = \dfrac{3T}{4}, \dfrac{7T}{4}$.

4.11e A uniform plane wave has electric field at $z = 0$ given as $E_x(0, t) = \cos \omega t + \frac{1}{2} \cos 3\omega t$. Plot E_x versus distance for a few periods in an ideal dielectric with no dispersion. Repeat for a dielectric in which phase velocity at frequency 3ω is $\frac{1}{3}$ that at frequency ω.

4.12 Application of Maxwell's Equations; Penetration of Electromagnetic Fields into a Good Conductor

In the previous section we considered a uniform plane wave propagating in free space. Here again we consider a uniform plane field but we shall study the penetration of the fields into a good conductor. The term *conductor* will be applied to those materials in which collisions, as noted below, determine the movement of the charges when an electric field is applied. Thus the current resulting from movement of the charges is given by Ohm's law:

$$\bar{i} = \sigma \bar{E}. \tag{1}$$

The constant σ is the conductivity of the conductor. Substitution of (1) in Eq. 4.06(4) gives

$$\nabla \times \bar{H} = \sigma \bar{E} + \frac{\partial \bar{D}}{\partial t}, \tag{2}$$

which can also be written in complex notation as

$$\nabla \times \bar{H} = (\sigma + j\omega\epsilon)\bar{E}. \tag{3}$$

It is easy to show that the assumption of Ohm's law implies the absence of free charges. Since the divergence of the curl of any vector is zero,

$$\nabla \cdot \nabla \times \bar{H} = (\sigma + j\omega\epsilon)\nabla \cdot \bar{E} = 0,$$

where we have assumed homogeneity of σ and ϵ. Thus

$$\nabla \cdot \bar{D} = \rho = 0. \tag{4}$$

The simple picture of the situation in a conductor is that mobile electrons drift through a lattice of positive ions encountering frequent collisions. On the average, over a volume large compared with the atomic dimensions but small compared with dimensions of interest in the system under study, the net charge is zero even though some of the charges are moving through the element and causing current flow. The net movement or "drift" in such cases is found proportional to the electric field.

The equations may be further simplified if displacement currents are negligible. They are negligible in good conductors up to the highest radio frequencies, but may not be at optical frequencies. For variations which are sinusoidal with time (of the form $e^{j\omega t}$), the terms to be compared in (3) are σ and $\omega\epsilon$. The precise values of ϵ for conductors are not known, yet most indications show that the range of dielectric constants is much the same for conductors as for dielectrics. For platinum, a relatively poor conductor, the term $\omega\epsilon$ would equal σ in the optical or ultraviolet range of frequencies if σ is taken as the low-frequency value and ϵ is of the same order as for dielectrics. Interactions between solids and fields in this frequency range must usually be studied by quantum mechanics. We see that for all but the poorest conductors (such as earth) the displacement current term is completely negligible compared with conduction current for radio frequencies at least.

Thus, to summarize, the following specializations are appropriate to Maxwell's equations applied to good conductors, and may in fact be taken as a definition of a good conductor.

1. The free-charge term is zero, $\rho = 0$.
2. Conduction current is given by Ohm's law, $\bar{\imath} = \sigma\bar{E}$.
3. Displacement current is negligible in comparison with conduction current, $\omega\epsilon \ll \sigma$.

To derive the differential equation which determines the penetration of the fields into the conductor we first take the curl of Eq. 4.06(3) and make use of a vector identity (see inside back cover) and the definition of permeability to obtain

$$\nabla \times \nabla \times \bar{E} = \nabla(\nabla \cdot \bar{E}) - \nabla^2\bar{E} = -\frac{\partial}{\partial t}\mu\nabla \times \bar{H}. \tag{5}$$

Then using (4) and substituting (2) in (5) with displacement current neglected, we find

$$\nabla^2\bar{E} = \mu\sigma\frac{\partial\bar{E}}{\partial t} \tag{6}$$

or, in phasor notation

$$\nabla^2\bar{E} = j\omega\mu\sigma\bar{E}. \tag{7}$$

Equations with forms identical with (6) and (7) can be found in a similar way for magnetic field and current density. In phasor notation

$$\nabla^2\bar{H} = j\omega\mu\sigma\bar{H} \tag{8}$$

$$\nabla^2\bar{\imath} = j\omega\mu\sigma\bar{\imath}. \tag{9}$$

These equations give the relation between space and time derivatives of magnetic field, electric field, and current density at any point in a good conductor. It remains to solve these differential equations subject to the boundary conditions imposed by certain physical shapes of interest for practical conductors.

The simplest case to solve, though possibly not the simplest to visualize, is that of a plane conductor of infinite depth, and with no field variations along the width or length dimension. This case is frequently taken as that

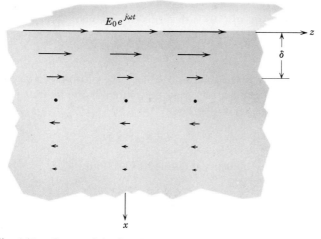

Fig. 4.12a   Penetration of uniform field into good conductor filling
half space $0 \leqslant x \leqslant \infty$.

of a conductor filling the half space $x > 0$ in a rectangular coordinate system with the y-z plane coinciding with the conductor surface, and is then spoken of as a "semi-infinite solid." In spite of the infinite depth requirement, the analysis of this case is of the greatest practical importance. It is important to many conductors of finite extent, and with curved surfaces, because at high frequencies the depth over which significant fields are concentrated is very small, so that radii of curvature and conductor depth may be taken as infinite in comparison. Moreover, any field variations along the length or width dimension due to curvature, edge effects, or variations along a wavelength are ordinarily so small compared with the variations into the conductor that they may be neglected.

For the uniform field situation shown in Fig. 4.12a with the electric field vector in the z direction, there are no variations with y or z and (7) becomes

$$\frac{d^2E_z}{dx^2} = j\omega\mu\sigma E_z = \tau^2 E_z \tag{10}$$

where

$$\tau^2 \equiv j\omega\mu\sigma. \tag{11}$$

$\sqrt{j} = (1 + j)/\sqrt{2}$ (taking the root with the positive sign),

$$\tau = (1 + j)\sqrt{\pi f \mu \sigma} = \frac{1 + j}{\delta} \tag{12}$$

where
$$\delta = \frac{1}{\sqrt{\pi f \mu \sigma}} \text{ meters.} \tag{13}$$

A complete solution of (10) is in terms of exponentials:

$$E_z = C_1 e^{-\tau x} + C_2 e^{\tau x}. \tag{14}$$

The field will increase to the impossible value of infinity at $x = \infty$ unless C_2 is zero. The coefficient C_1 may be written as the field at the surface if we let $E_z = E_0$ when $x = 0$. Then

$$E_z = E_0 e^{-\tau x}. \tag{15}$$

Or, in terms of the quantity δ defined by (12) and (13),

$$E_z = E_0 e^{-x/\delta} e^{-jx/\delta}. \tag{16}$$

Since the magnetic field and the current density are governed by the same differential equation as the electric field, forms identical with (16)

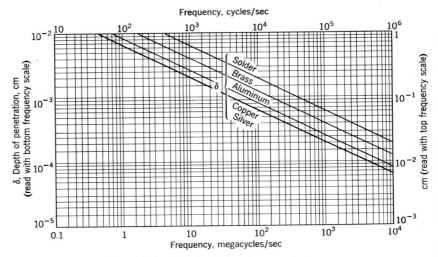

Fig. 4.12b   Skin depth for plane conductors.

apply; that is,

$$H_y = H_0 e^{-x/\delta} e^{-jx/\delta} \tag{17}$$

$$i_z = i_0 e^{-x/\delta} e^{-jx/\delta}, \tag{18}$$

where H_0 and i_0 are the magnitudes of the magnetic field and current density at the surface.

It is evident from the forms of (16) to (18) that the magnitudes of the fields and current decrease exponentially with penetration into the conductor, and δ has the significance of the depth at which they have decreased to $1/e$ (about 36.9 per cent) of their values at the surface. The quantity δ is accordingly called *depth of penetration* or *skin depth*. It is shown as a function of frequency for some common materials in Fig. 4.12b. The phases of the current and fields lag behind their surface values by x/δ radians at depth x into the conductor.

It is of interest to consider a physical explanation of the decay of fields and current which has been found mathematically. Imagine a high-frequency source as in Fig. 4.12c, producing an applied electric field E_0 in the neighborhood of the conductor. This must cause current flow in the conductor, producing a magnetic field at right angles to E_0. This changing magnetic field produces an induced electric field E' opposite to E_0. If a study is made of the two closed line integrals, 1–2–3–4–1 and 1—2'–3'–4–1, it is found that more magnetic flux is enclosed in the latter, so that induced voltage around this path is the greater, and it may be deduced that the induced field along 2'–3' is greater than that along 2–3. It follows that there is less net field, $E_0 + E'$, left to produce current flow as one progresses farther into the conductor.

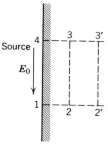

Fig. 4.12c

The student should retain these facts about skin depth:

1. Depth of penetration is smaller, the higher the conductivity, the higher the permeability, and the higher the frequency, since it is inversely proportional to the square root of each of these.

2. The fields and current do not fail to penetrate below the depth δ; this is merely the point at which they have decreased to $1/e$ of their values at the surface.

3. The concept as stated here applies strictly to plane solids. It may be extended, however, to conductors of other shapes so long as the value of δ calculated is much smaller than any curvatures of the surfaces.

4. In addition to its special significance for the plane solid, δ as defined by (13) may be considered simply a constant of a given material at frequency f, and it is useful as a parameter in exact analyses of other geometrical configurations, as will appear later.

Problems

4.12a Make a polar plot of $|i_z|$ versus the phase of i_z, with x/δ taken as the parameter.

4.12b Show that δ as defined by (13) does have the dimensions of meters, as indicated.

4.12c Defining wavelength λ as $v/f = (f\sqrt{\mu\epsilon})^{-1}$, show that, for a good conductor, depth of penetration is always a very small quantity compared with wavelength, $\delta \ll \lambda$.

4.12d The conductivity of graphite is about 0.12 mhos/meter. Take its dielectric constant as $5\epsilon_0$, and find the approximate frequency range over which it might be classed as a good conductor.

4.12e Take the divergence of Eq. 4.12(2) and interpret as a differential equation for ρ with respect to time. Give the solution of this equation and show that it predicts a decay of the free charge in a very short time (for good conductors). Since the decaying charge implies charge motion in some way, discuss the application of this model to real conductors.

4.12f Find the variation of magnitude of Poynting vector within the conductor of Art. 4.12 and interpret.

BOUNDARY CONDITIONS FOR TIME-VARYING SYSTEMS

4.13 Continuity Conditions for Fields at a Boundary

In Chapter 2, certain boundary and continuity conditions were stated for static fields. For the remainder of the book we shall be interested in the corresponding boundary and continuity conditions to be applied to the solutions of Maxwell's equations. These conditions may be deduced by referring to Maxwell's equations. Consider first Faraday's law in large-scale form, Eq. 4.07(3), applied to a path formed by moving distance Δl along one side of the boundary between any two materials, and returning on the other side, an infinitesimal distance into the second medium (Fig. 4.13a). The line integral of electric field is

$$\oint \bar{E} \cdot \bar{dl} = (E_{t1} - E_{t2})\Delta l. \tag{1}$$

Since the path is an infinitesimal distance on either side of the boundary, its area is zero, and therefore the contribution from changing magnetic

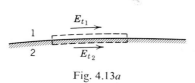

Fig. 4.13a

flux is zero so long as rate of change of magnetic flux density is finite.
Consequently,

$$(E_{t1} - E_{t2}) \Delta l = 0 \quad \text{or} \quad E_{t1} = E_{t2}. \quad (2)$$

Similarly, the generalized Ampère law in large-scale form, Eq. 4.07(4),
may be applied to a like path with its two sides on the two sides of the
boundary. Again there is zero area enclosed by the path, and, so long as
current density and rate of change of electric flux density are finite, the
integral is zero, and in like manner to the above

$$H_{t1} = H_{t2}. \quad (3)$$

Thus tangential components of electric and magnetic field must be equal
on the two sides of any boundary between physically real media. The
condition (3) may be modified for an idealized case such as the perfect
conductor where the current densities are allowed to become infinite.
This case is discussed separately in Art. 4.14.

The integral form of Gauss's law is Eq. 4.07(1). If two very small
elements of area ΔS are considered (Fig. 4.13b), one on either side of the
boundary between any two materials, with a surface charge density ρ_s
existing on the boundary, the application of Gauss's law to this elemental
volume gives

$$\Delta S(D_{n1} - D_{n2}) = \rho_s \Delta S$$

or

$$D_{n1} - D_{n2} = \rho_s. \quad (4)$$

For a charge-free boundary,

$$D_{n1} = D_{n2} \quad \text{or} \quad \epsilon_1 E_{n1} = \epsilon_2 E_{n2}. \quad (5)$$

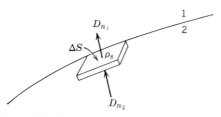

Fig. 4.13b   Surface charge ρ_s on a boundary
between two media.

That is, for a charge-free boundary, normal components of electric flux density are continuous; for a boundary with charges, they are discontinuous by the amount of the surface charge density.

With no magnetic charge term on the right of Eq. 4.07(2), a development corresponding to the above shows that always the magnetic flux density is continuous:

$$B_{n1} = B_{n2} \quad \text{or} \quad \mu_1 H_{n1} = \mu_2 H_{n2}. \tag{6}$$

For the time-varying case, which is of greatest importance to our study, the conditions on normal components are not independent of those given for the tangential components. The reason is that the former are derived from the two divergence equations (or their equivalent in large-scale form), and these may be obtained from the two curl equations in the time-varying case (Probs. 4.06b and c). The conditions on tangential components were derived from the large-scale equivalents of the curl equations. Hence, for the a-c solutions, it is necessary only to apply the continuity conditions on tangential components of electric and magnetic fields at a boundary between two media, and the conditions on normal components may be used as a check; or, if the normal components of D turn out to be discontinuous, (4) tells the amount of surface charge that is induced on the boundary.

4.14 Boundary Conditions at a Perfect Conductor

In Art. 4.12 it was shown that fields near the surface of a good conductor decay exponentially with distance into the conductor, falling to $1/e$ times the values at the surface in a distance called the skin depth. From Eq. 4.12(13) we see that, as the conductivity tends toward infinity, the skin depth approaches zero. Thus, the fields are excluded from the interior of a perfect conductor and all the currents flow in a vanishingly thin layer at the surface. Whereas only superconductors have infinite conductivity to the best of present day knowledge, it is a very good approximation in many practical problems to treat good conductors (such as copper) as though perfect in considering the fields outside the conductor.

Since the electric field inside the conductor is zero, Eq. 4.13(2) shows that at the conductor surface the tangential electric field intensity is zero;

$$E_t = 0 \tag{1}$$

and Eq. 4.13(4) gives the normal electric flux density as

$$D_n = \rho_s. \tag{2}$$

Furthermore, since magnetic fields also vanish inside the conductor, the statement of continuity of magnetic flux lines, Eq. 4.13(6) indicates that

$$B_n = 0 \qquad (3)$$

at the conductor surface. As was pointed out in the last article, however, the continuity condition on normal $\bar{B}$ is not independent of the condition on tangential $\bar{E}$ in the time-varying case. Thus, in the a-c solution, (3) follows from (1), but may sometimes be useful as a check, or as an alternative boundary condition.

The tangential component of magnetic field is likewise zero inside the perfect conductor but is not in general zero just outside. This discontinuity would appear to violate the condition of Eq. 4.13(3), but it will be recalled that a condition for that proof was that current density must remain finite. For the perfect conductor, the finite current J per unit width is assumed to flow as a current sheet of zero thickness, so that current *density* is infinite. The discontinuity in tangential magnetic field is found by a construction similar to that of Fig. 4.13a. The current enclosed by the path is the current per unit width J flowing on the surface of the conductor perpendicular to the direction of the tangential magnetic field at the surface. Then

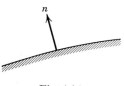

Fig. 4.14

$$\oint \bar{H} \cdot \overline{dl} = H_t \, dl = J \, dl$$

or

$$J = H_t. \qquad (4)$$

The direction and sense relations for (4) are given most conveniently by the vector form of the law below.

To write the relations of (1) and (4) in vector notation, a unit vector $\bar{n}$, normal to the conductor at any given point and pointing from the conductor into the region where fields exist, is defined (Fig. 4.14). Then conditions (1) to (4) become (5) to (8) below:

$$\bar{n} \times \bar{E} = 0 \qquad (5)$$

$$\bar{n} \cdot \bar{B} = 0 \qquad (6)$$

$$\rho_s = \bar{n} \cdot \bar{D} \qquad (7)$$

$$J = \bar{n} \times \bar{H}. \qquad (8)$$

For an a-c problem, (5) represents the only required boundary condition at a perfect conductor. Equation (6) serves as a check or sometimes as an alternative to (5). Equations (7) and (8) are used to give the charge and current induced on the conductor by the presence of the electromagnetic fields.

4.15 Use of Boundary Conditions and Uniqueness of Solution

As in the case of static fields, the continuity and boundary relations are used to join solutions at boundaries between different media and to insure uniqueness of the solutions. Thus in the diagramatic example of Fig. 4.15, a space is shown bounded everywhere except at the input surface III by a perfect conductor I, and filled with two dielectrics A and B which are separated by a surface II. It is assumed that electromagnetic fields in the region are excited by impressed fields at the boundary III, with tangential components given. Only the time-varying parts of the fields are of interest.

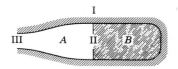

Fig. 4.15 Region containing two dielectrics partially enclosed by a conductor.

To obtain the distribution of fields, currents, and charges, various solutions of Maxwell's equations are now considered, and the process of selection of appropriate types and amounts of these solutions is ready to begin. In both regions A and B, we reject first those which fail to give zero tangential electric field on the boundary of the perfect conductor I. Of all the possible solutions that satisfy this boundary condition at the perfect conductor, those are retained which have continuity between the tangential electric and magnetic fields between regions A and B along the boundary II (Art. 4.13). Finally, of all the solutions which satisfy the boundary conditions on the perfect conductor and have continuity of tangential field components across the boundary II, one of these, or a sum, is retained to give continuity with the tangential components of the impressed fields at III. Then the charges and currents on the conductor can be found, if desired, by the normal component of $\bar{D}$ at the conductor and the tangential component of $\bar{H}$, respectively.

When the solutions found in the foregoing manner are tested for uniqueness, the procedure is to assume two possible solutions to Maxwell's equations with the same defined tangential fields on the boundary following the philosophy of Art. 3.03. The difference field is formed, and found to satisfy a Poynting's theorem of the form of Eq. 4.10(5). Stratton[3] shows that for linear, isotropic (but possibly inhomogeneous), media, specification of tangential $\bar{E}$ and $\bar{H}$ on the boundary and of initial values of all fields at time zero, is sufficient to specify fields uniquely within the region at all later times. The argument can be extended to anisotropic materials and certain classes of nonlinear materials, but not to materials that have

[3] J. A. Stratton, *Electromagnetic Theory*, McGraw-Hill, New York, 1941, pp. 486–488.

multivalued relations between D and E (or B and H) or to "active" materials that produce oscillations. In steady-state problems we are not much concerned with the specification of initial conditions required for the general uniqueness theorem. The reason will be explored when we discuss independent modes in Chapter 11.

Although the discussion has been given for a region with closed boundaries, uniqueness arguments also apply to open regions extending to infinity, provided certain *radiation conditions* are satisfied by the fields. These require that the products $r\bar{E}$ and $r\bar{H}$ remain finite as r approaches infinity,[4] and are satisfied by fields arising from real charge and current sources contained within a finite region. The extension to open regions is important to the potential formulation of the next section.

POTENTIALS USED WITH VARYING CHARGES AND CURRENTS

4.16 A Possible Set of Potentials for Time-Varying Fields

The set of differential equations known as Maxwell's equations, with certain auxiliary relations, gives the complete information for obtaining electric and magnetic effects due to currents and charges. It will sometimes be convenient to put the information in a different form by the introduction of new variables. In the study of static fields, it was found that new functions known as potentials helped in the solution of static problems. We might then look for similar potential functions which will help in the solution of more general problems. The potential functions of static fields were given in terms of integral expressions of charges and currents. They could be differentiated in certain specified ways to give the fields. We will then look for more general potential functions as integrals of the time-varying charges and currents, which potentials may be differentiated to give the time-varying fields. Because these potentials are largely used for homogeneous, isotropic materials, the discussion will be restricted to this case.

In speculating on the form which the potential function for electric field might take, we could hope to have one of the simple forms found useful in Chapter 2, such as gradient of a scalar or the curl of a vector. However, we are faced with this problem: the electric field for time-varying conditions cannot be derived alone as the gradient of scalar potential since this would require that it have zero curl, and it may actually

[4] S. Silver, *Microwave Antenna Theory and Design*, McGraw-Hill, New York, 1949, p. 85.

have a finite curl of value $-\partial \bar{B}/\partial t$; it cannot be derived alone as the curl of a vector potential since this would require that it have zero divergence, and it may have a finite divergence of value ρ/ϵ.

Since the divergence of magnetic field is zero in the general case as it was in the static, it seems that $\bar{B}$ may still be set equal to the curl of some magnetic vector potential, $\bar{A}$. Suppose that the substitution of $\bar{B} = \nabla \times \bar{A}$ is made in Maxwell's equations and an attempt is then made to obtain a value for the potential function of electric fields which vary with time. Equation 4.06(3) can be written

$$\nabla \times \left(\bar{E} + \frac{\partial \bar{A}}{\partial t} \right) = 0. \tag{1}$$

This equation states that the curl of a certain vector quantity is zero. But this is the condition that permits a vector to be derived as the gradient of a scalar, say Φ. That is,

$$\bar{E} + \frac{\partial \bar{A}}{\partial t} = -\nabla \Phi$$

or $$\bar{E} = -\nabla \Phi - \frac{\partial \bar{A}}{\partial t}. \tag{2}$$

The electric field $\bar{E}$ has consequently been obtained in terms of both a scalar and a vector potential.

Let us substitute (2) in another of Maxwell's equations, Eq. 4.06(1), to obtain

$$-\nabla^2 \Phi - \frac{\partial}{\partial t} (\nabla \cdot \bar{A}) = \frac{\rho}{\epsilon}. \tag{3}$$

Then substituting $\bar{B} = \nabla \times \bar{A}$ and (2) in Eq. 4.06(4), we find

$$\nabla \times \nabla \times \bar{A} = \mu \bar{\imath} + \mu \epsilon \left[-\nabla \left(\frac{\partial \Phi}{\partial t} \right) - \frac{\partial^2 \bar{A}}{\partial t^2} \right].$$

Using the vector identity

$$\nabla \times \nabla \times \bar{A} = \nabla(\nabla \cdot \bar{A}) - \nabla^2 \bar{A},$$

this becomes

$$\nabla(\nabla \cdot \bar{A}) - \nabla^2 \bar{A} = \mu \bar{\imath} - \mu \epsilon \nabla \left(\frac{\partial \Phi}{\partial t} \right) - \mu \epsilon \frac{\partial^2 \bar{A}}{\partial t^2}. \tag{4}$$

Equations (3) and (4) scarcely seem simple. However, it is realized that $\bar{A}$ is not unique until it is further specified. That is, there are any number of vector functions whose curl is the same. As was shown in Art. 2.37, it is necessary to specify also the divergence of $\bar{A}$ to make it unique and this may be done according to convenience. If the divergence of $\bar{A}$ is chosen as[5]

$$\nabla \cdot \bar{A} = -\mu\epsilon \frac{\partial \Phi}{\partial t} \tag{5}$$

(3) and (4) then simplify to

$$\nabla^2\Phi - \mu\epsilon \frac{\partial^2 \Phi}{\partial t^2} = -\frac{\rho}{\epsilon} \tag{6}$$

$$\nabla^2\bar{A} - \mu\epsilon \frac{\partial^2 \bar{A}}{\partial t^2} = -\mu\bar{\imath}. \tag{7}$$

And, repeating from the above,

$$\bar{B} = \nabla \times \bar{A} \tag{8}$$

$$\bar{E} = -\nabla\Phi - \frac{\partial \bar{A}}{\partial t}. \tag{9}$$

Thus the potentials $\bar{A}$ and Φ, defined in terms of the sources $\bar{\imath}$ and ρ by the differential equations (6) and (7), may be used to derive the electric and magnetic fields by (8) and (9). It is easy to see that they do reduce to the corresponding expressions of statics, for, if time derivatives are allowed to go to zero, the set of equations (6)–(9) becomes

$$\nabla^2\Phi = -\frac{\rho}{\epsilon} \qquad \bar{E} = -\nabla\Phi \tag{10}$$

$$\nabla^2\bar{A} = -\mu\bar{\imath} \qquad \bar{B} = \nabla \times \bar{A} \tag{11}$$

which are recognized as the appropriate expressions from Chapter 2.

Problems

4.16a A potential function commonly used in electromagnetic theory is the Hertz vector potential $\bar{\Pi}$, so defined that electric and magnetic fields are derived from it as follows, for a homogeneous medium:

$$\bar{H} = \epsilon \frac{\partial}{\partial t} (\nabla \times \bar{\Pi})$$

$$\bar{E} = \nabla(\nabla \cdot \bar{\Pi}) - \mu\epsilon \frac{\partial^2 \bar{\Pi}}{\partial t^2}$$

where

$$\nabla^2\bar{\Pi} - \mu\epsilon \frac{\partial^2 \bar{\Pi}}{\partial t^2} = -\frac{\bar{P}}{\epsilon}$$

and $\bar{P}$, the "polarization vector" associated with sources, is so defined that

$$\bar{\imath} = \frac{\partial \bar{P}}{\partial t} \qquad \rho = -\nabla \cdot \bar{P}.$$

[5] This choice is known as the *Lorentz condition* and has special significance in relativistic field theory. For our purposes, the choice leads to the symmetry of (6) and (7).

Show that $\bar{E}$ and $\bar{H}$ derived in this manner are consistent with Maxwell's equations. Comment on the relation of polarization defined here to that of Art. 2.38.

4.16b Show that $\bar{E}$ and $\bar{H}$ satisfy the following differential equations in a homogeneous medium containing charges and currents:

$$\nabla^2 \bar{E} - \mu\epsilon \frac{\partial^2 \bar{E}}{\partial t^2} = \frac{1}{\epsilon} \nabla \rho + \mu \frac{\partial \bar{i}}{\partial t}$$

$$\nabla^2 \bar{H} - \mu\epsilon \frac{\partial^2 \bar{H}}{\partial t^2} = -\nabla \times \bar{i}$$

4.17 The Retarded Potentials as Integrals over Charges and Currents

Although the potential functions $\bar{A}$ and Φ for time-varying fields are defined in terms of the currents and charges by the differential equations 4.16(6) and (7), it is also desirable to have expressions giving the potentials as integrals over the charges and currents as in the static case. The following discussion applies to the very important case of a single homogeneous region extending to infinity.

From Chapter 2, the integrals for the static potentials, which may be considered the solutions of Eqs. 4.16(10) and (11), are

$$\Phi = \int_V \frac{\rho \, dV}{4\pi\epsilon r} \tag{1}$$

$$\bar{A} = \mu \int_V \frac{\bar{i} \, dV}{4\pi r}. \tag{2}$$

A mathematical development to yield the corresponding integral solutions of the inhomogeneous wave equations, 4.16(6) and (7), is moderately difficult,[6] so only a qualitative discussion is given here. It can be shown that the solutions are

$$\Phi = \int_V \frac{\rho\left(t - \dfrac{r}{v}\right) dV}{4\pi\epsilon r} \tag{3}$$

$$\bar{A} = \mu \int_V \frac{\bar{i}\left(t - \dfrac{r}{v}\right) dV}{4\pi r} \tag{4}$$

where

$$v = (\mu\epsilon)^{-\frac{1}{2}} \tag{5}$$

(For free space, $v = c \approx 3 \times 10^8$ meters per second.)

[6] W. D. Jackson, *Classical Electrodynamics*, John Wiley and Sons, 1962, pp. 183–186.

In the above, $t - r/v$ denotes that, for an evaluation of Φ at time t, the value of charge density ρ at time $t - r/v$ should be used. That is, for each element of charge $\rho\, dV$, the equation says that the contribution to potential is of the same form as in statics, Eq. (1), except that we must recognize a finite time of propagating the effect from the charge element to the point P at which potential is being computed, distance r away. The effect travels with velocity $v = 1/\sqrt{\mu\epsilon}$, which, as we have seen, is just the velocity of a simple plane wave through the medium as predicted from the homogeneous wave equation. Thus, in computing the total contribution to potential Φ at a point P at a given instant t, we must use the values of charge density from points distance r away at an earlier time, $t - r/v$, since for a given element it is that effect which just reaches P at time t. The integral (3) states this. A similar interpretation applied to the computation of $\bar{A}$ from currents in (4). Because of this "retardation" effect, the potentials Φ

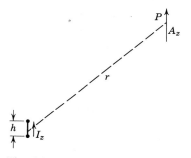

Fig. 4.17 Retarded potential from small current element.

and $\bar{A}$ are called the *retarded potentials*. Once the phenomenon of wave propagation predicted from Maxwell's equations is known, this is about the simplest revision of the static formulas (1) and (2) that could be expected.

One of the simplest examples illustrating the meaning of this retardation, and one which will be met again in the study of radiating systems, is that of a very short current element carrying an a-c current varying sinusoidally in time between two small spheres on which charges accumulate (Fig. 4.17). For a filamentary current in a small wire, the difference in distance from P to any point of a given cross section of the wire is unimportant, so that two of the integrations of the volume integral may be made by integrating current density over the cross section to yield the total current in the wire. Thus, for any filamentary current,

$$\bar{A} = \mu \int \frac{I\left(t - \dfrac{r}{v}\right) dl}{4\pi r} \tag{6}$$

For the particular case of Fig. 4.17, current is in the z direction only, so, by the above, $\bar{A}$ is also. If h is so small compared with r that it may be taken as infinitesimal, the remaining integration of (6) is performed by multiplying the current by h:

$$A_z = \frac{\mu h}{4\pi r} I_z\left(t - \frac{r}{v}\right). \tag{7}$$

Finally, if the current in the small element has the form

$$I_z = I_0 \cos \omega t,$$

substitution in (7) gives A_z as

$$A_z = \frac{\mu h I_0}{4\pi r} \cos \omega \left(t - \frac{r}{v} \right). \qquad (8)$$

From this value of $\bar{A}$ the magnetic field may be derived, and in fact the electric field also, but this part of the problem will be left for the chapter on radiation.

Problems

4.17a By analogy with the integral solutions for $\bar{A}$ and Φ, write the integral for the Hertz vector $\bar{\Pi}$ in terms of the polarization $\bar{P}$. (See Prob. 4.16a.)

4.17b Repeat the example of the small current element worked out above (Fig. 4.17), but in complex notation, $I_z = I_0 e^{j\omega t}$, finding the vector potential $\bar{A}$.

4.18 The Retarded Potentials for the Time-Periodic Case

If all electromagnetic quantities of interest are varying sinusoidally in time, in the complex notation with $e^{j\omega t}$ understood, the set of equations 4.16(8) and (9), 4.17(3) and (4), and 4.16(5) becomes

$$\bar{B} = \nabla \times \bar{A} \qquad (1)$$

$$\bar{E} = -\nabla\Phi - j\omega\bar{A} \qquad (2)$$

$$\Phi = \int_V \frac{\rho e^{-jkr}\, dV}{4\pi\epsilon r} \qquad (3)$$

$$\bar{A} = \int_V \frac{\mu \bar{i} e^{-jkr}\, dV}{4\pi r} \qquad (4)$$

$$\nabla \cdot \bar{A} = -j\omega\mu\epsilon\Phi \qquad (5)$$

where $k = \omega/v = \omega\sqrt{\mu\epsilon}$. Note that the retardation in this case is taken care of by the factor e^{-jkr} and amounts to a shift in phase of each contribution to potential according to the distance r from the contributing element to the point P at which potential is to be computed.

It is evident in this case of steady-state sinusoids that the relation between $\bar{A}$ and Φ [Eq. (5)] fixes Φ uniquely once $\bar{A}$ is determined. Thus, it is not necessary to compute the scalar potential Φ separately. Both $\bar{E}$ and $\bar{B}$ may be written in terms of $\bar{A}$ alone:

$$\bar{B} = \nabla \times \bar{A} \tag{6}$$

$$\bar{E} = -\frac{j\omega}{k^2} \nabla(\nabla \cdot \bar{A}) - j\omega\bar{A} \tag{7}$$

$$\bar{A} = \mu \int_V \frac{\bar{i}e^{-jkr}\,dV}{4\pi r}. \tag{8}$$

It is then necessary only to specifiy the current distribution over the system, to compute the vector potential $\bar{A}$ from it by (8), and then find the electric and magnetic fields by (6) and (7). It may appear that the effects of the charges of the system are being left out, but of course the continuity equation

$$\nabla \cdot \bar{i} = -j\omega\rho \tag{9}$$

relates the charges to the currents, and in fact, in this steady-state sinusoidal case, fixes ρ uniquely once the distribution of $\bar{i}$ is given. So an equivalent but lengthier procedure would be that of computing the charge distribution from the specified current distribution by means of the continuity equation (9), then using the complete set of equations (1) to (4).

Problems

4.18a Continuing Prob. 4.17b, find the charges that must exist on the ends of the current element to be consistent with the continuity equation. From these, find the retarded potential Φ at point P distance r away, making use of the inequalities $h/r \ll 1$ and $kh \ll 1$. Show that the same result is obtained for Φ by employing Eq. (5) and the result for $\bar{A}$ from Prob. 4.17b.

4.18b For a particular solution (the so-called TM_{111} mode) to be studied inside a rectangular cavity resonator of sides a, b, and d, the fields may be derived from a vector potential which has only a z component,

$$A_z = C \sin\frac{\pi x}{a} \sin\frac{\pi y}{b} \cos\frac{\pi z}{d}.$$

Find the corresponding electric and magnetic fields. (Time variations are as $e^{j\omega t}$.)

4.18c As in Prob. b, but for the so-called TE_{01} mode in a circular cylindrical waveguide where the vector potential has only a ϕ component,

$$A_\phi = CJ_1(k_c r)e^{-j\beta z},$$

find electric and magnetic fields.

4.18d Find the relation between the Hertz potential $\bar{\Pi}$ of Prob. 4.16a and the vector potential $\bar{A}$ when time variations are taken of the form $e^{j\omega t}$.

4.18e Use the result of Prob. 4.17b to find the components of $\bar{E}$ and $\bar{H}$ in spherical coordinates produced by an oscillating current element. Calculate the density of real average power flow outward at a distance large enough that only terms varying as $1/r$ need be retained.

4.19 Comparison of Voltage and Potential Difference

The concept of voltage between two points used in circuit theory and discussed further in the next chapter is defined as the negative line integral of the electric field taken along a path from 1 to 2:

$$V_{21} = -\int_1^2 \bar{E} \cdot \overline{dl}. \tag{1}$$

It is a convenient quantity which can be simply related to the current passing through an element of a circuit and is easily measured in many practical problems. If we utilize the expression for electric field in terms of the potential functions, Eq. 4.16(9), we have

$$V_{21} = -\int_1^2 \left(-\nabla\Phi - \frac{\partial \bar{A}}{\partial t} \right) \cdot \overline{dl}.$$

In evaluating the first term, it is recalled that the component of the gradient of a scalar in any direction gives the rate of change of the scalar with respect to that direction:

$$V_{21} = \int_1^2 \frac{\partial \Phi}{\partial l}\, dl + \frac{\partial}{\partial t} \int_1^2 \bar{A} \cdot \overline{dl}$$

or
$$V_{21} = (\Phi_2 - \Phi_1) + \frac{\partial}{\partial t} \int_1^2 \bar{A} \cdot \overline{dl}. \tag{2}$$

For static fields, the last term is zero and the voltage defined by (1) is exactly the difference in the scalar potential function Φ between the two points and so is independent of the path taken between 1 and 2. For time-varying fields we see by (2) that there is a term in addition to the difference in scalar potential, and this term will in general depend on the path taken between 1 and 2. Thus voltage in time-varying systems in general depends on the path taken between two specified points, and is usually not equal to a difference in scalar potential between these points. There are important cases for which the last term is exactly or approximately zero, and the identification between voltage and potential difference is correct and useful, but the justification must be supplied for each specific case if the fields are time-varying.

A slightly different approach which stresses this same point comes by evaluating the voltage along two paths C and C' between points 1 and 2 (Fig. 4.19). For, if the emf is evaluated about a closed path formed by

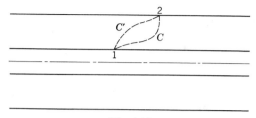

Fig. 4.19

integrating along C and returning on C', the result is just the difference in the voltages found along the two paths:

$$\oint \bar{E} \cdot \overline{dl} = \int_{1C}^{2} \bar{E} \cdot \overline{dl} - \int_{1C'}^{2} \bar{E} \cdot \overline{dl} = V_{21}' - V_{21}.$$

But by Faraday's law [Eq. 4.02(2)] this is just the negative rate of change of magnetic flux through the surface bounded by these paths:

$$V_{21}' - V_{21} = -\frac{\partial}{\partial t} \int_{S} \bar{B} \cdot \overline{dS}. \tag{3}$$

So we see that the voltages defined along the two paths will be different whenever there is any time-varying magnetic flux enclosed between the two paths. In such cases, voltage cannot be synonymous with potential difference.

The example of Fig. 4.19 might be considered a coaxial transmission line for which, as will be shown, there is magnetic field in the circumferential direction only. Hence, for all paths between the two conductors *lying in a given transverse plane*, the same result for voltage will be obtained since there is no changing magnetic flux included between any two of them. The voltage for such paths can then be interpreted as difference in potential between conductors *at a specified cross-sectional plane*. But, if voltage is desired between the two conductors for points 1 and 2 not in the same transverse plane, two paths C and C' will yield different results in general, since the circumferential magnetic field threads between the two paths and will in general yield a finite result for (3). The voltage between such points cannot then be defined until the path is specified, and it is not equal to the difference of potential between points 1 and 2.

4.20   Maxwell's Equations in Several Coordinate Systems

Rectangular Coordinates.

1. $\dfrac{\partial D_x}{\partial x} + \dfrac{\partial D_y}{\partial y} + \dfrac{\partial D_z}{\partial z} = \rho$

2. $\dfrac{\partial B_x}{\partial x} + \dfrac{\partial B_y}{\partial y} + \dfrac{\partial B_z}{\partial z} = 0$

3. $\dfrac{\partial E_z}{\partial y} - \dfrac{\partial E_y}{\partial z} = -\dfrac{\partial B_x}{\partial t}$

$\dfrac{\partial E_x}{\partial z} - \dfrac{\partial E_z}{\partial x} = -\dfrac{\partial B_y}{\partial t}$

$\dfrac{\partial E_y}{\partial x} - \dfrac{\partial E_x}{\partial y} = -\dfrac{\partial B_z}{\partial t}$

4. $\dfrac{\partial H_z}{\partial y} - \dfrac{\partial H_y}{\partial z} = i_x + \dfrac{\partial D_x}{\partial t}$

$\dfrac{\partial H_x}{\partial z} - \dfrac{\partial H_z}{\partial x} = i_y + \dfrac{\partial D_y}{\partial t}$

$\dfrac{\partial H_y}{\partial x} - \dfrac{\partial H_x}{\partial y} = i_z + \dfrac{\partial D_z}{\partial t}$

Cylindrical Coordinates.

1. $\dfrac{1}{r}\dfrac{\partial}{\partial r}(rD_r) + \dfrac{1}{r}\dfrac{\partial D_\phi}{\partial \phi} + \dfrac{\partial D_z}{\partial z} = \rho$

2. $\dfrac{1}{r}\dfrac{\partial}{\partial r}(rB_r) + \dfrac{1}{r}\dfrac{\partial B_\phi}{\partial \phi} + \dfrac{\partial B_z}{\partial z} = 0$

3. $\dfrac{1}{r}\dfrac{\partial E_z}{\partial \phi} - \dfrac{\partial E_\phi}{\partial z} = -\dfrac{\partial B_r}{\partial t}$

$\dfrac{\partial E_r}{\partial z} - \dfrac{\partial E_z}{\partial r} = -\dfrac{\partial B_\phi}{\partial t}$

$\dfrac{1}{r}\dfrac{\partial}{\partial r}(rE_\phi) - \dfrac{1}{r}\dfrac{\partial E_r}{\partial \phi} = -\dfrac{\partial B_z}{\partial t}$

4. $\dfrac{1}{r}\dfrac{\partial H_z}{\partial \phi} - \dfrac{\partial H_\phi}{\partial z} = i_r + \dfrac{\partial D_r}{\partial t}$

$\dfrac{\partial H_r}{\partial z} - \dfrac{\partial H_z}{\partial r} = i_\phi + \dfrac{\partial D_\phi}{\partial t}$

$\dfrac{1}{r}\dfrac{\partial}{\partial r}(rH_\phi) - \dfrac{1}{r}\dfrac{\partial H_r}{\partial \phi} = i_z + \dfrac{\partial D_z}{\partial t}$

Spherical Coordinates.

1. $\dfrac{1}{r^2}\dfrac{\partial}{\partial r}(r^2 D_r) + \dfrac{1}{r\sin\theta}\dfrac{\partial}{\partial \theta}(D_\theta \sin\theta) + \dfrac{1}{r\sin\theta}\dfrac{\partial D_\phi}{\partial \phi} = \rho$

2. $\dfrac{1}{r^2}\dfrac{\partial}{\partial r}(r^2 B_r) + \dfrac{1}{r\sin\theta}\dfrac{\partial}{\partial \theta}(B_\theta \sin\theta) + \dfrac{1}{r\sin\theta}\dfrac{\partial B_\phi}{\partial \phi} = 0$

3. $\dfrac{1}{r\sin\theta}\left[\dfrac{\partial}{\partial \theta}(E_\phi \sin\theta) - \dfrac{\partial E_\theta}{\partial \phi}\right] = -\dfrac{\partial B_r}{\partial t}$

$\dfrac{1}{r}\left[\dfrac{1}{\sin\theta}\dfrac{\partial E_r}{\partial \phi} - \dfrac{\partial}{\partial r}(rE_\phi)\right] = -\dfrac{\partial B_\theta}{\partial t}$

$\dfrac{1}{r}\left[\dfrac{\partial}{\partial r}(rE_\theta) - \dfrac{\partial E_r}{\partial \theta}\right] = -\dfrac{\partial B_\phi}{\partial t}$

4. $\dfrac{1}{r\sin\theta}\left[\dfrac{\partial}{\partial \theta}(H_\phi \sin\theta) - \dfrac{\partial H_\theta}{\partial \phi}\right] = i_r + \dfrac{\partial D_r}{\partial t}$

$\dfrac{1}{r}\left[\dfrac{1}{\sin\theta}\dfrac{\partial H_r}{\partial \phi} - \dfrac{\partial}{\partial r}(rH_\phi)\right] = i_\theta + \dfrac{\partial D_\theta}{\partial t}$

$\dfrac{1}{r}\left[\dfrac{\partial}{\partial r}(rH_\theta) - \dfrac{\partial H_r}{\partial \theta}\right] = i_\phi + \dfrac{\partial D_\phi}{\partial t}$

Forms for Steady State Sinusoids $(e^{j\omega t})$.

Differential Equation Form

$\nabla \cdot \bar{D} = \rho$

$\nabla \cdot \bar{B} = 0$

$\nabla \times \bar{E} = -j\omega\mu\bar{H}$

$\nabla \times \bar{H} = \bar{i} + j\omega\epsilon\bar{E}$

Retarded Potential Form

$\bar{B} = \nabla \times \bar{A}$

$\bar{E} = -j\omega\left[\bar{A} + \dfrac{1}{k^2}\nabla(\nabla \cdot \bar{A})\right]$

$\bar{A} = \displaystyle\int_V \dfrac{\mu\bar{i}}{4\pi r}e^{-jkr}\,dV$

$k = \omega\sqrt{\mu\epsilon}$

5 CIRCUIT CONCEPTS AND IMPEDANCE ELEMENTS

5.01 Introduction

From Chapter 4 we have a set of laws (Maxwell's equations) that contain the core of the classical theory of electricity and magnetism. As has been noted, it is the aim of the remainder of the book to apply these to a range of practical electromagnetic problems. The concepts, when understood, are remarkably simple, although there are admittedly mathematical difficulties in the solution of certain problems. The concepts should become well developed in the remaining chapters, and tools for solution of certain kinds of problems will be introduced. The solutions will often be in approximate form when exact results are impossible, or when they are difficult to interpret in physical terms.

Following the simple examples of the preceding chapter, we now choose to begin the application of field laws by studying the relation to circuit problems. These are not the simplest problems to start with, but they have been of primary importance in the development of electrical engineering. As reviewed in Chapter 1, classical circuit theory considers a voltage or current source applied to an interconnection of simple elements such as resistances, inductances, and capacitances. Solution is by means of differential equations. For linear circuits with sinusoidal sources, the powerful complex phasor method reviewed in Chapter 1 provides a most efficient method of solution. Because of the power of classical circuit analysis, skillful circuit designers have built up strong physical pictures, and an important philosophy of thinking in circuit terms.

Actual circuits, especially in modern systems, include nonlinear, active, nonreciprocal, or time-varying elements. At high frequencies most of the components are of distributed nature. Modern integrated circuits have the energy storage elements, dissipative units, and active parts built into the same crystal, or deposited by thin-film techniques on a common substrate.

270

Yet for many of these generalizations, lumped-element circuit *models* can be constructed, and because of the power of the circuit approach, become useful tools for analysis or qualitative thinking. Even when the specific circuit models are impractical, the cause and effect philosophy which is central to circuit thinking is useful in any of the problems with energy sources, and elements which transfer these or react to them.

Thus, in this chapter we will consider the relationship of classical circuit analysis to Maxwell's equations, and then study the field approach to resistance at high frequencies and to the inductive and capacitive energy storage elements of lumped circuitry.

THE FORMULATION OF A CIRCUIT CONCEPT CONSISTENT WITH MAXWELL'S EQUATIONS

5.02 Kirchhoff's First Law

In classical circuit theory, Kirchhoff's first law states that the algebraic sum of all currents flowing out of a junction must be zero. Thus, referring to Fig. 5.02,

$$\sum_{n=1}^{N} I_n = 0. \tag{1}$$

It is evident that the idea behind this law is that of continuity of current, so we should refer to the continuity equation implicit in Maxwell's equations, Eq. 4.03(5), or its large-scale equivalent,

$$\oint_S \bar{i} \cdot \overline{dS} = - \frac{\partial}{\partial t} \int_V \rho \, dV. \tag{2}$$

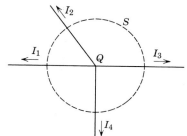

If we apply this to a surface S surrounding the junction, the only conduction current flowing out of the surface is that in the wires, so the left side of (2) becomes just the

Fig. 5.02   Current flow from a junction.

algebraic sum of the currents flowing out in the wires, as in (1). The right side is the negative time rate of change of charge Q, if any, accumulating at the junction. So (2) may be written

$$\sum_{n=1}^{N} I_n = - \frac{dQ}{dt}. \tag{3}$$

Comparison of (1) and (3) indicates an apparent difference. However, we know that, in the application of Kirchhoff's first law, we add a new branch, calling it a capacitance current of dQ/dt if there is charge accumulating at the junction, so in the practical application of the law it is entirely consistent with (3). That is, in interpreting (3), the current terms on the left are to be taken only as convection or conduction currents, whereas in (1) displacement or capacitance currents must be included. The explicit statement of the capacitance currents as in (3) makes it more obvious that the law is just a statement of the continuity equation for circuit junctions, but the form (1) is in other respects neater and is more common.

Problem

5.02 Show that the term on the right of (3) is just the displacement current flow out of the surface S.

5.03 Kirchhoff's Second Law: Single Loop with Lumped Elements

In classical circuit theory, Kirchhoff's second law states that the algebraic sum of voltages about a loop must equal zero or, equivalently,

applied voltage = sum of voltage drops about the circuit.

By analyzing circuits with the more general electromagnetic field relations, we will see how the limits on the validity of this "law" can be determined.

Let us look first at the simple case illustrated in Fig. 5.03 where we assume that all energy storage and dissipation in the circuit occurs within the lumped elements, Z_1, Z_2, and Z_3 which represent inductors, capacitors, and resistors. Losses and energy storage for the interconnecting leads will be neglected. Faraday's law can be written, for any closed line, in the form

$$-\oint \bar{E} \cdot \overline{dl} = \frac{\partial}{\partial t} \int_S \bar{B} \cdot \overline{dS}. \tag{1}$$

The voltage between two points was defined by Eq. 4.19(1) as

$$V_{21} = -\int_1^2 \bar{E} \cdot \overline{dl} \tag{2}$$

which is the quantity measured by a voltmeter when used properly between two points of a circuit. Combining (1) and (2), we see that

$$\sum_{n=1}^N V_n = \frac{\partial}{\partial t} \int_S \bar{B} \cdot \overline{dS}, \tag{3}$$

where the left side is the sum of the voltage drops around the chosen line. Let us consider the line to be the main rectangular loop in Fig. 5.03. Since we assumed at the outset that all energy storage occurs in the lumped elements, the magnetic field within the main loop is zero and (3) reduces to

$$\sum_{n=1}^{N} V_n = -V_0 + V_1 + V_2 + V_3 = 0, \qquad (4)$$

which is equivalent to Kirchhoff's second law. Thus we see that for this

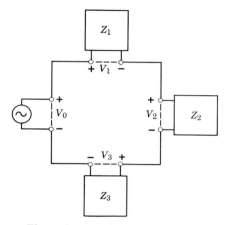

Fig. 5.03   Lumped element circuit.

simple case which is often closely approximated in practice by low-frequency circuits, the field equations lead to the circuit voltage law.

In the following sections we will examine more general circuits, identifying terms in the electromagnetic field expressions with those in circuit-theory equations. The concepts of inductance, capacitance, and impedance may then be examined from the basis of field theory.

5.04   Applied Field and Resultant Current Density

Perhaps the most important single relation that appears in classical circuit-theory is Ohm's law, which relates current flow to voltage drop in a conductor. This law may be generalized so that it applies to an infinitesimal conducting element and is then written [Eq. 4.06(6)]:

$$\bar{\imath} = \sigma \bar{E}. \qquad (1)$$

Equation (1) relates the current density at a point in a conductor to the electric field intensity at that point through the constant σ, known as the conductivity of the material. The electric intensity $\bar{E}$ is the *total* electric intensity at the point. The use of total field is emphasized because partial fields are superposed in the circuit approach. That is, in a circuit to which an external voltage has been applied, the notions of circuit theory have us subtract from this applied voltage the back voltages or voltage drops due to the varying currents of the system and the varying charges of the system, leaving a certain net voltage available for the ohmic drop. To set the background for an approach to circuit ideas from the field equations, such a division will be followed in the electric fields and the notions of voltages will be arrived at by way of the fields.[1]

Thus $\bar{E}$ may be made up of one part $\bar{E}_0$ applied from another system (the external generator) and another part $\bar{E}'$ arising from charges and currents in the circuit or system considered:

$$\bar{E} = \bar{E}_0 + \bar{E}'. \tag{2}$$

Recall that in Maxwell's equations, Art. 4.06, if all charges and currents are included in the equations, the electric intensity $\bar{E}$ appearing in the equations must be total electric intensity. If a system is considered which we have decided to call a circuit, and if this is influenced by another system which is the generator or source of applied voltage or applied field for the circuit, Maxwell's equations might, of course, be applied to the totality of the two systems, including all charges and currents for the circuit and its generator. Such an approach would be unnecessarily complicated if the generating system is, for all practical purposes, independent of the driven circuit. This is the case, for example, if the circuit obtains its applied field from an influencing system which is a distant antenna, a battery, a source of thermal emf, or a well-shielded signal generator. It is then easier to divide total field into two parts. There is the applied field which does not depend upon the charges and currents in the circuit, and there is an induced field which arises directly from these charges and currents. The basic laws applied only to the charges and currents of the circuit give only the amount of the induced field.

Total field, to be used in Ohm's law, is the sum of applied and induced components:

$$\frac{\bar{i}}{\sigma} = \bar{E}_0 + \bar{E}'. \tag{3}$$

The component $\bar{E}'$ due to charges and currents in the circuit may be stated

[1] This follows closely the procedure of Carson, *Bell Sys. Tech. J.*, **6**, 1–17 (Jan. 1927). For an alternate approach as a quasistatic approximation to the field equations by power series methods, see R. M. Fano, L. J. Chu, and R. B. Adler, *Electromagnetic Fields, Energy, and Forces*, John Wiley and Sons, New York, 1963, Chapter 6.

conveniently in terms of the potentials (Art. 4.16):

$$\bar{E}' = -\nabla\Phi - \frac{\partial \bar{A}}{\partial t},$$

where Φ is the scalar potential calculated from charges of the system, and $\bar{A}$ is the vector potential calculated from currents of the system as explained in Art. 4.17. Substituting these in (3), we have

$$\frac{\bar{i}}{\sigma} = \bar{E}_0 - \nabla\Phi - \frac{\partial \bar{A}}{\partial t}$$

or

$$\bar{E}_0 = \frac{\bar{i}}{\sigma} + \nabla\Phi + \frac{\partial \bar{A}}{\partial t}. \tag{4}$$

Equation (4) is the type of cause and effect relationship desired, since an applied field $\bar{E}_0$ results in an ohmic term and terms due to the charges and currents of the system. It is the first step in obtaining a circuit equation that relates voltages to currents and is based on rigorous field theory.

5.05 Applied Voltage and the Circuit Relations

We now consider an arbitrary set of elements in a single loop which may be represented as in Fig. 5.05. For any point on the path, the relation between cause and effect may be taken as that derived from Maxwell's equations, Eq. 5.04(4). To obtain a circuit equation it is necessary only to integrate this differential expression along the path chosen as the circuit:

$$\int_1^4 \bar{E}_0 \cdot \overline{dl} = \int_1^4 \frac{\bar{i}}{\sigma} \cdot \overline{dl} + \int_1^4 \frac{\partial \bar{A}}{\partial t} \cdot \overline{dl} + \int_1^4 \nabla\Phi \cdot \overline{dl}. \tag{1}$$

The first term of the equation is defined as the applied voltage of the circuit. (The sense is defined in such a way that the applied voltage is said to be positive at terminal 1 with respect to 4 when it produces a current flow into the circuit from terminal 1 for a pure resistance load.)

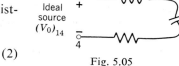

Fig. 5.05

$$(V_0)_{14} = \int_1^4 \bar{E}_0 \cdot \overline{dl} \tag{2}$$

For circuits containing a capacitor gap, as in Fig. 5.05, the integration of the current i through the gap gives zero contribution since the current is zero and the applied field is equal to the induced field.

The defined applied voltage of a circuit brings us to the first of several concepts which call for careful handling to avoid confusion. First let us look at the easy case of direct current. Suppose current is made to flow in a conducting loop connected across the terminals of a battery. The battery voltage causes the current flow, and it is the only thing causing such a flow, since there is no electric field due to alternating currents, and there is no electric field in the conducting loop due to charges. Usual circuit theory would say that the battery applies a voltage between the two ends of the loop. Field theory says first that the battery must produce an electric field in the conductor, otherwise there would be no current flow there. The two theories harmonize when applied voltage between two points is defined as the integral of applied electric field between those points. The circuit equations and concepts do not concern themselves with how the battery caused the voltage; neither do the field equations concern themselves with how it produced the applied field.

Consider next a closed loop of wire. Let magnetic flux through this loop be produced by some independent system which causes this flux to increase uniformly with time. The effect of this constant rate of change is to produce an applied d-c voltage, and, by Ohm's law, this yields a certain d-c flow. If the field in the loop is oscillating in time, as in a receiving antenna excited by the field of a distant transmitting antenna, it is again clear that the applied voltage is the integral around the loop of the electric field due to the distant transmitter.

For the applied voltage produced by the battery, we did not know or care exactly how it was produced; it was known only that this voltage was of a certain amount and was independent of the path chosen for its circuit. When the applied voltage arises from the field of a distant antenna, however, the amount of this voltage depends very definitely upon the path of the circuit. It may be different for different sizes, orientations, and positions of the circuit. So, in general, the applied voltage around any loop to which the circuit concept is applied may vary radically in magnitude as different loops are selected, even when voltage is from the same source.

Equation (1) has the form of Kirchhoff's second law if the integrals on the right side are defined as the voltage drops about a circuit. For frequencies low enough that the circuit dimensions are small compared with a wavelength, the following designations are useful for the terms in (1):

$$\int_1^4 \bar{E}_0 \cdot \overline{dl} = \text{applied voltage (1 taken as + terminal)};\tag{3}$$

$$\int_1^4 \frac{\bar{\imath}}{\sigma} \cdot \overline{dl} = \text{"internal-impedance" voltage drop};\tag{4}$$

$$\int_1^4 \frac{\partial \bar{A}}{\partial t} \cdot \overline{dl} = \text{"inductive" voltage drop};\tag{5}$$

$$\int_1^4 \nabla \Phi \cdot \overline{dl} = \text{"capacitive" voltage drop}.\tag{6}$$

For higher frequencies these terms lose their usual significance, as will be brought out in Section 5.12, but for the lower frequencies we recognize them as familiar terms from circuit theory.

5.06   Kirchhoff's Second Law for a D-C Circuit

For simplicity let us consider first the case of a d-c circuit for the interpretation of Eq. 5.05(1); the gap shown between 2 and 3 in Fig. 5.05 is eliminated. Time variations are zero so the inductive term Eq. 5.05(5) is zero. Since the circuit from 1 to 4 is a closed path and the voltage source is considered perfect, the capacitive term, Eq. 5.05(6), becomes just the integral of the gradient of a scalar about a closed path and is therefore zero.

$$\oint \nabla \Phi \cdot \overline{dl} \equiv 0.$$

In the internal-impedance term, Eq. 5.05(4), it is seen that, since the d-c current is distributed uniformly over the cross section, the current density is

$$i = \frac{I}{A},$$

where A is the cross-sectional area of the conductor or resistors, not necessarily constant about the path. So the term becomes

$$\int_1^4 \frac{i}{\sigma} \cdot \overline{dl} = \int_1^4 \frac{I\,dl}{\sigma A} = I \int_1^4 \frac{dl}{\sigma A}$$

Current I has been taken outside the integral since, by continuity, the d-c current must be constant about the path. A study of the integral multiplying I reveals that it is just the total d-c resistance of the path,

$$R = \int_1^4 \frac{dl}{\sigma A}, \tag{1}$$

so that the term is just IR, and Eq. 5.05(1) assumes the common form

$$V_0 = IR. \tag{2}$$

5.07   The Internal-Impedance Term at Low Frequencies

By "low frequencies" in the following discussion, we mean only that the circuits under discussion are small compared with wavelength (wavelength = velocity of light/frequency). The approximate forms to be developed may apply for certain circuits up to frequencies of thousands of megacycles per second. The two basic assumptions to be made in this and the two following articles which are a consequence of the above condition are:

1. Current is to be taken the same about the entire path.
2. Retardation is to be neglected in computing the potentials $\bar{A}$ and Φ.

We are concerned in this article with the "internal-impedance" term, Eq. 5.05(4). In Chapter 4, we have seen that for a-c effects the current does not distribute itself uniformly over the cross section of the conductor, so the current density cannot be found simply as it was for direct currents in the preceding article. If we choose as our circuit for the integration a path lying on the *surface* of the conductor, however, the term $\bar{i}_s/\sigma$ gives the electric field at the surface of the conductor, $\bar{E}_s$. If we define the internal impedance per unit length for the conductor as the ratio of this surface electric field (voltage per unit length) to the total current in the conductor

$$Z_i = \frac{E_s}{I}, \tag{1}$$

the term under consideration becomes the product of current and a total internal impedance Z:

$$\int_1^4 \frac{\bar{i}_s}{\sigma} \cdot \overline{dl} = I \int_1^4 \frac{\bar{E}_s}{I} \cdot \overline{dl} = I \int_1^4 Z_i \, dl = IZ. \tag{2}$$

By (2), the total internal impedance is equal to the integral of the internal impedance per unit length over the circuit. The steady-state form $(e^{j\omega t})$ has been implicitly assumed. As noted before, there is no contribution from the gap 2-3 in Fig. 5.05.

The internal impedance has an imaginary part as well as a real part since the surface field is not in phase with the total current in the conductor for a-c circuits because of the rate of change of magnetic flux within the conductor. The real part gives the a-c resistance of the wire, and the imaginary part gives the internal reactance (that part of the reactance arising from magnetic flux within the wire) for simple geometrical configurations where the magnetic flux can be divided in that manner. The complete internal-impedance term will be treated in considerable detail for several simple shapes of conductor in later articles in this chapter.

Finally, we should note that the choice of a path for the circuit along the surface of the wire was arbitrary, and could be made in other ways, say along the center of the conductor, or halfway in. The point is that it must be taken in the same place for the treatment of each of the terms of the circuit equation. The choice along the surface is convenient because it does give the separation between "internal inductance" and "external inductance" for many simple shapes.

5.08 The Inductive Term at Low Frequencies

Let us next consider the inductive term in the circuit equation, Eq. 5.05 (5), for the case of circuits small compared with wavelength. For such circuits, the time necessary to propagate electromagnetic effects over the extent of the circuit is a negligible part of a period of the a-c effects, since by definition a wavelength is the distance over which effects are propagated in a complete period. Retardation effects may then be neglected in computing the potentials in the vicinity of the circuit, as stated in one of the basic assumptions of Art. 5.07. The vector potential $\bar{A}$, Eq. 4.17(4), may then be written

$$\bar{A} = \int_V \frac{\mu \bar{i} \, dV}{4\pi r} . \tag{1}$$

The current density $\bar{i}$ may be written as the product of total current I and some vector function of the cross-sectional coordinates of the conductor, say $\bar{f}(x_1, x_2)$, so that $\bar{A}$ is proportional to the total current I, assumed constant about the circuit:

$$\bar{A} = I \int_V \frac{\mu \bar{f}(x_1, x_2) \, dV}{4\pi r} .$$

The integral multiplier of I is a function of the geometrical configuration and the *relative* distribution of current density. Then a coefficient L, a function of the circuit configuration, permeability, and the relative current distribution but not of total current, will be defined as follows:

$$L = \frac{\int_1^4 \bar{A} \cdot \overline{dl}}{I} . \tag{2}$$

With this coefficient defined, the term of Eq. 5.05(5) becomes

$$\int_1^4 \frac{\partial \bar{A}}{\partial t} \cdot \overline{dl} = \frac{d}{dt} \int_1^4 \bar{A} \cdot \overline{dl} = \frac{d}{dt}(LI) = L \frac{dI}{dt} . \tag{3}$$

The partial derivative has been changed to a total derivative since we are concerned here with stationary circuits. The term under consideration is seen to be of the form of the usual inductance drop of classical circuit theory, with the coefficient L the inductance of the whole circuit. Equation (2) then becomes a definition for inductance, and, although a useful form for many purposes, it is not the most common form. To identify it with more common forms, consider a closed circuit. From Stokes's theorem,

$$\oint \bar{A} \cdot \overline{dl} = \int_S \nabla \times \bar{A} \cdot \overline{dS}.$$

But

$$\bar{B} = \nabla \times \bar{A}$$

so

$$L = \frac{\int_S \bar{B} \cdot \overline{dS}}{I} \qquad . \tag{4}$$

Since $\int_S \bar{B} \cdot \overline{dS}$ is the amount of magnetic flux passing through the circuit, (4) is the exact equivalent of the usual low-frequency definition, which defines inductance as the flux linkage per unit current, $L = \psi/I$, and a complete identification with the classical inductance drop term has been shown for the assumptions of this article.

If the configuration of an inductor is such that the magnetic field is limited to the region of the windings, the points 1 and 2 on the circuit as used in this section can be considered to be voltage nodes as in Fig. 5.03. If there were neither losses nor free charges along the coil windings, the voltage would have the value given by (3) with the usual definition of inductance. The skin effect and capacitive effects, however, introduce important modifications of the voltage-current relation for an inductor at moderately high frequencies. The increase of losses caused by the skin effect can be accounted for by the internal impedance term of the previous section. The capacitive effects are discussed in Art. 5.09 for a general circuit. It should be pointed out that an exact equivalent circuit for an inductor, valid at all frequencies, is not possible and the equivalent for even one frequency may be difficult to calculate.

At this stage some clarification of this term in relation to the internal inductance of the preceding article is in order. Consider the wire circuit sketched in Fig. 5.08a. If the path of integration is taken along the inside

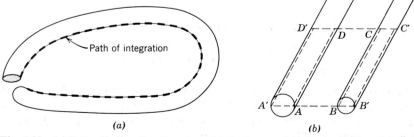

(a)   (b)

Fig. 5.08   (a) Path of integration for external inductance calculations. (b) Parallel-wire conductors.

surface of the wire, the magnetic flux to be used in computing inductance from (4) may be taken as flux flowing through the interior of the loop, not entering the conductor, for the surface S may be any bounded by the path. In this case, the inductance so calculated would be called "external inductance" since it arises from flux external to the wire. The remaining inductive term in the internal impedance of Art. 5.07 would then be associated with flux inside the wire and is called the "internal inductance." For other choices of the path the division between the two terms will be different, and the above names may not apply. The *sum* of all terms in the circuit equation will, however, be the same for all paths of integration. This division is useful primarily where the circuit has a certain symmetry, as will be demonstrated in the examples.

Problem

5.08 For a parallel-wire transmission line, the current density and surface electric field are greatest on the inside surfaces of the wires and least on the outside surfaces. If a path of integration is made along the inside surface $ABCD$ of Fig. 5.08b and internal impedance is defined as in Art. 5.07, a different result is obtained from that given by taking the path along the outer surface, as $A'B'C'D'$. Discuss the choice qualitatively, specifically answering the question: If the two paths are to be equally valid alternatives, how is the difference in the "internal impedance" obtained by the two paths accounted for?

5.09 The Capacitive Term at Low Frequencies

The remaining term of Eq. 5.05(1) may be identified with the "capacitive" voltage drop. As a reaction to the applied field, free charges are distributed along the circuit, particularly at the capacitor gap or gaps when such exist in the circuit. Since all charges on the circuit are considered as sources, the effect of the conductor on field distribution is taken into account and these charges can be considered to be distributed in free space as shown in Fig. 5.09 and the fields produced by the charges can be found using the integral appropriate to a region of uniform dielectric,

$$\Phi = \int_V \frac{\rho \, dV}{4\pi\epsilon r}. \qquad (1)$$

The gradient of this potential is used in the calculation of the capacitive voltage drop.

Fig. 5.09 Charge distribution in a circuit.

The integral in Eq. 5.05(6) can be evaluated as

$$\int_1^4 \nabla\Phi \cdot \overline{dl} = \oint \nabla\Phi \cdot \overline{dl} - \int_2^3 \nabla\Phi \cdot \overline{dl}. \tag{2}$$

The first integral on the right side vanishes since the closed line integral of the gradient of a scalar is zero. The remaining integral on the right side of (2) becomes

$$-\int_2^3 \nabla\Phi \cdot \overline{dl} = \int_3^2 \frac{\partial\Phi}{\partial l}\, dl = \Phi_2 - \Phi_3. \tag{3}$$

If stray capacitances are negligible so that all significant charge is concentrated at the discontinuity, Q on one plate and $-Q$ on the other, the value of Φ will be proportional to Q, and hence $\Phi_2 - \Phi_3$ will be also. Let $1/C$ be the constant of proportionality:

$$\Phi_2 - \Phi_3 = \frac{Q}{C}. \tag{4}$$

The charge at the discontinuity may be related to the current flowing toward the discontinuity by the continuity equation

$$Q = \int I\, dt,$$

so that the capacitive voltage drop may finally be written as

$$\int_1^4 \nabla\Phi \cdot \overline{dl} = \frac{1}{C} \int I\, dt. \tag{5}$$

This is the usual capacitance term in classical circuit theory, and (4) is the definition for electrostatic capacitance used in such circuit calculations. If there is significant charge distributed along the conductors at points other than the gap, the time variations of these charges constitutes a displacement current which follows a path different from the chosen circuit. Here there is not just a single loop and the current I cannot be considered constant about the circuit. This situation is clarified further in Art. 5.10.

To summarize, we have found in this and the two preceding sections all the types of terms included in the classical calculation of a single loop a-c circuit, the skin-effect resistance, the internal-inductance term, the external-inductance term, and the capacitive term. In steady-state notation ($e^{j\omega t}$), Kirchhoff's second law then reads

$$V_0 = I\left[(R + j\omega L_i) + j\omega L_e + \frac{1}{j\omega C}\right], \tag{6}$$

where L_i and L_e are internal and external inductances, respectively.

5.10 Extension to Multi-Loop Circuits and Distributed Constant Circuits

For simplicity, the case of a single-loop circuit with current constant about the path and no mutual effects was considered in the preceding articles relating classical circuit theory to field theory. It is now in order to see how some important extensions of classical circuit theory are related to the exact formulation based on Maxwell's equations.

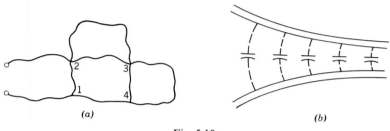

(a)   (b)

Fig. 5.10

For a multi-loop circuit, as indicated in Fig. 5.10a, the integral may be taken about any closed loop, as 1-2-3-4, but is broken into the four parts or branches, 1-2, 2-3, 3-4, and 4-1. For any one of these parts, the current is taken as constant, and the internal-impedance terms, external-inductance terms, and capacitance terms for that branch are calculated in terms of the current *in that branch* by the concepts of the preceding sections. That is, it is most often assumed that the induced fields along a given branch are related only to the current in that particular branch, and not to currents in other parts of the circuit. When this assumption is not justified, coupling effects from other branches are taken into account by mutual terms of the type to be described in the next article. The Kirchhoff first law (Art. 5.02) applied at each of the junctions, together with the circuit integration for each of the branches, gives the complete information necessary for solution by classical circuit theory.

For a distributed constant circuit as in Fig. 5.10b, circuit theory proceeds by approximating the distributed constants by a series of lumped constants, reducing this to a multi-loop circuit of the type just described. This approximation may be carried to the limit of infinitesimals, and may become exact for some systems such as certain ideal transmission lines, as will be shown in a following chapter. For more general shapes of circuits, the approximation may become poorer as one goes to higher frequencies. In any event, for such general circuits, it becomes very difficult to decide how the distributed constants should be calculated, and field theory must eventually be resorted to for an opinion.

5.11 Mutual Couplings in Low-Frequency Circuits

By a mutual inductive coupling we mean that current in one branch of the circuit produces a significant induced field in some other branch.

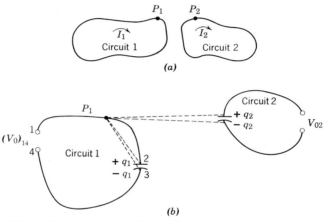

Fig. 5.11 (*a*) Two circuits coupled through inductive effects.
(*b*) Two circuits coupled through capacitive effects.

For example, in the two closed filamentary circuits of Fig. 5.11*a*, the induced electric field at point P_1 in circuit 1 may have one part related to the current I_1 of circuit 1, and another part related to the current I_2 of circuit 2. To compute the latter part, we consider the inductive term, Eq. 5.05(5),

$$\oint_{C_1} \frac{\partial \bar{A}_2}{\partial t} \cdot \overline{dl}_1 = \frac{d}{dt} \oint_{C_1} \bar{A}_2 \cdot \overline{dl}_1, \tag{1}$$

where $\bar{A}_2$ denotes the vector potential associated with the current I_2. For a filamentary current, neglecting retardation, it may be written [see Eq. 4.17(6)]

$$\bar{A}_2 = I_2 \oint_{C_2} \frac{\mu \, \overline{dl}_2}{4\pi r}. \tag{2}$$

The current I_2 has been taken as constant about the path. So $\bar{A}_2$ is proportional to I_2 through a constant which is a function of the circuit configuration, and therefore $\oint_{C_1} \bar{A}_2 \cdot \overline{dl}_1$ is also. Define

$$M_{12} = \frac{1}{I_2} \oint_{C_1} \bar{A}_2 \cdot \overline{dl}_1. \tag{3}$$

Then the term expressing the induced voltage in circuit 1 due to the changing current in circuit 2 may be written

$$\oint_{C_1} \frac{\partial \bar{A}_2}{\partial t} \cdot \overline{dl}_1 = \frac{d}{dt}(M_{12}I_2) = M_{12}\frac{dI_2}{dt}. \tag{4}$$

This is the usual mutual inductance term of classical circuit theory with (3) constituting the definition of mutual inductance. A more common form for the mutual inductance may be had by applying Stokes's theorem to (3):

$$M_{12} = \frac{1}{I_2} \int_{S_1} (\nabla \times \bar{A}_2) \cdot \overline{dS}_1 = \frac{\int_{S_1} \bar{B}_2 \cdot \overline{dS}_1}{I_2}. \tag{5}$$

In this form the mutual inductance is written as the magnetic flux linking circuit 1 from the current of circuit 2, per unit of current in 2. Still another form is obtained if (2) is substituted in (3):

$$M_{12} = \frac{\mu}{4\pi} \oint_{C_1} \oint_{C_2} \frac{\overline{dl}_1 \cdot \overline{dl}_2}{r}. \tag{6}$$

This is a classical form for mutual inductance of filamentary circuits and is known as the Neumann form. From the symmetry of this form one can immediately conclude the reciprocal relation,

$$M_{21} = M_{12}. \tag{7}$$

That is, the voltage induced in circuit 2 by a unit rate of change of current in circuit 1 is the same as the voltage induced in circuit 1 by a unit rate of change of current in circuit 2. Methods of calculating the mutual inductance of specific configurations are given in Art. 5.23.

Finally, by a mutual capacitance coupling we mean that the charge of one circuit produces a significant induced field in another. For example, in the two circuits of Fig. 5.11b, the induced electric field at P_1 from charges may have one part proportional to the charge of circuit 1 and another part proportional to the charge of circuit 2. These concepts will be explored more in the last section of this chapter.

5.12 Circuit Concepts at High Frequencies or Large Dimensions

Whereas the exact circuit equation given in Art. 5.05 is valid for all frequencies, the integrals of Eqs. 5.05(5) and (6) cannot be identified as "inductive" and "capacitive" voltage drops at frequencies high enough so that retardation must be considered in calculating the field potentials. That is, for frequencies at which kr is appreciable,

$$\bar{A} = \int_V \frac{\mu \bar{i} e^{-jkr}\, dV}{4\pi r}$$

and

$$\Phi = \int_V \frac{\rho e^{-jkr}\, dV}{4\pi \epsilon r}.$$

These expressions differ appreciably from the corresponding integrals with kr set equal to zero, as was done in the previous sections. The electric fields with kr finite are not wholly in quadrature with the current. This may occur both because the current is not uniform in phase about the circuit, and also because the retardation of fields resulting from the charges and currents causes time delays which are appreciable compared with a period of the current changes.

Where there is a component of the electric field in phase with the current, the integral of the electric field cannot be considered either as a pure "capacitive" or "inductive" voltage drop since there will be real energy transfer (radiation) from these terms. It is clear then that at high frequencies the usual low-frequency circuit concepts fail and must somehow be extended. The treatments of radiation in Chapter 12 involve detailed consideration of structures which are large compared with the wavelength. One method (the induced emf method) is a direct extension of this circuit point of view, but most often field methods must be used.

CIRCUIT ELEMENTS; SKIN EFFECT AND INTERNAL IMPEDANCE

5.13 Qualitative Considerations

Article 5.07 pointed out that the internal impedance of a wire is, in general, composed of real and imaginary parts. The mangitudes of these components are functions of frequency. The change of the impedance from its value at d-c is attributed to the *skin effect*. Skin effect is often introduced through the example of high-frequency current flow in a solid round conductor, in which it can be demonstrated that current flow at very high frequencies is essentially concentrated in a thin layer or skin near the surface. Students often leave such first introductions to the subject with the impression that this is the most important aspect of skin effect and, worse, believe erroneously that this phenomenon is caused by some sort of mutual repulsion between small filamentary current elements in the wire. With such a picture, they expect always to find current seeking the outside of any conducting system, an impression that would be unfortunate indeed as a preliminary to the study of resonant cavities, waveguides, shields, etc., in which currents may be concentrated on the inner, not outer, walls of the conductors.

The broad picture of skin effect is that of a phenomenon which tends to concentrate currents on the surfaces of conductors nearest to the field

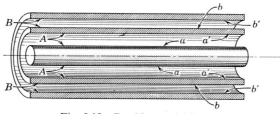

Fig. 5.13   Double coaxial line.

sources producing them. We saw in Art. 4.12 the mathematical and physical reasons for this concentration of the current. In practical conductors used at microwave frequencies, current density may decrease to one millionth of its surface value in a distance of only a few thousandths of an inch, so that any practical thickness of any good conductor becomes a nearly perfect shield between a region with a field source and one without a source. The classical example of current flow in a solid round conductor is now seen to be a special case of this general viewpoint; certainly, if the conductor is solid, the exciting sources must be on the outside, so current will concentrate near the outside. However, if exciting sources are on the inside of a hollow conductor, as they are for the outer conductor of a coaxial line, current will concentrate on the inner wall of that conductor. Finally, we might imagine a double coaxial line, as in Fig. 5.13, formed of good conductors and operated at very high frequencies. Currents due to the source A are concentrated on the walls a and a'; currents due to B are concentrated on the walls b and b'. For all practical purposes shielding between the two coaxial regions may be considered perfect, and phenomena of the two regions completely independent.

As mentioned previously, the general concentration of current into thin layers, as found in skin-effect phenomena, should have a marked effect on impedances, causing them to change with frequency. If current is concentrated over a smaller part of the cross section of a conductor than at low frequencies, the effective conductor cross section is decreased and resistance should increase. Also, if penetration of fields into the conductor becomes less as frequency increases, there should not be as much magnetic flux inside the conductor and internal inductance should decrease. All these phenomena will be studied quantitatively in the following articles.

5.14 Internal Impedance of a Plane Conductor

The internal impedance term, which includes the resistance and internal reactance as discussed in Art. 5.07, may now be found for the plane solid example of Art. 4.12. We shall compute the term for a unit length and unit width. As defined in Art. 5.07, the internal impedance term per unit length is the quotient of electric field at the surface and total current. The total current flowing in the plane conductor is found by integrating the current density, Eq. 4.12(18) from the surface to the infinite depth. For a unit width,

$$J_z = \int_0^\infty i_z \, dx = \int_0^\infty i_0 e^{-(1+j)(x/\delta)} \, dx = \frac{i_0 \delta}{(1+j)}. \tag{1}$$

The electric field at the surface is given by the current density at the surface,

$$E_{z0} = \frac{i_0}{\sigma}. \tag{2}$$

Internal impedance for a unit length and unit width is then

$$Z_s = \frac{E_{z0}}{J_z} = \frac{1+j}{\sigma \delta}. \tag{3}$$

Define

$$Z_s = R_s + j\omega L_i. \tag{4}$$

Then

$$R_s = \frac{1}{\sigma \delta} = \sqrt{\pi f \mu / \sigma} \tag{5}$$

$$\omega L_i = \frac{1}{\sigma \delta} = R_s. \tag{6}$$

The resistance and internal reactance of such a plane conductor are equal at any frequency. The internal impedance Z_s thus has a phase angle of 45°. Equation (5) gives another interpretation of depth of penetration δ, for this equation shows that the skin-effect resistance of the semi-infinite plane conductor is exactly the same as the d-c resistance of a plane conductor of depth δ. That is, resistance of this conductor with exponential decrease in current density is exactly the same as though current were uniformly distributed over a depth δ.

R_s, the resistance of the plane conductor for a unit length and unit width, is called the *surface resistivity*. For a finite area of conductor, the resistance is obtained by multiplying R_s by length, and dividing by width since the width elements are essentially in parallel. Thus the dimension of R_s is ohms or, as it is sometimes called, *ohms per square*. Like the depth of penetration δ, R_s as defined by (5) may also be a useful parameter in the analyses of conductors of other than plane shape, and may be thought of as a constant of the material at frequency f. Values of R_s and δ for several materials are summarized in Table 5.14.

TABLE 5.14

	Conductivity mhos/meter	Permeability henrys/meter	Depth of Penetration meters	Surface Resistivity ohms
	σ	μ	δ	R_s
Silver	6.17×10^7	$4\pi \times 10^{-7}$	$\dfrac{0.0642}{\sqrt{f}}$	$2.52 \times 10^{-7}\sqrt{f}$
Copper	5.80×10^7	$4\pi \times 10^{-7}$	$\dfrac{0.0660}{\sqrt{f}}$	$2.61 \times 10^{-7}\sqrt{f}$
Aluminum	3.72×10^7	$4\pi \times 10^{-7}$	$\dfrac{0.0826}{\sqrt{f}}$	$3.26 \times 10^{-7}\sqrt{f}$
Representative brass	1.57×10^7	$4\pi \times 10^{-7}$	$\dfrac{0.127}{\sqrt{f}}$	$5.01 \times 10^{-7}\sqrt{f}$
Representative solder	0.706×10^7	$4\pi \times 10^{-7}$	$\dfrac{0.185}{\sqrt{f}}$	$7.73 \times 10^{-7}\sqrt{f}$

Problem

5.14 Show that R_s as defined by $R_s = \sqrt{\pi f \mu / \sigma}$ does have the dimensions of ohms.

5.15 Power Loss in a Plane Conductor

To find average power loss per unit area of the plane conductor, we may apply the Poynting theorem of Art. 4.10. The field components E_z and H_y produce a power flow in the x direction, or into the conductor. Utilization of the field values at the surface gives the total power flowing from the field into the conductor. In complex phasor form,

$$W_L = \tfrac{1}{2} \, \text{Re} \, [\bar{E}_0 \times \bar{H}_0{}^*] = \tfrac{1}{2} \, \text{Re} \, (E_{z0} H_{y0}^*). \tag{1}$$

The surface value of magnetic field can readily be related to the surface current, as can be seen by taking the line integral of magnetic field about

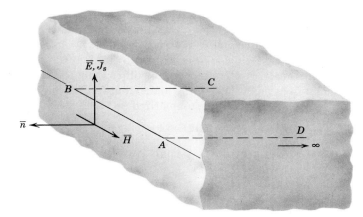

Fig. 5.15   Surface of plane conductor.

some path $ABCD$ of Fig. 5.15 (C and D at infinity). Since magnetic field will be in the y direction for this simple case, there is no contribution to $\bar{H} \cdot \overline{dl}$ along the sides BC and DA; there is no contribution along CD since field is zero at infinity. Hence, for a width w,

$$\oint_{ABCD} \bar{H} \cdot \overline{dl} = \int_{A}^{B} \bar{H} \cdot \overline{dl} = wH_y \Big|_{x=0}. \tag{2}$$

This line integral of magnetic field must be equal to the *conduction* current enclosed, since displacement current has been shown to be negligible in a good conductor. The current is just the width w times the current per unit width, J_z. A negative sign must be introduced since the right-hand sense associated with the direction of circulation $ABCD$ is the negative z direction. Then, utilizing (2),

$$wH_y \big|_{x=0} = -wJ_z \quad \text{or} \quad J_z = -H_y \big|_{x=0}. \tag{3}$$

This may be written in a vector form which includes the magnitude and sense information of (3), and the fact that $\bar{J}$ and $\bar{H}$ are mutually perpendicular:

$$\bar{J} = \bar{n} \times \bar{H}, \tag{4}$$

where $\bar{n}$ is a unit vector perpendicular to the conductor surface, pointing into the adjoining dielectric region and $\bar{H}$ is the magnetic field at the surface. Note that (4) is of the same form as for perfect conductors, Art. 4.14. Then using (1), (4), and Eq. 5.14(3) we obtain

$$W_L = \tfrac{1}{2} \operatorname{Re} [Z_s J_s J_s{}^*] = \tfrac{1}{2} R_s \, |J_s|^2 \text{ watts/meter}^2. \tag{5}$$

This is a form that might have been expected in that it gives loss in terms of resistance multiplied by square of current magnitude. An alternate derivation (Prob. 5.15a) is by the integration of power loss at each point of the solid from the known conductivity and current density function.

Equation (5) will be found of the greatest usefulness throughout this text for the computation of power loss in the walls of waveguides, cavity resonators, and other electromagnetic structures. Although the walls of these structures are not plane solids of infinite depth, the results of this section may be applied for all practical purposes whenever the conductor thickness and radii of curvature are much greater than δ, depth of penetration. This includes most important cases at high frequencies. In these cases the quantities which are ordinarily known are the fields at the surface of the conductor.

Problems

5.15a   The average power loss per unit volume at any point in the conductor is $|i_z|^2/2\sigma$. Show that (5) is correct by integrating over the conductor depth to obtain the total power loss per unit area.

5.15b   Find the magnetic field $\bar{H}$ for any point x in the plane conductor in terms of i_0 by first finding the electric field, and then utilizing the appropriate one of Maxwell's equations to give $\bar{H}$. Check the equation (3) by means of this result.

5.16 Current Distribution in a Wire of Circular Cross Section

Most common of the conductors used in electrical circuits are round wires, wires of circular cross section. If the round wire forms a conducting path with no very sharp curvatures, as in many circuit applications, any small portion may be treated as a straight circular cylinder. It will be assumed that external conditions are applied so that current is in the axial direction only, and that any variations in the axial direction or circumferentially are negligible compared with the variations into the wire (radially). The current distribution equation, 4.12(9), written in cylindrical coordinates with no ϕ or z variations is then (see inside cover):

$$\frac{d^2 i_z}{dr^2} + \frac{1}{r}\frac{di_z}{dr} = j\omega\mu\sigma i_z$$

$$\frac{d^2 i_z}{dr^2} + \frac{1}{r}\frac{di_z}{dr} + T^2 i_z = 0, \qquad (1)$$

where

$$T^2 = -j\omega\mu\sigma$$

or

$$T = j^{-\frac{1}{2}}\sqrt{\omega\mu\sigma} = j^{-\frac{1}{2}}\sqrt{2}/\delta. \qquad (2)$$

A direct comparison of (1) with Eq. 3.25(8) shows that both have exactly the form of the zero order Bessel equation, although T is complex. A complete solution may be written

$$i_z = AJ_0(Tr) + BH_0^{(1)}(Tr).$$ (3)

For a solid wire, $r = 0$ is included in the solution, and then it is necessary that $B = 0$ since a study of $H_0^{(1)}(Tr)$ shows that this would become infinite at $r = 0$, even though T is complex. Therefore,

$$i_z = AJ_0(Tr).$$ (4)

The arbitrary constant A may be evaluated in terms of current density at the surface. Let

$$i_z = i_0 \quad \text{at} \quad r = r_0.$$

Then from (4), $$A = \frac{i_0}{J_0(Tr_0)}$$

and $$i_z = \frac{i_0 J_0(Tr)}{J_0(Tr_0)}.$$ (5)

But T is complex, and it may seem troublesome to find a Bessel function of a complex quantity. As in cases where we are confronted with sines, cosines, and exponentials of complex quantities, however, we can resort to the power series definition for the proper function. Referring to the power series for J_0, it is seen that the function will have both real and imaginary parts if the argument is complex. These may be calculated separately. Define

$$Ber\,(v) \equiv \text{real part of } J_0(j^{-\frac{1}{2}}v)$$

$$Bei\,(v) \equiv \text{imaginary part of } J_0(j^{-\frac{1}{2}}v).$$

That is, $$J_0(j^{-\frac{1}{2}}v) \equiv Ber\,(v) + jBei\,(v).$$ (6)

$Ber\,(v)$ and $Bei\,(v)$ are tabulated in many references.[2] Using these definitions and (2), (5) may be written

$$i_z = i_0 \frac{Ber\,(\sqrt{2}r/\delta) + j\,Bei\,(\sqrt{2}r/\delta)}{Ber\,(\sqrt{2}r_0/\delta) + j\,Bei\,(\sqrt{2}r_0/\delta)}$$ (7)

Plots of current densities as functions of radius in a round wire are shown in Fig. 5.16a. Actually the magnitude of the ratio of current density to that at the outside of the wire is plotted as a function of the ratio of radius to outer radius of wire, for different values of the parameter (r_0/δ). Also, for purposes of the physical picture, these are interpreted in terms of current distribution for a 1-millimeter copper wire at different frequencies by the figures in parentheses.

[2] Dwight, *Tables of Integrals*, rev. ed., Macmillan, New York, 1961; McLachlan, *Bessel Functions for Engineers*, 2nd ed., Oxford Clarendon Press, New York, 1955.

As an example of the applicability of the plane analysis for curved conductors at high frequencies where δ is small compared with radii, we can take the present case of the round wire. If we are to neglect the

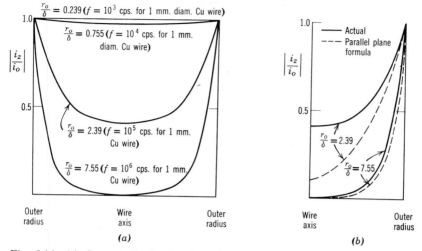

Fig. 5.16   (a) Current distribution in cylindrical wire for different frequencies. (b) Actual and approximate (parallel plane formula) distribution in cylindrical wire.

curvature and apply the plane analysis, the coordinate x, distance below the surface, is $(r_0 - r)$ for a round wire. Then Eq. 4.12(18) gives

$$\left| \frac{i_z}{i_0} \right| = e^{-(r_0-r)/\delta}. \qquad (8)$$

In Fig. 5.16b are plotted curves of $|i_z/i_0|$ by using this formula, and comparisons are made with curves obtained from the exact formula (7). This is done for two cases, $r_0/\delta = 2.39$ and $r_0/\delta = 7.55$. In the latter, the approximate distribution agrees well with the exact; in the former it does not. Thus, if ratio of wire radius to δ is large, it seems that there should be little error in analyzing the wire from the results developed for plane solids. This point will be pursued later in impedance calculations.

Problems

5.16a   Utilizing tables of the *Ber* and *Bei* functions, plot the phase of i_z/i_0 vs. r/r_0 for $r_0/\delta = 2.39$.

5.16b   Derive Eq. (8) for $r_0/\delta \gg 1$ by utilizing the asymptotic formulas for Bessel functions of large arguments in Eq. (5).

5.17 Impedance of a Round Wire at Very High or Very Low Frequencies

Very High Frequency. To show the usefulness of impedance formulas for a semi-infinite plane solid, we shall obtain from them the internal impedance of a round wire at very high frequencies. It has already been shown that, if the frequency is high enough, the curvature of the wire is unimportant. It may then be considered a plane solid of practically infinite depth, and width equal to its circumference. Thus, if Z_s, Eq. 5.14(3), is the internal impedance of the plane solid, per unit square, $Z_s/2\pi r_0$ is the impedance for a width $2\pi r_0$ (the circumference). So, for a round wire of radius r_0 at very high frequencies,

$$Z_{\text{h.f.}} = \frac{(1+j)}{2\pi r_0 \sigma \delta} = \frac{R_s(1+j)}{2\pi r_0}$$

or
$$R_{\text{h.f.}} = (\omega L_i)_{\text{h.f.}} = \frac{R_s}{2\pi r_0} \text{ ohms/meter,} \tag{1}$$

where R_s is as defined in Eq. 5.14(5).

Very Low Frequency. For very low frequencies the current has essentially a uniform distribution over the cross section, Fig. 5.16(a), and so the d-c resistance formula applies:

$$R_0 = \frac{1}{\pi r_0{}^2 \sigma} \text{ ohms/meter.} \tag{2}$$

Internal inductance will be shown in Art. 5.22 to be

$$(L_i)_0 = \frac{\mu}{8\pi} \text{ henrys/meter.} \tag{3}$$

The first correction term to resistance at moderately low frequencies may be obtained from series expansions of the exact results of the next article. This leads to

$$\frac{R}{R_0} = 1 + \frac{1}{48}\left(\frac{r_0}{\delta}\right)^4. \tag{4}$$

Equation (4) is good for small values of r_0/δ and has an error of about 6 per cent at $r_0/\delta = 2$ (that is, for a radius twice the depth of penetration).

Problems

5.17a Show that the ratio of very high-frequency resistance to d-c resistance of a round conductor of radius r_0 and material with depth of penetration δ can be written

$$\frac{R_{\text{h.f.}}}{R_0} = \frac{r_0}{2\delta}.$$

5.17b Using the approximate formula 5.17(4), find the value of r_0/δ below which R differs from d-c resistance R_0 by less than 2 per cent. To what size wire does this correspond for copper at 10 kc/sec? For copper at 1 Mc/sec? For brass at 1 Mc/sec?

5.18 Impedance of Round Wires Generally

The internal impedance of the round wire is found from total current in the wire and the electric intensity at the surface, according to the ideas of Art. 5.07. Total current may be obtained from an integration of current density, as for the plane conductor in Art. 5.14; however, it may also be found from the magnetic field at the surface, since the line integral of magnetic field around the outside of the wire must be equal to the total current in the wire:

$$\oint \bar{H} \cdot \overline{dl} = I$$

or

$$2\pi r_0 H_\phi \big|_{r=r_0} = I. \tag{1}$$

Magnetic field is obtained from the electric field by Maxwell's equations:

$$\nabla \times \bar{E} = -j\omega\mu\bar{H}. \tag{2}$$

For the round wire with the assumptions made in Art. 5.16, E_z and H_ϕ alone are present, and only r derivatives remain, so (2) is simply

$$H_\phi = \frac{1}{j\omega\mu}\frac{dE_z}{dr}. \tag{3}$$

An expression for current density has already been obtained in Eq. 5.16(5). Electric field is related to this through the conductivity σ:

$$E_z = \frac{i_z}{\sigma} = \frac{i_0}{\sigma}\frac{J_0(Tr)}{J_0(Tr_0)}. \tag{4}$$

By substituting in (3) and recalling that $T^2 = -j\omega\mu\sigma$,

$$H_\phi = \frac{i_0 T}{j\omega\mu\sigma}\frac{J_0'(Tr)}{J_0(Tr_0)} = -\frac{i_0}{T}\frac{J_0'(Tr)}{J_0(Tr_0)},$$

where $J_0'(Tr)$ denotes $\dfrac{d}{d(Tr)} J_0(Tr)$. From (1),

$$I = -\frac{2\pi r_0 i_0}{T} \frac{J_0'(Tr_0)}{J_0(Tr_0)}. \tag{5}$$

The internal impedance per unit length is

$$Z_i = \frac{E_z|_{r=r_0}}{I} = -\frac{TJ_0(Tr_0)}{2\pi r_0 \sigma J_0'(Tr_0)}. \tag{6}$$

where Z_i will be complex since T is complex [Eq. 5.16(2)]. To separate into real and imaginary parts, use Eq. 5.16(6):

$$Ber\ v + j\ Bei\ v = J_0(j^{-\frac{1}{2}}v)$$

Also let
$$Ber'\ v + j\ Bei'\ v = \frac{d}{dv}(Ber\ v + j\ Bei\ v)$$

$$= j^{-\frac{1}{2}} J_0'(j^{-\frac{1}{2}}v).$$

Then (6) may be written

$$Z_i = R + j\omega L_i = \frac{jR_s}{\sqrt{2}\pi r_0}\left[\frac{Ber\ q + j\ Bei\ q}{Ber'\ q + j\ Bei'\ q}\right]$$

where
$$R_s = \frac{1}{\sigma\delta} = \sqrt{\pi f\mu/\sigma} \qquad q = \frac{\sqrt{2}\,r_0}{\delta}$$

or
$$R = \frac{R_s}{\sqrt{2}\pi r_0}\left[\frac{Ber\ q\ Bei'\ q - Bei\ q\ Ber'\ q}{(Ber'\ q)^2 + (Bei'\ q)^2}\right]\ \text{ohms/meter}$$

$$\omega L_i = \frac{R_s}{\sqrt{2}\pi r_0}\left[\frac{Ber\ q\ Ber'\ q + Bei\ q\ Bei'\ q}{(Ber'\ q)^2 + (Bei'\ q)^2}\right]\ \text{ohms/meter}.$$

$$\tag{7}$$

These are the expressions for resistance and internal reactance of a round wire at any frequency in terms of the parameter q, which is $\sqrt{2}$ times the ratio of wire radius to depth of penetration. Curves giving the ratios of these quantities to the d-c and to the high-frequency values as functions of r_0/δ are plotted in Figs. 5.18a and 5.18b. A careful study of these will reveal the ranges of r_0/δ over which it is permissible to use the approximate formulas for resistance and reactance. For example, if a 10 per cent error can be tolerated, the high-frequency approximation for resistance, Eq. 5.17(1), may be used for $r_0/\delta > 5.5$; the high-frequency approximation for reactance, Eq. 5.17(1), may be used for $r_0/\delta > 2.2$. The d-c resistance formula, Eq. 5.17(2), may be used for $r_0/\delta < 1.5$, and the d-c inductance formula, Eq. 5.17(3), may be used for $r_0/\delta < 1.9$.

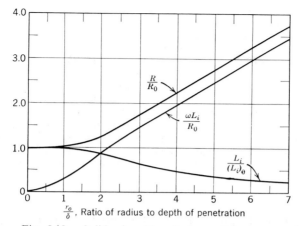

Fig. 5.18a Solid wire skin effect quantities compared
with d-c values.

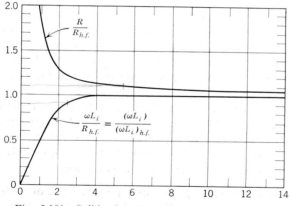

Fig. 5.18b Solid wire skin effect quantities compared
with values from high-frequency formulas.

Problems

5.18a For small values of Tr_0 (low frequencies) the Bessel functions may be approximated by only a few terms of the series, Eq. 3.25(11). Using three terms of the series for J_0 and J_0', show that these values, substituted in Eq. 5.18(6), lead to the expressions for low-frequency resistance and inductance stated in Eq. 5.17(3) and Eq. 5.17(4).

5.18*b* For large values of Tr_0 (high frequencies) the Bessel functions may be approximated by the asymptotic forms of Art. 3.27. Show that these, substituted in Eq. 5.18(6), lead to the expressions for resistance and internal inductance at high frequencies obtained in Eq. 5.17(1).

5.18*c* From Figs. 5.18*a* and 5.18*b*, investigate the ranges of r_0/δ over which it is permissible to use the approximate formulas of Eqs. 5.17(1), 5.17(2), and 5.17(3) if the error must be less than 5 per cent.

5.18*d* For two geometrically similar systems of good conductors of the same material, show that current distributions will be similar, and current densities equal in magnitude at similar points, if the applied voltage to the small system is $1/K$ in magnitude and K^2 in frequency that of the large system. Also show that the impedance of the small system will be K times that of the large system under these conditions. Check these conclusions for the case of two round wires of different radii. K is the ratio of linear dimensions.

5.19   Impedance of a Coated Conductor

Coated conductors appear in radio applications in the form of tinned copper wires, copper-plated iron or iron alloys in vacuum tube leads, silver-plated brass in resonant cavities, etc. Most often the problem is one of the following.

1. The coating material may be very thick compared with depth of penetration in that material. This requires no analysis since fields and currents in the coated metal are then negligible, and the impedance is governed only by the metal of the coating; the conductor is as good or as bad as a solid conductor of the coating material.

2. The coating may not be thick enough to prevent currents from flowing in the coated material, but penetration in both materials may be small compared with surface curvature so that the surfaces may be considered as planes, the coated material also being effectively infinite in depth. An analysis of this second case will follow.

In Fig. 5.19*a* is shown a plane solid material (conductivity σ_2, permeability μ_2) of effectively infinite depth coated with another material (conductivity σ_1, permeability μ_1) of thickness d. Solutions for the distribution equations must be found for both media and matched at the boundary between the two. The solution in either material is of the form of Eq. 4.12(18), but there can be no positive exponential term for the lower material since current density must become zero at infinite depth.

$$i_{z_2} = Ce^{-\tau_2 x}$$

$$\tau_2 = \frac{(1 + j)}{\delta_2} = (1 + j)\sqrt{\pi f \mu_2 \sigma_2}. \tag{1}$$

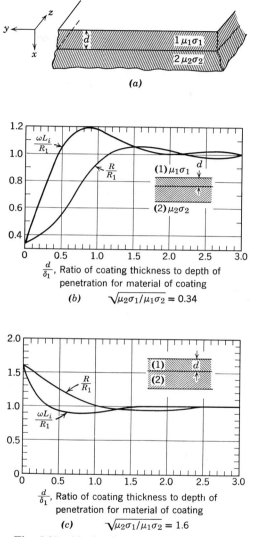

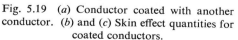

Fig. 5.19 (a) Conductor coated with another conductor. (b) and (c) Skin effect quantities for coated conductors.

In the coating material both exponentials must be present, but it is convenient to write the solution in terms of hyperbolic functions instead of the equivalent exponentials:

$$i_{z_1} = A \sinh \tau_1 x + B \cosh \tau_1 x$$

$$\tau_1 = \frac{(1 + j)}{\delta_1} = (1 + j)\sqrt{\pi f \mu_1 \sigma_1}. \tag{2}$$

For both materials,

$$E_z = \frac{i_z}{\sigma},$$

and, from Maxwell's equations,

$$H_y = \frac{1}{j\omega\mu}\frac{dE_z}{dx} = \frac{\sigma}{\tau^2}\frac{dE_z}{dx}.$$

Electric and magnetic fields in the two materials are then

$$E_{z_2} = \frac{C}{\sigma_2} e^{-\tau_2 x} \qquad E_{z_1} = \frac{1}{\sigma_1}(A \sinh \tau_1 x + B \cosh \tau_1 x)$$

$$H_y = -\frac{C}{\tau_2} e^{-\tau_2 x} \qquad H_{y_1} = \frac{1}{\tau_1}(A \cosh \tau_1 x + B \sinh \tau_1 x). \tag{3}$$

The constants may be evaluated since tangential electric and magnetic fields are continuous across the boundary (Art. 4.13):

$$E_{z1} = E_{z2} \quad H_{y1} = H_{y2} \quad \text{at} \quad x = d$$

Then
$$\frac{B}{A} = -\left[\frac{\sinh \tau_1 d + (\tau_2\sigma_1/\tau_1\sigma_2)\cosh \tau_1 d}{\cosh \tau_1 d + (\tau_2\sigma_1/\tau_1\sigma_2)\sinh \tau_1 d}\right]. \tag{4}$$

Total current in the two materials is obtainable from Eq. 5.15(4):

$$\bar{J} = \bar{n} \times \bar{H} \quad \text{or} \quad J_z = -H_y\big|_{x=0}$$

The impedance per square (per unit width and unit length) is

$$Z = \frac{E_z\big|_{x=0}}{J_z} = -\frac{E_z}{H_y}\bigg|_{x=0} = -\frac{B}{A}\frac{\tau_1}{\sigma_1}. \tag{5}$$

From (4) with τ_1 and τ_2 substituted,

$$\frac{Z}{R_{s1}} = (1 + j)\left[\frac{\sinh \tau_1 d + (R_{s2}/R_{s1})\cosh \tau_1 d}{\cosh \tau_1 d + (R_{s2}/R_{s1})\sinh \tau_1 d}\right]. \tag{6}$$

Curves of ratio of resistance and reactance of the composite conductor to resistance of a conductor made entirely of the coating material are plotted in Fig. 5.19*b* for $R_{s2}/R_{s1} = 0.34$, which corresponds roughly to solder on copper. Similar curves are given in Fig. 5.19*c* for a ratio of 1.6, which corresponds roughly to silver on brass. It is seen that in both cases the composite conductor becomes about as good, or as bad, as though the coating were of infinite depth when the coating thickness is greater than δ_1, depth of penetration for the material of the coating.

Problems

5.19a For the case of $R_{s2}/R_{s1} = 1.6$, find the ratio of the power loss in the coating material to that in the base when $d/\delta_1 = 1$.

5.19b For the conditions of Prob. *a*, find the ratio of energy stored in magnetic fields for the coating material to that in the base.

5.20 Impedance of Thin-Walled Tubular Conductors

A study of the current distribution in a solid round wire shows that at the higher frequencies the inner part of the conducting material plays little part in the conduction. There should consequently be little difference in impedance under such skin effect conditions between a solid round wire and a hollow tubular conductor of the same outer diameter. Certainly this is true when the wall thickness is very large compared with the depth of penetration of the conducting material, and we would use the same high-frequency equation, Eq. 5.17(1), that was developed for a round wire. If this criterion is not satisfied, the finite wall thickness must be taken into account. An exact solution may be carried through in terms of Bessel functions, but many times the wall thickness is small enough compared with wire radius so that the analysis of a flat plane conductor of finite thickness may be applied well enough. The result for this problem may be lazily found by setting conductivity of the lower material equal to zero in the result for the composite conductor of Art. 5.19. That is, in Eq. 5.19(6), set $R_{s2} = \infty$. Then, the surface impedance per square

$$Z = R + j\omega L_i = (1 + j)R_s \frac{\cosh \tau d}{\sinh \tau d} \tag{1}$$

$$= (1 + j)R_s \coth\left[\frac{d}{\delta}(1 + j)\right], \tag{2}$$

$$\frac{R}{R_s} = \frac{\sinh(2d/\delta) + \sin(2d/\delta)}{\cosh(2d/\delta) - \cos(2d/\delta)}. \tag{3}$$

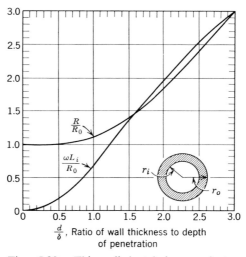

$\dfrac{d}{\delta}$, Ratio of wall thickness to depth of penetration

Fig. 5.20a Thin-walled tubular conductor. Skin effect quantities compared with d-c values.

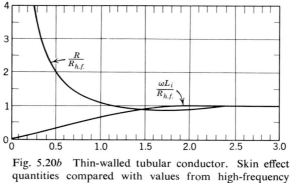

Fig. 5.20b Thin-walled tubular conductor. Skin effect quantities compared with values from high-frequency formulas.

For a tubular conductor satisfying the conditions of wall thickness small compared with radius of tube these results may be used directly to give impedance per unit length by dividing by the circumference:

$$R \approx \frac{R_s}{2\pi r}\left[\frac{\sinh(2d/\delta)+\sin(2d/\delta)}{\cosh(2d/\delta)-\cos(2d/\delta)}\right] \qquad (4)$$

$$\omega L_i \approx \frac{R_s}{2\pi r}\left[\frac{\sinh(2d/\delta)-\sin(2d/\delta)}{\cosh(2d/\delta)-\cos(2d/\delta)}\right], \qquad (5)$$

where r = outer radius if fields are applied along outside of tube; r = inner radius if fields are applied along inside of tube.

The high-frequency resistance of the tubular conductor is merely

$$R_{\text{h.f.}} = (\omega L_i)_{\text{h.f.}} = \frac{R_s}{2\pi r}$$

Curves of ratios of resistance and internal reactance to d-c resistance are given in Fig. 5.20a, and to high-frequency resistance in Fig. 5.20b.

Problems

5.20a Explain qualitatively why the ratio of a-c resistance for a tubular conductor to the a-c resistance of a solid conductor of the same outer radius is always less than the ratio of d-c resistances for the two conductors. Explain why the a-c resistance of the tubular conductor is always somewhat greater than the a-c resistance of the solid conductor.

5.20b The analysis of this article is equivalent to solving for the case of a slab conductor of finite depth d, with the boundary condition that tangential magnetic field is zero at $x = d$. Explain why this boundary condition is appropriate for the problem.

5.20c Show that for a tubular conductor of outer radius r_0, inner radius r_i with voltage applied from the outside, the exact expression for skin effect resistance and reactance is

$$R + j\omega L_i = \frac{j^{-\frac{1}{2}}\sqrt{2}R_s}{2\pi r_0}\left[\frac{J_0(Tr_0)H_0^{(1)\prime}(Tr_i) - J_0^\prime(Tr_i)H_0^{(1)}(Tr_0)}{J_0^\prime(Tr_0)H_0^{(1)\prime}(Tr_i) - J_0^\prime(Tr_i)H_0^{(1)\prime}(Tr_0)}\right],$$

with T as in Eq. 5.16(2).

5.20d For a case with $r_0/\delta = 1.25$ and $r_i/\delta = 1.0$, calculate the skin effect resistance from the result of the preceding problem and compare with that calculated from the approximate expression, Eq. 5.20(4).

5.20e Show that the result of Prob. 5.20c may be used for a tubular conductor with voltage applied at the inner radius, if r_0 and r_i are interchanged.

CIRCUIT ELEMENTS: INDUCTANCE

5.21 Inductance from Flux Linkages; Self-Inductance of Coaxial Line

The purpose of this section of the chapter is to demonstrate by example the several methods for finding the self- and mutual inductance coefficients of classical circuit theory discussed in previous articles. The examples to be chosen will be those for which results are of great interest in themselves. The first example will be the important one of a coaxial transmission line, and the method to be used will be the most familiar one of finding inductance from the flux linkages per unit current.

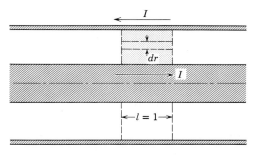

Fig. 5.21   Coaxial transmission line.

From Eq. 5.08(4), the inductance of a closed circuit is

$$L = \frac{1}{I} \int_S \bar{B} \cdot \overline{dS}, \tag{1}$$

or, in words, it is the magnetic flux linking current I, per unit of current I. For a coaxial line as pictured in Fig. 5.21 with axial current I flowing in the inner conductor and returning in the outer, the magnetic field is circumferential and for $a < r < b$ is (Art. 2.27)

$$H_\phi = \frac{I}{2\pi r}. \tag{2}$$

For a unit length the magnetic flux between radii a and b is, by integration over the shaded area in Fig. 5.21,

$$\int_S \bar{B} \cdot \overline{dS} = \int_a^b \mu\left(\frac{I}{2\pi r}\right) dr = \frac{\mu I}{2\pi} \ln \frac{b}{a}.$$

So, from (1), the inductance per unit length is

$$L = \frac{\mu}{2\pi} \ln \frac{b}{a} \text{ henrys/meter.} \tag{3}$$

The value obtained in (3) is of course the *external inductance* of the line, giving the contribution to inductance from flux external to conductors (in this case, between the two conductors). If total inductance is desired, the internal inductance of the solid inner conductor and of the tubular outer conductor (Arts. 5.18 and 5.20) must be added.

Problems

5.21a A coaxial transmission line has a solid copper inner conductor of radius 0.20 cm and a tubular copper outer conductor of inner radius 1 cm, wall thickness 0.1 cm. Find the total impedance per unit length of line for a frequency of 10 kc/sec, including the internal impedance of both conductors. Accuracy obtainable from curves given in the text will be acceptable.

5.21b For a coaxial transmission line as described in Prob. *a*, find the ratio of internal inductance from both conductors to the external inductance of the line for a frequency of 3000 Mc/sec.

5.22 Inductance from Energy Storage; Internal Inductance of Round Wire

An alternative method for computing inductance which is more convenient for many cases arises from a consideration of energy stored in the magnetic fields. From a circuit point of view, this is known to be $\frac{1}{2}LI^2$, where I is the instantaneous current flow through the inductance. It was shown in Art. 4.10 that the magnetic energy may be found by integrating an energy density of $\frac{1}{2}\mu H^2$ throughout the volume of significant fields. Equating these two forms gives

$$\tfrac{1}{2}LI^2 = \int_V \frac{\mu}{2} H^2 \, dV. \tag{1}$$

The form of (1) is especially convenient for problems that would require consideration of partial linkages if done by the method of flux linkages of the preceding article. As an example, consider the calculation of internal inductance of a round wire of radius r_0 at frequencies low enough so that current distribution may be considered uniform. The magnetic field (Prob. 2.27a and Prob. 2.33c) is

$$H_\phi = \frac{Ir}{2\pi r_0^2}, \qquad r < r_0. \tag{2}$$

For a unit length, substituting in (1),

$$\tfrac{1}{2}LI^2 = \int_0^{r_0} \frac{\mu}{2}\left(\frac{Ir}{2\pi r_0^2}\right)^2 2\pi r \, dr = \frac{\mu I^2}{4\pi r_0^4} \cdot \frac{r_0^4}{4}$$

or

$$L = \frac{\mu}{8\pi} \text{ henrys/meter.} \tag{3}$$

This is the result cited as Eq. 5.17(3), and is also obtainable as a limiting case from the a-c analysis of Art. 5.18.

Problems

5.22a Derive the formula for external inductance of the coaxial line by the energy method.

5.22b Derive the expression for internal inductance of the tubular outer conductor of Fig. 5.21 for low frequencies by the energy method.

5.22c Derive the formula for internal inductance of the plane conductor of infinite depth (Art. 5.14) by the energy method. *Suggestion:* Use average values of stored energy.

5.23 Mutual Inductance

Various formulas were given in Art. 5.11 for the mutual inductance between two circuits. Here we will give some broadly applicable examples of the use of the mutual inductance formulas in particular circuit configurations. One of these will be seen in the next article to be useful for the determination of the self-inductance of a single-loop conductor.

The most familiar mutual inductance formula is that giving M as the flux linking circuit 1 from a current in circuit 2, per unit of current in circuit 2, or vice versa. From Eq. 5.11(5), we see that

$$M = \frac{\int_{S_1} \bar{B}_2 \cdot \overline{dS}_1}{I_2}. \tag{1}$$

Since the concept of mutual inductance applies only where the fields may be calculated without considering retardation, any of the appropriate methods of Chapters 2 and 3 may be used to find the flux density B_2. For instance, if (1) were to be applied to two coaxial circular conductors of Fig. 5.23a, the flux B_2 could be obtained from Eq. 3.32(6).

A second derived form for mutual inductance is the Neumann form of Eq. 5.11(6):

$$M = \frac{\mu}{4\pi} \oint \oint \frac{\overline{dl}_1 \cdot \overline{dl}_2}{r}. \tag{2}$$

The integrations are performed about the two circuits, 1 and 2, with $\overline{dl}_1$ and $\overline{dl}_2$ representing differential elements of length about 1 and 2, respectively. To demonstrate the application of this form we shall find the mutual inductance between the two coaxial circular loops pictured in Fig. 5.23a. If $\overline{dl}_1$ is any element of circuit 1 and $\overline{dl}_2$ is any element of circuit 2

$$\overline{dl}_1 \cdot \overline{dl}_2 = dl_2 a \, d\theta \cos \theta$$

$$r = \sqrt{d^2 + (a \sin \theta)^2 + (a \cos \theta - b)^2}.$$

By substituting $\theta = \pi - 2\phi$ and

$$k^2 = \frac{4ab}{d^2 + (a + b)^2},$$

the integral will then be found to become

$$M = \mu\sqrt{ab}\, k \int_0^{\pi/2} \frac{(2 \sin^2 \phi - 1)\, d\phi}{\sqrt{1 - k^2 \sin^2 \phi}},$$

which can be written as

$$M = \mu\sqrt{ab}\left[\left(\frac{2}{k} - k\right) K(k) - \frac{2}{k} E(k)\right] \tag{3}$$

where

$$E(k) = \int_0^{\pi/2} \sqrt{1 - k^2 \sin^2 \phi}\, d\phi \tag{4}$$

$$K(k) = \int_0^{\pi/2} \frac{d\phi}{\sqrt{1 - k^2 \sin^2 \phi}}. \tag{5}$$

The definite integrals (4) and (5) are given in tables[3] as functions of k and are called *complete elliptic integrals* of the first and second kinds, respectively.

Finally, another method involves integration of the vector potential along circuit 1 resulting from the current in circuit 2. From Eq. 5.11(3), we see that

$$M = \frac{1}{I_2} \oint_{C_1} \bar{A}_2 \cdot \overline{dl}_1. \tag{6}$$

This form is convenient for calculating the approximate values of M for circuits with configurations which are not readily treated exactly. It is sometimes convenient to replace such a configuration with a circuit composed of straight sections such that the straight sections in the two circuits are either parallel or perpendicular to each other. We know that, for a straight current element, the potential $\bar{A}$ arising from that element must have the direction of that element. Where circuit 2 may be considered a filamentary path, $\bar{A}$ may be computed from Eq. 5.11(2). The induced field from changing magnetic effects,

$$\bar{E} = -\frac{\partial \bar{A}}{\partial t} = -j\omega\bar{A}, \tag{7}$$

has the direction of $\bar{A}$. Consequently in the system of Fig. 5.23b there can be no contribution to voltage in the sides a_2 and b_2 from current in the sides c_1 and d_1, nor any contribution in the sides c_2 and d_2 from current

[3] Dwight, *Tables of Integrals*, rev. ed., Macmillian, New York, 1961.

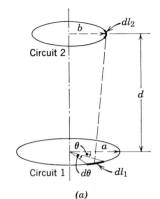

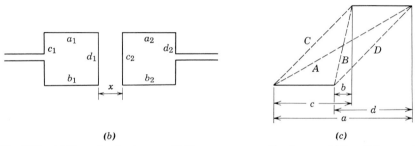

Fig. 5.23 (a) Two circular loops. (b) Two square coupling loops. (c) Parallel current elements displaced from one another.

in the sides a_1 and b_1. The picture obtained from visualizing these directive relations is frequently valuable where the circuit configuration is quite complicated.

Problems

5.23a Set up the integral for determining flux through circuit 1 when the complete series [(Eq. 3.32(6)] is to be used.

5.23b If d/b in Fig. 5.23a is much greater than a/b, or if a/b is much less than unity with any value of d, a study of the series in Eq. 3.32(6) shows that H_z can be assumed to be substantially constant over the area of the first loop. Find the mutual inductance for this case.

5.23c A coaxial line has the radius of the inner conductor as a and inside radius of outer conductor as b, and is closed by a conducting plane at $z = 0$. A square loop is introduced for coupling, lying in a longitudinal plane and extending from $z = 0$ to $z = d$ in length and from $r = r_1$ to $r = r_2$ in radius ($a < r_1 < r_2 < b$). Find the mutual inductance between loop and line.

5.23d From tables of the complete elliptic integrals given in the reference, plot the form of mutual inductance against d/a for $b/a = 1$.

5.23e Investigate the properties of the complete elliptic integrals from the reference for $k \ll 1$ and for $k \approx 1$, and obtain approximate expressions for mutual inductance for these two cases.

5.23f By integration of Eq. 5.23(6), show that the contribution to mutual inductance from two parallel line segments displaced as shown in Fig. 5.23c is

$$M = \frac{\mu}{4\pi}\left[\ln\left\{\frac{(A + a)^a(B + b)^b}{(C + c)^c(D + d)^d}\right\} + (C + D) - (A + B)\right].$$

5.23g Apply the result of Prob. f to the calculation of mutual inductance between two square loops used for coupling between open-wire transmission lines as shown in Fig. 5.23b. The length of each side is 0.03 meter; the separation x is 0.01 meter. Assume that the gaps at which the lines enter are small enough to be ignored.

5.23h For the coaxial line of Fig. 5.21, find vector potential for each of three regions by solving the Poisson equation as in Eq. 2.33(4) with proper continuity conditions between the regions. With $\bar{A}$ known, apply formula 5.08(2) to find self-inductance of the coaxial line (external) in terms of the vector potential.

5.24 Self-Inductance by Selected Mutual Inductance: Inductance of a Circular Loop

The external self-inductance of a loop conductor of finite cross section is defined as the ratio of the flux passing through the loop, external to the conductor, to the current flowing in the loop. Let us consider the arbitrarily shaped loop shown in Fig. 5.24a and see how the required flux may be found. It is the integral over the flux density, $\bar{B} = \mu\bar{H}$, normal to the surface bounded by the inside edge of the loop. We note that for a point P some distance from the wire, the field produced by a given total current in the conductor is essentially independent of the distribution of the current over the cross section of the conductor. In particular, for a point such as P, it is nearly correct to calculate the field intensity by assuming all current concentrated along the axis of the conductor as indicated in Fig. 5.24b. Similarly, at point Q near the wire, the field is $I/2\pi\rho$ where I is the total current and ρ is the distance from the axis of the conductor, *provided other portions of the conducting path are not near enough to disturb the circular symmetry of the current distribution in the conductor.* That is, the radius of curvature of the loop at each point should be large compared with the radius of the conductor.

We conclude that fields at any point inside the loop may be calculated approximately by assuming a current concentrated along the axis of the wire so long as the proximity effect from other portions of the conducting path is not great enough to disturb the current distribution in the conductor.

Then the problem of finding the contribution of self-inductance from the external flux is very nearly that of finding the mutual inductance between a line current along the axis of the wire and a line circuit selected along the

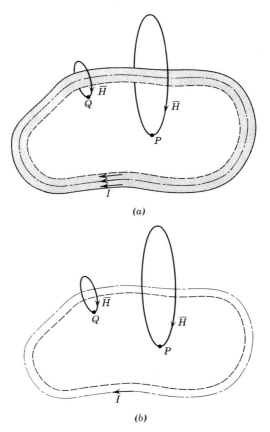

(a)

(b)

Fig. 5.24 (a) Conducting loop for which external self-inductance is to be found. (b) Equivalent filamentary circuits.

inner surface of the wire. Any of the methods of the past three articles may be used for the calculation.

As an example of this method, which might be called the selected mutual inductance method, let us find the inductance of a circular loop of wire. The wire radius is a, and the loop radius is r. The contribution to inductance from external flux, given by the mutual inductance between two concentric circles of radii r and $(r - a)$ may be obtained from Eq. 5.23(3):

$$L_0 = \mu(2r - a)\left[\left(1 - \frac{k^2}{2}\right)K(k) - E(k)\right] \tag{1}$$

$$k^2 = \frac{4r(r - a)}{(2r - a)^2},$$

where $E(k)$ and $K(k)$ are complete elliptic integrals of first and second kinds as defined by Eqs. 5.23(4) and 5.23(5). If a/r is very small, k is nearly unity, and K and E may be approximated by

$$K(k) \simeq \ln\left(\frac{4}{\sqrt{1 - k^2}}\right)$$

$$E(k) \simeq 1$$

so
$$L_0 \simeq r\mu\left[\ln\left(\frac{8r}{a}\right) - 2\right] \text{ henrys.} \tag{2}$$

To find total L, values of internal inductance, as listed in Arts. 5.17 or 5.18 must be added.

Problem

5.24 Suppose 1 mm-diameter copper wire is formed into a single circular loop having a radius of 10 cm. A voltage generator of one volt rms and 10 Mc/sec is connected to an infinitesimal gap in the loop. Find the current flowing in the loop, taking into account internal impedance as well as external inductance. Justify any approximations used.

5.25 Inductance of Practical Coils

A study of the inductance of coils at low frequencies involves no new concepts but only new troubles because of the complications in geometry. Certain special cases are simple enough for calculation by a straightforward application of previously outlined methods. For example, for a circular coil of N turns formed into a circular cross section (Fig. 5.25a) we may modify the formula for a circular loop of one turn, Eq. 5.24(2), provided the cross section is small compared with the coil radius. Magnetic field must be computed on the basis of a current NI; in addition, to compute the total induced voltage about the coil, N integrations must be made about the loop. Equation 5.24(2) is thus modified by a factor N^2. The external inductance for this coil is then

$$L_0 = N^2 R\mu\left[\ln\left(\frac{8R}{a}\right) - 2\right] \text{ henrys.} \tag{1}$$

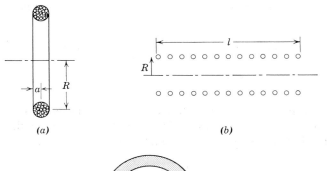

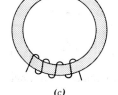

(c)

Fig. 5.25   (a) Coil of large radius-to-length ratio. (b) Solenoidal
coil. (c) Solenoidal coil on high-permeability core.

For the other extreme, the inductance of a very long solenoid (Fig.
5.25b) may be computed. If the solenoid is long enough, the magnetic
field on the inside is essentially constant, as for the infinite solenoid
(Prob. 2.27c):

$$H_z = \frac{NI}{l}, \tag{2}$$

where N is the total number of turns and l the length. The flux linkages
for N turns is then $N\pi R^2 \mu H_z$, and the inductance is

$$L_0 = \frac{\pi\mu R^2 N^2}{l} \text{ henrys.} \tag{3}$$

For coils of intermediate length to radius ratio, empirical or semi-
empirical formulas frequently have to be used.[4,5] The famous Nagaoka
formula[6] applies a correction factor K to the formula for the long solenoid,
(3). The factor K or its equivalent is tabulated in the references cited and in

[4] *Reference Data for Radio Engineers*, 4th ed., International Telephone and Telegraph
Corporation, New York, 1956.
[5] F. W. Grover, *Inductance Calculations*, Van Nostrand, Princeton, N.J., 1946.
[6] Nagaoka, *J. Coll. Sci. Tokyo*, **27**, Art. 6 (1909).

many standard handbooks.[7] Another simple approximate form useful for $l > 0.8R$ is[8]

$$L_0 = \frac{\pi\mu R^2 N^2}{l + 0.9R} \text{ henrys.} \tag{4}$$

If a coil is wound on a toroidal core of high permeability as shown in Fig. 5.25c, the flux essentially is restricted to the core region, independent of the length of the winding. The magnetic field intensity is again given by (2) and the inductance by (3) with $l = 2\pi r_0$ where r_0 is the mean radius of the toroid.

At higher frequencies the problem becomes more complex. When turns are relatively close together, the assumption made previously in calculating internal impedance (other portions of the circuit so far away that circular symmetry of current in the wire is not disturbed) certainly does not apply. Current elements in neighboring turns will be near enough to produce nearly as much effect upon current distribution in a given turn as the current in that turn itself. Values of skin effect resistance and internal inductance are then not as previously calculated. External inductance may also be different since changes in external fields result when current loses its symmetrical distribution with respect to the wire axis. In fact, the strict separation of internal and external inductance may not be possible for these coils, for a given field line may be sometimes inside and sometimes outside of the conductor. Finally, distributed capacitances may be important and further complicate matters (Art. 5.10).

Coils utilizing superconductors, which are materials giving zero resistance below some critical temperature near absolute zero, have recently become important because one can obtain with proper design very high values of uniform magnetic fields with them, without the use of iron. They may also be very efficient devices for storage of large energies. Cooling is simpler since conduction losses occur only in the lead-in wires which are outside of the low-temperature bath. The electromagnetic principles of design are the same as given for other coils—and in fact the approximations may be better satisfied by the thin wires typically used in superconducting magnets. The mechanical forces of the large currents must be considered in the design, and the transient behavior of a superconductor is very different from that of an ordinary conductor. Hempstead et al.[9] give examples of various coil configurations, with reference to the background literature.

[7] For example, F. E. Terman, *Radio Engineers' Handbook*, McGraw-Hill, New York 1943.
[8] H. A. Wheeler, *Proc. I.R.E.*, **16**, 1398–1400 (Oct. 1928).
[9] C. F. Hempstead, Y. B. Kim, and A. R. Strnad, "Inductive Behavior of Super-Conducting Magnets," *Journ. Appl. Phys.* **34**, 3226 (Nov. 1963).

CIRCUIT ELEMENTS; SELF- AND MUTUAL CAPACITANCES

5.26 The Coefficients of Potential, Capacitance, and Induction

The capacitance term of circuit theory was discussed in terms of field theory in Art. 5.09. Under the assumptions applicable to classical circuit theory, the term for a two-conductor capacitor assumed its common form with capacitance defined as the charge on one conductor divided by the

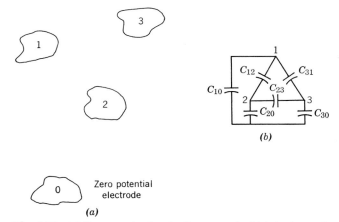

(b)

Zero potential
electrode

(a)

Fig. 5.26 (a) Four conducting bodies, one of which is chosen to have zero potential. (b) The equivalent circuit for (a).

difference of scalar potential between the two. This definition is so well known that it has been used for many electrostatic examples in Chapters 2 and 3, and no additional examples need be given here. However, the case of several conductors with capacitance coupling between them is also of interest, and will be discussed in this section.

In engineering practice, a problem of capacitance coupling between several conductors, as in Fig. 5.26a, is commonly handled by drawing an equivalent circuit with a capacitance between each pair of conductors. This is illustrated for the problem of Fig. 5.26a in Fig. 5.26b. The classical discussion of the several-conductor problem is that of Maxwell[10] in

[10] James Clerk Maxwell, *A Treatise on Electricity and Magnetism*, Vol. I, 3rd ed., Oxford, New York, 1892, pp. 107–118.

terms of defined coefficients of potential, capacitance, and induction. Since both points of view have usefulness, it is desirable to discuss the relation between the two. The present article will define the coefficients of Maxwell, and give certain of their properties.

From the basic equation for scalar potential Φ, Eq. 4.17(3), it is evident that, for a system with charge $Q_1, Q_2, \ldots, Q_n$ on n conductors, the potential at any point will be linearly related to the several charges. We may consider the potential of one of the electrodes to be the zero reference. The values of the coefficients depend on whether or not the zero reference is grounded but the forms of the general relations are not affected. The nature of a grounded conductor is that it implies an infinite reservoir of charge so that an excess of charge at one point does not imply a deficiency at some other point. Thus, for the potentials $\Phi_1, \Phi_2, \ldots, \Phi_n$ on the n conductors, we may write the set of linear equations

$$\Phi_1 = p_{11}Q_1 + p_{12}Q_2 + \cdots + p_{1n}Q_n$$
$$\Phi_2 = p_{21}Q_1 + p_{22}Q_2 + \cdots + p_{2n}Q_n$$
$$\cdots\cdots\cdots\cdots\cdots\cdots\cdots\cdots\cdots\cdots \tag{1}$$
$$\Phi_n = p_{n1}Q_1 + p_{n2}Q_2 + \cdots + p_{nn}Q_n.$$

The coefficients p_{rs} are the *coefficients of potential*, and are all real if retardation may be neglected in the computation of Φ.

The linear set of equations (1) may be solved for the charges, leading to another linear set relating charges to potentials:

$$Q_1 = c_{11}\Phi_1 + c_{12}\Phi_2 + \cdots + c_{1n}\Phi_n$$
$$Q_2 = c_{21}\Phi_1 + c_{22}\Phi_2 + \cdots + c_{2n}\Phi_n$$
$$\cdots\cdots\cdots\cdots\cdots\cdots\cdots\cdots\cdots \tag{2}$$
$$Q_n = c_{n1}\Phi_1 + c_{n2}\Phi_2 + \cdots + c_{nn}\Phi_n$$

where
$$c_{rs} = (-1)^{s+r}\frac{M_{sr}(p)}{\Delta(p)}, \tag{3}$$

$\Delta(p)$ is the determinant of the coefficients p_{rs}, and $M_{sr}(p)$ is the minor of the rth row and sth column. Above coefficients of the form c_{rr} are called coefficients of self-capacitance since such a term represents the ratio of charge on the rth body to potential on that body, all other conductors being set to zero potential. A term of the form c_{rs} ($r \neq s$) represents the ratio of charge on s to potential on r when all conductors but r are set to zero potential. Coefficients of the latter form are called *coefficients of induction* and are related to the mutual capacitances of the equivalent circuit, as will be shown in the following article.

Important properties of the coefficients of potential, capacitance, and induction are:

1. Reciprocity: $c_{rs} = c_{sr}$ and $p_{rs} = p_{sr}$.
2. All p's are positive or zero.
3. c_{rr} is positive or zero.
4. c_{rs} ($r \neq s$) is negative or zero.
5. The sum $c_{1s} + c_{2s} + \cdots + c_{ns}$ is positive or zero.

5.27 Capacitance Elements in the Equivalent Circuit

To study the relation between the coefficients of potential, capacitance, and induction, and the capacitances appearing in an equivalent circuit such as Fig. 5.26b, ahe first step is that of writing the charge equation for the various nodes of the equivalent circuit in terms of the potentials. Let us write them for the three-conductor problem of Figs. 5.26a, b:

$$Q_1 = C_{10}\Phi_1 + C_{13}(\Phi_1 - \Phi_3) + C_{12}(\Phi_1 - \Phi_2)$$
$$Q_2 = C_{20}\Phi_2 + C_{12}(\Phi_2 - \Phi_1) + C_{23}(\Phi_2 - \Phi_3)$$
$$Q_3 = C_{30}\Phi_3 + C_{23}(\Phi_3 - \Phi_2) + C_{13}(\Phi_3 - \Phi_1).$$

By comparison with the set of equations 5.26(2),

$$c_{11} = C_{10} + C_{12} + C_{13} \qquad c_{12} = -C_{12}$$
$$c_{22} = C_{20} + C_{12} + C_{23} \qquad c_{13} = -C_{13}$$
$$c_{33} = C_{30} + C_{13} + C_{23} \qquad c_{23} = -C_{23}$$

or

$$C_{10} = c_{11} + c_{12} + c_{13} \qquad C_{12} = -c_{12}$$
$$C_{20} = c_{22} + c_{12} + c_{23} \qquad C_{13} = -c_{13}$$
$$C_{30} = c_{33} + c_{13} + c_{23} \qquad C_{23} = -c_{23}$$

Generalizing, the capacitance from the rth conductor to the zero potential electrode is just the sum of the coefficient of self-capacitance and all the coefficients of induction for that conductor:

$$C_{r0} = \sum_{s=1}^{n} c_{rs}. \tag{1}$$

By the property 5 of Art. 5.26, each of these capacitances to the zero potential electrode is positive or zero. The mutual capacitance between element r and s is just the negative of the corresponding coefficient of induction:

$$C_{rs} = -c_{rs}. \tag{2}$$

5.28   Electrostatic Shielding

In electrostatic shielding between two bodies, as 1 and 3 of Fig. 5.28a, it is desired to decrease the capacitive coupling between these bodies to as small a value as possible. Of course, if a new conductor 2 is introduced into

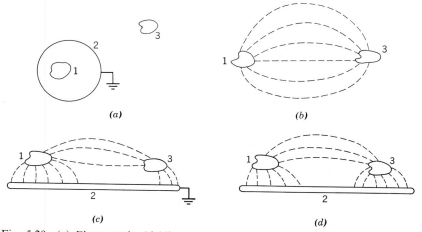

Fig. 5.28 (a) Electrostatic shielding by a grounded sphere. (b) Flux lines between a pair of conductors without shielding. (c) Partial shielding by a grounded conducting plane. (d) Ungrounded nearby conductor increases coupling.

the field and made to surround either body 1 or 3 completely, as in Fig. 5.28a, it is evident that a change in potential of 3 can in no way influence the charge on 1 and the mutual capacitance $C_{13} = 0$. Also, for the case pictured $C_{10} = 0$, and from Eq. 5.27(1)

$$c_{11} = -c_{12} = C_{12}.$$

These characteristics are typical of cases of perfect shielding.

More often the added conductor may not completely enclose any body, so that the capacitance coupling may not be made zero, but may only be reduced from its original value. It can be shown that any finite conductor as 2 introduced into the field acts to decrease the mutual capacitance C_{13} from its value prior to the introduction of 2, and hence provides some decrease in the capacitive coupling between 1 and 3. The reason is that fewer of the flux lines of the charge on 1 will terminate on 3 with a grounded conductor as shown by comparing Figs. 5.28b and c. However, if 2 is not connected to the ground (the infinite supply of charge), the effect of the added electrode will be to shorten the flux lines as seen in Fig. 5.28d. In terms of the equivalent circuit, the effective capacitance between 1 and 3 is seen from the equivalent circuit of Fig. 5.26b to be given by C_{13} in parallel with C_{12} and C_{23} in series:

$$(C_{13})_\text{eff} = C_{13} + \frac{C_{12}C_{23}}{C_{12} + C_{23}}.$$

This value is generally greater than the value of C_{13} prior to the introduction of 2 (though it need not be if 2 lies along an equipotential surface of the original field); so, if insulated from ground, the additional conductor may act to increase the effective capacitive coupling between 1 and 3. It often happens that electrodes, although grounded for direct current, may be effectively insulated or floating at radio frequencies because of impedance in the grounding leads. In such cases the new electrodes do not accomplish their shielding purposes but may in fact increase capacitive coupling.

Problems

5.28a Discuss qualitatively the case of Fig. 5.28c in which two bodies, 1 and 3, which are relatively far apart have a conducting plane brought in their vicinity. How can you prove that C_{13} is decreased when the plane is added?

5.28b Suppose that the bodies 1 and 3 of Fig. 5.28c are spheres of radii a separated by a distance d with $a/d \ll 1$. If the added plane is parallel to the line joining their centers and distance b from it ($a/b \ll 1$), find C_{13} before and after introduction of the plane when grounded, and the effective C_{13} with the plane present and insulated from ground.

5.29 Example: Interelectrode Capacitances of Triode

Consider the idealized triode with plane cathode, plane anode, and a grid of parallel wires as sketched in Fig. 5.29a. With the coordinates and dimensions as shown on the figure, this two-dimensional problem may be transformed to that of Fig. 5.29b by the complex function

$$Z' = e^{-2\pi Z/s} = e^{-2\pi x/s}e^{-j(2\pi y/s)}. \tag{1}$$

In the transformed figure, the anode and cathode have become coaxial cylinders of radii r'_a and r'_k, respectively, and each of the grid wires has transformed to a single nearly-circular cylindrical figure centered at $Z' = 1$. It will be assumed that r_g/s is less than about 0.2, in which case the transformed grid figure may be approximated well enough by a circle of radius b. Then, from (1),

$$r'_k = e^{2\pi d_{gk}/s} \tag{2}$$

$$r'_a = e^{-2\pi d_{ga}/s} \tag{3}$$

$$b = 2 \sin\left(\frac{\pi r_g}{s}\right). \tag{4}$$

The value of b in (4) is found by making the points A and B in the Z plane correspond to A' and B' in the Z' plane.

The problem in the Z' plane may be solved by utilizing a series of line images. Actually, for typical triode dimensions, r'_k as given by (2) is very large and r'_a from (3) is very small, so that the transformed anode may be

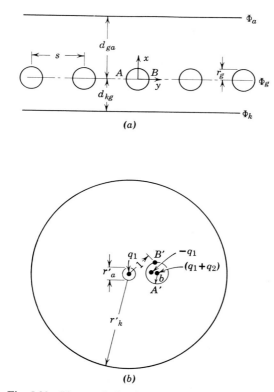

(a)

(b)

Fig. 5.29 Planar triode with parallel-wire grids and its transformed figure in the Z' plane.

considered a line charge and a single imaging of this in the transformed grid cylinder may be sufficient. The image is at distance $b^2/1$ from the center of the grid wire (Art. 2.19) so that the three line charges consist of q_1 at the origin, $-q_1$ at $Z' = 1 - b^2$, and $q_1 + q_2$ at $Z' = 1$. (The choice of the last value is made so that the net charge strength on the grid is q_2.) Potential is then (Art. 2.15)

$$\Phi = -\frac{1}{2\pi\epsilon}[q_1 \ln r_1 - q_1 \ln r_2 + (q_1 + q_2)\ln r_3] + C. \qquad (5)$$

Since r_k' is large, the potential on the cathode may be found by concentrating all charges at the axis. Since r_a' is small, potential on the anode may be found by considering only the charge q_1 on the axis. To find potential on the grid, some point such as $Z' = 1 - b$ on the grid wire is chosen:

$$\Phi_k = - \frac{1}{2\pi\epsilon}(q_1 + q_2) \ln r_k' + C \tag{6}$$

$$\Phi_a = - \frac{1}{2\pi\epsilon} q_1 \ln r_p' + C \tag{7}$$

$$\Phi_g = - \frac{1}{2\pi\epsilon}[q_1 \ln (1 - b) - q_1 \ln b(1 - b) + (q_1 + q_2) \ln b] + C$$

$$= - \frac{q_2}{2\pi\epsilon} \ln b + C. \tag{8}$$

Any of the three electrodes may be considered as the zero reference electrode. Let this be the cathode so that Φ_k of (6) is set equal to zero. The value of C thus determined may be substituted in (7) and (8):

$$\Phi_1 = \Phi_a = - \frac{1}{2\pi\epsilon}\left[q_1 \ln \left(\frac{r_p'}{r_k'}\right) - q_2 \ln r_k'\right] \tag{9}$$

$$\Phi_2 = \Phi_g = - \frac{1}{2\pi\epsilon}\left[-q_1 \ln r_k' + q_2 \ln \left(\frac{b}{r_k'}\right)\right]. \tag{10}$$

By comparing (9) and (10) with the set of equations 5.26(1), we may write the coefficients of potential for this problem

$$p_{11} = \frac{1}{2\pi\epsilon} \ln \left(\frac{r_k'}{r_p'}\right) = \frac{1}{2\pi\epsilon}\left(\frac{2\pi d_{kg}}{s} + \frac{2\pi d_{ag}}{s}\right) = \frac{d_{ka}}{\epsilon s} \tag{11}$$

$$p_{12} = p_{21} = \frac{1}{2\pi\epsilon} \ln r_k' = \frac{d_{kg}}{\epsilon s} \tag{12}$$

$$p_{22} = \frac{1}{2\pi\epsilon} \ln \left(\frac{r_k'}{b}\right) = \frac{d_{kg}}{\epsilon s} - \frac{1}{2\pi\epsilon} \ln \left(2 \sin \frac{\pi r_g}{s}\right). \tag{13}$$

Then by Eq. 5.26(3) the coefficients of capacitance and induction are

$$c_{11} = \frac{p_{22}}{\Delta(p_{rs})} = \frac{\dfrac{d_{kg}}{\epsilon s} - \dfrac{1}{2\pi\epsilon} \ln \left(2 \sin \dfrac{\pi r_g}{s}\right)}{\Delta(p_{rs})} \tag{14}$$

$$c_{12} = - \frac{p_{12}}{\Delta(p_{rs})} = - \frac{d_{kg}}{\epsilon s\,\Delta(p_{rs})} \tag{15}$$

$$c_{22} = \frac{p_{11}}{\Delta(p_{rs})} = \frac{d_{ka}}{\epsilon s\,\Delta(p_{rs})} \tag{16}$$

where

$$\Delta(p_{rs}) = p_{11}p_{22} - p_{12}^2 = \frac{d_{ka}}{\epsilon s}\left[\frac{d_{kg}}{\epsilon s} - \frac{1}{2\pi\epsilon}\ln\left(2\sin\frac{\pi r_g}{s}\right)\right] - \left(\frac{d_{kg}}{\epsilon s}\right)^2. \quad (17)$$

Finally, the interelectrode capacitances of the equivalent circuit (recalling that the cathode is taken as the zero potential electrode) are obtainable from Eqs. 5.27(1) and (2):

$$C_{ka} = C_{10} = c_{11} + c_{12} = -\frac{\ln\left(2\sin\frac{\pi r_g}{s}\right)}{2\pi\epsilon\,\Delta(p_{rs})} \quad (18)$$

$$C_{kg} = C_{20} = c_{22} + c_{12} = \frac{d_{ga}}{\epsilon s\,\Delta(p_{rs})} \quad (19)$$

$$C_{ga} = C_{12} = -c_{12} = \frac{d_{kg}}{\epsilon s\,\Delta(p_{rs})}. \quad (20)$$

It is also of interest to note the electrostatic amplification factor of the triode (an approximation to the amplification factor defined from tube characteristics) defined as the ratio C_{kg}/C_{ka}:

$$\mu_0 = \frac{C_{kg}}{C_{ka}} = -\frac{2\pi d_{ga}}{s\ln\left(2\sin\frac{\pi r_g}{s}\right)}. \quad (21)$$

This equation is a useful approximation for reasonably large values of s/r_g, $2\pi d_{kg}/s$, and $2\pi d_{ga}/s$.

Problems

5.29a Suppose that $2\pi d_{kg}/s$ is not large enough to justify the approximation used in computing Φ_k for Eq. (6). Describe the additional image charges that should be added for a next approximation. Describe the image charges that should be added if $2\pi d_{ga}/s$ is not large enough to justify the approximation used in computing Φ_a for (7).

5.29b Repeat the problem of this article, using the transformation $Z' = e^{2\pi Z/s}$ so that the cathode transforms to the inner cylinder, the anode to the outer.

6 PROPAGATION AND REFLECTION OF PLANE WAVES IN ISOTROPIC MEDIA

6.01 Introduction

The first example of the application of Maxwell's equations in Chapter 4 was that of electromagnetic wave propagation in space or a simple medium. In Chapter 5 this propagation effect entered only as a secondary consideration, adding radiation and other correction terms from "retardation" in electrical circuits. For the remainder of the book, wave effects will be the central issue. Thus we return to the plane wave example and extend it in this chapter, before considering the more general guided, resonant, and radiating waves in following chapters.

Plane waves are good approximations to real waves in many practical situations. Radio waves at large distances from the transmitter, or from diffracting objects, have negligible curvature and are well represented by plane waves. Much of optics utilizes the plane wave approximation. More complicated electromagnetic wave patterns can be considered as a superposition of plane waves, so in this sense the plane waves are basic building blocks for all wave problems. Even when that approach is not followed, the basic ideas of propagation, reflection, and refraction, which are met simply here, help the understanding of other wave problems.

Following a review and extension of the plane wave example of Chapter 4, we consider some dynamic models for materials in their interaction with waves. A large part of this chapter is then concerned with the reflection and refraction phenomena when waves pass from one medium to another, with examples for both radio waves and light. The chapter concludes with a discussion of the connection between wave propagation and ray optics to lay the foundation for a number of optical problems to be considered in later chapters.

322

WAVES IN UNBOUNDED REGIONS

6.02   Uniform Plane Waves in a Perfect Dielectric

The uniform plane wave was given in Chapter 4 as the first example of the use of Maxwell's equations. Here we will discuss, in more detail, the nature of the uniform plane wave. We restrict our attention to media for which ϵ and μ are scalar constants. For a uniform plane wave, variations in two directions, say x and y, are assumed to be zero. Maxwell's curl equations in rectangular coordinates reduce to

$$\nabla \times \bar{E} = -\mu \frac{\partial \bar{H}}{\partial t} \qquad \nabla \times \bar{H} = \epsilon \frac{\partial \bar{E}}{\partial t}$$

$$\frac{\partial E_y}{\partial z} = \mu \frac{\partial H_x}{\partial t} \qquad (1) \qquad\qquad \frac{\partial H_y}{\partial z} = -\epsilon \frac{\partial E_x}{\partial t} \qquad (4)$$

$$\frac{\partial E_x}{\partial z} = -\mu \frac{\partial H_y}{\partial t} \qquad (2) \qquad\qquad \frac{\partial H_x}{\partial z} = \epsilon \frac{\partial E_y}{\partial t} \qquad (5)$$

$$0 = \mu \frac{\partial H_z}{\partial t} \qquad (3) \qquad\qquad 0 = \epsilon \frac{\partial E_z}{\partial t} \qquad (6)$$

We see first from (3) and (6) that E_z and H_z must both be zero, except possibly for constant (static) parts which are not of interest to us in the wave solution. That is, the electric and magnetic fields of this simple wave are both transverse to the direction of propagation.

Next, if (2) is differentiated with respect to z, (4) with respect to t, and the two results combined, we obtain the one-dimensional form of the wave equation in E_x as written in Eq. 4.11(6).

$$\frac{\partial^2 E_x}{\partial z^2} = \mu\epsilon \frac{\partial^2 E_x}{\partial t^2} . \qquad (7)$$

This is to be expected, for the specializations leading to Eq. 4.11(6) are exactly the same as in this article, although the steps of the derivation are somewhat different. Then the solution is as in Eq. 4.11(8) and represents a wave traveling with velocity v in the positive z direction and another traveling with the same velocity in the negative z direction.

$$v = \frac{1}{\sqrt{\mu\epsilon}} \quad \text{meters/sec.} \qquad (8)$$

For free space,

$$v_0 = \frac{1}{\sqrt{\mu_0\epsilon_0}} \approx 3 \times 10^8 \text{ meters/sec,}$$

which is the velocity of light to the approximation taken. Let us concentrate for the moment on the positively traveling component of E_x:

$$E_{x+} = f_1\left(t - \frac{z}{v}\right). \tag{9}$$

From (2) we may find a relation for H_y in the positive wave:

$$\frac{\partial H_{y+}}{\partial t} = -\frac{1}{\mu}\frac{\partial E_{x+}}{\partial z} = \sqrt{\frac{\epsilon}{\mu}}f_1'\left(t - \frac{z}{v}\right).$$

Integrating, and again ignoring static constants of integration, we have

$$H_{y+} = \sqrt{\frac{\epsilon}{\mu}}f_1\left(t - \frac{z}{v}\right) = \frac{E_{x+}}{\eta} \tag{10}$$

where

$$\eta = \sqrt{\frac{\mu}{\epsilon}}. \tag{11}$$

The quantity η is thus seen to be the ratio of E_x to H_y in a single traveling wave of this simple type, and as defined by (11) it may also be considered a constant of the medium, and will be a useful parameter in the analysis of more complicated waves. It has dimensions of ohms and is known as the *intrinsic impedance* of the medium. For free space,

$$\eta_0 = \sqrt{\frac{\mu_0}{\epsilon_0}} \approx 120\pi \approx 377 \text{ ohms.} \tag{12}$$

If we start with the one-dimensional wave equation in E_y and utilize (1), we find that H_x for the positive wave is just $-E_y/\eta$. Combining this result with (10), we may write

$$\frac{E_{x+}}{H_{y+}} = -\frac{E_{y+}}{H_{x+}} = \eta. \tag{13}$$

Similarly, repeating the steps for a negatively traveling wave, we see that

$$\frac{E_{x-}}{H_{y-}} = -\frac{E_{y-}}{H_{x-}} = -\eta. \tag{14}$$

These results show a number of things. First, relations (13) and (14) are sufficient to require that $\bar{E}$ and $\bar{H}$ shall be perpendicular to one another in each of the traveling waves. They also require that the value of E at any instant must be η times the value of H at that instant, for each wave.

Finally we note that, if $\bar{E} \times \bar{H}$ is formed, it points in the positive z direction from (13), and in the negative z direction from (14), or in the direction of travel for each wave. These relations are indicated for a positively traveling wave in Fig. 6.02.

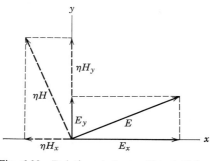

Fig. 6.02   Relations between E and H for a wave propagating in positive z direction (out of paper).

The energy relations are also of interest. The stored energy in electric fields per unit volume is

$$U_E = \frac{\epsilon E^2}{2} = \frac{\epsilon}{2}(E_x{}^2 + E_y{}^2), \tag{15}$$

and that in magnetic fields is

$$U_H = \frac{\mu H^2}{2} = \frac{\mu}{2}(H_x{}^2 + H_y{}^2). \tag{16}$$

By (13) or (14), U_E and U_H are equal, so the energy density at each point at each instant is equally divided between electric and magnetic energy. The Poynting vector for the positive traveling wave is

$$P_{z+} = E_{x+}H_{y+} - E_{y+}H_{x+} = \frac{1}{\eta}(E_{x+}^2 + E_{y+}^2) \tag{17}$$

and is always in the positive z direction except at particular planes where it may be zero for a given instant. Similarly, the Poynting vector for the negatively traveling wave is always in the negative z direction except where it is zero. The time-average value of the Poynting vector must be the same for all planes along the wave since no energy can be dissipated in the perfect dielectric, but the instantaneous values may be different at two different planes, depending on whether or not there is a net instantaneous rate of increase or decrease in the stored energy between those planes.

In most important cases the time variation has the complex exponential form, and the results of Art. 4.11 apply. Equation 4.11(10) for a wave traveling in the $+z$ direction can be expressed in complex form as

$$E_x = Ee^{-jkz}$$

where
$$k = \frac{\omega}{v} = \omega\sqrt{\mu\epsilon} \text{ meters}^{-1}. \qquad (18)$$

This constant is the phase constant for the uniform plane wave, since it gives the change in phase per unit length for each wave component. It may also be considered a constant of the medium at a particular frequency defined by (18), known as the *wave number*, and will be found useful in the analysis of all waves, as will be seen.

The *wavelength* is defined as the distance the wave propagates in one period. It is then the value of z which causes the phase factor to change by 2π:

$$k\lambda = 2\pi \qquad \text{or} \qquad k = \frac{2\pi}{\lambda} \qquad (19)$$

or
$$\lambda = \frac{2\pi}{\omega\sqrt{\mu\epsilon}} = \frac{v}{f}. \qquad (20)$$

This is the common relation between wavelength, phase velocity, and frequency. The *free-space wavelength* is obtained by using the velocity of light in free space in (20) and is frequently used at the higher frequencies as an alternative to giving the frequency.

To summarize the properties for a single wave of this simple type, which may be described as a *uniform plane wave*:

1. Velocity of propagation, $v = 1/\sqrt{\mu\epsilon}$.
2. No electric or magnetic field in direction of propagation.
3. Electric field normal to magnetic field.
4. Value of electric field η times that of magnetic field at each instant.
5. Direction of propagation given by direction of $\bar{E} \times \bar{H}$.
6. Energy stored in electric field per unit volume at any instant and any point is equal to energy stored in magnetic field per unit volume at that instant and that point.
7. Instantaneous value of Poynting vector given by $E^2/\eta = \eta H^2$, where E and H are the instantaneous values of total electric and magnetic field strengths.

Problems

6.02a Draw a sketch similar to Fig. 6.02 demonstrating the relations in a negatively traveling wave.

6.02b A step-function uniform plane wave is generated by suddenly impressing a constant electric field $E_x = C$ at $z = 0$ at time $t = 0$ and maintaining it thereafter. A perfectly conducting plane is placed normal to the z direction at $z = 600$ meters. Sketch total E_x and ηH_y versus z at $t = 1$ microsec and at $t = 3$ microsec.

6.03 Polarization of Plane Waves

Since the wave equation is a linear equation, any solution to it may be built up as the sum of other solutions. Many complex electromagnetic wave distributions might, if desired, be considered as made up of a large number of the simple plane waves with different magnitudes, phases, and directions of propagation. For most purposes this viewpoint is of little value except as a concept, and other methods to be given later will serve better for actual analysis. If we are studying the important practical case where a combination of plane waves exists such that all have the same direction of propagation, however, there is a definite advantage in considering these as a superposition of the individual plane waves and analyzing by obtaining the behavior of each individual wave. The orientations of the field vectors in these waves are often described by the *polarization* of the wave. In this discussion we are primarily concerned with sinusoidal waves of the same frequency.

For a single uniform plane wave, it has been seen that electric and magnetic field vectors are always at right angles and always maintain their respective orientations at every point along the wave. A combination of plane waves all propagating in the same direction, with arbitrary orientations of the field vectors, arbitrary magnitudes, and random phases is called an *unpolarized* wave (Fig. 6.03a).

If the electric field vector of the wave lies always in a given direction, the wave is said to be *plane polarized* (or, sometimes, *linearly polarized*). This condition results when all the superposed waves have electric fields in the same direction, or if they are in different directions but of exactly the same phase (Fig. 6.02). For radio waves, it is common to describe the polarization by the plane of the electric vector, so that a case as described in Figs. 6.03b,c would be described as *vertical* and *horizontal polarization*, respectively. In optics the convention utilizes the magnetic field to define the plane of polarization, but in either case it is best to avoid ambiguity by specifying explicitly, as "polarized with electric field in the vertical plane."

If there is a combination of two uniform plane waves of the same frequency, but of different phases, magnitudes, and orientations of the field vectors, the resultant combination is said to be an *elliptically polarized* wave. To see the reason for this, we may first break each wave into its

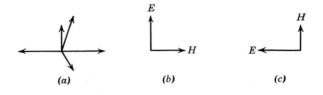

(a)   (b)   (c)

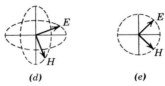

(d)   (e)

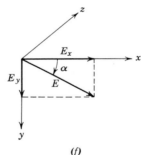

(f)

Fig. 6.03 (a) Unpolarized. (b) Vertically polarized. (c) Horizontally polarized. (d) Elliptically polarized. (e) Circularly polarized. (f) Coordinate for polarization angle.

two separate component waves, one with electric vector in the x direction, the other with electric vector in the y direction. The two x components add to produce a wave of given magnitude and phase angle. This will be written for this study directly in terms of cosines rather than in the exponential or complex form:

$$E_x = E_1 \cos \omega \left(t - \frac{z}{v} \right). \tag{1}$$

The two y components add to produce a wave of different magnitude and phase angle.

$$E_y = E_2 \cos \left[\omega \left(t - \frac{z}{v} \right) + \psi \right]. \tag{2}$$

In any given plane, say $z = 0$, these reduce to equations of the form

$$E_x = E_1 \cos \omega t$$
$$E_y = E_2 \cos (\omega t + \psi). \tag{3}$$

These are the parametric equations for an ellipse. The terminus of the electric field vector then traces an elliptic path in a plane normal to the direction of propagation. This is the reason for the name elliptic polarization (Fig. 6.03d).

If the two waves combine so that total x and y components are equal and 90° out of time phase, the ellipse reduces to a circle, and the wave is said to be *circularly polarized*. Thus, if

$$\psi = \pm \frac{\pi}{2} \quad \text{and} \quad E_1 = E_2$$
$$E_x{}^2 + E_y{}^2 = E_1{}^2 \tag{4}$$

which is the equation of a circle (Fig. 6.03e). The instantaneous angle α between the electric vector and the x axis can be found simply (Fig. 6.03f):

$$\alpha = \tan^{-1} \frac{E_y}{E_x} = \tan^{-1} \left(\frac{\mp E_1 \sin \omega t}{E_1 \cos \omega t} \right) = \mp \omega t. \tag{5}$$

Thus the vector is seen to rotate at a uniform rate with angular velocity equal to $2\pi f$. It rotates in a clockwise sense, looking in the direction of propagation, if ψ is $-\pi/2$, and in a counterclockwise sense if ψ is $+\pi/2$.

Problems

6.03a Show that any arbitrary elliptically polarized wave may be broken up into two oppositely rotating circularly polarized components instead of the two plane-polarized components.

6.03b Write the expressions corresponding to (1) and (2) in complex notation. Show that the general representation for an elliptically polarized wave in complex notation may then be written

$$\bar{E} = (\bar{E}_a + j\bar{E}_b)e^{-jkz},$$

where $\bar{E}_a$ and $\bar{E}_b$ are two real vectors, not in general mutually perpendicular. Relate $\bar{E}_a$ and $\bar{E}_b$ to E_1, E_2, and ψ.

6.03c Starting with the general complex representation for $\bar{E}$ of Prob. b, use Maxwell's equations to obtain the corresponding form for $\bar{H}$.

6.03d Sketch the locus of the vector for $E_1 = 1$, $E_2 = \frac{1}{2}$, and $\psi = \pi/2$; also for $E_1 = E_2 = 1$ and $\psi = \pi/4$.

MATERIALS AND WAVES

6.04 Imperfect Dielectrics and Conductors

In several articles of Chapter 2 we considered the effect of matter on static electric fields, and noted several mechanisms which contribute to the electric polarizability of materials. When fields are time varying, these mechanisms may be modified, both in their contribution to susceptibility or dielectric constant, and in damping or loss processes. The loss processes may be rather complicated, so the simple models should be considered only as introductions to the subject. Permittivity only will be discussed, since magnetic properties affecting waves are usually anisotropic, and will be discussed more in Chapter 9.

Of the contributions to polarizability, the electronic and ionic parts have similar models. The former arises from the shift of the electron charge cloud relative to the positive nucleus and the latter from the displacement of a positive ion and a negative ion from their neutral positions. The classical model for these processes is that of an oscillating system with losses. The resonance arises from inertia of the displaced charge system interacting with the restoring forces provided by the Coulomb interaction. The loss process in the classical model is taken as a damping proportional to velocity of the oscillating particles. In the quantum picture, the resonance arises from a transition between energy levels, and the loss processes may involve reradiation at various frequencies in addition to the excitation of phonons (the temperature increase of the material). In both models, however, the contribution to polarizability from the ith resonance has the form

$$(\alpha_e + \alpha_a)_i = \frac{F_i}{(\omega_i^2 - \omega^2) + j\omega\Gamma_i} \tag{1}$$

where F_i and ω_i are strength and angular frequency of the ith contribution, and Γ_i is a damping constant. Figure 6.04a shows the form of the real and imaginary parts contributed to α by a particular resonance of the electronic or ionic polarizability. The response is of course much like that of a tuned circuit with losses, the maximum of the losses occurring at the resonant frequency. The analysis of the classical model is in fact the exact analogue of such a circuit.

The dynamic response of the permanent dipole contribution to polarizability is different in that the force opposing the complete alignment of the dipoles in the direction of the field is that from thermal effects. If a static field is removed, the thermal effects would cause the alignment of the

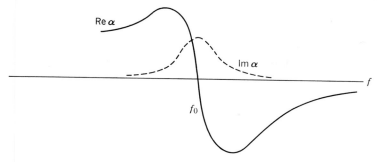

Fig. 6.04a   Real and imaginary parts of ionic or electronic polarizability
in the neighborhood of resonance.

dipoles to "relax" exponentially against viscous forces, with a characteristic
time τ required for the polarization to fall to $1/e$ of its original value. The
constant τ will similarly enter into any effects resulting from time variations
in the field. The classical analysis of Debye[1] showed the frequency
dependence of this effect to yield

$$\alpha_d = \frac{p^2}{3kT(1 + j\omega\tau)} . \tag{2}$$

The form of real and imaginary parts of this contribution are shown in
Fig. 6.04b. The relaxation of permanent dipoles is important largely in
gases and liquids, but may contribute in certain solids. Other poly-
crystalline solids may have a contribution with similar dynamic behavior
from the process of "site jumping" mentioned in Art. 2.38.

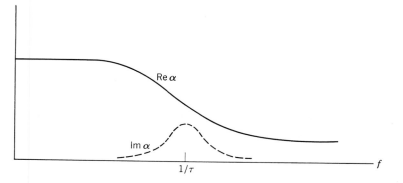

Fig. 6.04b   Real and imaginary parts of average polarizability resulting
from dipole alignment or ion site jumping.

[1] A. R. von Hippel, *Dielectrics and Waves*, John Wiley and Sons, New York, 1954.

The substitution of the dynamic values of α in the approximate Clausius-Mossotti relation, Eq. 2.41(5), leads to the equation that should describe the behavior of relative dielectric constant with frequency. There may actually be many resonances of the form (1), and a number of relaxation

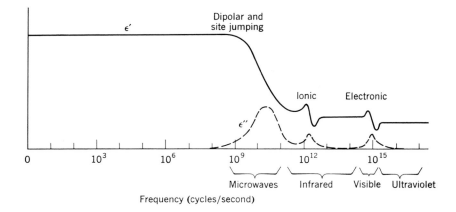

Fig. 6.04c   Real and imaginary part of relative permittivity for a hypothetical substance showing typical limiting frequencies for various polarization effects.

terms of the form (2). All those should be added to give the total polarizability α_T, to be used in Eq. 2.41(5)

$$\frac{\epsilon_r - 1}{\epsilon_r + 2} = \frac{N}{3}\,\alpha_T. \tag{3}$$

This is often known as the Debye equation in recognition of that author's contributions to the classical models described. Since polarizability is in general a complex number, permittivity is complex also. It may be written

$$\epsilon = \epsilon' - j\epsilon''. \tag{4}$$

Curves of real and imaginary parts of permittivity versus frequency are sketched for a hypothetical substance in Fig. 6.04c. For this, the dipolar relaxation is shown as occurring in the high microwave range of frequencies, as it does for water and some other materials,[1] although for most materials used as dielectrics at microwaves, ϵ is constant through the microwave range. The ionic resonances are typically in the infrared, and the electronic resonances near the visible range. Although this is typical, there may be some variation in the frequency ranges of the several contributions for various substances.

It is most interesting and important to note that the real and imaginary parts of ϵ are related by the fact that ϵ must be an analytic function in the right half of a complex frequency plane, so that real and imaginary parts are related by the Cauchy-Riemann equations (Art. 3.12). The relations applied to dielectric constant or index of refraction are known as the Kronig-Kramers relations[2] and are

$$\epsilon'(\omega) = \epsilon_0 + \frac{2}{\pi} \int_0^\infty \frac{\omega' \epsilon''(\omega') \, d\omega'}{\omega(\omega'^2 - \omega^2)} \tag{5}$$

$$\epsilon''(\omega) = -\frac{2\omega^2}{\pi} \int_0^\infty \frac{[\epsilon'(\omega) - \epsilon_0] \, d\omega'}{\omega'^2 - \omega^2}. \tag{6}$$

These are exactly analogous to relations between the real and imaginary parts of impedance functions, for which the presentation and discussion will be given in Chapter 11.

The loss mechanisms described apply to a model in which there are only bound charges. Materials in which there are an appreciable number of free charge carriers, as the electrons of an ordinary conductor, the ions of a solution, or the holes of a semiconductor, are described by the ordinary conductivity relating current density to applied field.

$$\bar{\imath} = \sigma \bar{E}. \tag{7}$$

The classical picture is one in which the free charges move randomly because of their thermal velocities, experiencing frequent collisions with the other constituents of the substance. The application of a force field causes a general drift in the direction of the field with an average velocity given by the product of applied force and a "mobility" for the substance. This component of velocity, and hence current, is in phase with applied field at frequencies low compared with collision frequency, and represents the usual ohmic loss. At any given frequency, this loss and that described for the bound charges add directly, so if one is interested only in macroscopic properties, it is common to include it in the ϵ'' term of (4), or alternatively to define an equivalent conductance representing all losses. The relationship is

$$\sigma = \omega \epsilon''. \tag{8}$$

If one is to be concerned with microscopic behavior, however, it is well to keep the two mechanisms separate.

The ratio ϵ''/ϵ' is also a common constant for dielectrics and is tabulated in certain tables[3] as tan δ. The properties of a lossy dielectric are also

[2] L. D. Landau and E. M. Lifshitz, *Electrodynamics of Continuous Media*, Pergamon Press, London, and Addison Wesley, Reading, Mass., 1960, pp. 256–260.
[3] A. R. von Hippel, *Dielectric Materials and Applications*, M.I.T. Press and John Wiley and Sons, New York, 1954.

sometimes given by the *power factor*, which is defined as sin δ. For small values, it is very nearly equal to ϵ''/ϵ'. Values of ϵ'/ϵ_0 and ϵ''/ϵ' for several materials at three different frequencies are given in Table 6.04.

TABLE 6.04

	ϵ'/ϵ_0			Loss tangent, $10^4 \, \epsilon''/\epsilon'$		
Material	$f = 10^6$	$f = 10^8$	$f = 10^{10}$	$f = 10^6$	$f = 10^8$	$f = 10^{10}$
Glass, Corning 707	4.00	4.00	4.00	8	12	21
Fused quartz	3.78	3.78	3.78	2	1	1
Ruby mica	5.4	5.4	—	3	2	—
Ceramic Alsimag 393	4.95	4.95	4.95	10	10	9.7
Titania	100	100	—	3	2.5	—
Polystyrene	2.56	2.55	2.54	0.7	1	4.3
Neoprene	5.7	3.4	—	950	1600	—

Problems

6.04a   For a single resonance of the form (1), show the relation between F_i, ω_i, Γ_i and the real and imaginary parts of ϵ defined in (4). Take a material with ϵ_r near unity so that $\epsilon_r + 2 \approx 3$ in Eq. (3).

6.04b   Repeat (a) for a single relaxation term, relating the quantities of (2) to ϵ' and ϵ''.

6.04c   For the result of (b), show that the locus of Re ϵ_r vs. Im ϵ_r in the complex ϵ_r plane is a circle, as ω is varied.

6.04d   It might be thought that relations similar to the Kronig-Kramers relations (5) and (6) might be written for real and imaginary parts of wave number k. This is not the case since k can have zeros and poles in both half planes. Discuss this in terms of the symmetry of positively and negatively traveling waves in space and the absence of this symmetry in time because of the "causality" concept.

6.05   Waves in Imperfect Dielectrics and Conductors

For substances with linear magnetic behavior, that is, the paramagnetic and diamagnetic materials, the permeability μ may be considered to be independent of the frequency of the fields since the fractional deviations from the free space permeability are only of the order of 10^{-3} to 10^{-5}. For the same reason, the magnetic behavior is substantially isotropic and homogeneous. We can therefore write the first of Maxwell's curl equations as

$$\nabla \times \bar{E} = -j\omega\mu\bar{H}. \qquad (1)$$

Since we are limiting our considerations in this chapter to isotropic materials, the scalar permittivity given by Eq. 6.04(4) will be used in writing Maxwell's second curl equation,

$$\nabla \times \bar{H} = j\omega\epsilon\bar{E} = j\omega(\epsilon' - j\epsilon'')\bar{E}, \tag{2}$$

where conduction currents are included in the loss factor ϵ''.

The wave number, Eq. 6.02(18), is complex in this case and is related to the complex permittivity by

$$k = \omega\sqrt{\mu(\epsilon' - j\epsilon'')}. \tag{3}$$

The wave number k may be separated into real and imaginary parts,

$$jk = \alpha + j\beta = j\omega\sqrt{\mu\epsilon'[1 - j(\epsilon''/\epsilon')]}, \tag{4}$$

where

$$\alpha = \omega\sqrt{(\mu\epsilon'/2)[\sqrt{1 + (\epsilon''/\epsilon')^2} - 1]} \tag{5}$$

and

$$\beta = \omega\sqrt{(\mu\epsilon'/2)[\sqrt{1 + (\epsilon''/\epsilon')^2} + 1]}. \tag{6}$$

According to Art. 6.02, the exponential propagation factor for phasor waves is e^{-jkz} which becomes, for this case,

$$e^{-jkz} = e^{-\alpha z}e^{-j\beta z}.$$

Thus the wave attenuates as it propagates through the material and the attenuation depends on the dielectric losses and the conduction losses, as would be expected.

The intrinsic impedance, or ratio of electric to magnetic field for a uniform plane wave, becomes

$$\eta = \sqrt{\frac{\mu}{\epsilon}} = \sqrt{\frac{\mu}{\epsilon'[1 - j(\epsilon''/\epsilon')]}} \tag{7}$$

An important parameter appearing in (4) through (7) is the ratio ϵ''/ϵ'. For low-loss materials such as the examples given in Table 6.04, the loss tangent is much less than unity. We may refer to such a material as an *imperfect dielectric*. Under these conditions, the attenuation constant (5) and the phase constant (6) may be approximated by

$$\alpha \approx \frac{k\epsilon''}{2\epsilon'} \tag{8}$$

$$\beta \approx k\left[1 + \frac{1}{8}\left(\frac{\epsilon''}{\epsilon'}\right)^2\right], \tag{9}$$

where $k = \omega\sqrt{\mu\epsilon'}$. It is seen that there is a small increase of the phase constant and, therefore, decrease of the phase velocity when losses are present in a dielectric. The intrinsic impedance in this case is, from (7),

$$\eta \approx \eta' \left\{\left[1 - \frac{3}{8}\left(\frac{\epsilon''}{\epsilon'}\right)^2\right] + j\frac{\epsilon''}{2\epsilon'}\right\} \qquad (10)$$

where $\eta' = \sqrt{\mu/\epsilon'}$.

For many important materials, particularly in and below the microwave frequency range (10^9 to 10^{11} cycles per second), the dominant factor in ϵ'' is conduction loss. In this case it is meaningful to write (2) as

$$\nabla \times \bar{H} = (j\omega\epsilon' + \sigma)\bar{E} = j\omega\epsilon'\left[1 - j\frac{\sigma}{\omega\epsilon'}\right]\bar{E}. \qquad (11)$$

For radian frequencies much larger than σ/ϵ' the loss term is small and the approximations (8) to (10) may be used with ϵ''/ϵ' replaced by $\sigma/\omega\epsilon'$. For frequencies much below σ/ϵ' the material may be considered a *good conductor*. If we make use of the fact that

$$\frac{\sigma}{\omega\epsilon'} \gg 1$$

in (4), we find

$$jk = j\sqrt{\frac{\mu\sigma}{j\omega}} = (1 + j)\sqrt{\pi f\mu\sigma} = \frac{1 + j}{\delta} \qquad (12)$$

where δ is the depth of penetration defined by Eq. 4.12(13) and used extensively in Chapter 5. The propagation factor for the wave shows that the wave decreases in magnitude exponentially, and has decreased to $1/e$ of its original value after propagating a distance equal to depth of penetration of the material. The phase factor corresponds to a very small phase velocity

$$v = \frac{\omega}{\beta} = \omega\delta = c\frac{2\pi\delta}{\lambda_0} \qquad (13)$$

where c is the velocity of light in free space; λ_0 is free-space wavelength. Since δ/λ_0 is usually very small (see Art. 4.12), this phase velocity is usually much less than the velocity of light.

Equation (7) gives, for a good conductor,

$$\eta = \sqrt{\frac{j\omega\mu}{\sigma}} = (1 + j)\sqrt{\frac{\pi f\mu}{\sigma}} = (1 + j)R_s, \qquad (14)$$

where R_s is the surface resistivity or high-frequency skin effect resistance per square of a plane conductor of great depth. Equation (14) shows that electric and magnetic fields are 45° out of time phase for the wave propagating in a good conductor. Also, since R_s is very small (0.014 ohm for copper at 3000 megacycles per second), the ratio of electric field to magnetic field in the wave is small.

The above mentioned results for the good conductor agree with those found in Chapter 4 by using a somewhat different analysis. In Art. 4.12

TABLE 6.05

Material Parameters for Frequencies below 10^5 Megacycles/Second

Material	Conductivity mhos/meter	$\dfrac{\epsilon'}{\epsilon_0}$	Frequency at which $\sigma = \omega\epsilon'$
Copper	5.80×10^7	—	(optical)
Platinum	0.94×10^7	—	(optical)
Germanium (pure)	2.2	16	2.5×10^9
Sea water	4	81	8.9×10^8
Fresh water	10^{-3}	81	2.2×10^5
Silicon (pure)	10^{-3}	12	1.5×10^6
Wet earth	10^{-3}	10	1.8×10^6
Dry earth	10^{-5}	5	3.6×10^6

the assumption that the conduction current greatly exceeds the displacement current is made at the outset with the result that the differential equation is not the wave equation but the so-called *diffusion equation*. The assumptions in both approaches are identical, however, so it is to be expected that the results would be the same.

Table 6.05 lists several materials for which the dominant losses are those resulting from finite conductivity. The values listed for conductivity and real part of permittivity are those applicable up through the microwave frequency range. The frequencies at which displacement currents equal conduction currents are listed and serve to indicate the range of frequencies in which the two above-mentioned approximations are valid.

Problems

6.05a For a uniform plane wave of frequency 10^4 Mc/sec propagating in polystyrene, calculate the attenuation constant, phase velocity, and intrinsic impedance.

6.05b Derive the expression for group velocity of a uniform plane wave propagating in a good conductor.

6.05c Determine the group velocity for uniform plane waves in a lossy dielectric, assuming σ and ϵ' independent of frequency; assuming ϵ''/ϵ' independent of frequency.

6.05d Plot a curve showing attenuation constant in sea water from 10^4 cps to 10^9 cps, assuming that the constants given do not vary over this range. Comment on the implications of the results to the problem of communicating by radio waves through sea water.

6.06   Plane Waves in an Ionized Gas

In the preceding articles we discussed the propagation of plane waves in dielectric and conducting materials with the implicit assumption that the constants describing the electrical behavior of the material are somehow known. For most substances the internal processes are so complicated that the constants must be experimentally obtained. It is of interest to examine one medium for which rather reliable calculations of the constants may be made. We will consider here an ionized gas in which the concentration of ions and electrons may be considered constant. The term *plasma* was applied by Tonks and Langmuir[4] to an ionized gas in which electron and ion densities are substantially equal. Present definition stresses the range over which collective action of the forces apply.[5] The distinction will not be important to the simple examples of this text, and much of the discussion is applicable both to a plasma and to the more general ionized gas. In many practical media, such as the earth's ionosphere, a steady magnetic field is present and causes the permittivity to be anisotropic. This more difficult problem is deferred to Chapter 9.

Certain assumptions or idealizations are made to simplify the study. The analyses of waves in ionized gases in this chapter are based on the "plasma" assumption that there is an equal concentration N of ions and electrons in the absence of the wave. In the analysis of this section the equality of the ion and electron densities is not disturbed by the wave. This is because fields are transverse and uniform, so there is no bunching of particles by a-c fields. The ions of all gases are at least 1840 times as heavy as the electrons and will be considered immobile. The concentration of ions and neutral atoms is typically so small in a gas that their induced electric and magnetic dipole moments cause only a small change of the free space permittivity and permeability, and this part will be neglected here. For fields that are not extremely strong, the electron motions are determined principally by the electric fields of the wave; the forces arising from the r-f magnetic field can be neglected. To show this let us assume an electron in free space and estimate the relative magnitudes of the force arising from the electric and magnetic fields. The Lorentz force equation

[4] L. Tonks and I. Langmuir, *Phys. Rev.* **33**, 195, 990 (1929).
[5] J. E. Drummond, *Plasma Physics*, McGraw-Hill, New York, 1961.

[Eq. 4.06(5)] is

$$\frac{d(m\bar{v})}{dt} = -e[\bar{E} + \bar{v} \times \bar{B}] = \bar{f}_e + \bar{f}_m, \tag{1}$$

where e is the magnitude of the electron charge. Then the ratio of magnitudes of the magnetic and electric forces is

$$\frac{f_m}{f_e} = \frac{vB}{E}.$$

But

$$B = \mu H = \mu \frac{E}{\eta} = \frac{E}{v_p},$$

where η is the intrinsic impedance. It will be seen from the results of the analysis to follow that the wave velocity v_p increases in the presence of the ionized gas, so

$$\frac{f_m}{f_e} = \frac{v}{v_p} < \frac{v}{c},$$

where c is the velocity of light in the absence of the gas. Ordinarily, the electron velocities are much less than the wave velocity, so the magnetic forces are neglected. This simplification is used extensively in the study of waves in ionized media.

We may modify (1) to apply to an average of the electrons rather than a single electron by introducing a force term which accounts for the average loss of energy to the gas molecules by collisions. The force is the rate of change of momentum. It is assumed that the entire momentum $m\bar{v}$ of the electron is transferred to the atom by an inelastic collision and that the collisions take place at a frequency ν. Thus the momentum loss per second is $m\bar{v}\nu$. Then if this force is introduced, the magnetic force neglected, and the mass assumed to be constant, (1) may be written as

$$m\frac{d\bar{v}}{dt} = -e\bar{E} - m\bar{v}\nu \tag{2}$$

The total time derivative is taken as we move with the particle and must in general be written as

$$\frac{d\bar{v}}{dt} = \frac{\partial \bar{v}}{\partial t} + \frac{\partial \bar{v}}{\partial x}\frac{dx}{dt} + \frac{\partial \bar{v}}{\partial y}\frac{dy}{dt} + \frac{\partial \bar{v}}{\partial z}\frac{dz}{dt}. \tag{3}$$

Since the applied forces here result from the electric fields of the uniform plane wave considered to be propagating in the z direction, the field is transverse and all velocity components are also in transverse directions. Thus the last term of (3), which contains the z-directed velocity dz/dt, vanishes. By virtue of the assumed uniformity of the fields in the transverse plane, the *variations* of velocity with respect to x and y are zero. Hence the total and partial derivatives with respect to time are equal here. Since we are considering the steady-state behavior of the system we may let $\bar{E} = \bar{E}e^{j\omega t}$ and $\bar{v} = \bar{v}e^{j\omega t}$. Equation (2) may then be rearranged to give the velocity in terms of the electric field as

$$\bar{v} = \frac{-e\bar{E}}{m(v + j\omega)} . \tag{4}$$

The electron density is undisturbed by the motions of the electrons since all paths lie in the transverse planes and are parallel with each other. Then the convection current density is

$$\bar{i} = -Ne\bar{v} = \frac{Ne^2\bar{E}}{m(v + j\omega)} . \tag{5}$$

Maxwell's curl equations are

$$\nabla \times \bar{E} = -j\omega\mu_0\bar{H} \tag{6}$$

and $\quad \nabla \times \bar{H} = j\omega\epsilon_0\bar{E} + \dfrac{Ne^2\bar{E}}{m(v + j\omega)}$

$$= j\omega\epsilon_0\left[1 - \frac{Ne^2}{\epsilon_0 m(v^2 + \omega^2)} + \frac{Ne^2 v}{j\omega\epsilon_0 m(v^2 + \omega^2)}\right]\bar{E}$$

$$= j\omega\epsilon\bar{E}. \tag{7}$$

It may be seen by comparing (7) with Eq. 6.05(11) that the real part of the permittivity is

$$\epsilon' = \epsilon_0\left[1 - \frac{Ne^2}{\epsilon_0 m(v^2 + \omega^2)}\right]. \tag{8}$$

The conductivity of the gas is given by this same comparison to be

$$\sigma = \frac{Ne^2 v}{\epsilon_0 m(v^2 + \omega^2)} . \tag{9}$$

The conductivity vanishes as the collision frequency v goes to zero.

Let us consider the important special case of a plane wave propagating in an homogeneous region of ionized gas in which the collisions may be neglected. Then $v = 0$ and (8) becomes

$$\epsilon = \epsilon' = \epsilon_0\left(1 - \frac{\omega_p^2}{\omega^2}\right), \tag{10}$$

where $\qquad \omega_p = \sqrt{Ne^2/\epsilon_0 m}. \tag{11}$

For $\omega < \omega_p$ the intrinsic impedance $\eta = \sqrt{\mu/\epsilon'}$ is imaginary so the magnetic field is out of phase with the electric field.

It may also be seen from Eq. 6.05(3) that for this case

$$k^2 = \omega^2 \mu \epsilon_0 \left(1 - \frac{\omega_p^{\,2}}{\omega^2}\right). \tag{12}$$

If $\omega < \omega_p$, k^2 is negative so $jk_c = \alpha$ and $\beta = 0$. Then

$$E_x = E_+ e^{-\alpha z} + E_- e^{\alpha z}. \tag{13}$$

That is, purely attenuated waves exist for $\omega < \omega_p$. For frequencies higher than ω_p, k^2 is positive and unattenuated waves propagate in the gas. The

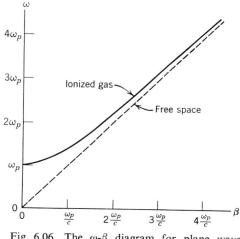

Fig. 6.06 The ω-β diagram for plane wave propagating through an ionized gas.

ω-β diagram for transverse plane waves in an ionized gas is shown in Fig. 6.06. It is seen that the phase velocity, which is measured by the slope of a line joining the ω-β curve and the origin, is always greater than the free-space velocity (velocity of light). Since the phase velocity depends on frequency, the medium is said to be dispersive. That is, the group velocity, which is the slope of the ω-β curve, is the velocity of a wave packet, but the packet disperses as it propagates since the various frequency components have different phase velocities. The concepts involved are the same as were introduced in Chapter 1. The ω-β diagram is modified when collisions are important, as is brought out in Prob. 6.06b.

Problems

6.06a Assume a neutral plasma in which all electrons in the region x to $x + dx$ are given a displacement Δx. Considering the forces acting to restore neutrality, show that the displaced sheet will oscillate at the "plasma frequency" ω_p given by (11).

6.06b Plot the loss tangent as a function of frequency at a level in the ionosphere where the concentration of free electrons is 10^{17} per cubic meter and the collision frequency is 10^{10} per second. (Assume zero steady magnetic field.)

6.06c The ω-β diagram is changed when collisions are considered. What is the minimum propagating frequency if $\nu = 0.1\omega_p$?

6.06d A simple model of the ionosphere may be formulated by assuming that the number density of free electrons increases linearly from zero at height z_0 to 10^{17} per cubic meter at a height of z_1 and then decreases linearly to zero at a height of $2z_1 - z_0$. The collisions may be neglected. A uniform plane wave traveling directly upward encounters the ionosphere. What is the highest frequency for which this wave will be at least partially reflected? Plot the maximum altitude of the wave as a function of frequency.

6.06e Suppose a plane wave of 6 Gc/sec is normally incident on the plane surface of the region $x > 0$ filled with a uniform ionized gas having zero collision frequency and electron density $N = 10^{12}$ per cm³. Find the variation of field intensities with x and compare this phenomenon with the skin effect introduced in Chapter 4. Assume free space outside the ionized region.

6.06f Consider a plane wave of variable frequency normally incident on the plane surface of the region $x > 0$ filled with a uniform ionized gas with negligible collision frequency. Find the power reflected as a fraction of incident power as frequency is varied from $0.5\omega_p$ to $1.5\omega_p$. Assume free space outside the ionized region.

REFLECTION AND REFRACTION OF WAVES AT BOUNDARIES

6.07 Reflection of Normally Incident Plane Waves from Perfect Conductors

If a single-frequency uniform plane wave is normally incident on a plane perfect conductor located at $z = 0$, we know that there must be some reflected wave in addition to the incident wave. One reason for this is that the boundary conditions cannot be satisfied by a single one of the traveling wave solutions, but will require just enough of the two so that the resultant electric field at the conductor surface will be zero for all time. From another point of view, we would expect the reflected wave since we know from the Poynting theorem that energy cannot pass the perfect conductor. Hence all energy brought by the incident wave must be returned in a reflected wave. In this simple case the incident and reflected waves are of equal amplitudes, and together form a standing wave pattern whose properties will now be studied.

For a single plane wave, select the orientation of axes so that total electric

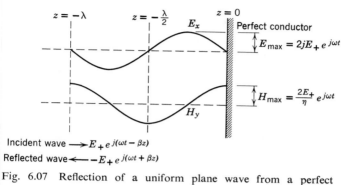

Incident wave $\longrightarrow E_+ e^{j(\omega t - \beta z)}$
Reflected wave $\longleftarrow -E_+ e^{j(\omega t + \beta z)}$

Fig. 6.07   Reflection of a uniform plane wave from a perfect conductor.

field lies in the x direction and include waves traveling in both the positive and negative z directions (Fig. 6.07),

$$E_x = E_+ e^{j(\omega t - \beta z)} + E_- e^{j(\omega t + \beta z)}.$$

If $E_x = 0$ at $z = 0$ for all values of time, $E_- = -E_+$.

$$E_x = E_+(e^{-j\beta z} - e^{j\beta z})e^{j\omega t}$$

but $e^{jx} = \cos x + j \sin x.$

So $E_x = -2jE_+ \sin \beta z\, e^{j\omega t}.$ (1)

The relation of the magnetic field to the electric field for the incident and reflected waves is given by Eqs. 6.02(13) and (14). Hence,

$$H_y = \left(\frac{E_+}{\eta} e^{j(\omega t - \beta z)} - \frac{E_-}{\eta} e^{j(\omega t + \beta z)} \right)$$

$$= \frac{E_+}{\eta} (e^{-j\beta z} + e^{j\beta z})e^{j\omega t}$$

$$= \frac{2E_+}{\eta} \cos \beta z e^{j\omega t}.$$ (2)

Equations (1) and (2) state that, although total electric and magnetic fields for the combination of incident and reflected waves are still mutually perpendicular in space and related in magnitude by η, they are now in time quadrature. The pattern is a standing wave pattern since a zero of electric field is always at the conductor surface, and also always at $\beta z = -n\pi$ or $z = -n\lambda/2$. Magnetic field has a maximum at the conductor surface, and there are other maxima each time there are zeros of electric field. Similarly, zeros of magnetic field and maxima of electric field are at $\beta z = (2n + 1)\pi/2$, or $z = -(2n + 1)\lambda/4$. This situation is sketched in Fig. 6.07, which shows a typical standing wave pattern such as was found for the shorted transmission line in Chapter 1. At an instant in time, occurring twice each cycle, all the energy of the line is in the magnetic field; 90° later the energy is stored entirely in the electric field. The *average* value of Poynting vector is zero at every cross-sectional plane; this emphasizes the fact that on the average as much energy is carried away by the reflected wave as is brought by the incident wave.

Problem

6.07   Write expressions for the instantaneous values of E_x, H_y, and the Poynting vector P_z. Evaluate the instantaneous stored energy in electric fields and in magnetic fields for a region extending from $z = -\lambda/4$ to $z = 0$. Note that the sum of these two energies is constant.

6.08   Transmission Line Analogy of Wave Propagation;   The Impedance Concept

In the problem of wave reflections from a perfect conductor, we found all the properties previously studied for standing waves on an ideal transmission line. The analogy between the plane wave solutions and the waves along an ideal line is in fact an exact and complete one. It is desirable to make use of this whether we start with a study of classical transmission line theory and then undertake the solution of wave problems, or proceed in the reverse order. In either case the algebraic steps worked out for the solution of one system need not be repeated in analyzing the other; any graphical aids (such as the Smith transmission line chart) developed for one may be used for the other; any experimental techniques applicable to one system will in general have their counterparts in the other system. We wish now to show the basis for this analogy.

Let us write side by side the equations for the field components in positively and negatively traveling uniform plane waves and the corresponding expressions found in Chapter 1 for an ideal transmission line.

For simplicity we orient the axes so that the wave has E_x and H_y components only:

$$E_x(z) = E_+ e^{-jkz} + E_- e^{jkz} \qquad (1) \qquad V(z) = V_+ e^{-j\beta z} + V_- e^{j\beta z} \qquad (5)$$

$$H_y(z) = \frac{1}{\eta} [E_+ e^{-jkz} - E_- e^{jkz}] \qquad (2) \qquad I(z) = \frac{1}{Z_0} [V_+ e^{-j\beta z} - V_- e^{j\beta z}] \qquad (6)$$

$$k = \omega\sqrt{\mu\epsilon} \qquad (3) \qquad \beta = \omega\sqrt{LC} \qquad (7)$$

$$\eta = \sqrt{\frac{\mu}{\epsilon}} \qquad (4) \qquad Z_0 = \sqrt{\frac{L}{C}} \qquad (8)$$

We see that, if in the field equations we replace E_x by voltage V, H_y by current I, permeability μ by inductance per unit length L, and dielectric constant ϵ by capacitance per unit length C, we get exactly the transmission line equations (5) to (8). To complete the analogy, we must consider the continuity conditions at a discontinuity between two regions. For the boundary between two dielectrics, we know that total tangential electric and magnetic field components must be continuous across this boundary. For the case of normal incidence (other cases will be considered separately later), E_x and H_y are the tangential components, so these continuity conditions are in direct correspondence to those of transmission lines which require that total voltage and current be continuous at the junction between two transmission lines.

To exploit this analogy fully, it is desirable to consider the ratio of electric to magnetic fields in the wave analysis, analogous to the ratio of voltage to current which is called impedance and used so extensively in the transmission line analysis. It is of course a good idea to use ratios such as this in the analysis, quite apart from the transmission line analogy or the name given these ratios, but in this case it will be especially useful to make the identification with impedance because of the large body of technique existing under the heading of "impedance matching" in transmission lines, most of which may be applied to problems in plane wave reflections. Credit for properly evaluating the importance of the wave impedance concept to engineers and making its use clear belongs to S. A. Schelkunoff.[6]

At any plane z, we shall define the field or wave impedance as the ratio of total electric field to total magnetic field at that plane.

$$Z(z) = \frac{E_x(z)}{H_y(z)}. \qquad (9)$$

For a single positively traveling wave this ratio is η at all planes, so that η, which has been called the intrinsic impedance of the medium, might also

[6] See, for instance, *Bell Sys. Tech. J.*, **17**, 17–48 (Jan. 1938).

be thought of as a *characteristic wave impedance* for uniform plane waves. For a single negatively traveling wave the ratio (9) is $-\eta$ for all z. For combinations of positively and negatively traveling waves, it will vary with z. The input value Z_i distance l in front of a plane at which the "load" value of this ratio is given as Z_L may be found from the corresponding transmission line formula, Eq. 1.18(10), taking advantage of the exact analogy. The intervening dielectric has intrinsic impedance η:

$$Z_i = \eta \left[\frac{Z_L \cos kl + j\eta \sin kl}{\eta \cos kl + jZ_L \sin kl} \right]. \tag{10}$$

It may be argued that in wave problems the primary concern is with reflections and not with impedances directly. This is true, but as in the transmission line case there is a one-to-one correspondence between reflection coefficient and impedance mismatch ratio. The analogy may again be invoked to adapt Eqs. 1.16(4) and (5) to give the reflection and transmission coefficients for a dielectric medium of intrinsic impedance η when it is terminated with some known load value of field impedance Z_L:

$$\rho = \frac{E_-}{E_+} = \frac{Z_L - \eta}{Z_L + \eta} \tag{11}$$

$$\tau = \frac{E_2}{E_{1+}} = \frac{2Z_L}{Z_L + \eta} \tag{12}$$

We see from this that there is no reflection when $Z_L = \eta$ (i.e., when impedances are matched). There is complete reflection, $|\rho| = 1$, when Z_L is zero, infinity, or is purely imaginary (reactive). Other important uses of formulas (10) to (12) will follow in succeeding articles.

Problems

6.08a Obtain the expression for the field impedance for any point z to the left of the conducting plane in Art. 6.07.

6.08b Write the formulas for a uniform plane wave with E_y and H_x only, and give the correspondence to voltage and current in the transmission line equations.

6.09   Normal Incidence on a Dielectric

If a uniform plane wave is normally incident on a single dielectric boundary from a medium with $\sqrt{\mu_1/\epsilon_1} = \eta_1$ to one with $\sqrt{\mu_2/\epsilon_2} = \eta_2$, the wave reflection and transmission may be found from the concepts and equations of Art. 6.08. Select the direction of the electric field as the x

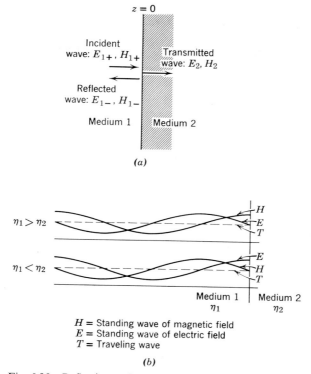

(a)

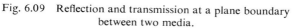

H = Standing wave of magnetic field
E = Standing wave of electric field
T = Traveling wave

(b)

Fig. 6.09   Reflection and transmission at a plane boundary
between two media.

axis, and the direction of propagation of the incident wave as the positive
z direction, with the boundary at $z = 0$ (Fig. 6.09a). The medium to the
right is assumed to be effectively infinite in extent, so that there is no
reflected wave in that region. The field impedance there is then just the
intrinsic impedance η_2 for all planes, and in particular this becomes the
known load impedance at the plane $z = 0$. Applying Eq. 6.08(11) to give
the reflection coefficient for medium 1 referred to $z = 0$,

$$\rho = \frac{E_{1-}}{E_{1+}} = \frac{\eta_2 - \eta_1}{\eta_2 + \eta_1}. \tag{1}$$

The transmission coefficient giving the amplitude of transmitted wave into
the second dielectric, from Eq. 6.08(12), is

$$\frac{E_2}{E_{1+}} = \frac{2\eta_2}{\eta_2 + \eta_1}. \tag{2}$$

From (1), we see that there is no reflection if there is a match of imped-ances, $\eta_1 = \eta_2$. This would of course occur for the trivial case of identical dielectrics, but also for the case of different dielectrics if they could be made with the same *ratio* of μ to ϵ. This latter case is not of practical importance since we do not commonly find high-frequency dielectric materials with permeability different from that of free space, but it is interesting since we might not intuitively expect a reflectionless trans-mission in going from free space to a dielectric with both permittivity and permeability increased by, say, ten times.

In the general case there will be a finite value of reflection in the first region, and from (1) we can show that the magnitude of ρ is always less than unity. (It approaches unity as η_2/η_1 approaches zero or infinity.) The reflected wave could then be combined with a part of the incident wave of equal amplitude to form a standing wave pattern as in the case of complete reflection studied in Art. 6.07. The remaining part of the incident wave could then be thought of as a traveling wave carrying the energy that passes on into the second medium. The combination of the traveling and standing wave parts then produces a space pattern with maxima and minima, but with the minima not zero in general. As for corresponding transmission lines, it is convenient to express the ratio of a-c amplitude at the electric field maximum to the minimum a-c amplitude (occurring a quarter-wavelength away) as a standing wave ratio S:

$$S = \frac{|E_x(z)|_{\max}}{|E_x(z)|_{\min}} = \frac{1 + |\rho|}{1 - |\rho|}. \tag{3}$$

By utilizing (1), it may be shown for real η that

$$S = \begin{cases} \eta_2/\eta_1 & \text{if} \quad \eta_2 > \eta_1 \\ \eta_1/\eta_2 & \text{if} \quad \eta_1 > \eta_2 \end{cases} \tag{4}$$

Since η_1 and η_2 are both real for perfect dielectrics, ρ is real and the plane $z = 0$ must be a position of a maximum or minimum. It is a maximum of electric field if ρ is positive, since reflected and incident waves then add, so it is a maximum of electric field and minimum of magnetic field if $\eta_2 > \eta_1$. The plane $z = 0$ is a minimum of electric field and a maximum of magnetic field if $\eta_1 > \eta_2$. These two cases are sketched in Fig. 6.09b.

Problems

6.09a Write the total electric field and total magnetic field for $z < 0$ and for $z > 0$ for the case of reflection from a single dielectric boundary as studied in Art 6.09.

6.09b For a certain dielectric material of effectively infinite depth, reflections of an incident plane wave from free space are observed to produce a standing wave ratio of 2.7 in the free space. The face is an electric field minimum. Find the dielectric constant.

6.09c Derive a formula for the fraction of incident energy passing into a conductor of conductivity σ, permeability μ, when a uniform plane wave is normally incident from a dielectric with intrinsic impedance η. Make approximations based on $\eta \gg R_s$. Compute the values for incidence from air to copper at 30 Mc/sec and 3000 Mc/sec.

6.09d Check the formula derived in Prob. c by assuming that the magnetic field at the surface is the same as for reflection from a perfect conductor, and computing the conductor losses due to currents compatible with this magnetic field.

6.09e Derive an approximate formula for the ratio of quadrature component in the reflected wave to the real component for a wave normally incident from a perfect dielectric onto a good conductor. Compute the ratios for incidence from air to copper at 30 and 3000 Mc/sec.

6.10 Reflection Problems with Several Dielectrics

We shall next be interested in considering the case of several parallel dielectric discontinuities with a uniform plane wave incident in some material to the left, as pictured in the case for three dielectric materials in Fig. 6.10. We might at first be tempted to treat the problem by considering a series of wave reflections, the incident wave breaking into one part reflected and one part transmitted at the first plane; of the part transmitted into region 2 some is transmitted at the second plane and some is reflected back toward the first plane; of the latter part some is transmitted and some reflected, and so on through an infinite series of wave reflections. This lengthy procedure can be avoided by considering total quantities at each stage of the discussion, and again the impedance formulation is useful in writing down the solution.

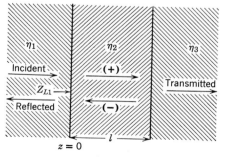

Fig. 6.10

If the region to the right has only a single outwardly propagating wave, the wave or field impedance at any plane in this medium is η_3, which then becomes the load impedance to place at $z = l$. The input impedance for region 2 is then given at once by Eq. 6.08(10), and, since this is the impedance at $z = 0$, it may also be considered the load impedance for region 1:

$$Z_{L1} = Z_{i2} = \eta_2 \left(\frac{\eta_3 \cos k_2 l + j\eta_2 \sin k_2 l}{\eta_2 \cos k_2 l + j\eta_3 \sin k_2 l} \right). \qquad (1)$$

The reflection coefficient in region 1, referred to $z = 0$, is given by Eq. 6.08(11):

$$\rho = \frac{Z_{L1} - \eta_1}{Z_{L1} + \eta_1}. \qquad (2)$$

In such problems we are often most interested in the ratio of power in the reflected wave to that in the incident wave, and this ratio is given by the square of the magnitude of (2), as can be shown by considering the Poynting vectors:

$$\frac{P_{z-}}{P_{z+}} = |\rho|^2. \qquad (3)$$

If there are more than the two parallel dielectric boundaries, the process is simply repeated, the input impedance for one region becoming the load value for the next, until one arrives at the region in which reflection is to be computed. It is of course desirable in many cases to utilize the Smith chart described in Art. 1.20 in place of (1) to transform load to input impedances, and to compute reflection coefficient or standing wave ratio once the impedance mismatch ratio is known, just as the chart is used in transmission line calculations.

We now wish to consider several special cases which are of importance.

Half-Wave Dielectric Window. If the input and output dielectrics are the same in Fig. 6.10, $\eta_1 = \eta_3$, and the intervening dielectric window is some multiple of a half-wavelength referred to medium 2, $k_2 l = m\pi$, (1) gives

$$Z_{L1} = \eta_3 = \eta_1,$$

and from (2)

$$\rho = 0.$$

Hence there is no reflection from such a window since the impedance seen at the input face is the same as that at the output.

Electrically Thin Window. If $\eta_1 = \eta_3$ and $k_2 l$ is so small compared with unity that all powers higher than the first may be neglected, (1) becomes to this approximation

$$Z_{L1} \approx \eta_2 \left(\frac{\eta_1 + j\eta_2 k_2 l}{\eta_2 + j\eta_1 k_2 l} \right) \approx \eta_1 \left[1 + jk_2 l \left(\frac{\eta_2}{\eta_1} - \frac{\eta_1}{\eta_2} \right) \right].$$

Substituting in (2), we see that

$$\rho \approx j \frac{k_2 l}{2}\left(\frac{\eta_2}{\eta_1} - \frac{\eta_1}{\eta_2}\right). \qquad (5)$$

The magnitude of reflection coefficient is thus proportional to the electrical length of the dielectric window for small values of $k_2 l$; and the fraction of incident power reflected is then proportional to the square of this length.

Quarter-Wave Coating for Eliminating Reflections. Another important case is that of a quarter-wave coating placed between two different dielectrics. If its intrinsic impedance is the geometric mean of those on the two sides, it will eliminate all wave reflections for energy passing from the first medium into the third. To show this, let

$$k_2 l = \frac{\pi}{2} \qquad \eta_2 = \sqrt{\eta_1 \eta_3}. \qquad (6)$$

From (1),

and from (2)

$$Z_{L1} = \frac{\eta_2^{\,2}}{\eta_3} = \frac{\eta_1 \eta_3}{\eta_3} = \eta_1,$$

$$\rho = 0. \qquad (7)$$

This technique is used, for example, in coating optical lenses to decrease the amount of reflected light, and is exactly analogous to the technique of matching transmission lines of different characteristic impedances by introducing a quarter-wave section having characteristic impedance the geometric mean of those on the two sides. In all cases the matching is perfect only at specific frequencies for which the length is an odd multiple of a quarter wave, but is approximately correct for bands of frequencies about these values. Multiple coatings are used to increase the frequency band obtainable with a specified permissible reflection.[7]

Problems

6.10a Calculate the reflection coefficient and per cent of incident energy reflected when a uniform plane wave is normally incident on a Plexiglas radome (dielectric window) of thickness $\frac{3}{8}$ in., relative permittivity $\epsilon_r = 2.8$, with free space on both sides. Frequency corresponds to free-space wavelength of 20 cm. Repeat for 10 cm; for 3 cm.

6.10b For a sandwich-type radome consisting of two identical thin sheets (thickness 1.5 mm, relative permittivity $\epsilon_r = 4$) on either side of a thicker foam-type dielectric (thickness 1.81 cm, relative permittivity $\epsilon_r = 1.1$), calculate the reflection coefficient for waves striking at normal incidence. Take frequency 3×10^9 cps; repeat for 6×10^9 cps. *Suggestion:* Use the Smith chart of Art. 1.20.

[7] J. M. Stone, *Radiation and Optics; an Introduction to the Classical Theory*, McGraw-Hill, New York, 1963.

6.10c A quarter-wave matching coating is designed to eliminate reflections for waves of frequency 3000 Mc/sec passing normally from space into the body of a material with relative permittivity 16. Find the thickness of the coating and its permittivity. Plot a curve showing percentage of incident energy reflected as a function of frequency for normally incident waves of frequencies in the range 1000 Mc/sec to 6000 Mc/sec.

6.10d Imagine two quarter-wave layers of intrinsic impedance η_2 and η_3 between dielectrics of intrinsic impedances η_1 and η_4. Show that perfect matching occurs if $\eta_2/\eta_3 = (\eta_1/\eta_4)^{1/2}$. For $\eta_4 = 4$, $\eta_3 = 3$, $\eta_2 = 1.5$, $\eta_1 = 1$, calculate reflection coefficient at a frequency 10% below that for perfect matching. Compare with the result for a single quarter-wave matching coating with $\eta = 2$.

6.10e A dielectric window of polystyrene (see Table 6.04) is made a half-wavelength thick (referred to the dielectric) at 10^8 cps, so that there would be no reflections for normally incident uniform plane waves from space, neglecting losses in the dielectric. Considering the finite losses, compute the reflection coefficient and fraction of incident energy reflected from the front face. Also determine the fraction of the incident energy lost in the dielectric window.

6.10f A slab of dielectric of length l, constants ϵ' and ϵ'', is backed by a conducting plane at $z = l$ which may be considered perfect. Determine the expression for field impedance at the front face, $z = 0$. Calculate the value for $\epsilon' = 4$, $\epsilon'' = 0.01$, $f = 3 \times 10^9$ cps, $l = 1.25$ cm.

6.10g A conducting film of impedance 377 ohms per square is placed a quarter-wave in air from a plane conductor to eliminate wave reflections for a 9000 Mc/sec wave. Assume negligible displacement currents in film. Plot a curve showing the fraction of incident power reflected versus frequency for frequencies from 6000 to 18,000 Mc/sec.

6.10h The common materials used for the conducting films in the application of Prob. *g* may not have a negligible dielectric constant. Study the effect of finite dielectric constant on a design that would otherwise produce no reflection.

6.11 Incidence at any Angle on Perfect Conductors

We now wish to remove the restriction to normal incidence which has been assumed in all the preceding examples. It is possible and desirable to extend the impedance concept to apply to this case also, but before doing this we shall consider the reflection of uniform plane waves at arbitrary incidence from a perfect conductor in order to develop certain ideas of the behavior at oblique incidence. It is also convenient to separate the discussion into two cases, polarization with electric field in the plane of incidence, and normal to the plane of incidence. Other cases may be considered a superposition of these two. The plane of incidence is defined by a normal to the surface on which the wave impinges, and a ray following the direction of propagation of the incident wave. That is, it is the plane of the paper as we have drawn sketches in this chapter. The case of waves obliquely incident on a surface between two media, one (or both) of which

is lossy is included in the development by substituting the appropriate complex values of intrinsic impedance and propagation constant. The interpretation of results becomes complicated and will not be given here.[8]
Polarization with Electric Field in the Plane of Incidence. In Fig. 6.11a the ray drawn normal to the incident wave front makes an angle θ with the normal to the conductor. We know that, since energy cannot pass into the perfect conductor, there must be some reflected wave, and we

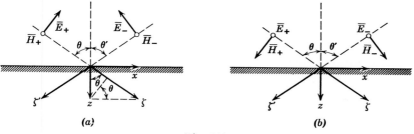

(a)   (b)

Fig. 6.11

draw its direction of propagation at some unknown angle θ'. The electric and magnetic fields of both incident and reflected wave must lie perpendicular to their respective directions of propagation by the properties of uniform plane waves (Art. 6.02), so the electric fields may be drawn as shown by $\bar{E}_+$ and $\bar{E}_-$. The corresponding magnetic fields $\bar{H}_+$ and $\bar{H}_-$ are then both normally out of the paper, so that $\bar{E} \times \bar{H}$ will give the direction of propagation for each wave. Moreover, with the senses as shown,

$$\frac{E_+}{H_+} = \frac{E_-}{H_-} = \eta. \qquad (1)$$

If we draw a ζ direction in the actual direction of propagation for the incident wave as shown, and a ζ' direction so that the reflected wave is traveling in the negative ζ' direction, we know that the phase factors for the two waves may be written as $e^{-jk\zeta}$ and $e^{jk\zeta'}$ respectively. The sum of incident and reflected waves at any point x, z ($z < 0$) could be written

$$\bar{E}(x, z) = \bar{E}_+ e^{-jk\zeta} + \bar{E}_- e^{jk\zeta'}, \qquad (2)$$

where $\bar{E}_+$ and $\bar{E}_-$ are reference values at the origin. We wish, however, to

[8] The interested reader is referred to a treatment of waves in free space obliquely incident on the plane surface of a lossy medium by R. B. Adler, L. J. Chu, and R. M. Fano, *Electromagnetic Energy Transmission and Radiation*, John Wiley and Sons, New York, 1960, p. 442.

express all coordinates in terms of the rectangular system aligned with the conductor surface. The conversion of ζ and ζ' from the diagram is

$$\zeta = x \sin \theta + z \cos \theta \qquad (3)$$

$$\zeta' = -x \sin \theta' + z \cos \theta' \qquad (4)$$

so that, if these are substituted in the phase factors of (2), and the two waves broken into their x and z components, we have

$$E_x(x, z) = E_+ \cos \theta e^{-jk(x \sin \theta + z \cos \theta)} - E_- \cos \theta' e^{jk(-x \sin \theta' + z \cos \theta')}, \qquad (5)$$

$$E_z(x, z) = -E_+ \sin \theta e^{-jk(x \sin \theta + z \cos \theta)} - E_- \sin \theta' e^{jk(-x \sin \theta' + z \cos \theta')}. \qquad (6)$$

The magnetic field in the two waves is

$$H_y(x, z) = H_+ e^{-jk(x \sin \theta + z \cos \theta)} + H_- e^{jk(-x \sin \theta' + z \cos \theta')}. \qquad (7)$$

The next step is the application of the boundary condition of the perfect conductor, which is that, at $z = 0$, E_x must be zero for all x. From (5),

$$E_x(x, 0) = E_+ \cos \theta e^{-jkx \sin \theta} - E_- \cos \theta' e^{-jkx \sin \theta'} = 0. \qquad (8)$$

This equation can be satisfied for all x only if the phase factors in the two terms are equal, and this in turn requires that

$$\theta = \theta'. \qquad (9)$$

That is, *the angle of reflection is equal to the angle of incidence.* With this result in (8), it follows that the two amplitudes must be equal:

$$E_+ = E_-. \qquad (10)$$

If the results (9) and (10) are substituted in (5), (6), and (7), we have the final expressions for field components at any point $z < 0$,

$$E_x(x, z) = -2jE_+ \cos \theta \sin (kz \cos \theta) e^{-jkx \sin \theta}, \qquad (11)$$

$$E_z(x, z) = -2E_+ \sin \theta \cos (kz \cos \theta) e^{-jkx \sin \theta}, \qquad (12)$$

$$\eta H_y(x, z) = 2E_+ \cos (kz \cos \theta) e^{-jkx \sin \theta}. \qquad (13)$$

The foregoing field has the character of a traveling wave with respect to the x direction, but that of a standing wave with respect to the z direction. That is, E_x is zero for all time at the conducting plane, and also in parallel planes distance nd in front of the conductor, where

$$d = \frac{\lambda_1}{2 \cos \theta} = \frac{1}{2f\sqrt{\mu\epsilon} \cos \theta}. \qquad (14)$$

The a-c amplitude of E_x is a maximum in planes an odd multiple of $d/2$ in front of the conductor. H_y and E_z are maximum where E_x is zero, are zero where E_x is maximum, and are everywhere 90° out of time phase with respect to E_x. Perhaps the most interesting result from this analysis is that the distance between successive maxima and minima, measured normal to the plane, becomes *greater* as the incidence becomes more oblique. A superficial survey of the situation might lead one to believe that they would be at projections of the wavelength in this direction, which would become smaller with increasing θ. This point will be pursued more in the following article.

Polarization with Electric Field Normal to the Plane of Incidence. In this polarization (Fig. 6.11b), $\bar{E}_+$ and $\bar{E}_-$ are normal to the plane of the paper, and $\bar{H}_+$ and $\bar{H}_-$ are then as shown. Proceeding exactly as before, we can write the components of the two waves in the x, z system of coordinates as

$$E_y(x, z) = E_+ e^{-jk(x \sin \theta + z \cos \theta)} + E_- e^{jk(-x \sin \theta' + z \cos \theta')}, \tag{15}$$

$$\eta H_x(x, z) = -E_+ \cos \theta e^{-jk(x \sin \theta + z \cos \theta)} + E_- \cos \theta' e^{jk(-x \sin \theta' + z \cos \theta')}, \tag{16}$$

$$\eta H_z(x, z) = E_+ \sin \theta e^{-jk(x \sin \theta + z \cos \theta)} + E_- \sin \theta' e^{jk(-x \sin \theta' + z \cos \theta')}. \tag{17}$$

The boundary condition at the perfectly conducting plane is that E_y is zero at $z = 0$ for all x, which by the same reasoning as before leads to the conclusion that $\theta = \theta'$ and $E_+ = -E_-$. The field components, (15) to (17), then become

$$E_y = -2jE_+ \sin (kz \cos \theta) e^{-jkx \sin \theta} \tag{18}$$

$$\eta H_x = -2E_+ \cos \theta \cos (kz \cos \theta) e^{-jkx \sin \theta}, \tag{19}$$

$$\eta H_z = -2jE_+ \sin \theta \sin (kz \cos \theta) e^{-jkx \sin \theta}. \tag{20}$$

This set again shows the behavior of a traveling wave in the x direction and a standing wave pattern in the z direction with zeros of E_y and H_z and maxima of H_x at the conducting plane and at parallel planes distance nd away, with d given by (14).

Problems

6.11a Write the instantaneous values of the field components corresponding to (11) to (13) in Art 6.11. Write the average and instantaneous components of Poynting vector in the x direction; in the z direction.

6.11b Repeat Prob. *a* for the other polarization, (18) to (20).

6.12 Phase Velocity and Impedance for Waves
at Oblique Incidence

Phase Velocity. Let us consider an incident wave, such as that of Art. 6.11, traveling with velocity $v = 1/\sqrt{\mu\epsilon}$ in a positive direction, which makes angle θ with a desired z direction aligned normally to some reflecting surface. We saw that it was possible to express the phase factor in terms of the x and z coordinates:

$$\bar{E}(x, z) = \bar{E}_+ e^{-jk\xi} = \bar{E}_+ e^{-jk(x\sin\theta + z\cos\theta)}. \tag{1}$$

For many purposes it is desirable to concentrate on the change in phase as one moves in the x direction, or in the z direction. We may then define the two phase constants for these directions:

$$\beta_x = k\sin\theta \tag{2}$$

$$\beta_z = k\cos\theta. \tag{3}$$

Wave (1) may then be written (putting in $e^{j\omega t}$ explicitly)

$$\bar{E}(x, z, t) = \bar{E}_+ e^{j(\omega t - \beta_x x - \beta_z z)}. \tag{4}$$

If we wish to keep the instantaneous phase constant as we move in the x direction, we keep $\omega t - \beta_x x$ constant (the last term does not change if we move only in the x direction), and the velocity required for this is defined as the phase velocity referred to the x direction:

$$v_{px} = \left.\frac{\partial x}{\partial t}\right|_{(\omega t - \beta_x x) = \text{const}} = \frac{\omega}{\beta_x}$$

or

$$v_{px} = \frac{\omega}{k\sin\theta} = \frac{1}{\sqrt{\mu\epsilon}\sin\theta} = \frac{v}{\sin\theta}. \tag{5}$$

Similarly for the z direction,

$$v_{pz} = \frac{\omega}{\beta_z} = \frac{v}{\cos\theta}, \tag{6}$$

where v is the velocity normal to its wave front, $1/\sqrt{\mu\epsilon}$.

We see that in both cases the phase velocity is *greater* than the velocity measured normal to the wave front, and will in fact be so for any oblique direction. There is no violation of relativistic principles by this result, since no material object moves at this velocity. It is the velocity of a fictitious point of intersection of the wave front and a line drawn in the selected direction. Thus in Fig. 6.12, if a plane of constant phase aa moves to $a'a'$ in a given interval of time, the distance moved normal to the wave front is XX', but the distance moved by this constant phase reference along the z direction BO is the greater distance YY'. Since

$$YY' = XX' \sec \theta,$$

this picture would again lead to the result (6) for phase velocity in the z direction.

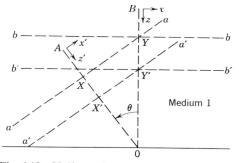

Fig. 6.12   Uniform plane wave moving at angle θ toward a plane.

The concept of a phase velocity, and the understanding of why it may be greater than the velocity of light, is very necessary to the discussion of guided waves in later chapters, as well as to the remainder of this chapter.

Wave Impedance. In the problems of oblique incidence on a plane boundary between different media, it is also useful to define the wave or field impedance as the ratio of electric to magnetic field components in planes parallel to the boundary. The reason for this is the continuity of the *tangential* components of electric and magnetic fields at a boundary, and the consequent equality of the above defined ratio on the two sides of the boundary. That is, if the value of this ratio is computed as an input impedance for a region to the right in some manner, it is also the value of load impedance at that plane for the region to the left, just as in the examples of normal incidence.

Thus, for incident and reflected waves making angle θ with the normal as in Art. 6.11, we may define a characteristic wave impedance referred to the z direction in terms of the components in planes transverse to that direction. From Eqs. 6.11(5) and (7) *for waves polarized with electric field in the plane of incidence,*

$$Z_z = \frac{E_{x+}}{H_{y+}} = -\frac{E_{x-}}{H_{y-}} = \eta \cos \theta. \tag{7}$$

Superscripts $+$ and $-$ refer, respectively, to incident and reflected wave; the sign of the ratio is chosen for each wave to yield a positive result. From Eqs. 6.11(15) and (16) *for waves polarized with electric field normal to the plane of incidence,*

$$Z_z = -\frac{E_{y+}}{H_{x+}} = \frac{E_{y-}}{H_{x-}} = \eta \sec \theta. \tag{8}$$

We see that, for the first type of polarization, the characteristic wave impedance is always less than η, as we would expect since only a component of total electric field lies in the transverse x-y plane, whereas the total magnetic field lies in that plane. In the latter polarization, the reverse is true and Z_z is always greater than η.

The interpretation of the example of the last article from the foregoing point of view is then that the perfect conductor amounts to a zero impedance or short to the transverse field component E_x. We would then expect a standing wave pattern in the z direction with other zeros at multiples of a half-wavelength away, this wavelength being computed from phase velocity in the z direction. This leads again to the result Eq. 6.11(14).

6.13 Incidence at any Angle on Dielectrics

Law of Reflection. For a uniform plane wave incident at angle θ with the normal to the plane boundary between two dielectrics ϵ_1 and ϵ_2, Fig. 6.13, there will be a reflected wave at some angle θ' with the normal, and a transmitted (or *refracted*) wave into the second medium which is drawn at some angle θ'' with the normal. For either type of polarization, the continuity condition on tangential components of electric and magnetic

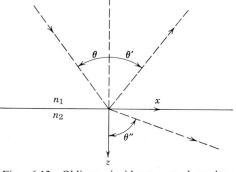

Fig. 6.13 Oblique incidence on boundary between two isotropic media.

field at the boundary $z = 0$ must be satisfied for all values of x. As in the argument applied to the problem of reflection from the perfect conductor, this is possible for all x only if incident, reflected, and refracted waves all have the same phase factor with respect to the x direction, and hence the same phase velocity in the x direction. Using the result of Eq. 6.12(5), we conclude that

$$\frac{v_1}{\sin \theta} = \frac{v_1}{\sin \theta'} = \frac{v_2}{\sin \theta''}. \tag{1}$$

The first pair in (1) gives the result

$$\theta' = \theta, \tag{2}$$

or the angle of reflection is equal to the angle of incidence.

Snell's Law of Refraction. From the last pair of (1) we find a relation between the angle of refraction θ'' and the angle of incidence θ:

$$\frac{\sin \theta''}{\sin \theta} = \frac{v_2}{v_1} = \frac{n_1}{n_2}. \tag{3}$$

This relation is a familiar one in optics and is known as Snell's law. The *refractive index* n is defined to be unity for free space so its value for any other dielectric is a measure of the phase velocity of electromagnetic waves in the medium, relative to free space. It is common to use the refractive index to characterize properties of dielectrics in the infrared and optical frequency ranges. At microwave and lower frequencies it is more common to express the velocities in (3) in terms of permittivity and permeability. For common dielectrics n_1/n_2 may be replaced by $(\epsilon_1/\epsilon_2)^{1/2}$ since $\mu_1 \approx \mu_2 \approx \mu_0$.

Reflection and Transmission for Polarization with E in Plane of Incidence. To compute the amount of the wave reflected and the amount transmitted, we may use the impedance concept as extended for oblique incidence in the last article. To show the validity of this procedure, we write the continuity conditions for total E_x and H_y, including both incident and reflected components in region 1:

$$E_{x+} + E_{x-} = E_{x2}, \tag{4}$$

$$H_{y+} + H_{y-} = H_{y2}. \tag{5}$$

Following Art. 6.12, if we define wave impedances in terms of the tangential components,

$$Z_{z1} = \frac{E_{x+}}{H_{y+}} = -\frac{E_{x-}}{H_{y-}}, \tag{6}$$

$$Z_L = \frac{E_{x2}}{H_{y2}}. \tag{7}$$

Equation (5) may be written

$$\frac{E_{x+}}{Z_{z1}} - \frac{E_{x-}}{Z_{z1}} = \frac{E_{x2}}{Z_L}. \tag{8}$$

An elimination between (4) and (8) results in equations for reflection and transmission coefficients:

$$\rho = \frac{E_{x-}}{E_{x+}} = \frac{Z_L - Z_{z1}}{Z_L + Z_{z1}}, \tag{9}$$

$$\tau = \frac{E_{x2}}{E_{x+}} = \frac{2Z_L}{Z_L + Z_{z1}}. \tag{10}$$

For the present case, since there is no returning wave in medium 2, the load impedance Z_L is just the characteristic wave impedance for the refracted wave referred to the z direction, obtainable from Eq. 6.12(7),

$$Z_L = \eta_2 \cos \theta'' = \eta_2 \sqrt{1 - \left(\frac{v_2}{v_1}\right)^2 \sin^2 \theta}. \tag{11}$$

And the characteristic wave impedance for medium 1 referred to the z direction is

$$Z_{z1} = \eta_1 \cos \theta. \tag{12}$$

The second form of (11) is obtained by substituting the Snell's law relation (3) between θ'' and θ, and is applicable even when the result for Z_L is complex. Note that, for dielectrics with $\mu_1 = \mu_2$,

$$\frac{\eta_2}{\eta_1} = \frac{v_2}{v_2} = \sqrt{\frac{\epsilon_1}{\epsilon_2}}. \tag{13}$$

The total fields in region 1 may then be written as the sum of incident and reflected waves, utilizing (9) and the basic properties of uniform plane waves. We shall use H_{y+} (denoted H_+) of the incident wave as the reference component since it is parallel to the boundary.

$$E_x = \eta_1 H_+ \cos \theta e^{-j\beta_x x}[e^{-j\beta_z z} + \rho e^{j\beta_z z}] \tag{14}$$

$$H_y = H_+ e^{-j\beta_x x}[e^{-j\beta_z z} - \rho e^{j\beta_z z}] \tag{15}$$

$$E_z = \eta_1 H_+ \sin \theta e^{-j\beta_x x}[-e^{-j\beta_z z} + \rho e^{j\beta_z z}] \tag{16}$$

$$\beta_x = k_1 \sin \theta \qquad \beta_z = k_1 \cos \theta. \tag{17}$$

This field again has the character of a traveling wave field in the x direction and a standing wave field in the z direction, but here the minima in the z direction do not in general reach zero. The ratio of maxima to minima could be expressed as a standing wave ratio and would be related to the magnitude of reflection coefficient by the usual expression, Eq. 6.09(3).

Reflection and Transmission for Polarization with E Normal to Plane of Incidence. For this polarization, the basic relations (9) and (10) between impedances and reflection or transmission may also be shown to apply. Note that they were first introduced in connection with transmission line waves in Chapter 1 but have now found usefulness for many wave problems through the impedance concept applied to wave phenomena:

$$\rho = \frac{E_{y-}}{E_{y+}} = \frac{Z_L - Z_{z1}}{Z_L + Z_{z1}} \tag{18}$$

$$\tau = \frac{E_{y2}}{E_{y+}} = \frac{2Z_L}{Z_L + Z_{z1}}. \tag{19}$$

For this polarization, the proper wave impedances are obtained from Eq. 6.12(8):

$$Z_L = \eta_2 \sec \theta'' = \eta_2 \left[1 - \left(\frac{v_2}{v_1} \right)^2 \sin^2 \theta \right]^{-\frac{1}{2}} \tag{20}$$

$$Z_{z1} = \eta_1 \sec \theta. \tag{21}$$

The total fields in region 1 are (E_+ denotes the value of E_{y+} in the incident wave)

$$E_y = E_+ e^{-j\beta_x x}[e^{-j\beta_z z} + \rho e^{j\beta_z z}] \tag{22}$$

$$H_x = -\left(\frac{E_+ \cos \theta}{\eta} \right) e^{-j\beta_x x}[e^{-j\beta_z z} - \rho e^{j\beta_z z}] \tag{23}$$

$$H_z = \left(\frac{E_+ \sin \theta}{\eta} \right) e^{-j\beta_x x}[e^{-j\beta_z z} + \rho e^{j\beta_z z}] \tag{24}$$

$$\beta_x = k_1 \sin \theta \qquad \beta_z = k_1 \cos \theta. \tag{25}$$

Problems

6.13a Write the expressions for field components in region 2 for both types of polarization.

6.13b For the first type of polarization, evaluate the average Poynting vector in both regions, and show the power balance.

6.13c For both polarizations, give the conditions for which the standing wave pattern in z shows a minimum of tangential electric field at the boundary surface; repeat for a maximum of tangential E at the surface.

6.13d Derive formulas (18) and (19) for polarization with electric field normal to the plane of incidence.

6.14 Total Reflection

A study of the general results from Art. 6.13 shows that there are several particular conditions of incidence of special interest. The first is one which leads to a condition of total reflection. From the basic formula for reflection coefficient, Eq. 6.13(9) or (18), we know that there is complete reflection ($|\rho| = 1$) if the load impedance Z_L is zero, infinity, or purely imaginary. To show the last condition, let $Z_L = jX_L$ and note that Z_{z1} is real:

$$|\rho| = \left| \frac{jX_L - Z_{z1}}{jX_L + Z_{z1}} \right| = \frac{\sqrt{X_L{}^2 + Z_{z1}^2}}{\sqrt{X_L{}^2 + Z_{z1}^2}} = 1. \qquad (1)$$

The value of Z_L for polarization with electric field in the plane of incidence, given by Eq. 6.13(11), is seen to become zero for some critical angle $\theta = \theta_c$ such that

$$\sin \theta_c = \frac{v_1}{v_2}. \qquad (2)$$

The value of Z_L for polarization with electric field normal to the plane of incidence, given by Eq. 6.13(20), becomes infinite for this same condition. For both polarizations, Z_L would be imaginary for angles of incidence greater than θ_c, so there would be total reflection for such angles of incidence.

For common dielectrics having $\mu_1 = \mu_2$, (2) reduces to

$$\sin \theta_c = \sqrt{\epsilon_2/\epsilon_1}. \qquad (3)$$

It is seen that there are real solutions for the critical angle in this case only when $\epsilon_1 > \epsilon_2$, or when the wave passes from an optically dense to an optically rarer medium. From Snell's law, Eq. 6.13(3), we would find that the angle of refraction would be $\pi/2$ for $\theta = \theta_c$, and would become imaginary for greater angles of incidence. So from this point of view also we would expect no transfer of energy into the second medium. Although there is no energy transfer, there are finite values of field in the second region as required by the continuity conditions at the boundary. These die off exponentially with distance from the boundary as the phase constant β_z becomes imaginary.

Although the reflected wave has the same amplitude as the incident wave for angles of incidence greater than the critical, it does not in general have the same phase. The phase relation between E_{x-} and E_{x+} for the first type of polarization is also different from that between E_{y-} and E_{y+} for the second type of polarization incident at the same angle. Thus, if the incident wave has both types of polarization components, 'the reflected wave under these conditions will be elliptically polarized (Art. 6.03).

The phenomenon of total reflection is very important at optical frequencies, as it provides reflection with less loss than from conducting mirrors. (As noted in Table 6.05, conductors can no longer be considered ideal at optical frequencies.) The use in total reflecting prisms is a well-known example.

Problems

6.14a Calculate the critical angle for an electromagnetic wave passing from the following dielectrics into air.

Material	ϵ/ϵ_0 (ratio of permittivity to that of air)
Distilled water	81.1
Ethyl alcohol	25.8
Glass (high-density)	9
Glass (low-density)	6
Mica	6
Quartz	5
Petroleum oil	2.1

6.14b Defining ψ as the phase E_{x-}/E_{x+} and ψ' as the phase of E_{y-}/E_{y+}, find expressions for ψ and ψ' under conditions of total reflection. Show that the phase difference between these two polarization components, $\delta = \psi - \psi'$, is given by

$$\tan\left(\frac{\delta}{2}\right) = \frac{(\eta_2/\eta_1)[(v_2/v_1)^2 - 1]\sin^2\theta}{[(\eta_2/\eta_1)^2 - 1]\cos\theta\sqrt{(v_2/v_1)^2\sin^2\theta - 1}}.$$

6.14c Find, in such form as to disclose the exponential decay of fields with penetration into the second dielectric, the expressions for the fields in the second dielectric when the incident angle is such as to yield imaginary Z_L.

6.15 Polarizing or Brewster Angle

Let us next ask under what conditions there might be no reflected wave when the uniform plane wave is incident at angle θ on the dielectric boundary. We know that this occurs for a matching of impedances between the two media, $Z_L = Z_{z1}$. For the wave polarized with electric field in the plane of incidence, and for a medium with $\mu_1 = \mu_2$, Eqs. 6.13(11) and (12) become

$$Z_L = \sqrt{\mu_1/\epsilon_2}\sqrt{1 - (\epsilon_1/\epsilon_2)\sin^2\theta} \tag{1}$$

$$Z_{z1} = \sqrt{\mu_1/\epsilon_1}\cos\theta. \tag{2}$$

These two quantities may be made equal for a particular angle $\theta = \theta_p$ such that

$$\cos \theta_p = \frac{\epsilon_1}{\epsilon_2} \sqrt{1 - (\epsilon_1/\epsilon_2) \sin^2 \theta_p}. \qquad (3)$$

This equation has a solution:

$$\theta_p = \sin^{-1} \sqrt{\epsilon_2/(\epsilon_1 + \epsilon_2)} = \tan^{-1} \sqrt{\epsilon_2/\epsilon_1}. \qquad (4)$$

Note that (4) yields real values of θ_p for either $\epsilon_1 > \epsilon_2$ or $\epsilon_2 > \epsilon_1$, and so, for polarization with electric field in the plane of incidence, there is always some angle for which there is no reflection; all energy incident at this angle passes into the second medium.

For polarization with electric field normal to the plane of incidence, a study of Eqs. 6.13(20) and (21) would show that there is no angle yielding an equality of impedances for materials with different dielectric constants but like permeabilities. Hence, a wave incident at angle θ_p with both polarization components present has some of the second polarization component but none of the first reflected. The reflected wave at this angle is thus plane polarized with electric field normal to the plane of incidence, and the angle θ_p is correspondingly known as the *polarizing angle*. It is also alternatively known as the *Brewster angle*. Gas lasers typically use windows placed at the Brewster angle to allow oscillation for only one of the two possible polarizations, since for this polarization there will be low reflection from the ends of the tube, and the external optical resonator (Art. 10.15) will govern the behavior.

Problems

6.15a For the dielectrics listed in Prob. 6.14a, determine the polarizing angle for waves passing from each of the dielectrics into air, and also for waves passing from air into the dielectrics.

6.15b Imagine a material with $\epsilon_1 = \epsilon_2$, but $\mu_1 \neq \mu_2$. Which polarization component would then yield a solution for incident angle giving no reflections? Give the angle.

6.15c For the wave with E polarized in the plane of incidence, note the change of phase between E_x in reflected and incident waves for angles in the vicinity of θ_p. What effect does this have on the standing wave pattern in the z direction in the first dielectric?

6.15d Show that there will be no reflections from the second surface of a window with parallel faces if the radiation is properly polarized and incident from one side at the Brewster angle.

6.16   Multiple Dielectric Boundaries with Oblique Incidence

If there are several dielectric regions with parallel boundaries, the problem may be solved by successively transforming impedances through the several regions, using the standard transmission line formula, Eq. 1.18(10), or a graphical aid such as the Smith chart. For each region the phase constant and characteristic wave impedance must include the function of angle from the normal as well as the properties of the dielectric material. Thus for the ith region, from the concepts of Art. 6.12, the phase constant is

$$\beta_{zi} = k_i \cos \theta_i, \tag{1}$$

and the characteristic wave impedance is

$$Z_{zi} = \eta_i \cos \theta_i \qquad \text{for } E \text{ in plane of incidence} \tag{2}$$

$$Z_{zi} = \eta_i \sec \theta_i \qquad \text{for } E \text{ normal to plane of incidence.} \tag{3}$$

When the impedance is finally transformed to the surface at which it is desired to find reflection, the reflection coefficient is calculated from the basic reflection formula, Eq. 6.13(9), and the fraction of the incident power reflected is just the square of its magnitude. The angles in the several regions are found by successively applying Snell's law, starting from the first given angle of incidence.

Problems

6.16a   A uniform plane wave of free-space wavelength 3 cm is incident from space on a window of permittivity 3, and thickness equal to a half-wavelength referred to the dielectric material so that it gives no reflections for normal incidence. For general angles of incidence, plot the fraction of incident energy reflected versus θ for polarization with E in the plane of incidence, and also for polarization normal to the plane of incidence.

6.16b   An incident wave in medium 1 of permittivity ϵ_1 makes angle θ_1 with the normal. Find the proper length and permittivity of a medium 2 to form a "quarter-wave matching section" to a medium of permittivity ϵ_3.

6.16c   For the design described in Prob. 6.10g, plot a curve showing fraction of incident power reflected versus angle of incidence for 9000 Mc/sec waves at oblique incidence and polarized with electric field in the plane of incidence. Repeat for electric field normal to plane of incidence.

6.16d   By use of the transmission line analogies, determine the spacing between a thin film and a parallel perfect conductor, and the conductivity properties of that film if reflections are to be perfectly eliminated for a wave incident at an angle θ from the normal for the two types of polarization.

6.17 Geometrical or Ray Optics and the Lens

The law of reflection and Snell's law of refraction, although derived and applied in the last few articles from the point of view of electromagnetic wave theory, were first observed experimentally on rays of light striking various materials. They formed the basis for a very extensive art and the beginnings for a science of optics before the wave theory was fully developed. As the concentration in such an approach is on rays of light and their geometrical paths, it is often known as geometrical or ray optics. It is useful for electromagnetic waves of any frequency provided dimensions of the body of concern are large compared with wavelength. The formal identity of geometrical and wave optics in such cases has been established.[9]

As an example, consider one of the most useful tools of classical optics, the ideal lens, which focuses a plane wave to a point (or line, for a cylindrical lens). Figure 6.17a illustrates an axially symmetric converging lens, with index of refraction of the lens material greater than that of the surrounding medium. Let us consider that a portion of a plane wave moving parallel with the axis is incident on the lens at point A. Wavelength is small compared with lens dimensions. Application of Snell's law to the two surfaces of the lens yields

$$\frac{\sin \theta_2}{\sin \theta_1} = \frac{n_1}{n_2} = \frac{\sin \theta_3}{\sin \theta_4}, \tag{1}$$

with angles defined in the figure. The angles are also related by the sum law for angles in the triangle ABC:

$$\theta_3 = \pi - (\pi - 2\theta_1 + \theta_2) = 2\theta_1 - \theta_2. \tag{2}$$

The relation (2) depends on the lens being thin so A and B can be considered to be at the same distance from the axis. The portion of the wave entering the lens at A reaches the axis at a distance f from the lens. (Distance may be measured from lens center for a *thin lens*.)

$$f \approx r \cot (\theta_4 - \theta_1). \tag{3}$$

If the angles are now assumed small enough so that sines and tangents may be replaced by the angles themselves, substitution among (1) to (3) leads to

$$\frac{1}{f} \approx \frac{\theta_4 - \theta_1}{r} \approx \frac{2\theta_1}{r}\left(\frac{n_2}{n_1} - 1\right). \tag{4}$$

[9] M. Born and E. Wolf, *Principles of Optics*, Pergamon Press-Macmillan, New York, 2nd ed., 1964, pp. 109–121.

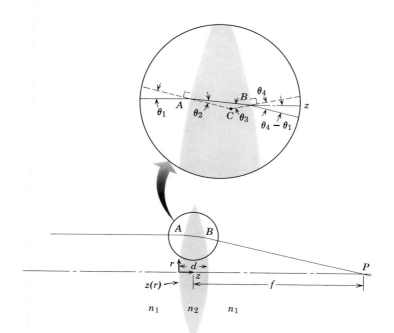

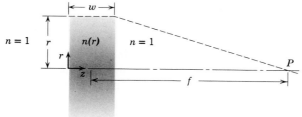

(a)

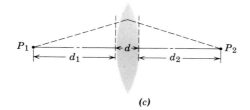

(b)

(c)

Fig. 6.17 (a) Focusing of light rays by a thin lens. (b) Focusing with a planar lens having radially varying refractive index. (c) Object and image locations for a thin lens.

If θ_1 is proportional to r, the distance f is the same for portions of the incident plane wave reaching various points on the left surface of the lens. In this case all portions of the plane wave focus to a common point on the axis at distance f from the center of the lens. The distance f is called the

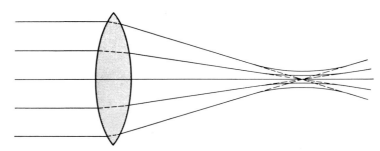

Fig. 6.17d Minimum of spot size at focus set by diffraction effects.

focal length of the lens. Since θ_1 is the slope of the lens face dz/dr, the curve for the lens face under these approximations is then

$$z(r) = \int_0^r \theta_1 \, dr = \frac{r^2}{4f[(n_2/n_1) - 1]} \tag{5}$$

which is a paraboloid of revolution.

This purely geometrical point of view may also be considered from a simple wave viewpoint, with the focus defined as the axial point for which all rays have the same phase, and thus add. Parallel rays incident from the left at different values of r reach P with phase from a plane $z = 0$ given as follows:

$$\phi = \frac{\omega}{c} [2n_1 z + n_2(d - 2z) + n_1(f^2 + r^2)^{\frac{1}{2}}].$$

If $r^2 \ll f^2$

$$\phi \approx \frac{\omega}{c}\left[n_2 d + 2z(n_1 - n_2) + n_1 f\left(1 + \frac{r^2}{2f^2}\right)\right] = \frac{\omega}{c}[n_2 d + n_1 f]. \tag{6}$$

The last result is by substitution of (5) and shows phase independent of r.

The wave point of view is especially useful in considering a lens in which focusing arises from an index of refraction which varies with position. Thus consider Fig. 6.17b, which illustrates a plane slab of material of width w with index of refraction varying parabolically with radius r from an axis,

$$n(r) = n_0\left[1 - \delta\left(\frac{r}{a}\right)^2\right]. \tag{7}$$

Phase from $z = 0$ to a focal point P is

$$\phi = \frac{\omega}{c} \left\{ wn_0 \left[1 - \delta\left(\frac{r}{a}\right)^2 \right] + n_1(r^2 + f^2)^{1/2} \right\}$$

$$\approx \frac{\omega}{c} \left[wn_0 \left(1 - \frac{\delta r^2}{a^2} \right) + n_1\left(f + \frac{r^2}{2f} \right) \right].$$

This yields a constant phase if focal length is

$$f = \frac{a^2 n_1}{2wn_0}. \tag{8}$$

The above is closely related to the important principle of classical optics, Fermat's so-called *principle of least time*. Fermat postulated that the ray path between two points will be that which minimizes the propagation time between the points. (Later formulations recognize that, under some circumstances, the time for a ray path may be a relative maximum compared with paths slightly shifted in space, or the time may be at an inflection point compared with times for neighboring paths.) This may be illustrated by deriving for the thin lens the relation between "object" and "image" distances, d_1 and d_2, for points on the axis as illustrated in Fig. 6.17c. The phase delay for the ray sketched is

$$\phi = \frac{\omega}{c} [2n_1 z + n_2(d - 2z) + n_1(d_1^2 + r^2)^{1/2} + n_1(d_2^2 + r^2)^{1/2}], \tag{9}$$

which for $r^2 \ll d_1^2$ and $r^2 \ll d_2^2$ is approximately

$$\phi \approx \frac{\omega}{c} \left[n_2 d - 2z(n_1 - n_2) + n_1(d_1 + d_2) + \frac{n_1 r^2}{2}\left(\frac{1}{d_1} + \frac{1}{d_2} \right) \right]. \tag{10}$$

Again using the result for the lens shape derived in (5), we have

$$\phi = \frac{\omega}{c} \left[n_2 d + n_1(d_1 + d_2) + \frac{r^2 n_1}{2}\left(\frac{1}{d_1} + \frac{1}{d_2} - \frac{1}{f} \right) \right].$$

Minimization of time also means minimization of phase delay,

$$\frac{d\phi}{dr} = n_1 r \left(\frac{1}{d_1} + \frac{1}{d_2} - \frac{1}{f} \right) = 0,$$

which leads to the classical thin lens formula,

$$\frac{1}{d_1} + \frac{1}{d_2} = \frac{1}{f}. \tag{11}$$

The idealizations leading to the thin lens formulas illustrate the point of classical optics, and will be sufficient for the applications of other simple lens ideas in this text. However, practical lenses may be "thick," requiring another parameter,[10] and possess various aberrations giving departures from the ideal focusing property.[11]

Geometrical optics, in a lens without aberration, would predict focus of incident parallel rays to a point, thus predicting infinite energy density there. As this result is physically impossible, such point focusing does not occur, but the rays diverge in the vicinity of the focus by diffraction effects as sketched in Fig. 6.17d. The spot, although small, will be finite and determined in size by the angle of convergence of the lens and the wavelength of the light. The approximate wave solution for optical modes to be discussed in Art. 10.15 will be useful for quantitative analysis of this diffraction effect.

Problems

6.17a Derive the formula (11) for the lens illustrated in Fig. 6.17b.

6.17b Derive the equation representing the face of a diverging thin lens analogous to Fig. 6.17a. Show the constant phase property (6) for this lens, and explain how the inhomogeneous dielectric of Fig. 6.17b would be modified to give a diverging lens.

6.17c What are the shapes corresponding to the derived thin converging and diverging lenses if cylindrical lenses are desired, with the plane wave focused to a line?

6.17d From Fermat's principle, show that (11) applies for the diverging lens with proper interpretation of focal length.

[10] *Ibid.*, pp. 161–163.
[11] *Ibid.*, Chapter V.

7 GUIDED ELECTROMAGNETIC WAVES

7.0I Introduction

In Chapter 6 we were interested primarily in electromagnetic waves in boundless dielectrics except insofar as reflecting discontinuities were concerned. Actually, no wave is ever truly free from the effect of conductors and dielectrics, but one may be to a good approximation, as in the example of a radio wave at a great distance from the ground in the region between transmitter and receiver. We now wish, however, to study specifically the behavior of electromagnetic waves in the immediate vicinity of conducting and dielectric boundaries when the configurations of these boundaries have the effect of guiding the waves along their surfaces.

By a guided wave, we mean first that the direction of energy flow must be primarily along the direction of the guiding system, although there must of course be some energy flow from the wave into the imperfectly conducting metal and dielectric boundaries for any real system. But, more important, if the wave is said to be guided by the boundaries, we infer that a change in the direction of these boundaries, within reasonable limits, will cause the wave to follow the new direction of the guide. We know, for example, that this is true for the transmission line used to transfer energy between the transmitter and an antenna, where the wave energy follows the path of the line, at least for paths with only reasonable discontinuities. This guiding of the wave is accomplished in all such systems by an intimate connection between the fields of the wave and the currents and charges of the boundary, or by some condition of special reflection at the boundary.

In the field picture, we imagine the energy as being transmitted through the electromagnetic fields of the wave in the dielectric region between boundaries, those boundaries being of primary importance in forming the characteristics of a particular wave. In the mathematical analysis, we wish to find solutions of the wave equation which fit the boundary conditions

371

imposed by the conducting and dielectric boundaries of the guides, concentrating on those solutions which represent energy transfer along the direction of the guide and which are intimately tied to the guide through some condition of current flow, charge induction, or special reflection at the boundary of the guide. Analysis will be confined here to guides which are straight and uniform, with the recognition that the waves will follow these with little change in characteristics if there are only reasonable changes in direction of the guides.

In the two articles following this, we shall write the relations from Maxwell's equations in the special form suitable for studying guided waves, and consider the classification of basic wave types. We shall then try to develop many of the important physical pictures and techniques of analysis for guided waves by considering the simple boundary conditions imposed by parallel conducting planes. We shall devote the remainder of the chapter to the discussion of some of the general properties of the basic wave types applicable to any shape of a guiding boundary before going on in the next chapter to the most commonly used shapes of guides for electromagnetic energy.

7.02 Basic Equations for Waves along Uniform Systems

In view of the concept of guided waves discussed in Art. 7.01, we would like to describe the waves propagating along a uniform guiding system in terms of a propagation factor $e^{(j\omega t - \gamma z)}$, such as was found for transmission line waves in Chapter 1. The character of the propagation constant γ tells much about the properties of the wave, such as the degree of attenuation, the phase velocity, and the group velocity. We shall begin by writing Maxwell's equations for the dielectric region in rectangular coordinates (without inferring here any limitation to rectangular shapes of boundaries), with the factor $e^{(j\omega t - \gamma z)}$ substituted. Then by solution subject to the boundary conditions of particular guides we may find what waves exist in this propagating form, and the character of γ as well as the distributions of electric and magnetic fields in the wave.

The curl equations with the assumed functions $e^{(j\omega t - \gamma z)}$ are written below for fields in the dielectric of the system.

$$\nabla \times \bar{E} = -j\omega\mu\bar{H}$$

$$\frac{\partial E_z}{\partial y} + \gamma E_y = -j\omega\mu H_x \quad (1)$$

$$-\gamma E_x - \frac{\partial E_z}{\partial x} = -j\omega\mu H_y \quad (2)$$

$$\frac{\partial E_y}{\partial x} - \frac{\partial E_x}{\partial y} = -j\omega\mu H_z \quad (3)$$

$$\nabla \times \bar{H} = j\omega\epsilon\bar{E}$$

$$\frac{\partial H_z}{\partial y} + \gamma H_y = j\omega\epsilon E_x \quad (4)$$

$$-\gamma H_x - \frac{\partial H_z}{\partial x} = j\omega\epsilon E_y \quad (5)$$

$$\frac{\partial H_y}{\partial x} - \frac{\partial H_x}{\partial y} = j\omega\epsilon E_z. \quad (6)$$

It must be remembered, in all analysis to follow, that these coefficients, E_x, H_x, E_y, etc., are functions of x and y only, by our agreement to take care of the z and time functions in the assumed $e^{(j\omega t - \gamma z)}$.

From the foregoing equations, it is possible to solve for E_x, E_y, H_x, or H_y in terms of E_z and H_z. For example, H_x is found by eliminating E_y from (1) and (5), and a similar procedure gives the other components.

$$H_x = \frac{1}{\gamma^2 + k^2}\left(j\omega\epsilon\,\frac{\partial E_z}{\partial y} - \gamma\,\frac{\partial H_z}{\partial x}\right) \qquad (7)$$

$$H_y = -\frac{1}{\gamma^2 + k^2}\left(j\omega\epsilon\,\frac{\partial E_z}{\partial x} + \gamma\,\frac{\partial H_z}{\partial y}\right) \qquad (8)$$

$$E_x = -\frac{1}{\gamma^2 + k^2}\left(\gamma\,\frac{\partial E_z}{\partial x} + j\omega\mu\,\frac{\partial H_z}{\partial y}\right) \qquad (9)$$

$$E_y = \frac{1}{\gamma^2 + k^2}\left(-\gamma\,\frac{\partial E_z}{\partial y} + j\omega\mu\,\frac{\partial H_z}{\partial x}\right) \qquad (10)$$

where $k^2 = \omega^2\mu\epsilon$.

If the dielectric has finite losses it is merely necessary to substitute $\epsilon' - j\epsilon''$ for ϵ in the above expressions (Art. 6.05).

All waves propagating in the positive z direction according to the factor $e^{(j\omega t - \gamma z)}$ must have components related by these equations, since nothing has been assumed but this factor and Maxwell's equations. [For a wave traveling in the negative z direction, substitute $-\gamma$ for γ in (1) to (6) or (7) to (10).] The total electric and magnetic intensities in the charge-free regions between the conducting boundaries must also satisfy the wave equation (Art. 4.11):

$$\nabla^2\bar{E} = -k^2\bar{E} \qquad \nabla^2\bar{H} = -k^2\bar{H}.$$

The three-dimensional ∇^2 may be broken into two parts:

$$\nabla^2\bar{E} = \nabla_{xy}^2\bar{E} + \frac{\partial^2\bar{E}}{\partial z^2}.$$

The last term is the contribution to ∇^2 from derivatives in the axial direction. The first term is the two-dimensional Laplacian in the transverse plane, representing contributions to ∇^2 from derivatives in this plane. By the assumed propagation function, $e^{-\gamma z}$, in the axial direction,

$$\frac{\partial^2\bar{E}}{\partial z^2} = \gamma^2\bar{E}.$$

The foregoing wave equations may then be written

$$\nabla^2_{xy}\bar{E} = -(\gamma^2 + k^2)\bar{E} \tag{11}$$

$$\nabla^2_{xy}\bar{H} = -(\gamma^2 + k^2)\bar{H}. \tag{12}$$

Equations (11) and (12) are the differential equations that must be satisfied in the dielectric regions of the transmission lines or guides. The boundary conditions imposed on these differential equations follow from the configuration and the electrical properties of the boundaries. Equations (1) to (6) or (7) to (10) then give the relations between any desired components in the wave.

7.03 Basic Wave Types

In studying guided waves along uniform systems, it is common to classify the wave solutions into the following types:

1. Waves that contain neither electric nor magnetic field in the direction of propagation. Since electric and magnetic field lines both lie entirely in the transverse plane, these may be called *transverse electromagnetic waves* (abbreviated *TEM*). They are the usual *transmission line waves* along a multi-conductor guide, and are also known as *principal waves*.

2. Waves that contain electric field but no magnetic field in the direction of propagation. Since the magnetic field lies in transverse planes, they are known as *transverse magnetic (TM)* waves. They have also been referred to in the literature as *E* waves, or waves of electric type.

3. Waves that contain magnetic field but no electric field in the direction of propagation. These are known as *transverse electric (TE)* waves, and have also been referred to as *H* waves or waves of magnetic type.

The above is not the only way in which the possible wave solutions may be divided, but is a useful way in that any general field distribution excited in an ideal guide may be divided into a number (possibly an infinite number) of the above types with suitable amplitudes and phases. The propagation constants of these tell how the individual waves change phase and amplitude as they travel down the guide, so that they may be superposed at any later position and time to give the total resultant field there. Of course, only one of the possible infinite number may propagate along the guiding system if it alone is excited and if conditions are favorable for its propagation. This is in fact the condition we try to approximate in most practical uses of wave guiding systems.

SIMPLE WAVES GUIDED BY PARALLEL PLANES

7.04 *TEM* Waves Guided by Ideal Parallel Plane Conductors

We wish to develop our physical pictures and techniques for analysis of guided waves by considering the simplest of all guiding systems, that of two infinite parallel conducting planes separated by a dielectric. Although

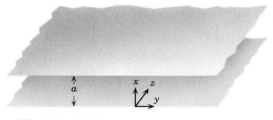

Fig. 7.04   Infinite parallel plane guide.

this is an idealization, there are physical systems for which it is a good approximation. One of these is represented by the region between two coaxial conducting cylinders with only slightly different radii. Following the division of Art. 7.03, we shall begin with a study of those waves which have both electric and magnetic fields confined to the transverse plane.

Without explicitly solving the equations of Art. 7.02, it is evident that, if the planes are perfectly conducting, there is a solution of the transverse electromagnetic type (*TEM*) for the region between planes, for we may introduce a portion of a uniform plane wave as studied in Chapter 6, propagating in the z direction and polarized with its electric field in the x direction (Fig. 7.04). This is known to be a solution of the wave equation, and it obviously fulfills the requirements for a *TEM* wave. We know also that it must propagate with the velocity of light in the dielectric and that it has a ratio of electric field to magnetic field given by the intrinsic impedance η of the dielectric. We may then write the expressions for the fields ($e^{j\omega t}$ understood):

$$E_x(z) = E_0 e^{\mp jkz} \tag{1}$$

$$\eta H_y(z) = \pm E_0 e^{\mp jkz} \tag{2}$$

where
$$\eta = \sqrt{\mu/\epsilon} \quad k = \omega\sqrt{\mu\epsilon}. \tag{3}$$

The upper signs in these equations apply to a wave propagating in the positive z direction, and the lower signs to one propagating in the negative z direction.

The electric field E_x passing normally between planes induces equal and opposite charge densities on the two planes at a given value of z; the uniform magnetic field H_y corresponds to equal and opposite currents flowing in the z direction in the two planes. These are properties we commonly associate with a two-conductor transmission line, so the wave studied here is recognized as the ordinary transmission line wave for this two-conductor system. The identification may be completed by deriving voltage and current from the field solution, comparing with the results from a classical transmission line solution. The voltage of the upper plate with respect to the lower may be found by integrating the electric field,

$$V(z) = -\int_0^a E_x(z)\, dx = -aE_0 e^{\mp jkz}. \tag{4}$$

Note that this result is independent of the path of integration *for all paths confined to the transverse plane*, since there is no H_z (Art. 4.19). The current per unit width in the upper plane is found from the rule $\bar{J} = \bar{n} \times \bar{H}$ developed in Art. 4.14,

$$J_z = -H_y.$$

Thus, if a width b is taken in the y direction, the current in the upper plane is

$$I(z) = -bH_y = \mp \frac{bE_0}{\eta} e^{\mp jkz}. \tag{5}$$

A direct solution of the transmission line equations (Art. 1.18) yields

$$V(z) = V_0 e^{\mp j\beta z} \tag{6}$$

$$I(z) = \left(\pm \frac{V_0}{Z_0}\right) e^{\mp j\beta z} \tag{7}$$

$$Z_0 = \sqrt{L/C} \quad \beta = \omega\sqrt{LC}. \tag{8}$$

But, for the parallel planes, the capacitance and inductance per unit length, for a width b, are

$$C = \frac{\epsilon b}{a} \text{ farads/meter} \tag{9}$$

$$L = \frac{\mu a}{b} \text{ henrys/meter.} \tag{10}$$

So, from (8),

$$Z_0 = \sqrt{\left(\frac{\mu a}{b}\right)\left(\frac{a}{\epsilon b}\right)} = \frac{\eta a}{b} \text{ ohms} \tag{11}$$

$$\beta = \omega\sqrt{\left(\frac{\mu a}{b}\right)\left(\frac{\epsilon b}{a}\right)} = k. \tag{12}$$

With these values and $V_0 = -aE_0$, (6) and (7) become identical with the results of the field solution, (4) and (5).

The power transferred by the wave may be calculated from the fields or from the classical transmission line solution. From the field viewpoint, the Poynting vector is found and integrated over the dielectric region between planes. Here it has a z component only, so that the average power transmitted by a single positive traveling wave is

$$W_T = b \int_0^a \tfrac{1}{2} \operatorname{Re}(E_x H_y^*) \, dx = \frac{ba}{2} \frac{E_0^2}{\eta} \text{ watts.} \tag{13}$$

From the voltage-current viewpoint, the average power transmitted by a single positively traveling wave is

$$W_T = \tfrac{1}{2} \operatorname{Re}(VI^*) = \frac{V_0^2}{2Z_0} = \frac{E_0^2 ab}{2\eta}, \tag{14}$$

so that the expressions for power computed from these two points of view are also identical.

Problem

7.04 Starting from the equations of Art. 7.02, obtain the *TEM* wave solutions for this parallel-plane system and compare with (1) and (2) in Art 7.04. Show that there can be no *TEM* solution for this case with finite E_y.

7.05 *TEM* Waves between Lossy Parallel Planes: Physical Approximations

In the analysis of the preceding article, the conductor and dielectric were taken as ideal. For any actual guide, conductor and dielectric must have finite conductivities, and the resulting loss effects, which may be negligible for some applications, may not be for others. An exact solution will be set up in the following article. We are most often interested in guides for which the losses are small, so that approximations may be made which greatly simplify the solution and which provide good physical pictures for the effects of losses. The approximate techniques to be applied will be of great importance in the analysis of all guides to follow.

If the dielectric region between planes has losses, we may proceed as in Art. 6.05, replacing $j\omega\epsilon$ by $j\omega(\epsilon' - j\epsilon'')$, or equivalently by $(\sigma + j\omega\epsilon)$, in the loss-free solution. The propagation constant and wave impedance E_x/H_y may be written as

$$\gamma = \alpha + j\beta = \sqrt{j\omega\mu(\sigma + j\omega\epsilon)} \tag{1}$$

$$Z_z = \sqrt{j\omega\mu/(\sigma + j\omega\epsilon)}. \tag{2}$$

For low-loss dielectrics, $\sigma/\omega\epsilon = \epsilon''/\epsilon' \ll 1$, these become

$$\alpha \approx \frac{\eta\sigma}{2} = \frac{k\epsilon''}{2\epsilon'} \tag{3}$$

$$\beta \approx k\left[1 + \frac{\sigma^2}{8\omega^2\epsilon^2}\right] = k\left[1 + \frac{1}{8}\left(\frac{\epsilon''}{\epsilon'}\right)^2\right] \tag{4}$$

$$Z_z \approx \eta\left\{\left[1 - \frac{3}{8}\left(\frac{\sigma}{\omega\epsilon}\right)^2\right] + j\frac{\sigma}{2\omega\epsilon}\right\}. \tag{5}$$

where k and η contain only the real part of permittivity.

If the conductor has a finite conductivity, the main effect will be an attenuation caused by the power loss in the conducting boundaries. The value of this attenuation may be estimated by the method of Art. 1.22, if the ratio of power loss per unit length to the average power transferred by the wave can be found. For a good conductor, it is reasonable to assume that the expression for power transfer derived for the ideal guide in Art. 7.04 applies well enough to the actual guide, and that power loss may be computed by taking the current flow of the ideal guide as flowing in the walls of the actual guide with known conductivity.

Let us assume that the conducting plates are thick compared with depth of penetration in the conducting material, and that the surface resistivity R_s is known. The average power loss per unit area would be $\frac{1}{2}R_s|J_z|^2$, so for a unit length and width b, counting both plates,

$$W_L = 2b[\tfrac{1}{2}R_s|J_z|^2] = bR_s|H_y|^2 = \frac{bR_sE_0^2}{\eta^2}. \tag{6}$$

The average power transfer is given by Eq. 7.04(13). Attenuation constant is then

$$\alpha = \frac{W_L}{2W_T} \tag{7}$$

$$\alpha = \frac{1}{2}\left(\frac{bR_sE_0^2}{\eta^2}\right)\left(\frac{2\eta}{abE_0^2}\right) = \frac{R_s}{\eta a}. \tag{8}$$

Note that the wave we are considering in the presence of finite conducting boundaries is not strictly a transverse electromagnetic wave since a small but finite axial electric field E_z is required to force the axial current flow along the conductors. The designation *TEM* is still ordinarily retained, since the fields are so nearly the same as those for the *TEM* wave of the ideal guide. The ratio of longitudinal to transverse electric field can be estimated. At the surface of the upper conductor,

$$E_z = J_z Z_s = -H_y R_s (1 + j) = -(1 + j) \frac{R_s E_0}{\eta}$$

or
$$\frac{E_z}{E_x} = \frac{E_z}{E_0} = -(1 + j) \frac{R_s}{\eta}. \qquad (9)$$

This ratio is around 4×10^{-5} for copper conductor and air dielectric at 3000 megacycles per second and is thus exceedingly small for most practical systems.

If losses are present in both conductor and dielectric, attenuation may be found by adding (3) and (8) so long as both are small. The result is the same as would be obtained from the approximate transmission line formula, Eq. 1.23(13):

$$\alpha \approx \frac{R}{2Z_0} + \frac{GZ_0}{2}. \qquad (10)$$

The proof of this is left for a problem.

Problems

7.05a Show that the transmission line formula for attenuation constant (10) gives precisely the same result as the approximate wave analysis of this article for the wave under consideration.

7.05b Derive the approximate formula for attenuation constant due to dielectric losses by using Eq. (7).

7.05c Since E_z is equal and opposite at top and bottom conductors, it is reasonable to assume a linear variation between the two values,

$$E_z = (1 + j) \frac{R_s E_0}{\eta} \left(1 - \frac{2x}{a} \right).$$

Find the modification in the distribution for E_x to satisfy the divergence equation for $\bar{E}$. Find the corresponding modification in H_y from Maxwell's equations. Describe qualitatively the average Poynting vector as a function of position in the guide.

7.06 *TEM* Waves between Lossy Parallel Planes: Mathematical Approximations

The physical approximations for low-loss guides utilized in the preceding article are of first importance since they will be applied to nearly all the types of wave guiding systems to be studied in this book. It is consequently well to compare them with results from a rigorous solution for this simple case where an analysis can be performed. The model is that shown in Fig. 7.06, in which the upper and lower conductors are infinite in depth. The field pattern for a wave which deviates by a small amount from a pure *TEM* wave is illustrated by the arrows. The current flowing in the conductors, as necessary to be compatible with the magnetic field of the wave,

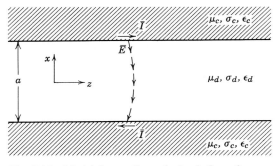

Fig. 7.06   Model for mathematical solution of waves between imperfectly conducting planes.

requires a z component of $\bar{E}$ at the boundaries as indicated in the sketch. The odd symmetry of the z component of $\bar{E}$, evident in the figure, requires that it be zero at the plane midway between the boundaries where the origin of the x coordinate has been chosen.

The approach to the solution of problems involving abrupt changes of the characteristics of the medium is to find general solutions for each of the regions and evaluate constants by satisfying the boundary conditions across interfaces and at outer boundaries. The characteristics of imperfect dielectrics and conductors can be expressed by introducing complex permittivities as discussed in Chapter 6. The form of variation in the z direction is taken as $e^{-\gamma z}$, where γ must be the same for all regions so that boundary conditions can be satisfied for all values of z. The odd symmetry of the z component of $\bar{E}$ may be used to simplify the problem since in this case it is only necessary to satisfy conditions in one-half of the system and to insure odd symmetry in the solution. Where variations in the y direction are assumed to be zero, Eq. 7.02(11) may be written for the z-component in the conductor as

$$\frac{d^2E_z}{dx^2} + (\gamma^2 + k_c^2)E_z = 0. \tag{1}$$

The same form applies to the dielectric with k_d replacing k_c. The general solutions for the two regions may be taken in the form of sines and cosines or complex exponentials. It will be advantageous to choose

$$E_{zd} = C_1 \sin K_d x + D_1 \cos K_d x \tag{2}$$

and

$$E_{zc} = C_2 e^{-jK_c x} + D_2 e^{jK_c x} \tag{3}$$

for the dielectric and conductor, respectively, where

$$K_d^2 = \gamma^2 + \omega^2 \mu_d \epsilon_d; \quad K_c^2 = \gamma^2 + \omega^2 \mu_c \epsilon_c. \tag{4}$$

To satisfy the requirement of odd symmetry for E_z, $D_1 = 0$. Since the fields must decay and not grow with distance into the conductor, we set $D_2 = 0$ and choose the root of K_c^2 in (4) so that jK_c has a real positive part. The propagation constant γ appearing in both K_c and K_d and the relation between C_2 and C_1 may be found by applying the two remaining boundary conditions, continuity of tangential electric and magnetic fields at the boundary.

Since we will limit ourselves to finding γ, only the ratios of tangential electric and magnetic fields need be matched at the boundary. The tangential magnetic field in the two regions may be found from Eq. 7.02(8),

$$H_{yd} = -\frac{j\omega\epsilon_d}{K_d} C_1 \cos K_d x \tag{5}$$

$$H_{yc} = -\frac{\omega\epsilon_c}{K_c} C_2 e^{-jK_c x}. \tag{6}$$

Equating the ratios E_z/H_y at the position $x = a/2$, we have

$$\tan\left(K_d \frac{a}{2}\right) = j \frac{K_c \epsilon_d}{K_d \epsilon_c}. \tag{7}$$

Since in (7) all quantities but γ are known, the equation in principle determines the value of propagation constant. However, since (7) is a transcendental equation containing complex quantities, it is not easy to solve in the general case. We shall then go to the special low-loss case which is of greatest interest to us where losses in the dielectric, and the displacement current in the conductor are negligible. We also keep in mind that the propagation constant γ with small losses should not differ much from its value $j\omega\sqrt{\mu\epsilon_d}$ for no losses. The permittivity of the dielectric will be considered real and $\epsilon_c \approx \sigma_c/j\omega$. We find from (4):

$$jK_c \approx \omega\sqrt{\mu\epsilon_d}\left[1 - \left(\frac{\sigma_c}{j\omega\epsilon_d}\right)\right]^{\frac{1}{2}} \approx \frac{1+j}{\delta_c} \tag{8}$$

where μ_d and μ_c are assumed equal, ratio of real parts of ϵ_d and ϵ_c is of order unity, and δ_c is the skin depth for the conductor. Also,

$$K_d^2 = \gamma^2 + \omega^2 \mu\epsilon_d = \gamma^2 + k_d^2.$$

Since γ^2 is approximately the same as without losses, K_d must be small and the tangent in (7) may be approximated by its argument. (The validity of this approximation may be checked when the results are obtained.) Equation (7) then becomes, with $R_{sc} = 1/\sigma_c \delta_c$,

$$\frac{K_d^2 a}{2} \approx \left(\frac{j\omega\epsilon_d}{\sigma_c}\right) j K_c$$

$$(\gamma^2 + k_d^2) \approx \frac{2j\omega\epsilon_d(1 + j)}{a(\sigma_c\delta_c)} = \frac{2j(1 + j)\omega\epsilon_d R_{sc}}{a}$$

$$\gamma^2 = -k_d^2\left[1 - \frac{2j(1 + j)R_{sc}}{k_d a \eta_d}\right].$$

It can be checked that the last term is small so long as frequency is high enough that $k_d a$ is not less than, say, 10^{-3}, so the square root may be approximated by two terms of the binomial expansion.

$$\gamma \approx jk_d\left[1 - \frac{j(1 + j)R_{sc}}{k_d a \eta_d}\right]$$

$$\alpha + j\beta \approx \frac{R_{sc}}{a\eta_d} + jk_d\left(1 + \frac{R_{sc}}{k_d a \eta_d}\right). \tag{9}$$

The expression for α is the same as that of the last article where approximations were made on a physical basis. By the analysis of this article we can see that these approximations are justified whenever

$$\frac{\sigma_d}{\omega\epsilon_d'} \ll 1, \qquad \frac{\omega\epsilon_c'}{\sigma_c} \ll 1, \tag{10}$$

where ϵ_d' and ϵ_c' are real parts of the dielectric and conductor permittivities, respectively. That is, conduction current should be small compared with displacement current in the dielectric, but displacement current should be small compared with conduction current in the conductor. A study of the field expressions shows that electric field is very nearly transverse in the dielectric ($E_{zd} \ll E_{xd}$) and very nearly longitudinal in the conductor ($E_{xc} \ll E_{zc}$).

Problems

7.06a Find the ratios E_{zd}/E_{xd} and E_{xc}/E_{zc} for the low-loss case at $x = a/2$. What type of polarization is represented in each case?

7.06b For the low-loss case show that the fields in the dielectric have nearly the form assumed in Prob. 7.05c.

7.07 Transverse Magnetic Waves between Parallel Planes

In the second classification given in Art. 7.03, the waves are to have an electric field component but no magnetic field in the direction of propagation. We can find many of the important properties for these TM waves by studying them in the simple guiding system formed by parallel-plane conductors, as we did for the TEM waves in preceding articles. We shall first give a fairly straightforward solution of the equations subject to the boundary conditions of the planes, and then give a physical picture for arriving at the same results by considering the waves as made up of a superposition of uniform plane waves.

Since the TM wave is to have a non-zero E_z, let us write Eq. 7.02(11) in terms of E_z. We are assuming no variations with y.

$$\nabla^2_{xy} E_z = \frac{d^2 E_z}{dx^2} = -K^2 E_z \tag{1}$$

$$K^2 = \gamma^2 + k^2 = \gamma^2 + \omega^2 \mu \epsilon. \tag{2}$$

The solution to (1) may be written in terms of either sinusoids or exponentials, but, since the perfectly conducting planes require that E_z be zero at $x = 0$ and $x = a$, we shall select the sinusoidal form because of its repeated zeros. The cosine terms may also be eliminated if the bottom plate is taken as $x = 0$.

$$E_z = A \sin Kx. \tag{3}$$

But E_z must also be zero at the upper plate, $x = a$. There must then be a half-period of the sine wave or a multiple thereof between the planes.

$$Ka = n\pi \tag{4}$$

The remaining field components may be found from Eqs. 7.02(7) to (10), remembering that $H_z = 0$ and $\partial/\partial y = 0$.

$$E_z = A \sin\left(\frac{n\pi x}{a}\right)$$

$$E_x = -\frac{\gamma}{K^2} \frac{\partial E_z}{\partial x} = -\frac{\gamma}{K} A \cos\left(\frac{n\pi x}{a}\right)$$

$$H_y = -\frac{j\omega\epsilon}{K^2} \frac{\partial E_z}{\partial x} = -\frac{j\omega\epsilon}{K} A \cos\left(\frac{n\pi x}{a}\right) \tag{5}$$

$$H_x = 0$$

$$E_y = 0.$$

The above set of fields satisfies Maxwell's equations for the dielectric region, and for n an integer fulfills the boundary condition that electric field tangential to the planes shall be zero. Hence, there are many "modes" of this TM type, one for each integer n. A particular one with n half-sine variations between the plates may be designated as TM_{n0} (the zero to denote that there are no variations with y).

The propagation constant for the nth mode may now be found from (2) and (4):

$$\gamma = \sqrt{K^2 - k^2} = \sqrt{\left(\frac{n\pi}{a}\right)^2 - \omega^2\mu\epsilon}. \tag{6}$$

A study of this form reveals a very important characteristic which we will find for TM and TE waves in all closed guides. For a particular spacing, a and mode number n, $(n\pi/a)^2$ is a real number. For frequencies low enough so that $k < n\pi/a$, γ will have a real result representing attenuation only. As frequency is increased, we come to a condition (called the cutoff of the mode) where $k = n\pi/a$ and $\gamma = 0$, so that there is neither phase shift nor attenuation along the guide. As frequency is increased, $k > n\pi/a$ and (6) yields a purely imaginary result so that the mode propagates without attenuation. Thus the cutoff condition may be written

$$k_c = 2\pi f_c\sqrt{\mu\epsilon} = \frac{2\pi}{\lambda_c} = \frac{n\pi}{a}, \tag{7}$$

where λ_c is the wavelength of a uniform plane wave in the dielectric at the cutoff frequency. We can then write (6) in terms of the cutoff frequency for the particular mode of interest.

$$\gamma = \alpha = \frac{n\pi}{a}\sqrt{1 - (f/f_c)^2}, \qquad f < f_c \tag{8a}$$

$$\gamma = j\beta = jk\sqrt{1 - (f_c/f)^2}, \qquad f > f_c. \tag{8b}$$

For the propagating range $f > f_c$, phase and group velocities are (Art. 1.24)

$$v_p = \frac{\omega}{\beta} = v/\sqrt{1 - (f_c/f)^2} \tag{9}$$

$$v_g = \frac{d\omega}{d\beta} = v\sqrt{1 - (f_c/f)^2}. \tag{10}$$

The wavelength measured along the guide in the z direction is the distance represented by a phase shift of 2π, and is denoted λ_g:

$$\lambda_g = \frac{\lambda}{\sqrt{1 - (f_c/f)^2}}. \tag{11}$$

The wave or field impedance is another useful concept (Art. 6.08) and is here defined as the ratio of transverse electric to magnetic field components:

$$Z_z = \frac{E_x}{H_y} = \frac{\gamma}{j\omega\epsilon} = \frac{-jn\pi}{a\omega\epsilon}\sqrt{1-(f/f_c)^2} \quad f < f_c \qquad (12a)$$

$$Z_z = \eta\sqrt{1-(f_c/f)^2} \qquad\qquad f > f_c. \qquad (12b)$$

Note that it is real in the propagating range and imaginary in the attenuating range, so that there is average power transferred where $f > f_c$ but not where $f < f_c$.

Problem

7.07 Derive expressions for the average energy stored per unit length (z) and unit width (y), and the power transfer for a unit width, for *TM* waves traveling between parallel planes. Show that the energy velocity, the ratio of power transfer to energy storage, is the same as group velocity for these waves.

7.08 Physical Discussion of Transverse Magnetic Wave

Let us study the field distribution in a single positively traveling *TM* mode having one half-sine variation in x (i.e., $n = 1$). It will be convenient to write the field expressions in true instantaneous form by taking the real part of the complex expressions of Art. 7.07 (see Art. 4.08):

$$E_z(x, z, t) = \mathrm{Re}\left[A \sin\frac{\pi x}{a} e^{j(\omega t - \beta z)}\right] = A\sin\frac{\pi x}{a}\cos(\omega t - \beta z)$$

$$E_x(x, z, t) = \mathrm{Re}\left[-\frac{j\beta a}{\pi}A\cos\frac{\pi x}{a}e^{j(\omega t-\beta z)}\right] = \frac{\beta a}{\pi}A\cos\frac{\pi x}{a}\sin(\omega t-\beta z)$$

$$H_y(x, z, t) = \mathrm{Re}\left[-\frac{j\omega\epsilon a A}{\pi}\cos\frac{\pi x}{a}e^{j(\omega t-\beta z)}\right] = \frac{\omega\epsilon a}{\pi}A\cos\frac{\pi x}{a}\sin(\omega t-\beta z).$$

Let us consider the distribution at a particular instant of time, say $t = 0$:

$$E_z(x, z, 0) = A\sin\frac{\pi x}{a}\cos\beta z \qquad (1)$$

$$E_x(x, z, 0) = \frac{-\beta a A}{\pi}\cos\frac{\pi x}{a}\sin\beta z \qquad (2)$$

$$H_y(x, z, 0) = \frac{-\omega\epsilon a A}{\pi}\cos\frac{\pi x}{a}\sin\beta z. \qquad (3)$$

The slope of the electric field lines in the x-z plane are

$$\frac{dx}{dz} = \frac{E_x}{E_z} = -\frac{\beta a}{\pi}\cot\frac{\pi x}{a}\tan\beta z. \qquad (4)$$

The lines may be sketched either by drawing in the direction of the tangents at a number of points throughout the field, or by integrating (4)

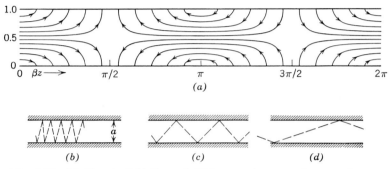

Fig. 7.08 (a) Electric field lines of TM_{10} wave between plane conductors. (b, c, d) Waves guided by two parallel conducting planes.

to give the equation of the family of electric field lines (Prob. 7.08a). A few of these field lines are shown in Fig. 7.08a.

Note that in this mode electric field lines start from charges on the guide walls and pass to charges of opposite sign, not on the opposite plane as in the TEM mode, but on the same plane a half guide wavelength along in the z direction. The axial displacement currents are surrounded by magnetic field lines (considering the magnetic field lines as closing at $y = \pm\infty$). Note that displacement current and H_y are maximum, not at $\beta z = 0$ where E_z is a maximum, but at $\beta z = \pm\pi/2$ where its rate of change is a maximum.

A somewhat different physical picture in terms of wave reflections may be developed for the TM modes between parallel planes by reference to Art. 6.11. That article was concerned with the reflection of a uniform plane wave from a perfectly conducting plane when incident at any angle θ from the normal. It was found that the tangential component of electric field was zero at the conductor, and also at planes parallel to the conductor and distance $n\lambda/2\cos\theta$ away. Hence a second perfectly conducting plane could be placed at any of the positions characterized by a given value of n without disturbing the fields. The field solution found in that article, Eqs. (11) to (13), should then apply directly to the parallel-plane guide. (The x and z coordinates must be interchanged to correspond to the coordinate system set up for the present analysis.)

Thus, if the spacing between plates is a,

$$a = \frac{n\lambda}{2 \cos \theta}$$

or
$$\cos \theta = \frac{n\lambda}{2a}. \tag{5}$$

For the $n = 1$ mode, for example, θ will be zero if the spacing between plates is just a half-wavelength; the wave will bounce back and forth between the plates with nodes at $x = 0$ and $x = a$; and there will be no tendency for propagation in the z direction. This is the condition we have called cutoff. As frequency is raised (λ decreased), $\lambda/2a$ will be less than unity and θ will take on a finite value representing some component of propagation in the z direction as pictured in Figs. 7.08b, c. That is, since the spacing a is greater than a half-wavelength measured normal to a wave front, the wave must tip somewhat to make the distance between zeros of E_z still correspond to a. This is accomplished since the phase velocity measured in the x direction is $v/\cos \theta$ and is consequently greater than v (where $v = 1/\sqrt{\mu\epsilon}$). If frequency is raised so that $\lambda/2a$ is very small, $\cos \theta$ must also be small and the plane wave components propagate nearly in the axial direction of the guide (Fig. 7.08d).

The phase velocity in the z direction may be obtained from this picture:

$$v_{pz} = \frac{v}{\sin \theta} = v/\sqrt{1 - \cos^2 \theta}. \tag{6}$$

But
$$\cos \theta = \frac{n\lambda}{2a} = \frac{\lambda}{\lambda_c} = \frac{f_c}{f}, \tag{7}$$

so
$$v_{pz} = v/\sqrt{1 - (f_c/f)^2}. \tag{8}$$

Therefore this result is the same as that obtained by the detailed analysis of Art. 7.07. In fact, all the properties of the TM mode in the propagating range could be similarly derived from this analysis of the TM wave into component uniform plane waves propagating and reflecting at an angle from the boundary.

Problems

7.08a Show that the curve of an electric field line corresponding to (1) and (2) is expressed by

$$\cos \beta z = \frac{\cos (\pi x_0/a)}{\cos (\pi x/a)}.$$

Plot a few lines for selected values of x_0/a (x_0 is the value of x for a particular curve at $z = 0$).

7.08b Sketch the form of electric and magnetic field lines, showing sense, for a single positively traveling *TM* mode between planes with $n = 2$.

7.08c By suitably changing coordinates and notation, show that the field distributions of Art. 7.07 for the *TM* wave and of Eqs. 6.11(11) to (13) for uniform plane waves reflected at oblique incidence are identical.

7.08d Obtain the expressions for wave impedance, using the picture of uniform plane waves reflecting at an angle.

7.09 Effect of Losses on *TM* Waves Between Planes

It will be assumed that dielectric and conductor are reasonably good so that attenuation may be calculated in the approximate manner demonstrated previously for the *TEM* wave (Art. 7.05).

Losses in the dielectric may be taken into account by substituting $(\sigma + j\omega\epsilon)$ for $j\omega\epsilon$ in the loss-free analysis. The expression for propagation constant, Eq. 7.07(6), becomes

$$\gamma = \left[\left(\frac{n\pi}{a}\right)^2 - \omega^2\mu\epsilon\left(1 - \frac{j\sigma}{\omega\epsilon}\right)\right]^{1/2}$$

$$\approx \left[\left(\frac{n\pi}{a}\right)^2 - \omega^2\mu\epsilon\right]^{1/2}\left\{1 + \frac{j\omega\mu\sigma}{2}\left[\left(\frac{n\pi}{a}\right)^2 - \omega^2\mu\epsilon\right]^{-1}\right\}. \tag{1}$$

This approximation retains only two terms of the binomial expansion and is valid for

$$\omega\mu\sigma \ll \left|\left(\frac{n\pi}{a}\right)^2 - \omega^2\mu\epsilon\right|. \tag{2}$$

Utilizing the cutoff frequency defined in Eq. 7.07(7), we see that

$$\left(\frac{n\pi}{a}\right) = 2\pi f_c\sqrt{\mu\epsilon}$$

$$\gamma = \frac{\omega\mu\sigma}{2\omega\sqrt{\mu\epsilon}\sqrt{1 - (f_c/f)^2}} + j\omega\sqrt{\mu\epsilon}\sqrt{1 - (f_c/f)^2}. \tag{3}$$

The phase constant (imaginary part of γ) is the same as that obtained in the loss-free case to the extent of this approximation. The attenuation constant (real part of γ) is

$$\alpha_d = \frac{\eta\sigma}{2\sqrt{1 - (f_c/f)^2}} = \frac{k\epsilon''}{2\epsilon'\sqrt{1 - (f_c/f)^2}} \text{ nepers/meter}, \tag{4}$$

where $\eta = \sqrt{\mu/\epsilon}$, $\epsilon'' = \sigma/\omega$, $k = \omega\sqrt{\mu\epsilon}$.

Note that α apparently approaches infinity as the frequency approaches cutoff, but this does not actually happen since condition (2) breaks down for any finite σ as the cutoff frequency is approached.

To compute the attenuation caused by conductor losses, the power transfer for the loss-free case will be found, and also the power loss per unit length, taking the currents flowing in the actual conductors the same as in the ideal conductors. The average power transfer for a width b is found by a Poynting integration:

$$W_T = b \int_0^a \tfrac{1}{2}(E_x H_y^*) \, dx$$

$$= \frac{b}{2} \int_0^a \left(-\frac{j\beta a}{n\pi} A \cos\frac{n\pi x}{a} e^{-j\beta z}\right)\left(\frac{j\omega\epsilon a}{n\pi} A \cos\frac{n\pi x}{a} e^{j\beta z}\right) dx$$

$$= \frac{b}{2}\frac{\omega\epsilon\beta a^2 A^2}{n^2\pi^2} \int_0^a \cos^2\frac{n\pi x}{a}\, dx = \left(\frac{b\omega\epsilon\beta a^2 A^2}{2\pi^2 n^2}\right)\frac{a}{2}. \qquad (5)$$

The current flow in upper and lower planes has the same magnitude. For the lower plane the current per unit width is

$$|J_z| = |H_y|_{x=0} = \frac{\omega\epsilon a A}{n\pi}.$$

The total power loss for a unit length and width b, counting both planes, is

$$W_L = \frac{2bR_s |J_z|^2}{2} = \frac{bR_s\omega^2\epsilon^2 a^2 A^2}{n^2\pi^2}. \qquad (6)$$

The attenuation arising from conductor losses is then approximately

$$\alpha_c = \frac{W_L}{2W_T} = \frac{2R_s\omega\epsilon}{\beta a}$$

$$\alpha_c = \frac{2R_s\omega\epsilon}{a\omega\sqrt{\mu\epsilon}\sqrt{1-(f_c/f)^2}} = \frac{2R_s}{\eta a\sqrt{1-(f_c/f)^2}} \text{ nepers/meter}, \qquad (7)$$

where, in terms of μ_2 and σ_2 of the conductor,

$$R_s = \sqrt{\pi f \mu_2/\sigma_2}.$$

The expression for attenuation caused by conductor losses also approaches infinity at cutoff, but again the approximations entering into its derivation break down in that region so that the expression does not apply there. The attenuation will, however, be high at cutoff and decrease with frequency until a frequency of $\sqrt{3}f_c$ is reached beyond which the surface resistivity in the numerator takes over and attenuation again increases with frequency. The form of the curve is shown in Fig. 7.09.

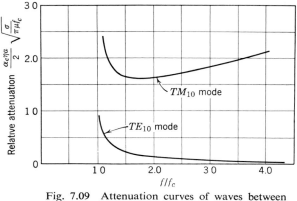

Fig. 7.09 Attenuation curves of waves between imperfectly conducting planes.

Problem

7.09 Prove that the frequency of minimum attenuation due to conductor losses for the *TM* mode is at $f = \sqrt{3}f_c$, and find the expression for this minimum attenuation. Calculate its value for copper conductors 5 cm apart with air dielectric for the $n = 1$, 2, and 3 modes.

7.10 Transverse Electric Waves between Parallel Planes

Since the analysis and characteristics of the transverse electric waves are very similar to those for the transverse magnetic waves, they will be treated more briefly. Equation 7.02(12) may be written in terms of the non-zero H_z:

$$\nabla_{xy}^2 H_z = \frac{d^2 H_z}{dx^2} = -K^2 H_z \tag{1}$$

$$K^2 = \gamma^2 + k^2. \tag{2}$$

The solution will again be written in terms of sinusoids, but this time only the cosine term is retained since E_y, proportional to the derivative of H_z with x, must become zero at the perfectly conducting plane $x = 0$:

$$H_z = B \cos Kx. \tag{3}$$

From Eqs. 7.02(7) to (10), remembering that E_z is zero,

$$H_x = -\frac{\gamma}{K^2}\frac{\partial H_z}{\partial x} = \frac{\gamma}{K} B \sin Kx \qquad (4)$$

$$E_y = \frac{j\omega\mu}{K^2}\frac{\partial H_z}{\partial x} = -\frac{j\omega\mu}{K} B \sin Kx \qquad (5)$$

$$E_x = 0 \qquad (6)$$

$$H_y = 0. \qquad (7)$$

E_y must be zero at the conducting plane $x = a$ also, so K is determined from (5) as some multiple of π/a. As with the TM wave, this is identified from (2) as the value of k at cutoff.

$$K = 2\pi f_c \sqrt{\mu\epsilon} = \frac{n\pi}{a}. \qquad (8)$$

Propagation constant from (2) may then be written

$$\gamma = \alpha = \left(\frac{n\pi}{a}\right)\sqrt{1 - (f/f_c)^2}, \qquad f < f_c \qquad (9)$$

$$\gamma = j\beta = jk\sqrt{1 - (f_c/f)^2}, \qquad f > f_c. \qquad (10)$$

The forms for attenuation constant in the cutoff range and phase constant in the propagating range are thus exactly the same as for the TM waves, and by (8) conditions for cutoff are the same for TE modes as for TM modes of the same order. The expressions for phase velocity, group velocity, and guide wavelength in the propagating range follow from (10) and are exactly the same as Eqs. 7.07(9) to (11).

Wave or field impedance for the TE wave is

$$Z_z = -\frac{E_y}{H_x} = \frac{j\omega\mu}{\gamma} = \frac{j\omega\mu}{j\omega\sqrt{\mu\epsilon}\sqrt{1 - (f_c/f)^2}}$$

$$Z_z = \frac{\eta}{\sqrt{1 - (f_c/f)^2}}. \qquad (11)$$

For frequencies below cutoff this wave impedance is imaginary, but for frequencies above cutoff it is real and always greater than η, as contrasted to the wave impedance for TM waves, which is always less than η.

The form of the field lines for the first order TE mode is indicated in Fig. 7.10. Here the magnetic field lines form closed curves surrounding the y-direction displacement current. There is no charge induced on the conducting plates and only a y component of current corresponding to the finite H_z tangential to the plates. The *TE* waves may also be considered as made up of uniform plane waves propagating and reflecting from the planes at an angle θ from the normal, as pictured in Figs. 7.08*b*–*d*, but here the component plane waves are polarized with the electric field normal to the plane of incidence so that Eqs. 6.11(18) to (20) apply. The relation between angle θ and f_c/f is, as for the *TM* waves, Eq. 7.08(7).

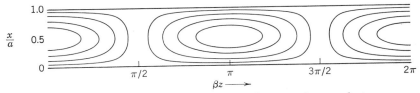

Fig. 7.10   Magnetic field lines of TE_{10} wave between plane conductors.

If the dielectric is lossy, the approximate expression for attenuation constant is the same as for *TM* waves, Eq. 7.09(4), since this was derived from the formula for propagation constant which is common to both types of waves.

If the conductor has finite conductivity, the attenuation constant may be computed in terms of power loss and power transfer as before. The power loss per unit length, for a width b of both planes, is

$$W_L = 2bR_s \frac{|H_z|^2_{x=0}}{2} = bR_sB^2. \tag{12}$$

The average power transferred by the wave is

$$W_T = \frac{b}{2} \int_0^a (-E_y H_x{}^*)\, dx = \frac{b}{2}\frac{a}{2}\frac{\beta a}{\pi}\frac{\omega\mu a}{\pi} B^2. \tag{13}$$

So the attenuation constant arising from conductor losses is

$$\alpha_c = \frac{W_L}{2W_T} = \frac{4\pi^2 R_s}{2\beta\omega\mu a^3} = \frac{4R_s\omega_c{}^2\mu\epsilon\sqrt{\epsilon}}{2\omega^2\mu\epsilon\sqrt{\mu}a\sqrt{1-(f_c/f)^2}}$$

$$= \frac{2R_sf_c{}^2}{\eta af^2\sqrt{1-(f_c/f)^2}}. \tag{14}$$

Note that, unlike that for *TM* waves, this expression shows a continually decreasing attenuation with increasing frequency (Fig. 7.09).

Problems

7.10a Derive the expression for the curves in the x-z plane corresponding to the magnetic field lines. Sketch a few for a single positively traveling $n = 2$ *TE* mode. Show sense and indicate position and sense of electric field.

7.10b By suitably changing coordinates and notation, show that the expressions 6.11(18) to (20) for plane waves reflecting from a plane at an oblique angle give exactly the fields of the *TE* modes of this article.

7.10c In the curve showing the attenuation caused by conductor losses as a function of f/f_c (Fig. 7.09), explain qualitatively the reason for the decrease of attenuation with increasing frequency.

GENERAL ANALYSIS OF GUIDED WAVES

7.11 Transverse Electromagnetic or Transmission Line Waves

Now that certain points of view toward guided waves have been developed through the study of the special case of parallel-plane conductors, it is desirable to study those properties of *TEM*, *TM*, and *TE* waves which can be found independently of the shape of the cylindrical guiding conductor. The general analysis follows quite closely that given by Schelkunoff.[1]

The first of the basic wave types to be studied is that with neither electric nor magnetic field in the direction of propagation. This has been termed a transverse electromagnetic wave. In the simple case of propagation between perfectly conducting parallel planes, such a wave was identified exactly with the ordinary wave expected from transmission line theory. It will now be shown that this must be true for any general cross section of a uniform guiding line with perfect conductors along which this wave type may exist. (The types of guides on which it may not exist will be apparent once its characteristics are found.)

The general relations between wave components as expressed by Eq. 7.02(7) to (10) show that, with E_z and H_z zero, all other components must of necessity also be zero, unless $\gamma^2 + k^2$ is at the same time zero. Thus, a transverse electromagnetic wave must satisfy the condition

$$\gamma^2 + k^2 = 0$$

or

$$\gamma = \pm jk = \pm \frac{j\omega}{v} = \pm j\omega\sqrt{\mu\epsilon}. \tag{1}$$

[1] S. A. Schelkunoff, "Transmission Theory of Plane Electromagnetic Waves," *Proc. I.R.E.*, **25**, 1457–1492 (Nov. 1937).

For a perfect dielectric, the propagation constant γ is thus a purely imaginary quantity, signifying that any completely transverse electromagnetic wave must propagate unattenuated, and with velocity v, the velocity of light in the dielectric bounded by the guide.

With (1) satisfied, the wave equations, as written in the form of Eqs. 7.02(11) and (12), reduce to

$$\nabla_{xy}^2 \bar{E} = 0 \qquad \nabla_{xy}^2 \bar{H} = 0. \tag{2}$$

These are exactly the form of the two-dimensional Laplace's equation written for $\bar{E}$ and $\bar{H}$ in the transverse plane. Since E_z and H_z are zero, $\bar{E}$ and $\bar{H}$ lie entirely in the transverse plane. In Art. 3.02 it was found that electric and magnetic fields both satisfy Laplace's equation under static conditions. Consequently it may be concluded that the field distribution in the transverse plane is exactly a static distribution, if it can be shown that boundary conditions to be applied to the differential equations (2) are the same as those for a static field distribution. The boundary condition for the *TEM* wave on a perfect conducting guide is that electric field at the surface of the conductor can have a normal component only, which is the same as the condition at a conducting boundary in statics. The line integral of the electric field between conductors is the same for all paths lying in a given transverse plane, and may be thought of as corresponding to a potential difference between the conductors for that value of z.

To study the character of the magnetic field, note Eqs. 7.02(1) and (4) with zero E_z and H_z.

$$H_y = \frac{j\omega\epsilon}{\gamma} E_x = \frac{E_x}{\eta} \tag{3}$$

and

$$H_x = -\frac{\gamma}{j\omega\mu} E_y = -\frac{E_y}{\eta}. \tag{4}$$

[The signs of (3) and (4) are for a positively traveling wave; for a negatively traveling wave they are opposite.] Study shows that (3) and (4) are conditions which require that electric and magnetic field be everywhere normal to each other. In particular, magnetic field must be tangential to the conducting surfaces since electric field is normal to them. The magnetic field pattern in the transverse plane then corresponds exactly to that arising from static currents flowing entirely on the surfaces of the perfect conductors.

These characteristics show that a transverse electromagnetic wave may be guided by two or more conductors, or outside a single conductor, but not inside a closed conducting region, since it can have only the distributions of the corresponding two-dimensional static problem, and no electrostatic field can exist inside a source-free region completely closed by a conductor (see Prob. 7.11b).

In addition to the foregoing general properties of *TEM* waves along perfectly conducting guides for which this type may exist, we may show an exact identity with the ordinary transmission line equations for such cases. As a definite example, consider a line consisting of two conductors A and B of any general shape, Fig. 7.11. We shall, for the demonstration, be quite general regarding time and z functions, merely requiring that E_z and H_z be zero. The voltage between the two lines may be found by integrating electric field over any path between lines, such as that shown, 1-0-2. It will have the same value

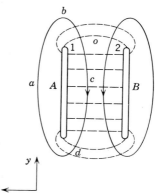

Fig. 7.11 Two-conductor transmission line with integration paths.

no matter which path is chosen, since $\bar{E}$ does satisfy Laplace's equation in the transverse plane and so may be considered the gradient of a scalar potential in so far as variations in the transverse plane are concerned.

$$V = -\int_1^2 \bar{E} \cdot \overline{dl} = -\int_1^2 (E_x \, dx + E_y \, dy).$$

Differentiate the above equation with respect to z.

$$\frac{\partial V}{\partial z} = -\int_1^2 \left(\frac{\partial E_x}{\partial z} \, dx + \frac{\partial E_y}{\partial z} \, dy \right). \tag{5}$$

But the curl relation,

$$\nabla \times \bar{E} = -\frac{\partial \bar{B}}{\partial t},$$

shows that, if E_z is zero,

$$\frac{\partial E_y}{\partial z} = \frac{\partial B_x}{\partial t} \quad \text{and} \quad \frac{\partial E_x}{\partial z} = -\frac{\partial B_y}{\partial t}. \tag{6}$$

By substituting (6) in (5), we have

$$\frac{\partial V}{\partial z} = -\frac{\partial}{\partial t} \int_1^2 (-B_y \, dx + B_x \, dy). \tag{7}$$

A study of Fig. 7.11 reveals that the quantity inside the integral is the magnetic flux flowing across the path 1-0-2, per unit length in the z

direction. According to the usual definition of inductance, this may be written as the product of inductance L per unit length and the current I so (7) becomes

$$\frac{\partial V}{\partial z} = \frac{\partial}{\partial t}(LI) = -L\frac{\partial I}{\partial t}. \tag{8}$$

Equation (8) is one of the differential equations used as a starting point for conventional transmission line analysis (Art. 1.13). The other may be developed by starting with current in line A as the integral of magnetic field about a path a-b-c-d-a. (There is no contribution from displacement current since there is no E_z.)

$$I = \oint \bar{H} \cdot \bar{dl} = \oint (H_x\,dx + H_y\,dy).$$

Differentiate with respect to z.

$$\frac{\partial I}{\partial z} = \oint \left(\frac{\partial H_x}{\partial z}\,dx + \frac{\partial H_y}{\partial z}\,dy\right). \tag{9}$$

From the curl equation,

$$\nabla \times \bar{H} = \frac{\partial \bar{D}}{\partial t},$$

it follows that, if $H_z = 0$,

$$\frac{\partial H_y}{\partial z} = -\frac{\partial D_x}{\partial t} \quad \text{and} \quad \frac{\partial H_x}{\partial z} = \frac{\partial D_y}{\partial t}. \tag{10}$$

Substituting, (10) in (9), we have

$$\frac{\partial I}{\partial z} = -\frac{\partial}{\partial t}\oint (D_x\,dy - D_y\,dx). \tag{11}$$

Inspection of Fig. 7.11 shows that this must be the electric displacement flux per unit length of line crossing from one conductor to the other. Since it corresponds to the charge per unit length on the conductors, it may be written as the product of capacity per unit length and the voltage between lines and (11) becomes

$$\frac{\partial I}{\partial z} = -C\frac{\partial V}{\partial t}. \tag{12}$$

Equations (8) and (12) are exactly the equations used as a beginning for transmission line analysis, if losses are neglected (Art. 1.13). It is seen that these equations may be derived exactly from Maxwell's equations provided the conductors are perfect, and, since fields in the transverse plane satisfy Laplace's equation, the inductance and capacitance appearing in the equations are the same as those computed in statics. So, in this very important case of guiding of electromagnetic energy (transmission lines with negligible imperfections in conductivity of conductors), the well-known method of analysis based on low-frequency circuit notions gives the correct answer, since it is actually equivalent to an analysis starting from Maxwell's equations—despite the use of *static* L's and C's for a problem certainly not static. As we shall see, this situation will not be true for other more general types of waves.

Problems

7.11a Demonstrate that, although in a *TEM* wave $\bar{E}$ does satisfy Laplace's equation in the transverse plane and so may be considered a gradient of a scalar in so far as variations in the transverse plane are concerned, $\bar{E}$ is *not* the gradient of a scalar when variations in all directions (x, y, and z) are included.
7.11b Demonstrate that electrostatic field will be zero inside any source-free region closed by a conductor as constant potential C. *Hint:* Make use of the uniqueness theorem, Art. 3.03.

7.12 Transmission Line Waves along Imperfect Lines

We have found that the classical analysis for a transmission line wave (*TEM*), made in terms of voltage and current along the line and the distributed inductance and capacitance calculated for direct current, is equivalent to one made directly from Maxwell's equations provided the conductor and dielectric are perfect.

This conclusion might not have been expected, for, if one had wished to be skeptical, it would have been easy to question the validity of the transmission line equations on at least two counts.

1. A voltage drop due to current flow through the distributed inductance of the line is calculated, but none is included because of mutual effects from any other part of the line; similarly, no mutual charging effects are considered.

2. Inductance and capacitance used in the equations are those calculated for direct current. It might seem doubtful that such constants could be of any use for extremely high frequencies; certainly we found that it is not permissible to neglect frequency effects when considering lumped inductances and capacitances at the highest frequencies in circuit equations (Chapter 5).

The first objection is answered once one finds from the field equations that there are no axial field components in the wave, and consequently no mutual effects. The second objection is answered by the discovery that the field distribution for the wave in the transverse plane is actually one corresponding to the static field pattern for that configuration, no matter what the frequency may be. The necessary condition is that the propagation be with light velocity in the dielectric of the line, a condition the conventional approach to transmission lines is very happy to grant.

If the transmission line is not ideal, but has resistance and conductance of finite amount, classical transmission line theory would have us take account of these by setting the voltage change along the line equal to a resistance plus an inductance drop, and the current change equal to a capacitance plus a conductance leakage current (Art. 1.23):

$$\frac{\partial V}{\partial z} = -(j\omega LI + RI)$$

$$\frac{\partial I}{\partial z} = -(j\omega CV + GV).$$

It is usually assumed that inductance and capacitance calculated on the basis of d-c distributions are still used in these equations. Although it is true that a contribution to inductance from the flux inside the conductors (the internal inductance of Chapter 5) may now be included, that part of the inductance arising from flux in the space between conductors is still calculated from the d-c distributions.

It will now be shown that such an analysis is equivalent to one made from Maxwell's equations if a line has uniform conductance but no resistance; it will also be shown that, if resistance of the conductors is important, the two analyses cannot be exactly equivalent. We should not undermine our confidence in the usual transmission line expressions too quickly, however, for the error will be infinitesimal for efficient transmission lines.

If the transmission line has a dielectric with uniform losses, occupying all the space between conductors, previous field analyses can be corrected by replacing $j\omega\epsilon$ by $(\sigma + j\omega\epsilon)$ in all results (Art. 6.05). This is exactly what is done in a conventional analysis, however, where $j\omega C$ for the ideal line is replaced by $(G + j\omega C)$ for the line with conductance. For a line with uniform dielectric, G has the same form as C, with conductivity in place of dielectric constant:

$$(G + j\omega C) = (\sigma + j\omega\epsilon) \times \text{function of configuration.}$$

It follows that the two analyses have then actually considered the effect of losses of the dielectric in the same manner.

If the current-carrying conductors of the transmission line have finite conductivity, one trouble is immediately apparent. There must be at least some small component of electric field in the direction of propagation to force the current through the conductors. By referring again to Eqs. 7.02(7) to (10), we see that with E_z finite, $\gamma^2 + k^2$ must then also be finite. The quantity on the right of the wave equation cannot then be exactly zero, but must be some small but finite amount.

$$\nabla_{xy}^2 \bar{E} = \text{finite quantity.}$$

This conclusion indicates that the field distributions are disturbed from the Laplace distributions somewhat by the axial field required to produce current flow. It is then no longer correct to calculate values of capacitance and inductance from the static distributions.

Although the nature of an exact analysis from Maxwell's equations is apparent, it is difficult to apply to practical lines. One must first obtain the wave solutions which apply inside the dielectric and those which apply inside the conductor, matching the two at the boundary. The difficulties with most geometrical configurations are obvious. Schelkunoff has carried through this attack for coaxial lines,[2] determining the extent of the approximations which must be made to reduce the problem to the classical analysis. We have carried through the similar procedure for the parallel-plane transmission line in Art. 7.06. Studies of more general configurations might be made by the method of successive perturbations. That is, the first correction to the perfect conductor case is the required axial electric field, which may be estimated simply from the resistivity times the approximate current flow. An idea is thus obtained of E_z's distribution and magnitude and consequently of $\nabla^2 E_z$. A next approximation is then obtained for the distribution of E_x, H_y, etc., as well as γ. From the new H's thus computed, a new current is computed and the whole process is again repeated. From the results of such studies it becomes apparent that an exact analysis from Maxwell's equations is fortunately unnecessary for lines which are at all efficient for energy transfer. The difference in results between such an exact analysis and the usual classical analysis including distributed resistance is extremely small.[3]

The classical transmission line analysis for imperfectly conducting boundaries is similar to methods previously introduced in this book, in which the first correction arising from the resistance is applied, but the

[2] S. A. Schelkunoff, "The Electromagnetic Theory of Coaxial Transmission Lines and Cylindrical Shields," *Bell Sys. Tech. J.*, **13**, 532–579 (Oct. 1934).

[3] J. R. Carson, "The Guided and Radiated Energy in Wire Transmission," *J.A.I.E.E.*, **43**, 906–913 (Oct. 1924).

major field distributions are assumed essentially unchanged. When this type of approximation was used for a wave analysis in Art. 7.06, the two criteria for its use were the following:

1. Displacement currents in the conductor negligible compared to conduction currents.

2. The intrinsic impedance of the dielectric much greater than the skin effect surface resistivity of the conductor.

These are also a measure of the excellence of the conventional transmission line analysis including distributed resistance. Stated in another way, such an analysis assumes that transverse electric field components *in the conductor* are negligible compared with the axial, and that axial electric field components *in the dielectric* are small compared with the transverse. These are equivalent to the criteria 1 and 2 above which may be stated mathematically as

$$\frac{\sigma_2}{\omega\epsilon_2} \gg 1, \qquad \frac{R_s}{\eta} \ll 1,$$

where R_s is surface impedance of the conductor, and η intrinsic impedance of the dielectric. These inequalities are nearly always satisfied by the materials of common transmission lines, but, if they are not, one must examine critically any results predicted by the usual transmission line equations.

Problems

7.12a Two perfectly conducting cylinders of arbitrary cross-sectional shape are parallel and separated by a dielectric of conductivity σ and permittivity ϵ. Show that the ratio of electrostatic capacitance per unit length to d-c conductance per unit length is ϵ/σ.

7.12b If the conductors are perfect but the dielectric has conductivity σ as well as permittivity ϵ, show that γ must have the following value in order for a *TEM* wave to exist ($E_z = 0$, $H_z = 0$):

$$\gamma = \pm[j\omega\mu(\sigma + j\omega\epsilon)]^{1/2}.$$

Explain why the distribution of fields may be a static distribution as in the loss-free line, unlike the case for a lossy conducting boundary.

7.13 Transverse Magnetic Waves

As the next possibility, let us consider generally those waves that may exist with electric field but no magnetic field in the direction of propagation. These have been named transverse magnetic (*TM*) waves, and examples have been given for the parallel-plane guide (Arts. 7.07 to 7.09).

The Differential Equation. With the assumed propagation constant $e^{(j\omega t - \gamma z)}$, the finite axial component of electric field for the *TM* waves must satisfy the wave equation in the form of Eq. 7.02(11):

$$\nabla_{xy}^2 E_z = -k_c^2 E_z \tag{1}$$

$$k_c^2 = (\gamma^2 + k^2) = \gamma^2 + \omega^2 \mu\epsilon. \tag{2}$$

The value of k_c, which should be a constant for a particular mode, is determined by the boundary condition to be applied to (1).

Boundary Condition for a Perfectly Conducting Guide. As in the examples, the first step in the solution of a practical waveguide problem is to assume that the waveguide boundaries are perfectly conducting. Then E_z must certainly be zero at the conducting boundary of the guide:

$$E_z = 0 \quad \text{at boundary.} \tag{3}$$

There are transverse components of electric field in the waves which must enter the conducting boundaries normally, but this need not be put on as a separate condition since it turns out to follow from (3). To show this, let us write all field components from the general relations of Art. 7.02 with H_z set equal to zero. Upper and lower signs are for positively and negatively traveling waves, respectively.

$$E_x = \mp \frac{\gamma}{k_c^2} \frac{\partial E_z}{\partial x} \qquad E_y = \mp \frac{\gamma}{k_c^2} \frac{\partial E_z}{\partial y} \tag{4}$$

$$H_x = \frac{j\omega\epsilon}{k_c^2} \frac{\partial E_z}{\partial y} \qquad H_y = -\frac{j\omega\epsilon}{k_c^2} \frac{\partial E_z}{\partial x}. \tag{5}$$

Relation (4) may be written in the vector form:

$$\bar{E}_t = \mp \frac{\gamma}{k_c^2} \nabla_t E_z, \tag{6}$$

where $\bar{E}_t$ is the transverse part of the electric field vector, and ∇_t represents the transverse part of the gradient. By the nature of the gradient, the transverse electric vector $\bar{E}_t$ is normal to any line of constant E_z. It is then normal to the conducting boundary, as required, once the boundary is made a curve of constant $E_z = 0$. Thus (3) is the only required boundary condition for solutions of (1).

Cutoff Properties of TM Waves. Solution of the homogeneous differential equation (1) subject to the boundary condition (3) at a given boundary is possible only for discrete values of the constant k_c. These are the *characteristic values, allowed values,* or *eigenvalues* of the problem, any one of which determines a particular *TM mode* for the given guide. In the example of the plane conductors (Art. 7.07), the allowed values of k_c

were defined by $n\pi/a$, and a particular mode was described by the appropriate integer n. It will be shown below that, for any dielectric region which is completely closed by perfect conductors, the allowed values, k_c, must always be real. Hence the propagation constant from (2),

$$\gamma = \sqrt{k_c^2 - k^2}, \tag{7}$$

always exhibits cutoff properties. That is, for a particular mode in a perfect dielectric γ is real for the range of frequencies such that $k < k_c$, γ is zero for $k = k_c$, and γ is imaginary for $k > k_c$. The cutoff frequency of a given mode is then given by

$$2\pi f_c \sqrt{\mu\epsilon} = \frac{2\pi}{\lambda_c} = k_c, \tag{8}$$

and (7) may be written in terms of frequency f and cutoff frequency f_c:

$$\gamma = \alpha = k_c\sqrt{1 - (f/f_c)^2}, \qquad f < f_c \tag{9}$$

$$\gamma = j\beta = jk\sqrt{1 - (f_c/f)^2}, \qquad f > f_c. \tag{10}$$

The phase velocity for all TM modes in an ideal guide then has the form

$$v_p = \frac{\omega}{\beta} = v\left[1 - \left(\frac{f_c}{f}\right)^2\right]^{-\frac{1}{2}}. \tag{11}$$

The group velocity is

$$v_g = \frac{d\omega}{d\beta} = v\left[1 - \left(\frac{f_c}{f}\right)^2\right]^{\frac{1}{2}}. \tag{12}$$

Universal curves for attenuation constant, phase velocity, and group velocity as functions of f/f_c are shown in Fig. 7.13a. Phase velocity is infinite at cutoff frequency and is always greater than the velocity of light in the dielectric; group velocity is zero at cutoff and is always less than the velocity of light in the dielectric. As the frequency increases far beyond cutoff, phase and group velocities both approach the velocity of light in the dielectric.

It remains to be shown that k_c is real for all TM modes in a cylindrical dielectric region completely enclosed by perfect conductors. In this proof we will be concerned with the multipliers of $e^{(j\omega t - \gamma z)}$ independent of the axial coordinate. If the divergence theorem (Art. 2.13) is applied to a vector of this type, the integration in the axial direction is equivalent to multiplication by the length. Dividing both sides of the divergence relation by the length and noting that ∇ reduces to ∇_t for this case, it may be written as

$$\int_{c.s.} (\nabla_t \cdot \bar{F})\, dS = \oint F_n\, dl. \tag{13}$$

In (13), the integral on the left is taken over the cross-sectional area of the cylindrical region, and the integral on the right is the line integral of the component of $\bar{F}$ normal to the boundary, taken about the boundary of the region. All vector operations are confined to the transverse plane.

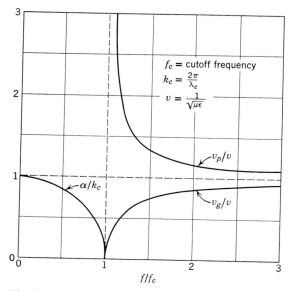

f_c = cutoff frequency
$$k_c = \frac{2\pi}{\lambda_c}$$
$$v = \frac{1}{\sqrt{\mu\epsilon}}$$

Fig. 7.13a   Frequency characteristics of all *TE* and *TM* wave types.

Since $\bar{F}$ may be any vector which does not vary in the axial direction, let it be the vector $E_z \nabla_t E_z$. (Recall that E_z is the multiplier of $e^{(j\omega t - \gamma z)}$ and so does not vary with z.)

$$\int_{\text{c.s.}} \nabla_t \cdot (E_z \nabla_t E_z)\, dS = \oint E_z \frac{\partial E_z}{\partial n}\, dl = 0.$$

The right-hand integral is zero since E_z is zero on the perfectly conducting boundary. The left side may be transformed (see inside back cover):

$$\int_{\text{c.s.}} [(\nabla_t E_z)^2 + E_z \nabla_t^2 E_z]\, dS = 0.$$

The value of $\nabla_t^2 E_z$ is supplied by (1).

$$\int_{\text{c.s.}} (\nabla_t E_z)^2\, dS = k_c^2 \int_{\text{c.s.}} E_z^2\, dS. \tag{14}$$

For plane waves that are of the same phase in any given transverse section, $E_z{}^2$ and $(\nabla_t E_z)^2$ are real and positive, so $k_c{}^2$ must also be real and positive. Hence, k_c is real under the conditions stated.

Magnetic Fields of the Waves. Once the distribution of E_z is found by solution of the differential equation (1) subject to the boundary condition (3), the transverse electric field of a given mode may be found from relation (6) or (4). The transverse magnetic field may be found from relations (5). By comparing (4) and (5), we see that

$$\frac{E_x}{H_y} = -\frac{E_y}{H_x} = \pm\frac{\gamma}{j\omega\epsilon}. \tag{15}$$

These relations show that transverse electric and magnetic fields are at right angles, and that their magnitudes are related by the quantity $\gamma/j\omega\epsilon$, which may be thought of as the wave impedance or field impedance of the mode. The usefulness of this type of quantity has already been demonstrated, and will appear in additional discussions.

$$Z_{TM} = \frac{\gamma}{j\omega\epsilon} = \eta\sqrt{1 - (f_c/f)^2} \tag{16}$$

$$\eta = \sqrt{\mu/\epsilon}.$$

The latter form is found by substitution of relation (10).

The wave impedance is imaginary (reactive) for frequencies less than the cutoff frequency, and purely real for frequencies above cutoff, approaching the intrinsic impedance of the dielectric at infinite frequency. This type of behavior is also found in the study of lumped-element filters, and again emphasizes that the wave can produce no average power transfer for frequencies below cutoff where the impedance is imaginary.

The relations between electric and magnetic fields may also be expressed in the following vector form, which expresses the properties described above:

$$\bar{H} = \pm\frac{\bar{a}_z \times \bar{E}_t}{Z_{TM}}, \tag{17}$$

where $\bar{a}_z$ is the unit vector in the z direction. The upper sign is for positively traveling waves, the lower sign for negatively traveling waves.

Power Transfer in the Waves. The power transfer down the guide has been shown to be zero below cutoff if the conductor of the guide is perfect. Above cutoff it may be obtained in terms of the field components by integrating the axial component of the Poynting vector over the cross-sectional area. Since it has been shown that transverse components of electric and magnetic fields are in phase and normal to each other, the axial component of the average Poynting vector is one-half the product of the transverse field magnitudes. For a positively traveling wave,

$$W_T = \int_{\text{c.s.}} \tfrac{1}{2}\text{Re}\,[\bar{E} \times \bar{H}^*]_z \, dS = \tfrac{1}{2}\int_{\text{c.s.}} |E_t|\,|H_t| \, dS$$

$$= \frac{Z_{TM}}{2} \int_{\text{c.s.}} |H_t|^2 \, dS. \quad (18)$$

By (5), this may be written

$$W_T = \frac{Z_{TM}\omega^2\epsilon^2}{2k_c^4} \int_{\text{c.s.}} |\nabla_t E_z|^2 \, dS.$$

By substitution of (14), this is

$$W_T = \frac{Z_{TM}\omega^2\epsilon^2}{2k_c^2} \int_{\text{c.s.}} E_z^2 \, dS = \frac{Z_{TM}}{2\eta^2}\left(\frac{f}{f_c}\right)^2 \int_{\text{c.s.}} E_z^2 \, dS. \quad (19)$$

It is often as easy to use the transverse field distributions of a mode in the Poynting integration (18) as to use the form (19). But form (19) does emphasize that, for a given power transfer in the mode, the axial component of field E_z must decrease as f/f_c approaches infinity.

Attenuation Due to Imperfectly Conducting Boundaries. When the conducting boundaries are imperfect, an exact solution would require solution of Maxwell's equations in both the dielectric and conducting regions as was done for the parallel-plane guide in Art. 7.06. Because this procedure is impractical for most geometrical configurations, we take advantage of the fact that most practical conductors are good enough to cause only a slight modification of the ideal solution, and the approximate formula 7.05(7) may be used. To compute the average power loss per unit length, we require the current flow in the guide walls, which is taken the same as that in the ideal guide. By the $\bar{n} \times \bar{H}$ rule, the current in the boundary is equal to the transverse magnetic field at the boundary, and flows in the axial direction since magnetic field is entirely transverse:

$$W_L = \oint_{\text{bound}} \frac{R_s}{2}|J_z|^2 \, dl = \frac{R_s}{2}\oint_{\text{bound}} |H_t|^2 \, dl. \quad (20)$$

The attenuation constant is then approximately

$$\alpha = \frac{W_L}{2W_T} = \frac{R_s \oint_{\text{bound}} |H_t|^2 \, dl}{2Z_{TM}\int_{\text{c.s.}} |H_t|^2 \, dS}. \quad (21)$$

If desired, the power loss and hence the attenuation constant may be written in terms of the distribution of E_z only. By (5),

$$W_L = \frac{R_s}{2}\frac{\omega^2\epsilon^2}{k_c^4} \oint_{\text{bound}} |\nabla E_z|^2 \, dl. \tag{22}$$

Since E_z is zero at all points along the boundary, there is no tangential derivative of E_z there; E_z consists merely of the derivative normal to the conductor:

$$W_L = \frac{R_s\omega^2\epsilon^2}{2k_c^4} \oint_{\text{bound}} \left[\frac{\partial E_z}{\partial n}\right]^2 dl = \frac{R_s}{2\eta^2 k_c^2}\left(\frac{f}{f_c}\right)^2 \oint \left[\frac{\partial E_z}{\partial n}\right]^2 dl. \tag{23}$$

An alternative form for the attenuation constant is then

$$\alpha = \frac{R_s}{2k_c^2 Z_{TM}}\left[\oint \left(\frac{\partial E_z}{\partial n}\right)^2 dl \Big/ \int_{\text{c.s.}} E_z^2 \, dS\right]. \tag{24}$$

Attenuation Due to Imperfect Dielectric. It is noted that the general form for propagation constant (7) is exactly the same as that for the special case of the parallel-plane guide, Eq. 7.07(6). Hence, the modification caused by an imperfect dielectric, taken into account by replacing $j\omega\epsilon$ by $\sigma + j\omega\epsilon$, yields the same form for attenuation as Eq. 7.09(4):

$$\alpha_d = \frac{k\epsilon''/\epsilon'}{2\sqrt{1-(f_c/f)^2}} = \frac{\sigma\eta}{2\sqrt{1-(f_c/f)^2}} \quad \text{nepers/meter.} \tag{25}$$

It is especially interesting to note that the form of the attenuation produced by an imperfect dielectric is the same for all modes and all shapes of guides, though of course the amount of attenuation is a function of the cutoff frequency, which does depend on the guide and the mode.

Summary. For TM modes, the differential equation (1) is solved subject to the boundary condition (3), which determines certain allowed distributions of E_z (modes) and corresponding allowed values of the constant k_c. The latter determine cutoff frequencies for the various modes, which placed in (9), (11), (12), (16), (24), and (25), determine attenuation below cutoff, phase and group velocities above cutoff, wave impedance, attenuation due to conductors, and attenuation due to dielectric, respectively. All this may be done without explicitly finding the transverse fields. It is usually desirable, however, to study the form of the transverse components of field, which may be done by means of (6) and (17). These may in turn be used to compute power transfer, power loss, and attenuation due to conductors by (18), (20), and (21) as alternatives to (19), (22), and (24).

Problems

7.13a Show that the circuit of Fig. 7.13b may be used to represent the propagation characteristics of the transverse magnetic wave, if the characteristic wave impedance and propagation constant are written by analogy with

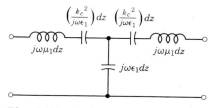

Fig. 7.13b Equivalent circuit for the transverse magnetic wave.

transmission line results in terms of an impedance Z_1, and an admittance Y_1 per unit length.

$$Z_{TM} = \sqrt{Z_1/Y_1} \qquad \gamma = \sqrt{Z_1 Y_1}.$$

Note the similarity between this and the circuits of conventional filter sections, remembering of course that all constants in this circuit are in reality distributed constants.

7.13b Show that all field components for a TM wave may be derived from the axial component of the vector potential $\bar{A}$. Obtain the expressions relating E_x, H_x, etc., to A_z, the differential equation for A_z, and the boundary conditions to be applied at a perfect conductor.

7.13c Repeat Prob. b, using the axial component of the Hertz potential as defined in Prob. 4.16a.

7.13d Show that the magnetic field distribution in the transverse plane can be derived from a scalar flux function, and relate this to E_z. With transverse electric field derivable from a scalar potential function and transverse magnetic field derivable from a scalar flux function, does it follow that both are static type distributions as in the TEM wave? Explain.

7.13e Note that we have essentially used E_z as a potential function for derivation of other components in the preceding article. How is this related to the A_z of Prob. b and the Π_z of Prob. c?

7.13f Show that the energy velocity equals the group velocity for the TM modes in a waveguide of general cross section.

7.13g Plot the ω-β diagram for loss-free TM waves and discuss group velocity and phase velocity as a function of frequency as illustrated by the diagram. Plot ω versus attenuation constant α on the same diagram.

7.14 Transverse Electric Waves

Finally, we consider waves that have magnetic field but no electric field in the axial direction. Because of the similarly of treatment to that of TM waves in the preceding article, it will be given more briefly.

The Differential Equation. The finite H_z of the waves must satisfy the wave equation in the form of Eq. 7.02(12):

$$\nabla_t^2 H_z = -k_c^2 H_z \tag{1}$$

$$k_c^2 = \gamma^2 + k^2. \tag{2}$$

Boundary Conditions for a Perfectly Conducting Guide. Allowable solutions to (1) are determined by the single boundary condition that at perfect conductors the normal derivative of H_z must be zero:

$$\frac{\partial H_z}{\partial n} = 0 \quad \text{at boundary.} \tag{3}$$

To show that (3) is the required boundary condition, write the transverse fields of the wave from Eqs. 7.02(7) to (10).

$$E_x = -\frac{j\omega\mu}{k_c^2}\frac{\partial H_z}{\partial y} \qquad E_y = \frac{j\omega\mu}{k_c^2}\frac{\partial H_z}{\partial x} \tag{4}$$

$$H_x = \mp\frac{\gamma}{k_c^2}\frac{\partial H_z}{\partial x} \qquad H_y = \mp\frac{\gamma}{k_c^2}\frac{\partial H_z}{\partial y}. \tag{5}$$

Relation (5) may be written in the vector form,

$$\bar{H}_t = \mp\frac{\gamma}{k_c^2}\nabla_t H_z. \tag{6}$$

If H_z has no normal derivative at the boundary, its transverse gradient has only a component tangential to the boundary, so, by (6), $\bar{H}_t$ does also. Comparison of (4) and (5) shows that transverse electric and magnetic field components are normal to one another, so electric field is normal to the conducting boundary as required.

Cutoff Properties of TE Waves. If in the two-dimensional divergence theorem, Eq. 7.13(13), the general vector F is set equal to $H_z \nabla_t H_z$, the following relation may be derived for a cylindrical region closed by a perfectly conducting boundary:

$$\int_{\text{c.s.}} (\nabla_t H_z)^2 \, dS = k_c^2 \int_{\text{c.s.}} H_z^2 \, dS. \tag{7}$$

For plane waves, H_z and $\nabla_t H_z$ are real, so k_c^2 must be real and positive. By (2), γ then shows cutoff properties exactly the same as for *TM* waves:

$$\gamma = \sqrt{k_c^2 - k^2}. \tag{8}$$

Formulas for attenuation constant below cutoff, phase constant, phase and group velocities above cutoff then follow exactly as in Eqs. 7.13(9) to (12).

$$\gamma = \alpha = k_c\sqrt{1 - (f/f_c)^2}, \qquad f < f_c \qquad (9)$$

$$\gamma = j\beta = jk\sqrt{1 - (f_c/f)^2}, \qquad f > f_c \qquad (10)$$

$$v_p = v\left[1 - \left(\frac{f_c}{f}\right)^2\right]^{-\frac{1}{2}} \qquad (11)$$

$$v_g = v\left[1 - \left(\frac{f_c}{f}\right)^2\right]^{\frac{1}{2}} \qquad (12)$$

where
$$2\pi f_c\sqrt{\mu\epsilon} = k_c = \frac{2\pi}{\lambda_c}. \qquad (13)$$

The universal curves of Fig. 7.13a then apply directly.

Electric Field of the Wave. The electric field is everywhere transverse, and everywhere normal to the transverse magnetic field components. Transverse components of electric and magnetic field may again be related through a field or wave impedance:

$$\frac{E_x}{H_y} = -\frac{E_y}{H_x} = Z_{TE}, \qquad (14)$$

where, from (4) and (5),

$$Z_{TE} = \frac{j\omega\mu}{\gamma} = \eta\left[1 - \left(\frac{f_c}{f}\right)^2\right]^{-\frac{1}{2}}. \qquad (15)$$

This impedance is imaginary for frequencies below cutoff, infinite at cutoff, and purely real for frequencies above cutoff, approaching the intrinsic impedance η as f/f_c becomes large.

Electric field may also be written in the vector form

$$\bar{E} = \mp Z_{TE}(\bar{a}_z \times \bar{H}_t), \qquad (16)$$

where $\bar{a}_z$ is the unit vector in the z direction, and the upper and lower signs apply respectively to positively and negatively traveling waves.

Power Transfer in TE Waves. Average power transfer in the propagating range is, as usual, obtained from the Poynting vector:

$$W_T = \tfrac{1}{2}\int_{\text{c.s.}} \text{Re}\,[\bar{E} \times \bar{H}^*] \cdot \overline{dS} = \tfrac{1}{2}\int_{\text{c.s.}} |E_t|\,|H_t|\,dS$$

$$= \frac{Z_{TE}}{2}\int |H_t|^2\,dS. \qquad (17)$$

By (6) and (7), this may be transformed to

$$W_T = \frac{\eta^2(f/f_c)^2}{2Z_{TE}} \int_{\text{c.s.}} H_z^2 \, dS. \tag{18}$$

Attenuation Due to Imperfectly Conducting Boundaries. As with the *TEM* mode, there cannot be a true transverse electric wave in most guides with imperfect conductors, since most (but not all) of the *TE* modes have axial currents which require a certain finite axial electric field when conductitivy is finite. This axial field is very small compared with the transverse field, however, so the waves are not renamed.

The axial component of current arises from the transverse component of magnetic field at the boundary:

$$|J_z| = |H_t| = \frac{\beta}{k_c^2}|\nabla_t H_z| = \frac{\beta}{k_c^2}\frac{\partial H_z}{\partial l}. \tag{19}$$

The last form follows since it has been shown that the transverse gradient of H_z has only a tangential component $\partial/\partial l$ at the boundary. There is in addition a transverse current arising from the axial magnetic field:

$$|J_t| = |H_z|. \tag{20}$$

The power loss per unit length is then

$$W_L = \frac{R_s}{2} \oint [|H_z|^2 + |H_t|^2] \, dl. \tag{21}$$

$$W_L = \frac{R_s}{2} \oint \left\{ H_z^2 + \left(\frac{f}{f_c}\right)^2 \frac{[1 - (f_c/f)^2]}{k_c^2}\left[\frac{\partial H_z}{\partial l}\right]^2 \right\} dl. \tag{22}$$

Attenuation due to the loss is

$$\alpha = \frac{R_s Z_{TE}}{2\eta^2} \frac{\oint \left\{ (f_c/f)^2 H_z^2 + (1/k_c)^2[1 - (f_c/f)^2]\left[\frac{\partial H_z}{\partial l}\right]^2 \right\} dl}{\int_{\text{c.s.}} H_z^2 \, dS}. \tag{23}$$

If the transverse field components have been calculated explicitly, it is usually as easy to use forms (17) and (21) as the derived forms (18) and (22).

Attenuation Due to Imperfect Dielectrics. Since propagation constant of the *TE* waves has the same form as for the *TM* waves, it follows that the form for attenuation due to an imperfect dielectric does also. For a reasonably good dielectric, the approximate form, Eq. 7.13(25), may be used:

$$\alpha_d = \frac{k\epsilon''/\epsilon'}{2\sqrt{1 - (f_c/f)^2}} = \frac{\sigma\eta}{2\sqrt{1 - (f_c/f)^2}}. \tag{24}$$

Problems

7.14a As in Prob. 7.13a, show that the equivalent circuit for transverse electric waves in terms of distributed constants is as pictured in Fig. 7.14.

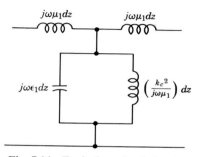

Fig. 7.14   Equivalent circuit for the transverse electric wave.

7.14b Show that fields satisfying Maxwell's equations in a homogeneous, charge-free, current-free dielectric may be derived from a vector potential $\bar{F}$,

$$\bar{E} = -\frac{1}{\epsilon} \nabla \times \bar{F}$$

$$\bar{H} = \frac{1}{j\omega\mu\epsilon} \nabla(\nabla \cdot \bar{F}) - j\omega\bar{F}$$

$$(\nabla^2 + k^2)\bar{F} = 0.$$

Obtain expressions for all field components of a *TE* wave from the axial component F_z of the above potential function, and give the differential equation and boundary conditions for F_z.

7.14c Show that, if one utilizes the potential function $\bar{A}$ instead of the $\bar{F}$ of Prob. *b* for derivation of a *TE* wave, more than one component is required.

7.14d Show that transverse distribution of electic field can be derived from a scalar flux function. How is this related to H_z?

7.14e Show that the energy velocity equals the group velocity for the *TE* modes in a waveguide of general cross section.

7.14f Plot the ω-β diagram for loss-free *TE* waves (including attenuation) and compare with the result of Prob. 7.13g. Discuss similarities and differences of ω-β diagrams and equivalent circuits for the two problems.

7.15   General Wave Types in Rectangular Coordinates

The general solutions for guided waves may be written in rectangular coordinates for application to waves between parallel planes, parallel bar transmission lines, waveguides of rectangular section, etc.

For transverse magnetic waves, Eq. 7.13(1) in rectangular coordinates is

$$\nabla^2_{xy} E_z = \frac{\partial^2 E_z}{\partial x^2} + \frac{\partial^2 E_z}{\partial y^2} = -k_c^2 E_z. \tag{1}$$

This is a partial differential equation which may be solved by the method used in Chapter 3. Assume that the solution may be written as a product of two terms, one a function of x only, the other a function of y only:

$$E_z = XY,$$

where X is a function of x only and Y is a function of y only. Substitute in (1):

$$X''Y + XY'' = -k_c^2 XY$$

or
$$\frac{X''}{X} + \frac{Y''}{Y} = -k_c^2. \tag{2}$$

The primes indicate derivatives. If this equation is to hold for all values of x and y, since x and y may be changed independently of each other, each of the ratios X''/X and Y''/Y can be only a constant. There are then several forms for the solutions, depending on whether these ratios are both taken as negative constants, both positive, or one negative and one positive. If both are taken as negative, say k_x^2 and k_y^2 respectively, then

$$\frac{X''}{X} = -k_x^2$$

$$\frac{Y''}{Y} = -k_y^2.$$

The solutions to these ordinary differential equations are sinusoids, and by (2) the sum of k_x^2 and k_y^2 is k_c^2.

Thus three forms of the wave solution for rectangular coordinates in the transverse plane are listed below, with $e^{(j\omega t - \gamma z)}$ understood. They apply as well to H_z in transverse electric or H waves, since H_z satisfies an equation identical to (1).

$$\left.\begin{array}{l} E_z \ \text{for } TM \text{ waves} \\ H_z \ \text{for } TE \text{ waves} \end{array}\right\} = XY \tag{3}$$

where
$$X = A \cos k_x x + B \sin k_x x$$
$$Y = C \cos k_y y + D \sin k_y y \tag{4}$$
$$k_x^2 + k_y^2 = k_c^2;$$

or
$$X = A_1 \cos k_x x + B_1 \sin k_x x$$
$$Y = C_1 \cosh K_y y + D_1 \sinh K_y y \tag{5}$$
$$k_x^2 - K_y^2 = k_c^2;$$

or

$$X = A_2 \cosh K_x x + B_2 \sinh K_x x$$

$$Y = C_2 \cosh K_y y + D_2 \sinh K_y y \qquad (6)$$

$$-(K_x^2 + K_y^2) = k_c^2.$$

Note that solutions in the form of (6) have a negative value of k_c^2, which does not violate previous proofs that k_c^2 must be positive for solutions applying within a closed region, since (6) would not be applicable inside a region closed by a perfect conductor.

All other components, H_x, H_y, E_x, and E_y, are obtained from (3) to (6) and Eqs. 7.02(7) to (10). For a negatively traveling wave, reverse the sign of all terms containing γ in those equations.

Problem

7.15 Discuss the types of geometrical configurations to which each of the forms of Eqs. 7.15(4) to (6) might be applied.

7.16 General Wave Types in Cylindrical Coordinates

In cylindrical structures, such as coaxial lines or wave guides of circular sections, the wave components will be most conveniently expressed in terms of cylindrical coordinates. The two-dimensional Laplacian ∇^2_{xy} in Eq. 7.13(1) should be written in cylindrical coordinates:

$$\nabla^2_{xy} E_z = \nabla^2_{r\phi} E_z = \frac{\partial^2 E_z}{\partial r^2} + \frac{1}{r}\frac{\partial E_z}{\partial r} + \frac{1}{r^2}\frac{\partial^2 E_z}{\partial \phi^2},$$

so that

$$\frac{\partial^2 E_z}{\partial r^2} + \frac{1}{r}\frac{\partial E_z}{\partial r} + \frac{1}{r^2}\frac{\partial^2 E_z}{\partial \phi^2} = -k_c^2 E_z. \qquad (1)$$

For this partial differential equation, we shall again substitute an assumed product solution and attempt to separate variables in order to obtain two ordinary differential equations.

Assume

$$E_z = R F_\phi$$

where R is a function of r alone and F_ϕ is a function of ϕ alone.

$$R''F_\phi + \frac{R'F_\phi}{r} + \frac{F_\phi''R}{r^2} = -k_c^2 R F_\phi.$$

Separating variables, we have

$$r^2 \frac{R''}{R} + \frac{rR'}{R} + k_c^2 r^2 = \frac{-F_\phi''}{F_\phi}.$$

The left side of the equation is a function of r alone; the right of ϕ alone. If both sides are to be equal for all values of r and ϕ, both sides must equal a constant. Let this constant be ν^2. There are then the two ordinary differential equations:

$$\frac{-F_\phi''}{F_\phi} = \nu^2 \tag{2}$$

and

$$r^2 \frac{R''}{R} + \frac{rR'}{R} + k_c^2 r^2 = \nu^2$$

or

$$R'' + \frac{1}{r} R' + \left(k_c^2 - \frac{\nu^2}{r^2}\right) R = 0. \tag{3}$$

The solution to (2) is in sinusoids. By comparing with Eq. 3.26(3), we see that solutions to (3) may be written in terms of Bessel functions of order ν. Since H_z for transverse electric or H waves satisfies the same equation as (1), solutions to H_z will also be in the same form. Thus, with $e^{(j\omega t - \gamma z)}$ understood,

$$\left.\begin{array}{l} E_z \text{ (for } TM \text{ waves)} \\ H_z \text{ (for } TE \text{ waves)} \end{array}\right\} = RF_\phi \tag{4}$$

where

$$R = AJ_\nu(k_c r) + BN_\nu(k_c r)$$
$$F_\phi = C \cos \nu\phi + D \sin \nu\phi \tag{5}$$

or

$$R = A_1 H_\nu^{(1)}(k_c r) + B_1 H_\nu^{(2)}(k_c r)$$
$$F_\phi = C \cos \nu\phi + D \sin \nu\phi; \tag{6}$$

or

$$R = A_2 J_\nu(k_c r) + B_2 H_\nu^{(1)}(k_c r)$$
$$F_\phi = C \cos \nu\phi + D \sin \nu\phi. \tag{7}$$

The Hankel function form of (6) is useful when one desires to look at waves as though propagation were in the radial direction, as will be seen in the study of radial transmission lines. The form of (7) is useful for problems in which the constant k_c may be imaginary, since J_ν and $H_\nu^{(1)}$ of imaginary arguments are tabulated.[4]

[4] See E. Jahnke, F. Emde, and F. Lösch, *Tables of Higher Functions*, Sixth edition revised by F. Lösch, McGraw-Hill, New York, 1945.

Other components, E_r, E_ϕ, H_r and H_ϕ, are obtainable from the foregoing solutions by the following equations, which are the cylindrical coordinate equivalents of Eqs. 7.02(7) to (10).

$$E_r = -\frac{1}{k_c^2}\left[\gamma \frac{\partial E_z}{\partial r} + \frac{j\omega\mu}{r}\frac{\partial H_z}{\partial \phi}\right] \qquad (8)$$

$$E_\phi = \frac{1}{k_c^2}\left[-\frac{\gamma}{r}\frac{\partial E_z}{\partial \phi} + j\omega\mu\frac{\partial H_z}{\partial r}\right] \qquad (9)$$

$$H_r = \frac{1}{k_c^2}\left[\frac{j\omega\epsilon}{r}\frac{\partial E_z}{\partial \phi} - \gamma\frac{\partial H_z}{\partial r}\right] \qquad (10)$$

$$H_\phi = -\frac{1}{k_c^2}\left[j\omega\epsilon\frac{\partial E_z}{\partial r} + \frac{\gamma}{r}\frac{\partial H_z}{\partial \phi}\right]. \qquad (11)$$

For a negatively traveling wave, reverse the sign of all terms containing γ in the preceding equations.

Problem

7.16 Demonstrate, making use of the form of Eq. 7.16(7), that a solution with k_c imaginary cannot apply inside a closed region.

7.17 Comparisons of General Wave Behavior and Physical Explanations of Wave Types

Many characteristics have been found in the past articles for waves along uniform guiding systems by mathematical analyses starting from Maxwell's equations. It has been found, for instance, that transverse electromagnetic waves (waves with no field components in the direction of propagation) may propagate along an ideal guide with the velocity of light for the dielectric of the guide. In the transverse plane, these may have any field distributions which correspond to static field distributions. Thus such waves may propagate along a system of two or more conductors, or outside a single conductor, but not inside any hollow pipe, since a static field distribution cannot exist inside an infinitely long, hollow, closed conductor. Moreover, it has been verified that the usual transmission line equations written with distributed inductance and capacitance calculated for direct current are exact for ideal lines, and the usual equations with distributed inductance, capacitance, resistance, and conductance are excellent approximations for any practical transmission line efficient for energy transfer.

We have known of these *principal* or *transmission-line* waves, although without assurance, from the conventional line equations, and have seen them verified by Maxwell's equations. In addition, waves have been found which could not have been predicted from the classical transmission line equations based on circuit notions. These waves have either electric or magnetic field components in the direction of propagation. They may propagate inside closed hollow conductors, but only above certain critical or cutoff frequencies for which cross-sectional dimensions between conductors are of the order of a half-wavelength. Below these cutoff frequencies the waves, even if started, attenuate extremely rapidly, so that for ordinary transmission lines where spacing between conductors is much smaller than a half wavelength, these waves should not enter into energy propagation. They may be important at discontinuities, in end effects, or in the radiation field at a long distance from the line. Above the cutoff frequency, however, these waves may be quite satisfactory for energy transfer in any system, and are the only waves which may exist inside closed hollow conductors.

These and other characteristics were obtained by mathematical analysis. It will be profitable to pause now, attempting to understand physically the basis for this behavior and the comparisons between the several types of waves.

It should first be recalled that at the frequencies of interest—at least for the profitable use of hollow pipe waveguides—current flow in the conducting walls will be completely governed by skin effect. For many purposes the conductors may be considered perfect, so that there is no penetration whatever into the conductors, but all currents and charges reside on the surface. Even when actual conductivities of practical conducting materials are taken into account, it is found that at such frequencies depth of penetration is of the order of 10^{-4} inch, and the outside of the pipe is perfectly shielded from the fields which are being retained on the interior.

For the dielectric space inside the pipe, the following should be recalled:

1. Electric field lines may begin and end on charges. If an electric field ends on a conductor, it must represent a charge induced on that conductor.

2. Magnetic field lines can never end since magnetic charges are not known physically. Magnetic fields must always form continuous closed paths, surrounding either a conduction current or a changing electric field (displacement current).

3. Electric field lines may form continuous closed paths, surrounding a changing magnetic field.

In a transverse electromagnetic field, by definition, there are no axial field components; both electric and magnetic fields must lie in the transverse plane. Since electric field is transverse, it would be impossible for magnetic field to surround it without having a component in the axial direction. Consequently all magnetic fields must surround axial conduction currents and not displacement currents. This is the result checked by the analysis for these waves and explains physically why the magnetic fields satisfy a Laplacian equation in the transverse plane outside of the current-carrying region. Similarly, since magnetic fields are transverse, electric

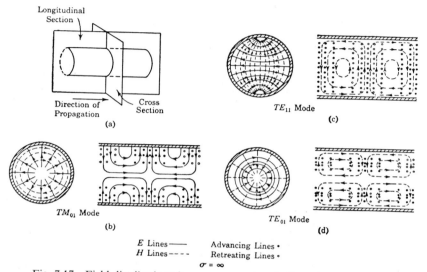

Longitudinal Section

Direction of Propagation

Cross Section

(a)

TE_{11} Mode

(c)

TM_{01} Mode

(b)

TE_{01} Mode

(d)

E Lines ——   Advancing Lines •
H Lines ----   Retreating Lines •
$\sigma = \infty$

Fig. 7.17 Field distributions for some waves in a hollow circular cylinder.

fields could not enclose them without having an axial component of electric field. Consequently, in a given transverse plane, all electric field lines must begin on a certain number of positive charges and end on the same number of negative charges. So electric field also must satisfy Laplace's equation in the transverse plane for the region between conductors.

We can also see quite easily that there can be no transverse electromagnetic waves inside hollow closed conductors. Consider, for a specific case, the round hollow pipe of Fig. 7.17a. If the conductor of the pipe is perfect, magnetic field must be tangential to the conductor. Since magnetic field must also form closed lines, any magnetic field line just inside the pipe would have to be a closed circle tangential to the pipe; it could cut no part of the conductor, and so could surround no conduction current. For a wave with no axial electric field, it cannot surround displacement current (or changing electric field). Consequently, it cannot exist at all.

It is evident as an extension of the foregoing reasoning that there may be a value of magnetic field inside the pipe if there is an axial electric field, since the axial displacement current could then account for magnetic field. The electric field might start from positive charges at one section of the guide, turn and go down the guide axially, and finally end on negative charges farther down the guide (Fig. 7.17b). It is recognized that such a wave is a transverse magnetic wave analyzed in Art. 7.13. (The subscript notation will be defined in Chapter 8.) Note particularly that, since the line integral of magnetic field is proportional to *rate of change* of electric flux enclosed, magnetic field for a single traveling wave is a maximum, not in the plane where axial electric field is a maximum, but rather in the plane where rate of change of axial electric field is a maximum as the entire pattern moves down the guide. If this wave is symmetrical, there must be only axial current flow, produced by the transverse magnetic field at the conductor surface. This is also evident by the current which must flow to account for the lumps of induced charge. From still another point of view, we have agreed that the conducting wall acts as a perfect shield so that no magnetic field due to influences on the inside can exist outside it. Thus, at any section, there must flow a current in the conductor exactly equal and opposite to the total axial displacement current inside the guide at that section.

Let us now consider the field distribution for waves with axial magnetic field and transverse electric field. First, as in Fig. 7.17c, notice that, if electric field lines start from positive charges on one side of the hollow pipe and go directly across to negative charges on the opposite side, magnetic field lines may exist inside the hollow pipe if they surround these electric field lines. In this type of wave there must exist currents flowing circumferentially between the positive and negative charges at any given section in addition to those which flow axially. The former are accounted for by the axial magnetic field at the surface of the conductor; the latter are accounted for by the transverse component of magnetic field at the surface of the conductor.

The wave just described is, of course, a transverse electric or *H* wave. Another wave of this same type may appear, however, if the electric field lines in the transverse plane do not end on any charges, but always close upon themselves. In this wave (Fig. 7.17d) the electric field lines and the magnetic field lines surround each other. There are then no charges induced on the conductors and no axial currents. There are circulating currents arising from the axial component of magnetic field. Since we have found that this axial component becomes very small for frequencies far above cutoff, so will the circulating current become small, and under this condition there will be but slight losses in the guide even though conductors are imperfect. Of course, such a situation indicates that the type of wave described is not so intimately tied to the guide. If it is attempted to make a bend in such a guide, current must flow at the discontinuity, and the new wave generated at the bend may be of an entirely different type. Because of this reason it is often pointed out that the type of wave is unstable. This is the TE_{01} wave of circular guides which will be studied in more detail later.

We might next ask if it is possible to have a transverse magnetic or E wave with no charges induced on the guide, but with electric and magnetic fields surrounding each other. A little study of this shows that, although it may be possible for the fields to surround each other on the interior of the guide for the higher order TM waves, the field nearest the conductor must turn to enter the conductor normally, thus inducing charges as described previously.

All the above general characteristics will be further clarified in later study of the specific waves which may propagate inside guides of circular and rectangular shapes. However, the preceding general study is particularly important in showing that similar types of waves should be found in guides of different cross sections, since the above discussions did not require the specification of the shape of guide.

8 CHARACTERISTICS OF COMMON WAVEGUIDES AND TRANSMISSION LINES

8.01 Introduction

Chapter 7 illustrated guided waves on idealized structures and gave some of the general properties of the various classes of guided waves. Here we wish to look in more detail at the characteristics of a few specific forms of guides. First we shall consider the two most commonly used forms of hollow guides—rectangular and circular cylindrical forms. Then we will look at characteristics of commonly used transmission lines for both the principal and higher-order waves.

This chapter continues with consideration of a variety of wave guiding systems. In the selection of these examples, there are generally two objectives. The first is that the structures in themselves be of some practical use. The second and more important is that each example illustrate some principle concerning wave guiding that is not necessarily obvious from the examples of the preceding chapter and the first parts of this chapter. Thus the radial line is a simple but important example of the nonuniform system. The region between inclined planes is another, but also illustrates how the principle of duality can be used to obtain the solution for one set of guide boundaries from that for boundaries where $\bar{E}$ and $\bar{H}$ are exchanged. The ridge waveguides show that cross sections of closed guides do not necessarily have to be of the order of a half-wave in size for propagation. The dielectric guides illustrate guiding phenomena with open structures. The surface guides and slow-wave structures are extensions of this important principle. There are articles on periodic microwave and optical guides as illustrations of the effect of spatially repetitive physical characteristics along a wave guiding system. None of these treatments can be exhaustive, but they show the variety of phenomena included in the study of guided waves.

420

The chapter concludes with a discusion of wave propagation through inhomogeneous media. Though the treatment is not restricted to the case of guided waves, the approach has much in common with nonuniform guides and some solutions found in the preceding articles lead directly to results for some special forms of inhomogeneity. The basis of the ray optic treatment of propagation through inhomogeneous media is explained.

COMMON WAVEGUIDES

8.02   Rectangular Waveguides

Hollow conducting pipes of rectangular cross section are the most commonly used of the hollow-pipe waveguides. It has been pointed out in Chapter 7 that for such hollow pipes the dielectric interior can support *TM* and *TE* waves, but not *TEM* waves. With the coordinate system chosen as in Fig. 8.02a, the wave equation may be solved in rectangular coordinates as in Art. 7.15. For *TM* waves the boundary conditions require zero E_z at $x = 0$ and at $y = 0$, so only sine terms can be present. Other components are derived by the relations 7.02(7) to (10).

Transverse Magnetic Waves

$$E_z = A \sin k_x x \sin k_y y$$

$$H_x = j\frac{k_y f}{k_c \eta f_c} A \sin k_x x \cos k_y y$$

$$H_y = -j\frac{k_x f}{k_c \eta f_c} A \cos k_x x \sin k_y y \quad (1)$$

$$E_x = Z_{TM} H_y$$

$$E_y = -Z_{TM} H_x$$

Transverse Electric Waves

$$H_z = B \cos k_x x \cos k_y y$$

$$E_x = j\frac{\eta k_y f}{k_c f_c} B \cos k_x x \sin k_y y$$

$$E_y = -j\frac{\eta k_x f}{k_c f_c} B \sin k_x x \cos k_y y \quad (2)$$

$$H_x = -\frac{E_y}{Z_{TE}}$$

$$H_y = \frac{E_x}{Z_{TE}}$$

In (1) and (2), the propagation factor $e^{(j\omega t - \gamma z)}$ is understood, and

$$Z_{TM} = \eta[1 - (f_c/f)^2]^{1/2} \qquad Z_{TE} = \eta[1 - (f_c/f)^2]^{-1/2} \quad (3)$$

$$\gamma = \sqrt{k_c^2 - k^2} = j\frac{\omega}{v}\sqrt{1 - (f_c/f)^2}. \quad (4)$$

If the wave is negatively traveling, $e^{(j\omega t + \gamma z)}$ is understood and the signs of Z_{TM} or Z_{TE} should be reversed.

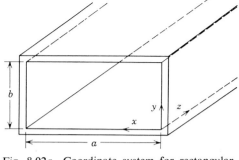

Fig. 8.02a Coordinate system for rectangular
guide.

In addition to the boundary conditions just utilized, there remain the
conditions at $x = a$ and $y = b$. For the TM waves, E_z must be zero here
also, requiring that $k_x a$ and $k_y b$ be multiples of π.

$$k_x = \frac{m\pi}{a} \qquad k_y = \frac{n\pi}{b}.$$

The requirement of $\partial H_z/\partial x = 0$ at $x = a$ and $\partial H_z/\partial y = 0$ at $y = b$ leads
to the same values of k_x and k_y for TE waves. From Eq. 7.15(4) for either
TM or TE waves,

$$(k_c)_{m,n} = \sqrt{k_x{}^2 + k_y{}^2} = \sqrt{(m\pi/a)^2 + (n\pi/b)^2}. \tag{5}$$

Then cutoff wavelength and frequency may be written

$$(\lambda_c)_{m,n} = \frac{2\pi}{k_c} = \frac{2}{\sqrt{(m/a)^2 + (n/b)^2}} = \frac{2ab}{\sqrt{(mb)^2 + (na)^2}} \tag{6}$$

$$(f_c)_{m,n} = \frac{k_c}{2\pi\sqrt{\mu\epsilon}} = \frac{1}{2\sqrt{\mu\epsilon}}\sqrt{(m/a)^2 + (n/b)^2}. \tag{7}$$

There are then a doubly infinite number of possible waves of each type,
corresponding to all the combinations of the integers m and n. An E or
transverse magnetic wave with m half-sine variations in the x direction
and n half-sine variations in the y direction is denoted as an E_{mn} or
TM_{mn} wave. An H or transverse electric wave with m half-sine variations
in x, n in y, is denoted by H_{mn} or TE_{mn}. Note that by (1) and (2) TE waves
may exist with either m or n (but not both) zero, whereas in a TM wave
neither m nor n can be zero or the entire wave disappears. The lowest
order TE wave, TE_{10}, is of enough special engineering interest to be studied
in more detail in a following article. For the moment, however, we see
from (6) that the cutoff (free space) wavelength of such a wave is

$$[\lambda_c]_{TE_{10}} = 2a. \tag{8}$$

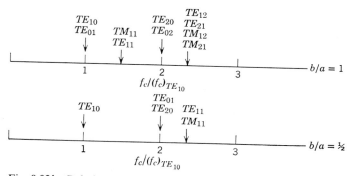

Fig. 8.02*b*   Relative cutoff frequencies of waves in rectangular guides.

That is, the cutoff frequency is that frequency for which the width of the guide is a half-wavelength. It does not depend at all on the other dimensions. This TE_{10} mode is frequently referred to as the *dominant* mode of the rectangular guide.

Figure 8.02*b* shows a line diagram indicating the cutoff frequencies of several of the lowest-order modes for a square guide, $a = b$, referred to the cutoff frequency of the dominant TE_{10} mode, and for a guide of ratio $b/a = \frac{1}{2}$.

The phase and group velocities, attenuation below cutoff, and attenuation due to imperfect dielectrics above cutoff for any wave type are given in terms of the cutoff frequency of that wave type by the general expressions of Art. 7.13. For attenuation above cutoff due to imperfect conductivity, we evaluate the integrals of Eqs. 7.13(19) to (24) in a straightforward manner. The results are

$$(\alpha_c)_{TE_{m0}} = \frac{R_s}{b\eta\sqrt{1 - (f_c/f)^2}}\left[1 + \frac{2b}{a}\left(\frac{f_c}{f}\right)^2\right] \tag{9}$$

$$(\alpha_c)_{TE_{mn}}$$
$$= \frac{2R_s}{b\eta\sqrt{1 - (f_c/f)^2}}\left\{\left(1 + \frac{b}{a}\right)\left(\frac{f_c}{f}\right)^2 + \left[1 - \left(\frac{f_c}{f}\right)^2\right]\left[\frac{\frac{b}{a}\left(\frac{b}{a}m^2 + n^2\right)}{\frac{b^2m^2}{a^2} + n^2}\right]\right\} \tag{10}$$

$$(\alpha_c)_{TE_{mn}} = \frac{2R_s}{b\eta\sqrt{1 - (f_c/f)^2}}\frac{[m^2(b/a)^3 + n^2]}{[m^2(b/a)^2 + n^2]}. \tag{11}$$

Curves of attenuation in decibels per meter (8.686 times the values of α in nepers per meter given in the foregoing equations) are plotted for a few modes and b/a ratios in Fig. 8.02c. Note that all curves show a minimum value of attenuation, after which attenuation increases with frequency. Field distributions in several of the modes are shown in

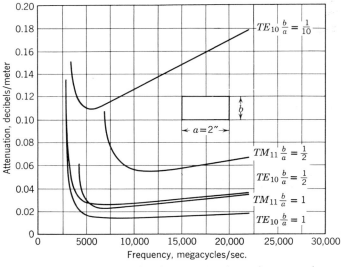

Fig. 8.02c   Attenuation due to copper losses in rectangular waveguides of fixed width.

Table 8.02. It will be useful to become familiar with this table, and especially to make comparisons with the similar table to be given in Art. 8.04 for circular guides.

Problems

8.02a Derive in detail the expressions for attenuation due to imperfect conductors, Eqs. 8.02(9) to (11).

8.02b Recalling that surface resistivity R_s is a function of frequency, find the frequency of minimum attenuation for a TM_{mn} mode. Show that the expression for attenuation of a TE_{mn} mode must also have a minimum.

8.02c Of the wave types studied so far, those transverse magnetic to the axial direction were obtained by setting $H_z = 0$; those transverse electric to the axial direction were obtained by setting $E_z = 0$. For the rectangular waveguide, obtain the lowest-order mode with $H_x = 0$ but all other components present. This may be called a wave transverse magnetic to the x direction. Show that it may also be obtained by superposing the TM and TE waves given previously of just sufficient amounts so that H_x from the two waves exactly cancel. Repeat for a wave transverse electric to the x direction. These wave types are also called *longitudinal section waves*.

8.03   The TE_{10} Wave in a Rectangular Guide

One of the simplest of all the waves which may exist inside hollow-pipe waveguides is the dominant TE_{10} wave in the rectangular guide. It is also of great engineering importance, partly for the following reasons.

1. Cutoff frequency is independent of one of the dimensions of the cross section. Consequently for a given frequency this dimension may be made small enough so that the TE_{10} wave is the only wave which will propagate, and there is no difficulty with higher-order waves that end effects or discontinuities may cause to be excited.

2. The polarization of the field is definitely fixed, electric field passing from top to bottom of the guide. This fixed polarization may be required for certain applications.

3. For a given frequency the attenuation due to copper losses is not excessive compared with other wave types in guides of comparable size.

Let us now rewrite the expressions from the previous article for general TE waves in rectangular guides, Eq. 8.02(2), setting $m = 1$, $n = 0$, and substituting the value of cutoff for this combination.

$$E_y = E_0 \sin \frac{\pi x}{a} \tag{1}$$

$$H_x = -\left(\frac{E_0}{Z_{TE}}\right) \sin\left(\frac{\pi x}{a}\right) \tag{2}$$

$$H_z = \frac{jE_0}{\eta}\left(\frac{\lambda}{2a}\right) \cos\frac{\pi x}{a} \tag{3}$$

$$H_y = 0 = E_x \tag{4}$$

$$Z_{TE} = \frac{\eta}{\sqrt{1 - (\lambda/2a)^2}} \tag{5}$$

$$v_p = \frac{1}{\sqrt{\mu\epsilon}\sqrt{1 - (\lambda/2a)^2}} \tag{6}$$

$$v_g = \frac{1}{\sqrt{\mu\epsilon}}\sqrt{1 - (\lambda/2a)^2} \tag{7}$$

$$\lambda_c = 2a \tag{8}$$

$$f_c = \frac{1}{2a\sqrt{\mu\epsilon}}. \tag{9}$$

Attenuation due to imperfect dielectric,

$$\alpha_d = \frac{\sigma \eta}{2\sqrt{1 - (f_c/f)^2}} = \frac{k\epsilon''/\epsilon'}{2\sqrt{1 - (f_c/f)^2}}. \tag{10}$$

Attenuation due to imperfect conductor,

$$\alpha_c = \frac{R_s}{b\eta\sqrt{1 - (f_c/f)^2}} \left[1 + \frac{2b}{a}\left(\frac{f_c}{f}\right)^2 \right]. \tag{11}$$

In these relations, v_p is phase velocity, v_g is group velocity, μ, ϵ, and η are permeability, permittivity, and intrinsic impedance respectively for the dielectric filling the guide, R_s is the skin effect surface resistivity of the conducting walls, and ϵ''/ϵ' is the ratio of loss factor to real part of permittivity of the dielectric.

A study of the field distributions (1) to (3) shows the field patterns for this wave sketched in Table 8.02. First it is noted that no field components vary in the vertical or y direction. The only electric field component is that vertical one E_y passing between top and bottom of the guide. This is a maximum at the center and zero at the conducting walls, varying as a half-sine curve. The corresponding charges induced by the electric field lines ending on conductors are:

1. Charges zero on side walls.
2. A charge distribution on top and bottom corresponding to E_y.

$$\rho_s = -\epsilon E_y \text{ coulombs/meter}^2 \text{ on top}$$
$$= \epsilon E_y \text{ coulombs/meter}^2 \text{ on bottom.}$$

The magnetic field forms closed paths surrounding the vertical electric displacement currents arising from E_y, so that there are components H_x and H_z. Component H_x is zero at the two side walls and a maximum in the center, following the distribution of E_y. Component H_z is a maximum at the side walls and zero at the center. Component H_x corresponds to a longitudinal current flow down the guide in the top, and opposite in the bottom; H_z corresponds to a current from top to bottom around the periphery of the guide. These current distributions are sketched in Fig. 8.03a.

1. Longitudinal current flow:
   On top $J_z = H_x$ amperes per meter.
   On bottom $J_z = -H_x$ amperes per meter.
2. Transverse current flow from top to bottom:
   On walls $J_y = -H_z|_{x=0}$ amperes per meter.
   On top $J_x = -H_z$ amperes per meter.
   On bottom $J_x = H_z$ amperes per meter.

This simple wave type is a convenient one to study in order to strengthen some of our physical pictures of wave propagation. First note that this is one of the types predicted by physical reasoning in Art. 7.17. Electric

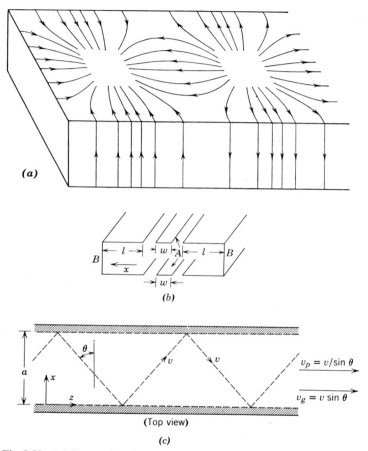

(a)

(b)

(Top view)

(c)

Fig. 8.03   (a) Current flow in walls of rectangular guide with TE_{10} mode. (b) Guide roughly divided into axial- and transverse-current regions. (c) Path of uniform plane wave component of TE_{10} wave in rectangular guide.

field is confined to the transverse plane and so passes between equal and opposite charge densities lying on different parts of the walls in the same transverse plane. Currents flow around the periphery of the guide between these opposite charges; currents also flow longitudinally down the guide between a given charge and that of opposite sign, a half-wave farther down the guide. The magnetic fields surround the electric displacement currents inside the guide and so must have an axial as well as a transverse component.

As a fairly crude way of looking at the problem, one might also think of this mode being formed by starting with a parallel-plate transmission line of width w to carry the longitudinal current in the center of the guide, and then adding shorted troughs B of depth l on the two sides to close the region, as pictured in Fig. 8.03b. Since one would expect the lengths l to be around a quarter-wavelength to provide a high impedance at the center, the overall width should be something over a half-wavelength, which we know to be true for propagation. The picture is only a rough one because the fields in the two regions are not separated, and propagation is not purely longitudinal in the center portion or transverse in the side portions.

A third viewpoint follows from that used in studying the higher-order waves between parallel planes. There it was pointed out that one could visualize the TM and TE waves in terms of plane waves bouncing between the two planes at such an angle that the interference pattern maintains a zero of electric field tangential to the two planes. Similarly, the TE_{10} wave in the rectangular guide may be thought of as arising from the interference between incident and reflected plane waves, polarized so that the electric vector is vertical, and bouncing between the two sides of the guide at such an angle with the sides that the zero electric field is maintained at the two sides. One such component uniform plane wave is indicated in Fig. 8.03c. As in the result of Art. 7.08, when the width a is exactly $\lambda/2$, the waves travel exactly back and forth across the guide with no component of propagation in the axial direction. At slightly higher frequencies there is a small angle θ such that $a = \lambda/2 \cos \theta$, and there is a small propagation in the axial direction, a very small group velocity in the axial direction $v \sin \theta$, and a very large phase velocity $v/\sin \theta$. At frequencies approaching infinity, θ approaches $90°$, so that the wave travels down the guide practically as a plane wave in space propagating in the axial direction.

All the foregoing points of view explain why the dimension b should not enter into the determination of cutoff frequency. Since the electric field is always normal to top and bottom, the placing of these planes plays no part in the boundary condition. However, this dimension b will be important from two other points of view.

1. The smaller b is (all other parameters constant), the greater is the electric field across the guide for a given power transfer, and so the danger of voltage breakdown is greater.

2. The smaller b is (all other parameters constant), the greater is the attenuation due to conductor losses.

The first point is easily seen since it was shown that the power transfer can be written as the integral over the cross-sectional area of E^2/Z_{TE}. Z_{TE} does not change with b, so, as cross-sectional area decreases, E must increase, if power is to be constant.

The second point follows from an approximate picture in which the attenuation is roughly proportional to the ratio of perimeter to cross-sectional area. This picture is a logical one as the conductor losses occur on the perimeter, and the power transfer occurs through the cross-sectional area. Of course, field distributions enter, and we can look at this case more rigorously by noting that, if the strength of magnetic field is maintained constant as b is decreased, the magnitude of currents in the walls is maintained constant. A large part of the losses occur along the top and bottom, and this part is consequently unchanged as b decreases, but power transfer for this constant H decreases directly with b. Therefore the ratio of power loss to power transfer increases as b decreases.

Problems

8.03a For $\lambda = 10$ cm, design a rectangular waveguide with copper conductor and air dielectric so that the TE_{10} wave will propagate with a 30 per cent safety factor ($f = 1.30f_c$) but also so that the wave type with next higher cut-off will be 30 per cent below its cutoff frequency. Calculate the attenuation due to copper losses in decibels per meter.
8.03b Repeat the above for $\lambda = 5$ cm.
8.03c Design a guide for use at 3000 Mc/sec with the same requirements as in *a* except that the guide is to be filled with a dielectric having a permittivity 4 times that of air. Calculate the increase in attenuation due to copper losses alone, assuming that the dielectric is perfect. Calculate the additional attenuation due to this dielectric, if $\epsilon''/\epsilon' = 0.01$.

8.04 Waveguides of Circular Cross Section

For a circular guide, cylindrical coordinates will be selected so that the appropriate solutions for the waves may be taken directly from Art. 7.16. There can be no term in $N_n(k_c r)$ since the solution must in this case apply at the origin, $r = 0$ and $N_n(0) = \infty$. For TM waves, E_z is then given by Eqs. 7.16(4) and 7.16(5) with $B = 0$. For TE waves, H_z is given by a like expression. Other field components for the two types of waves follow from Eqs. 7.16(8) to 7.16(11) respectively. General solutions for the two types of waves are then as follows.

Transverse Magnetic Waves

$$E_z = AJ_n(k_c r) \begin{cases} \cos n\phi \\ \sin n\phi \end{cases}$$

$$H_r = -j\frac{nf}{k_c \eta r f_c} AJ_n(k_c r) \begin{cases} \sin n\phi \\ -\cos n\phi \end{cases}$$

$$H_\phi = -j\frac{f}{f_c \eta} AJ'_n(k_c r) \begin{cases} \cos n\phi \\ \sin n\phi \end{cases} \quad (1)$$

$$E_\phi = -H_r Z_{TM}$$

$$E_r = H_\phi Z_{TM}$$

Transverse Electric Waves

$$H_z = BJ_n(k_c r) \begin{cases} \cos n\phi \\ \sin n\phi \end{cases}$$

$$E_r = j\frac{n\eta f}{k_c r f_c} BJ_n(k_c r) \begin{cases} \sin n\phi \\ -\cos n\phi \end{cases}$$

$$E_\phi = jn\frac{f}{f_c} BJ'_n(k_c r) \begin{cases} \cos n\phi \\ \sin n\phi \end{cases} \quad (2)$$

$$H_\phi = \frac{E_r}{Z_{TE}}$$

$$H_r = -\frac{E_\phi}{Z_{TE}}$$

In all the preceding expressions $e^{j\omega t - \gamma z}$ is understood, and γ, Z_{TM}, and Z_{TE} are:

$$\gamma = j\frac{\omega}{v}\left[1 - \left(\frac{f_c}{f}\right)^2\right]^{1/2}$$

$$Z_{TM} = \eta\left[1 - \left(\frac{f_c}{f}\right)^2\right]^{1/2}$$

$$Z_{TE} = \eta\left[1 - \left(\frac{f_c}{f}\right)^2\right]^{-1/2}.$$

For a negatively traveling wave ($e^{j\omega t + \gamma z}$ understood), the signs of terms in (1) and (2) containing Z_{TM} or Z_{TE} should be reversed.

For transverse magnetic waves, the boundary condition of zero electric field tangential to the conducting boundary, $E_z = 0$ at $r = a$, must require that

$$J_n(k_c a) = 0. \quad (3)$$

Since the Bessel function $J_n(x)$ has an infinite number of values of x for which it becomes zero, (3) may be satisfied by any one of these. That is, if p_{nl} is the lth root of $J_n(x) = 0$, (3) is satisfied if

$$(k_c)_{nl} = \frac{p_{nl}}{a}. \quad (4)$$

Equation (4) defines a doubly infinite set of possible values for k_c, one for each combination of the integers n and l. Each of these combinations defines a particular wave type by Eqs. (1), in general differing from all others in field distributions, cutoff frequencies, and propagation properties. A particular E or transverse magnetic wave corresponding to two integers n and l is denoted by E_{nl} or TM_{nl}. The integer n describes the number of variations circumferentially; the integer l describes the number of variations radially. The cutoff wavelength or frequency for a particular wave type follows from (4).

$$(\lambda_c)_{TMnl} = \frac{1}{\sqrt{\mu\epsilon}(f_c)_{TMnl}} = \frac{2\pi a}{p_{nl}}. \qquad (5)$$

The lowest value of p_{nl} is the first root of the zero-order Bessel function, $p_{01} = 2.405$, so that this TM_{01} wave has the lowest cutoff frequency of all transverse magnetic waves in a given circular pipe. From (5), this cutoff wavelength is $2.61a$. Note that this wavelength is measured at velocity of light in the dielectric filling the guide, $1/\sqrt{\mu\epsilon}$.

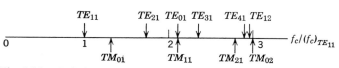

Fig. 8.04a Relative cutoff frequencies of waves in a circular guide.

For transverse electric or H waves the required boundary condition is that normal derivative of H_z be zero at all conducting surfaces. This requires

$$J'_n(k_c a) = 0, \qquad (6)$$

so that, if p'_{nl} is the lth root of $J'_n(x) = 0$, (6) is satisfied by

$$(k_c)_{nl} = \frac{p'_{nl}}{a}. \qquad (7)$$

Equation (7) again defines a doubly infinite number of possible TE wave types corresponding to all the possible combinations of the integers n and l, n describing the number of circumferential variations, l the number of radial variations. A particular H or transverse electric wave type is labeled H_{nl} or TE_{nl}. Cutoff wavelength and frequency are

$$(\lambda_c)_{TEnl} = \frac{1}{\sqrt{\mu\epsilon}(f_c)_{TEnl}} = \frac{2\pi a}{p'_{nl}}. \qquad (8)$$

The lowest value of p'_{nl} is p'_{11}, which is 1.84, so that the TE_{11} wave has the lowest cutoff frequency of all transverse electric waves in a given diameter of pipe. From (8) this corresponds to a cutoff wavelength of $3.41a$. This is also a lower frequency of cutoff than that found for the lowest-order TM wave in a given size of pipe. Stated in another way, the TE_{11} wave of a given frequency will propagate in a pipe only 76.6 per cent as big as that required to support a TM_{01} wave of the same frequency.

A line diagram showing positions of the cutoff frequencies of some of the lower-order modes as compared with the dominant TE_{11} mode is given for a circular guide in Fig. 8.04a. Field distributions for several of the modes with other important data are shown in Table 8.04. In comparing this with the similar table for rectangular guides, note that analogous modes in the two shapes of guides do not have corresponding subscripts. Thus, a TE_{11} circular mode is analogous to the TE_{10} rectangular, a TM_{01} circular is analogous to a TM_{11} rectangular, the TM_{11} circular is analogous to the TM_{21} rectangular, etc.[1]

To demonstrate the calculation of the attenuation arising from imperfect conductors, we will carry through the steps for a TM_{nl} mode. To compute power transfer, the expression for E_z in (1) may be substituted in Eq. 7.13(19).

$$W_T = \frac{Z_{TM}}{2\eta^2}\left(\frac{f}{f_c}\right)^2 \int_{c.s.} E_z^2 \, dS$$

$$= \frac{(f/f_c)^2\sqrt{1 - (f_c/f)^2}}{2\eta} \int_0^{2\pi} \int_0^a A^2 J_n^2(k_c r) \cos^2(n\phi) \, r \, dr \, d\phi. \quad (9)$$

The integral of the $\cos^2$ term gives a value of π. The integral of the Bessel function is evaluated by Eq. 3.27(22).

$$\int_0^a J_n^2(k_c r) r \, dr = \frac{a^2}{2}\left[J_n'^2(k_c a) + \left(1 + \frac{n^2}{k_c^2 a^2}\right)J_n^2(k_c a)\right]. \quad (10)$$

The second term in this integral is zero because of (3). So

$$W_T = \frac{\pi(f/f_c)^2\sqrt{1 - (f_c/f)^2}\, a^2}{4\eta} A^2 J_n'^2(k_c a). \quad (11)$$

The power loss per unit length due to the conductors, by Eq. 7.13(23), is

$$W_L = \frac{R_s}{2\eta^2 k_c^2}\left(\frac{f}{f_c}\right)^2 \oint \left(\frac{\partial E_z}{\partial n}\right)^2 dl$$

$$= \frac{R_s}{2\eta^2 k_c^2}\left(\frac{f}{f_c}\right)^2 k_c^2 A^2 J_n'^2(k_c a) \int_0^{2\pi} \cos^2(n\phi) \, a \, d\phi$$

$$= \frac{R_s \pi a}{2\eta^2}\left(\frac{f}{f_c}\right)^2 A^2 J_n'^2(k_c a). \quad (12)$$

The attenuation is then

$$\alpha_{TM_{nl}} = \frac{W_L}{2W_T} = \frac{R_s}{a\eta}\frac{1}{\sqrt{1 - (f_c/f)^2}} \quad \text{nepers/meter.} \quad (13)$$

[1] C. T. Tai (*Proc. I.R.E.*, **49**, 1442, September 1961) suggests a numbering system which is logical and establishes greater parallelism, but which does not yet appear to be generally adopted in practical use of round guides.

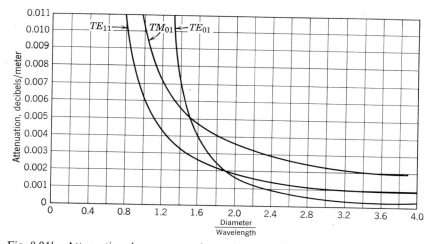

Fig. 8.04b Attenuation due to copper losses in circular waveguides at 3000 Mc/sec.

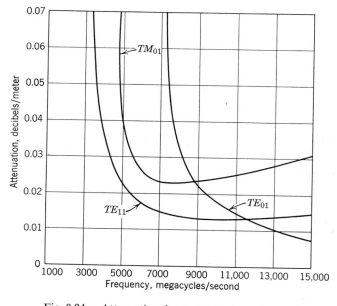

Fig. 8.04c Attenuation due to copper losses in circular
waveguides; diameter = 2 in.

A similar use of the equations gives the attenuation for a TE_{nl} wave,

$$\alpha_{TEnl} = \frac{R_s}{a\eta} \frac{1}{\sqrt{1 - (f_c/f)^2}} \left[\left(\frac{f_c}{f}\right)^2 + \frac{n^2}{p_{nl}^{'2} - n^2} \right]. \tag{14}$$

Some representative curves of attenuation versus diameter are plotted in Fig. 8.04b for different wave types at a fixed frequency; and, in Fig. 8.04c, for different wave types in a guide of fixed diameter, attenuation is plotted vs. frequency. The TE_{01} wave is interesting because it shows an attenuation which decreases indefinitely with increasing frequency. It is interesting enough to deserve special treatment in the next article along with other TE_{0l} modes.

Problems

8.04a Derive Eq. 8.04(14) for attenuation of TE_{nl} waves in an imperfectly conducting guide.

8.04b Show that for all TM_{nl} waves the minimum attenuation arising from imperfect conductors occurs at a frequency

$$f = \sqrt{3} f_c.$$

Study the dependence of the value of attenuation at this frequency on f_c. (Recall that R_s is a function of frequency.)

8.04c For $\lambda = 7$ cm, select a pipe size to propagate with a reasonable safety factor the TE_{11} wave, but no other wave type. Compare the dissipative attenuation in this TE_{11} wave (copper guide) with the reactive attenuation in the next higher-order wave.

8.05 The Circular Electric Mode and Other Oversize Guides

It was noted in Art. 8.04 that the TE_{01} mode yields a decreasing attenuation for a pipe of fixed size as frequency is increased. This property is one shared by all TE modes with $n = 0$, and is expected, since Eq. 8.04(2) shows that for such modes the only magnetic field component tangential to the conductors is H_z. As frequency increases, H_z decreases for a constant value of power transfer and approaches zero at infinite frequency. Currents and conductor losses in the guide walls therefore approach zero. Because of this property, the waves have received a good deal of attention for possible long-distance propagation of energy, especially at millimeter waves and attenuations as low as 2 db per mile were attained.[2] Since electric field lines are circular, modes of this class are often described as "circular electric" modes.

[2] S. E. Miller, *Bell Syst. Tech. J.*, **33**, 1209–1265 (November 1954).

One of the major problems in the use of the TE_{01} or other circular electric modes arises because it is not the mode of lowest cutoff frequency, so must always be used in a guide capable of propagating a number of modes. Such guides are known as "oversize" guides, and will be discussed in their use with other waves later in the article. For the TE_{01} mode, Fig. 8.04a shows that there will be at least four other modes (TE_{11}, TM_{01}, TE_{21}, and TM_{11}) propagating if the TE_{01} mode is above cutoff. Moreover, to use the potentially very low attenuation constants, the operating frequency must be well above cutoff, so many more modes than the above are in the propagating range. The situation is still worse if one goes to a TE_{0l} mode with higher l.

The practical problems raised by the multimode character are several. In the first place one must have a method of exciting the desired mode with reasonable purity, since the attenuating character of cutoff modes cannot be counted on to eliminate other modes excited at the input as it can when only a single mode propagates. Secondly, one must guard against coupling from the desired TE_{0l} mode, once excited, to undesired modes. These not only cause higher losses, but the different phase velocities of the several modes may produce distortion of the signal. Coupling to the undesired modes comes chiefly from irregularities in the guide shape or direction. Some irregularities will inevitably exist, and the guide is not of much use if it cannot guide around a corner of reasonable curvature. The corner problem has been solved in a very ingenious way so that there is mode conversion in entering the corner, but a corresponding conversion back to the desired TE_{0l} mode in leaving it.[2]

A more general solution to both asymmetry and corner problems is to devise mode filters which discriminate against the undesired modes, but cause negligible attenuation to the desired one. The principle in devising these is to produce cuts perpendicular to current paths in the guide wall for undesired modes, maintaining them parallel to currents of the desired mode. Or attenuating sheets may be introduced inside the guide, along the direction of electric field for the mode to be damped but normal to electric fields of the mode to be favored. An example of the latter for the TE_{01} mode is a set of thin conducting sheets placed on radial planes as illustrated by Fig. 8.05a. The E_ϕ is normal to these planes, but modes with either E_r or E_z would be damped by the conductors.

A second type of mode filter, considering current directions, would be formed by producing frequent cuts in the guide wall perpendicular to the axis. Expressed differently, a series of closely spaced parallel conducting rings (Fig. 8.05b) would propagate a TE_{0l} mode very well, but would discourage any mode requiring an axial component of current flow. It has been found in practice that a closely wound helical wire (Fig. 8.05c) works nearly as well and is much more practical to construct. Analysis of this guide[3] shows attenuation of the TE_{01} mode little more than in the solid pipe, but attenuations of unwanted modes hundreds of times greater.

For the very short millimeter or submillimeter wavelengths, single-mode guides of any shape are small and difficult to construct and have

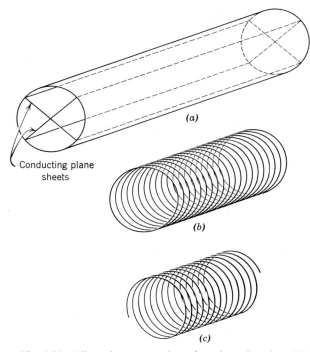

Conducting plane
sheets

Fig. 8.05   Filters for suppression of modes other than TE_{01}.

high attenuation. Thus for other shapes, and modes, also, one may wish to go to oversize guides in order to obtain larger sizes. These have the capability of propagating more than the mode to be utilized, and the principle is much the same as that discussed for maintaining a single mode. The mode is usually excited by flaring gradually from a single-mode guide of the desired form. Mode filters may be introduced according to the foregoing principles. Any discontinuities placed in the guide for matching, reflecting, or coupling should extend uniformly over the cross section of the guide so that they will not couple energy to undesired modes. The guide, if large compared with wavelength, is coupled little to the wave and acts

[3] S. P. Morgan and J. A. Young, *Bell Syst. Tech. J.*, **35**, 1347–1384 (November 1956).

largely as a shield. The axial components of field are small so that the wave is essentially a *TEM* mode. The techniques then become essentially those of handling a uniform plane wave in space and are often referred to as "quasioptical" techniques.[4,5] Some of those discussed in Art. 8.07 may be particularly applicable.

8.06 Excitation and Reception of Waves in Guides

The problems of exciting waves in waveguides and of absorbing their energy in a receiver are usually not simple field problems. The quantitative treatment, to the extent appropriate to this book, will be reserved for Chapter 11. However, some qualitative discussion of the approaches to excitation and reception may be helpful at this point. To excite any particular desired wave, one should study the field pattern and use one or more of the following concepts.

1. Introduce the excitation in a probe or antenna oriented in the direction of electric field. The probe is most often placed near a maximum of the electric field of the mode pattern, but exact placing is a matter of impedance matching. Examples are shown in Figs. 8.06a and b.

2. Introduce the excitation through a loop oriented in a plane normal to magnetic field of the mode pattern (Fig. 8.06c).

3. Couple to the desired mode from another guiding system, by means of a hole or iris, the two guiding systems having some common field component over the extent of the hole. An example of coupling between waveguides using a large iris is shown in Fig. 8.06d. The coupling is sometimes done with a small hole as for coupling to resonant cavities (Art. 10.12).

4. Introduce currents from transmission lines or other sources in a manner to excite desired current directions in the guide walls (Fig. 8.06e). (It is true that any scheme based on currents may also be looked at as one of exciting by the related fields, but occasionally the concentration on currents gives a clearer picture.)

5. For higher-order waves combine as many of the exciting sources as are required, with proper phasings (Fig. 8.06f).

6. For oversize guides which may propagate a number of modes, taper carefully from a smaller single-mode system as discussed in Art. 8.05.

[4] J. J. Toub, H. J. Hindin, O. F. Hinckelmann, M. L. Wright, *I.R.E. Trans. MTT* 11, 338–350 (1963).
[5] *Proceedings of the Symposium on Quasi-Optics*, Microwave Research Institute Symposia Series, Vol. XIV, Polytechnic Press, Brooklyn, N.Y., 1964.

Since any of these exciting methods are in the nature of concentrated sources, they will not in general excite purely one wave, but all waves which have field components in a favorable direction for the particular exciting source. From another point of view, we see that one wave alone will not suffice to satisfy the boundary conditions of the guide complicated by the exciting source, so that many higher-order waves must be added for

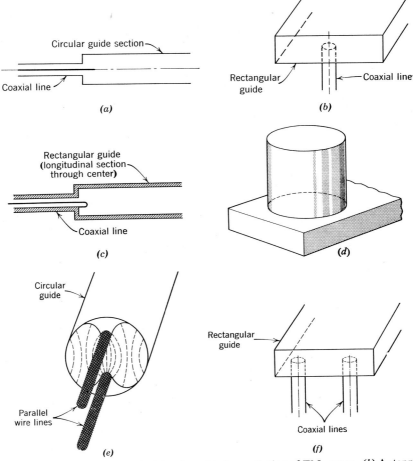

Fig. 8.06   (a) Antenna in end of circular guide for excitation of TM_{01} wave. (b) Antenna in bottom of rectangular guide for excitation of the TE_{10} wave. (c) Loop in end of rectangular guide for excitation of TE_{10} wave. (d) Junction between circular guide (TM_{01} wave) and rectangular guide (TE_{10} wave); large-aperture coupling. (e) Parallel wire line for excitation of TE_{11} wave in circular guide. (f) Excitation of the TE_{20} wave in rectangular guide by two oppositely phased antennas.

this purpose. If the guide is large enough, several of these waves will then proceed to propagate. Most often, however, only one of the excited waves is above cutoff. This will propagate down the guide, and (if absorbed somewhere) will represent a resistive load on the source, comparable to the radiation resistance of antennas which we shall encounter further in Chapter 12. The higher-order waves which are excited, if all below cutoff, will be localized in the neighborhood of the source and will represent purely reactive loads on the source. For practical application, it is then necessary to add, in the line which feeds the probe or loop or other exciting means, an arrangement for matching to the load which has a real part representing the propagating wave and an imaginary part representing the localized reactive waves.

The receiving problem is the reverse of the exciting problem, and in general any method which works well for exciting will also work well for receiving.

Problem

8.06 Sketch examples of mode couplings by each of the six methods described in Art. 8.06 using for each a system different from the one utilized in Fig. 8.06 to illustrate it.

8.07 Simple Transmission Line Techniques Applied to Guides

Equivalent networks for general junctions such as those of the last article are very important in general impedance-matching problems, and will be discussed in Chapter 11. However, certain simple problems may be handled in terms of the wave impedance, defined as the ratio of transverse electric field to transverse magnetic field, and given for various wave types in preceding articles. These problems are characterized by the fact that any discontinuity should be the same over an entire transverse section of the guide, so that matching of E and H for one point of the transverse plane produces a match for all points of that plane. This is of course similar to the study of plane wave reflection problems by impedance techniques in Chapter 6. Several examples will follow. Guide wavelength λ_g and wave impedances to be used are

$$\lambda_g = \frac{\lambda}{\sqrt{1 - (f_c/f)^2}} = \frac{1}{f\sqrt{\mu\epsilon}\sqrt{1 - (f_c/f)^2}} \tag{1}$$

Transverse electromagnetic waves $Z_{TEM} = \eta = \sqrt{\mu/\epsilon}$ $\tag{2}$

Transverse magnetic (E) waves $Z_{TM} = \eta\sqrt{1 - (f_c/f)^2}$ $\tag{3}$

Transverse electric (H) waves $Z_{TE} = \frac{\eta}{\sqrt{1 - (f_c/f)^2}}.$ $\tag{4}$

Short-Circuited Guide. A waveguide may be considered as truly short circuited if a conducting plate is placed across the entire section of the guide so that the transverse component of electric field is reduced to zero over all that section. This corresponds to a shorted transmission line, so that at once we may draw the forms of the resulting standing wave pattern (Fig. 8.07a). Transverse electric field is zero at the conducting plate and at multiples of $\lambda_g/2$ in front of it. It is a maximum at odd multiples of $\lambda_g/4$ in front of the plate. Transverse magnetic field is a maximum at the plate and

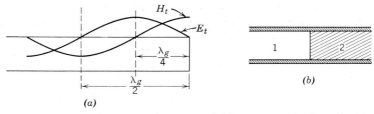

(a)   (b)

Fig. 8.07   (a) Standing waves of transverse field components in shorted guide.
(b) Guide with dielectric discontinuity.

has other maxima at $n\lambda_g/2$; minima at $(2n + 1)\lambda_g/4$ before the plate. Other phase relations show that E_z for *TM* waves has the same axial distribution pattern as the magnetic field, and H_z for *TE* waves has the same axial distribution pattern as the electric field.

Guide with Dielectric Discontinuity. If there is a discontinuity from one dielectric to another in a guide (Fig. 8.07b), the amount of reflection into the first region and the transmission to the second region may be determined from the mismatch in impedances Z_1 and Z_2. The expressions in terms of transverse field components are

$$\frac{E_{t-}}{E_{t+}} = \frac{Z_2 - Z_1}{Z_2 + Z_1} = -\frac{H_{t1-}}{H_{t1+}}$$

$$\frac{E_{t2}}{E_{t1+}} = \frac{2Z_2}{Z_2 + Z_1} = \frac{Z_2 H_{t2}}{Z_1 H_{t1+}}.$$

(5)

Region (1) then has both a standing wave and a traveling wave. The other standard expressions for input impedance, and voltage and current along the line, from Chapter 1, may be applied to calculation of input impedance on a field basis and of values of electric and magnetic fields along the guide.

Quarter-Wave Matching Sections. It is of course possible to match between one section of a guide and another section with different dielectric constant for any of the wave types at any single frequency. This is accomplished by the technique of quarter-wave matching sections developed for transmission lines in Prob. 1.18(*b*) and for plane waves in Art. 6.10. Thus in Fig. 8.07*c* it is possible to match between the regions 1 and 3, if a region 2 is introduced, a quarter wavelength long (measured at the phase velocity in that region) and having an impedance the geometric mean of those on the two sides. Note that, in calculating these impedances, the different cutoff frequencies for the three sections must be taken into account in (3) or (4).

This matching may be used, for instance, in a case where it is desired to absorb power in the third section, which may be filled with water or some

(c)   (d)

Fig. 8.07   (*c*) Insertion of matching section in a guide. (*d*) Conducting film for terminating a guide.

other material with a small but finite conductivity. A quarter-wave section of a proper material (certain special glasses, for example) may then be used to match this section to the portion of the guide with air dielectric.

Elimination of Reflections from Dielectric Slabs. If dielectric slabs must be placed in an otherwise uniform guide (for example, because a section must be evacuated), these may be designed in certain ways so that they cause no reflections, just as may insulators in transmission lines. The simplest arrangement is to make the dielectric slabs a half-wavelength in thickness ($\lambda_g/2$ for the material of the slab). The impedance at the front is then exactly the impedance of the guide following the slab. From another point of view, the reflections from the front and back surfaces exactly cancel under these conditions.

This method of eliminating reflections requires that the dielectric slab be a half-wavelength in thickness, measured in the material of that slab. For certain applications it may be undesirable to use slabs of that thickness. For slabs of any thickness, reflections may be eliminated by cancelling the reflected wave from one slab by that from another placed a proper distance from it. For slabs of thickness small compared with wavelength, or of a material with properties not too greatly different from that of region 1, this spacing is such that the total phase angle corresponding to the length of guide between insulators and one insulator is very nearly 90°.

Termination of Waveguides. Another important technique of transmission lines is the termination of a line by means of a proper resistor to eliminate the reflected wave. All energy is completely absorbed according to the simple line theory if this resistor is equal to the characteristic wave impedance of the line. If the line must be closed at the end, the terminating resistor may be placed a quarter-wavelength from the shorted end, since for perfect conductors the shorted quarter-wave line represents an infinite impedance in parallel with the resistance. Similarly, a waveguide may be terminated by a conducting sheet having a resistance per unit square equal to the characteristic wave impedance of the wave type to be matched. This sheet is placed a quarter-wavelength from the shorted end (Fig. 8.07d).

$$d_3 = \frac{\lambda_{g3}}{4}$$

$$\frac{1}{\sigma_2 d_2} = Z_1.$$

Notice that the conducting film must be made of some material of relatively low conductivity if its thickness is not to be absurdly small. That is, for a material like copper, d_2 would be only of the order of 10^{-10} meter.

Problems

8.07a Show, for a *TM* wave in any shape of guide passing from one dielectric material to another, that at one frequency the change in cutoff factor may cancel the change in η, and the wave may pass between the two media without reflection, even though no intervening matching section is present. Identify this condition with the case of incidence at polarizing angle in Art. 6.16. Determine the requirement for a similar situation with *TE* waves, and show why it is not practical to obtain this.

8.07b A rectangular waveguide of inside dimensions 4 cm by 2 cm is to propagate a TE_{10} mode of frequency 5000 Mc/sec. A dielectric of constant $\epsilon_r = 3$ fills the guide for $z > 0$, with an air dielectric for $z < 0$. Assuming the dielectric-filled part to be matched, find the reflection coefficient at $z = 0$ and the standing wave ratio in the air-filled part.

8.07c Find the length and dielectric constant of a quarter-wave matching section to be placed between the air and given dielectric of Prob. *b*.

8.08   Waves Below and Near Cutoff

The higher-order waves which may exist in transmission lines and all waves which may exist in hollow pipe waveguides are characterized by cutoff frequencies. If the waves are to be used for propagating energy, we are of course interested only in the behavior above cutoff. However, the behavior of these reactive or local waves below cutoff is important in at least two practical cases:

1. Application to waveguide attenuators.
2. Effects of discontinuities in transmission systems.

The attenuation properties of these waves below cutoff have been developed in the previous analyses. It has been found that below the cutoff frequency there is an attenuation only and no phase shift in an ideal guide. The characteristic wave impedance is a purely imaginary quantity—a reemphasis of the fact that no energy can propagate down the guide. This is not a dissipative attenuation as is that due to resistance and conductance in transmission systems with propagating waves. It is a purely reactive attenuation, analogous to that in a filter section made of reactive elements, when this is in the cutoff region. The energy is not lost but is reflected back to the source so that the guide acts as a pure reactance to the source.

The expression for attenuation below cutoff in an ideal guide, Eq. 7.13(9), may be written

$$\gamma = \alpha = k_c\sqrt{1 - (f/f_c)^2} = \frac{2\pi}{\lambda_c}\sqrt{1 - (f/f_c)^2}. \tag{1}$$

As f is decreased below f_c, α increases from a value of 0 approaching the constant value

$$\alpha = \frac{2\pi}{\lambda_c}, \tag{2}$$

when $(f/f_c)^2 \ll 1$. This is an important point in the use of waveguide attenuators, since it shows that the amount of this attenuation is substantially independent of frequency if the operating frequency is very far below the cutoff frequency. In addition, the amount of this attenuation is determined only by the cutoff wavelength of the guide, which is in general proportional to the transverse size of the guide, so that the value of α may be made almost as large as one pleases by selecting a low cutoff wavelength (small pipe size). Since (1) holds for any wave in any shape of guide, it follows that choices of wave type and guide shape cannot influence the attenuation constant except in so far as they fix the cutoff wavelength λ_c.

Note that, if a waveguide attenuator is designed with $(f/f_c) \ll 1$ so that attenuation is independent of frequency, attenuation must necessarily be very great in a wavelength since α will be much greater than the free space phase constant,

$$\frac{\alpha}{k} = \frac{2\pi/\lambda_c}{2\pi/\lambda} = \frac{\lambda}{\lambda_c} \gg 1.$$

Now let us look for a moment at the relations among the fields of both transverse magnetic and transverse electric waves below cutoff. If $\gamma = \alpha$ as given by (1) is substituted in the expressions for field components of transverse magnetic waves, Eqs. 7.13(4) and (5),

$$H_x = \frac{j}{\eta}\left(\frac{f}{f_c}\right)\frac{1}{k_c}\frac{\partial E_z}{\partial y} \qquad E_x = -\sqrt{1-(f/f_c)^2}\,\frac{1}{k_c}\frac{\partial E_z}{\partial x}$$

$$H_y = -\frac{j}{\eta}\left(\frac{f}{f_c}\right)\frac{1}{k_c}\frac{\partial E_z}{\partial x} \qquad E_y = -\sqrt{1-(f/f_c)^2}\,\frac{1}{k_c}\frac{\partial E_z}{\partial y}. \tag{3}$$

For a given distribution of E_z across the guide section, which is determined once the guide shape and size and the wave type are determined, it is evident from relations (3) that, as frequency decreases, $f/f_c \to 0$, the components of magnetic field approach zero whereas the transverse components of electric field approach a constant value. We draw the conclusion that only electric fields are of importance in transverse magnetic or E waves far below cutoff. Similarly, only magnetic fields are of importance in transverse electric or H waves far below cutoff.

Suppose that a TM wave is excited by some source in a waveguide, extending down the guide a certain distance to a suitable receiver. If the frequency is far enough below cutoff so that $(f/f_c)^2$ is negligible compared with unity, the entire problem may be looked upon as one of electric coupling between the source and the receiver, calculated by d-c or low-frequency methods (of course, taking into account the presence of the guide as a shield). Similarly, a TE wave between a source and receiver in a guide far below cutoff may be looked upon as a problem of ordinary magnetic coupling between the source and receiver (of course, taking into account the presence of the guide as a shield). If the waves are far below cutoff, the dimensions of the guide must be small compared with wavelength. For any such region small compared with wavelength, the wave equation will reduce to Laplace's equation so that low-frequency analyses neglecting any tendency toward wave propagation are applicable. Only when $(f/f_c)^2$ is comparable to unity must the effects of magnetic fields be considered in TM waves, and the effects of electric fields in TE waves.

The presence of losses in the guide below cutoff causes the phase constant to change from the zero value for an ideal guide to a small but finite value, and modifies slightly the formula for attenuation. These modifications are most important in the immediate vicinity of cutoff, for with losses there is no longer a sharp transition but a more gradual change from one region to another, as indicated by the dotted curves in Fig. 8.08. It should be emphasized again that the approximate formulas developed in previous articles may become extremely inaccurate in this region. For example, the approximate formulas for attenuation caused by conductor or dielectric

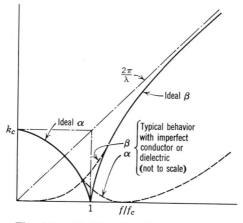

Fig. 8.08 Modification of propagation characteristics due to losses.

losses would yield an infinite value at $f = f_c$. The actual value is large compared with the minimum attenuation in the pass range since it is approaching the relatively larger magnitude of attenuation in the cutoff regime, but it is nevertheless finite. Previous formulas have also shown an infinite value of phase velocity at cutoff, and with losses it too will be finite.

COMMON TRANSMISSION LINES

8.09 Coaxial Lines, Parallel-Wire Lines, and Shielded Pairs

From the conclusions of Arts. 7.11 and 7.12 the analysis for ordinary transmission line waves along practical transmission systems may be correctly made from the distributed circuit constant concepts of Chapter 1. For use of the formulas of Chapter 1, it is necessary to calculate values for the inductance, capacitance, resistance, and conductance per unit length. The calculation of such constants was studied in Chapter 5. However, for convenience, some results for the commonly used transmission lines will be listed in Table 8.09 with configurations shown.

Coaxial lines are among the most commonly used of all transmission lines, particularly at the higher frequencies. This is largely because of the convenient construction and the practically perfect shielding between fields inside and outside of the line. The range of impedances that may be obtained most conveniently by coaxial lines is about 30 to 100 ohms.

Somewhat higher impedances may be obtained conveniently with parallel-wire lines, and these find wide application, although the shielding and radiation problems make them undesirable at the highest frequencies. It is also difficult to attain the lowest impedances conveniently with them. Unlike the coaxial line, the parallel-wire line is a balanced line, which is sometimes desirable.

If the parallel-wire line is placed inside a conducting pipe as shield, the radiation and shielding difficulties are eliminated. The impedance of the line with shield is in general somewhat lower than the same line without the shield. The resulting shielded pair is also a balanced line, assuming symmetrical location of the lines in the shield.

The parallel-bar transmission line is sometimes used when balanced lines of low impedance are desired. Like the parallel-wire line, it is not perfectly shielded.

Table 8.09 lists some of the constants for these lines. Many of these formulas are approximate, applying at the highest frequencies. For lower frequencies, values of resistance and internal inductance should be calculated by the methods of Chapter 5 and substituted in the formulas of Chapter 1.

$$\gamma = \alpha + j\beta = \sqrt{(R + j\omega L)(G + j\omega C)}$$

$$Z_0 = \sqrt{\frac{(R + j\omega L)}{(G + j\omega C)}} \quad \text{ohms.}$$

8.10 Higher-Order Modes on Transmission Lines

In addition to the TEM wave on a two-conductor transmission line, higher-order TE and TM mode solutions may exist also. These are usually cut off and are important only as reactive effects near junctions of the line (see Art. 8.08), but they ocassionally may enter as additional propagating modes in the transmission system.

The study of the parallel-plane system in Chapter 7 has shown TM and TE waves in addition to the TEM wave. As another example consider the higher-order modes in a coaxial line, Fig. 8.10a. The general forms for the TM and TE modes in circular cylindrical coordinates are listed in Art. 7.16. The boundary conditions require that E_z for TM waves be zero at r_0 and r_i (Fig. 8.10a).

For TM waves,

$$A_n J_n(k_c r_i) + B_n N_n(k_c r_i) = 0$$
$$A_n J_n(k_c r_0) + B_n N_n(k_c r_0) = 0$$

or
$$\frac{N_n(k_c r_i)}{J_n(k_c r_i)} = \frac{N_n(k_c r_0)}{J_n(k_c r_0)}. \tag{1}$$

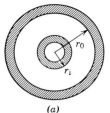

(a)

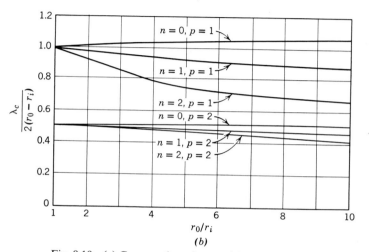

(b)

Fig. 8.10   (a) Cross section of a coaxial line. (b) Cutoff wavelength for some higher order TM waves in coaxial lines.

For TE waves, the derivative of H_z normal to the two conductors must
be zero at the inner and outer radii. Then, in place of (1),

$$\frac{N'_n(k_c r_i)}{J'_n(k_c r_i)} = \frac{N'_n(k_c r_0)}{J'_n(k_c r_0)} .$$ (2)

Solutions to the transcendental equations (1) and (2) determine the
values of k_c and hence cutoff frequency, for any wave type and any
particular values of r_i and r_0. Solution of the transcendental equations is
accomplished by graphical methods or by consulting published tables. By
analogy with the parallel-plane guide, we would expect to find certain
modes with a cutoff such that the spacing between conductors is of the
order of p half-wavelengths. Figure 8.10b shows that this is so for the TM
modes so long as radii of curvature are large.

$$\lambda_c \approx \frac{2}{p}(r_0 - r_i) \qquad p = 1, 2, 3, \ldots .$$ (3)

This is verified by Fig. 8.10b for values of r_0/r_i near unity.

Probably more important is the lowest order *TE* wave with circumferential variations. This is analogous to the TE_{10} wave of a rectangular waveguide, and physical reasoning from the analogy leads one to expect cutoff for this wave type when the average circumference is about equal to wavelength. The field picture of the TE_{10} mode given in Art. 8.03 should make this reasonable. Solution of (2) reveals this simple rule to be within about 4 percent accuracy for r_0/r_i up to 5. In general, for the *n*th order *TE* wave with circumferential variations,

$$\lambda_c \approx \frac{2\pi}{n}\left(\frac{r_0 + r_i}{2}\right), \qquad n = 1, 2, 3, \ldots . \tag{4}$$

There are, of course, other *TE* waves with further radial variations, and the lowest order of these has a cutoff about the same as the lowest order *TM* wave.

Once cutoff is found by solution of (1) and (2) or the foregoing approximations, propagation characteristics are determined by the expressions of Art. 7.13, 7.14. Of course, for the majority of coaxial line applications, dimensions are small enough compared with wavelength so that the waves are far below cutoff. They then do not propagate energy, but attenuate rapidly so that they are important only at end effects, discontinuities, or in the radiation field. For microwave applications, however, the line size may sometimes be large enough to propagate the circumferential mode determined by $n = 1$ in (4). Care must then be taken to avoid its excitation or its interference with the desired mode.

Problem

8.10 How many *TEM* waves may exist on a three-conductor transmission line? On an *N*-conductor line? Discuss the number and character of *TEM*, *TM*, and *TE* modes for the shielded pair pictured in Table 8.09.

MISCELLANEOUS WAVE-GUIDING SYSTEMS

8.11 Dielectric Rod or Slab Guides

The study of waves in the rectangular guide from the point of view of plane waves reflected between top and bottom (Art. 8.03) suggests that under certain conditions a wave may be guided without loss of energy by a slab of perfect dielectric having no metal boundaries. This follows from the concept of total reflection of Art. 6.14, where it was found that, if a wave traveling in a dense dielectric strikes the boundary of a less dense dielectric at an angle of incidence greater than a certain critical angle, all energy is reflected. This critical angle, Eq. 6.14(2), where 1 refers to the dense medium and 2 to the less dense medium, is

$$\theta_c = \sin^{-1}(\sqrt{\mu_2\epsilon_2/\mu_1\epsilon_1}).$$

Thus in a dielectric slab as in Fig. 8.11a, which is assumed infinite in the direction normal to the paper, suppose that plane waves are excited inside

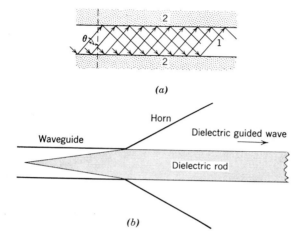

(a)

(b)

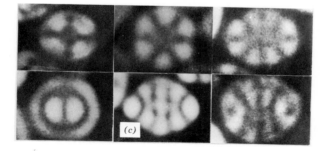

(c)

(d)

Fig. 8.11   (a) Wave paths in slab guide.   (b) Excitation of rod guide.
(c) Photographs of fiber optics modes[8].   (d) Rod guide section.

the dielectric in some manner so that they travel as shown, striking the surface at an angle of incidence, θ. If $\theta > \theta_c$, all energy will be reflected at each reflection and all will be retained in the slab.

This point of view is a very useful physical picture and could be made to give exact quantitative relationships. However, it is probably as easy to go directly to Maxwell's equations, writing appropriate wave solutions for the two dielectrics and matching tangential fields at the boundaries. If the propagating energy is to be confined to medium 1, the solutions in medium 2 must be "reactive," decaying exponentially away from the boundary. The field solutions in the slab may be broken into even and odd types, and there may be TM and TE mode types to consider. The appropriate fields for TM and TE waves having even and odd symmetries of their axial components are given in Eqs. (1) to (18). The subscripts 1 and 2 refer to the bounded and unbounded regions shown in Fig. 8.11a. They may be checked by the planar Maxwell's equations of Eqs. 7.02(1) to (6) or the equivalent forms of Eqs. 7.02(7) to (10). The determinantal equation is obtained by equating tangential fields at $x = d$, resulting in the continuity relations,

$$TM: \left. \frac{E_{z1}}{H_{y1}} \right|_{x=d} = \left. \frac{E_{z2}}{H_{y2}} \right|_{x=d}, \qquad TE: \left. \frac{H_{z1}}{E_{y1}} \right|_{x=d} = \left. \frac{H_{z2}}{E_{y2}} \right|_{x=d}.$$

The relations for the TM modes with axial components having odd symmetry are:

$$E_{z1} = A \sin k_x x \tag{1}$$

$$H_{y1} = \frac{\omega \epsilon_1}{\beta} E_{x1} = \frac{-j\omega\epsilon_1 A}{k_x} \cos k_x x \tag{2}$$

$$E_{z2} = C e^{-K_x(x-d)} \tag{3}$$

$$H_{y2} = \frac{\omega \epsilon_1}{\beta} E_x = \frac{-j\omega\epsilon_2 C}{K_x} e^{-K_x(x-d)} \tag{4}$$

$$K_x = \frac{\epsilon_2}{\epsilon_1} k_x \tan k_x d. \tag{5}$$

For TM modes with even symmetry of axial components:

$$E_{z1} = B \cos k_x x \tag{6}$$

$$H_{y1} = \frac{\omega \epsilon_1}{\beta} E_{x1} = \frac{j\omega\epsilon_1 B}{k_x} \sin k_x x \tag{7}$$

Other components have same form as (3) and (4) for region 2.

$$K_x = -\frac{\epsilon_2}{\epsilon_1} k_x \cot k_x d. \tag{8}$$

For *TE* modes with odd symmetry of axial components:

$$H_{z1} = D \sin k_x x \tag{9}$$

$$E_{y1} = \frac{-\omega\mu_1}{\beta} H_{x1} = \frac{j\omega\mu_1 D}{k_x} \cos k_x x \tag{10}$$

$$H_{z2} = F e^{-K_x(x-d)} \tag{11}$$

$$E_{y2} = -\frac{\omega\mu_1}{\beta} H_{x1} = \frac{j\omega\mu_2}{K_x} F e^{-K_x(x-d)} \tag{12}$$

$$K_x = \frac{\mu_2}{\mu_1} k_x \tan k_x d. \tag{13}$$

For *TE* modes with even symmetry of axial components:

$$H_{z1} = E \cos k_x x \tag{14}$$

$$E_{y1} = \frac{-\omega\mu_1}{\beta} H_{x1} = \frac{-j\omega\mu_1 D}{k_x} \cos k_x x \tag{15}$$

Other components have same form as (11) and (12) for region 2.

$$K_x = \frac{-\mu_2}{\mu_1} k_x \cot k_x d. \tag{16}$$

In these relations

$$k_x{}^2 = k_1{}^2 - \beta^2 > 0 \tag{17}$$

$$k_x{}^2 = \beta^2 - k_2{}^2 > 0. \tag{18}$$

There are several important points that may be found from the solutions in (1) to (18) whereby dielectric rod guides differ from guides closed by conducting pipes. The first fact is that the lowest-order *TM* and *TE* modes with axial components having odd symmetry have no cutoff frequency but may exist for slab thicknesses very small compared with wavelength. Consider for example the odd *TM* mode with determinantal equation (5). If $k_x d \ll 1$, this reduces to

$$K_x \approx \frac{\epsilon_2}{\epsilon_1} k_x{}^2 d. \tag{19}$$

Approximate solution of this equation combined with (17) and (18) yields

$$K_x \approx \frac{\epsilon_2}{\epsilon_1} (k_1{}^2 - k_2{}^2)d, \qquad \beta \approx k_2. \tag{20}$$

Thus as d becomes small, and/or $k_1 \to k_2$, the constant K_x becomes small, indicating that energy extends very far into the outer medium. The propagation constant in such cases becomes very close to the wave number in the outer region, since most of the energy is there. A similar solution exists for the lowest order TE mode defined by (13), but not for the even modes defined by (8) and (16). This is seen since no positive value of K_x is given by these equations until $k_x d$ is at least $\pi/2$.

A second point is that any of the Eqs. (5), (8), (13), and (16) have only a finite number of solutions (Prob. 8.11e) as compared with the infinite number in closed-pipe guides. Closely related to this is the fact that this finite number may not be sufficient to represent the total fields in the vicinity of an exciting source, as represented by the waveguide and horn excitation system of Fig. 8.11b. The difference is a set of waves reflected from and diffracted into the dielectric over a continuous range of angles, as explained in Art. 6.13. These reflected waves do not die off at infinity as the "trapped" modes do. The total result does not constitute a complete orthogonal set in the sense of closed pipe guides, but results may nevertheless be useful in representing practical fields over a limited region.[6,7]

Practical dielectric guides have been used in guiding of light waves with a bundle of fine quartz fibers used for this purpose.[8] The fibers are of the order of light wavelengths in diameter, and photographs have shown the various modes that may exist (Fig. 8.11c). Analysis of the circular shape is in principle just as for the slab except for the use of Bessel functions. For example, the fields of the circularly symmetric TM mode for the rod (Fig. 8.11d) are

$r < a$

$$E_{z1} = A J_0(k_r r)$$

$$H_{\phi 1} = \frac{\omega \epsilon_1}{\beta} E_{r1} = \frac{j \omega \epsilon_1 A J_1(k_r r)}{k_r}$$

$$k_r^2 = k_1^2 - \beta^2$$

$r < a$

$$E_{z2} = B K_0(\tau r)$$

$$H_{\phi 2} = \frac{\omega \epsilon_2}{\beta} E_{r2} = \frac{j \omega \epsilon_2 B K_1(\tau r)}{\tau} \quad (21)$$

$$\tau^2 = \beta^2 - k_2^2.$$

Continuity conditions on E_z/H_ϕ at $r = a$ give the determinantal equation

$$\frac{J_0(k_r a)}{J_1(k_r a)} = \frac{\epsilon_1}{\epsilon_2} \frac{\tau}{k_r} \frac{K_0(\tau r)}{K_1(\tau r)}. \quad (22)$$

The mode used in the dielectric radiators is a "hybrid" or combination TM and TE mode.[9] The angular variation is that with $n = 1$, which

[6] J. Brown, "The types of waves which may exist over a guiding surface," *Proc. IEE (London)* **100**, part III, 363 (1953).

[7] N. Marcuvitz, "On field representations in terms of leaky modes or eigenmodes," *IRE Trans.*, **AP-4**, 192 (1956).

[8] N. S. Kapany, "Fiber optics IX. waveguide effects," *Jour. of the Optical Society of America*, **51**, 1067 (1961).

[9] G. E. Mueller and W. A. Tyrrell, "Polyrod Antennas," *Bell Syst. Tech. J.*, **26**, 837–851 (October 1947).

yields fields inside the rod somewhat like the TE_{11} mode in a hollow-pipe guide but which are more complex outside. Most interesting is the fact that, as with two of the modes in the dielectric slab, this mode has no cutoff frequency. To analyze, one may start with both E_z and H_z in both regions,

$$r < a \qquad\qquad\qquad r > a$$
$$E_{z1} = AJ_1(k_r r) \cos \phi \qquad E_{z2} = CK_1(\tau r) \cos \phi$$
$$H_{z1} = BJ_1(k_r r) \sin \phi \qquad H_{z2} = DK_1(\tau r) \sin \phi \qquad (23)$$
$$k_r^2 = k_1^2 - \beta^2 \qquad\qquad \tau^2 = \beta^2 - k_2^2.$$

The remaining field components $(E_r, H_r, E_\phi, H_\phi)$ may be obtained by application of Eqs. 7.16(8) to (11). Continuity of tangential components at $r = a$ gives the determinantal equation

$$\frac{J_1'^2(k_r a)}{J_1^2(k_r a)} + \frac{k_r^2 \mu_2 \epsilon_2 K_1'^2(\tau a)}{\tau^2 \mu_1 \epsilon_1 K_1^2(\tau a)} + \frac{k_r}{\tau}\left(\frac{\mu_2}{\mu_1} + \frac{\epsilon_2}{\epsilon_1}\right)\frac{J_1'(k_r a)K_1'(\tau a)}{J_1(k_r a)K_1(\tau a)}$$
$$= \left(1 + \frac{\alpha^2}{\beta^2}\right)\left(\frac{1}{k_r^2 a^2} + \frac{\mu_2 \epsilon_2}{\mu_1 \epsilon_1 \tau^2 a^2}\right). \quad (24)$$

This equation has a solution $\beta = 0$ at $\omega = 0$, yielding also $\tau = 0$ and $k_r = 0$, which supports the assertion that cutoff frequency of this mode is zero.

Problems

8.11a Using the approximation (19) for thin slabs, verify the approximate formulas (20). Derive similar formulas for the lowest order TE mode with odd symmetry and $k_x d \ll 1$.

8.11b Plot the value of x at which fields decrease to e^{-1} of the value at $x = d$ vs. $k_1 d$. Use the approximations (19), (20) and take $\epsilon_1/\epsilon_2 = 1.01$, 1.1, 2.

8.11c For a circular dielectric rod with small but finite losses, $\sigma_1 \ll \omega \epsilon_1$, study equation (22) by means of Taylor series methods from the point of view of attenuation of the TM_{01} mode caused by dielectric losses.

8.11d Obtain the equations for all field components of the $n = 1$ mode in a circular dielectric rod discussed in Art. 8.11.

8.11e Show that Eq. 8.11(5) has only a finite number of solutions.

8.12 Radial Transmission Lines

Another guide of practical importance consists of two circular, parallel, conducting plates, separated by a dielectric and used for guiding electromagnetic energy radially (Figs. 8.12a and b). The simplest wave that may be guided by these plates is one with no field variations circumferentially or axially. There are then no field components in the radial direction, but field components E_z and H_ϕ only. The component E_z, having no variations in the z direction, corresponds to a total voltage $E_z d$ between plates. The component H_ϕ corresponds to a total radial current $2\pi r H_\phi$, outward in one plate and inward in the other. This wave is then analogous to an ordinary transmission line wave and thus derives its name, radial transmission line.

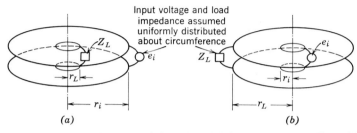

Fig. 8.12   (a) Radial transmission line with input at outer radius. (b) Radial transmission line with input at inner radius.

For the simple wave described there are no radial field components, and analysis may be made by the nonuniform transmission line theory of Art. 1.26, allowing L and C to vary with radius. However, the wave solution for fields may also be obtained directly from the results of Art. 7.16. Since there are no ϕ or z variations, ν and γ may be set equal to zero. Special linear combinations of Bessel functions have been defined particularly for this problem,[10] but for occasional solution of radial line problems, known forms of the Bessel functions are satisfactory. The form of Eq. 7.16(6) in the Hankel functions is particularly suitable since these have been shown to have the character of waves traveling radially inward or outward (Art. 3.26). The constant k_c by Eq. 7.13(2) reduces to $k = \omega\sqrt{\mu\epsilon}$ since $\gamma = 0$.

$$E_z = AH_0^{(1)}(kr) + BH_0^{(2)}(kr). \tag{1}$$

With ν and γ zero, the only remaining field component in Eqs. 7.16(8) to (11) is H_ϕ.

$$H_\phi = \frac{1}{j\omega\mu}\frac{\partial E_z}{\partial r} = \frac{j}{\eta}[AH_1^{(1)}(kr) + BH_1^{(2)}(kr)]. \tag{2}$$

The $H_n^{(1)}$ terms are identified as the negatively traveling wave and the $H_n^{(2)}$ terms as the positively traveling wave because of the asymptotic forms

[10] N. Marcuvitz in: Montgomery, Dicke, Purcell, *Principles of Microwave Circuits*, McGraw-Hill, New York, 1947, Chapter 8.

which approach complex exponentials (Art. 3.26). It is convenient to utilize the magnitudes and phases of these functions,

$$H_0^{(1)}(x) = J_0(x) + jN_0(x) = G_0(x)e^{j\theta(x)} \tag{3}$$

$$H_0^{(2)}(x) = J_0(x) - jN_0(x) = G_0(x)e^{-j\theta(x)} \tag{4}$$

$$jH_1^{(1)}(x) = -N_1(x) + jJ_1(x) = G_1(x)e^{j\psi(x)} \tag{5}$$

$$jH_1^{(2)}(x) = N_1(x) + jJ_1(x) = -G_1(x)e^{-j\psi(x)} \tag{6}$$

where $\quad G_0(x) = [J_0^2(x) + N_0^2(x)]^{\frac{1}{2}}, \qquad \theta(x) = \tan^{-1}\left[\dfrac{N_0(x)}{J_0(x)}\right] \tag{7}$

$$G_1(x) = [J_1^2(x) + N_1^2(x)]^{\frac{1}{2}}, \qquad \psi(x) = \tan^{-1}\left[\dfrac{J_1(x)}{-N_1(x)}\right]. \tag{8}$$

Expressions (1) and (2) then become

$$E_z = G_0(kr)[Ae^{j\theta(kr)} + Be^{-j\theta(kr)}] \tag{9}$$

$$H_\phi = \frac{G_0(kr)}{Z_0(kr)}[Ae^{j\psi(kr)} - Be^{-j\psi(kr)}] \tag{10}$$

where

$$Z_0(kr) = \eta\,\frac{G_0(kr)}{G_1(kr)}. \tag{11}$$

Evaluation of the constants A and B follows from specification of two field values at given radii. For example, given E_a at r_a, and H_b at r_b, the fields at any radius r are

$$E = E_a\frac{G_0\cos(\theta - \psi_b)}{G_{0a}\cos(\theta_a - \psi_b)} + jZ_{0b}H_b\frac{G_0\sin(\theta - \theta_a)}{G_{0b}\cos(\theta_a - \psi_b)} \tag{12}$$

$$H = H_b\frac{G_1\cos(\psi - \theta_a)}{G_{1b}\cos(\theta_a - \psi_b)} + j\frac{E_aG_1\sin(\psi - \psi_b)}{Z_{0a}G_{1a}\cos(\theta_a - \psi_b)}. \tag{13}$$

These are similar in form to the ordinary transmission line equations except for the use of the special magnitudes and phases. A plot of these special radial line quantities vs. kr is given in Fig. 8.12c. This is not very accurate for small values of kr, so that the following approximations are useful for kr small compared with unity:

$$G_0(x) \approx \frac{2}{\pi}\ln\left(\frac{\gamma x}{2}\right) \qquad \theta(x) \approx \tan^{-1}\left[\frac{2}{\pi}\ln\left(\frac{\gamma x}{2}\right)\right] \tag{14}$$

$$G_1(x) \approx \frac{2}{\pi x} \qquad \psi(x) \approx \tan^{-1}\left(\frac{1}{\pi x^2}\right) \tag{15}$$

where $\gamma = 0.5772\ldots$. More accurate values can be calculated from the definitions (7) and (8) utilizing tables of J and N, although some tables give magnitude and phase of $H_n^{(1)}$ and $H_n^{(2)}$ directly.

Forms similar to (12) and (13) can be derived for two values of E specified at different radii, or two values of H. The most useful form,

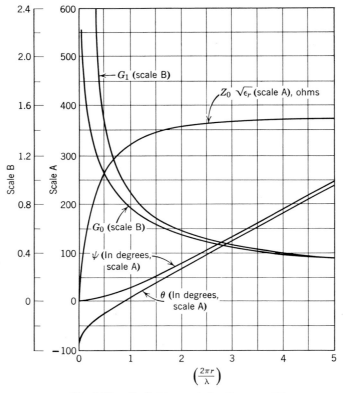

Fig. 8.12c Radial transmission line quantities.

however, is that defining an input impedance $Z_i = E_{zi}/H_{\phi i}$ when load impedance $Z_L = E_{zL}/H_{\phi L}$ is given. This is

$$Z_i = Z_{0i} \left[\frac{Z_L \cos(\theta_i - \psi_L) + jZ_{0L} \sin(\theta_i - \theta_L)}{Z_{0L} \cos(\psi_i - \theta_L) + jZ_L \sin(\psi_i - \psi_L)} \right]. \qquad (16)$$

Special forms of this for output shorted ($Z_L = 0$) or open ($Z_L = \infty$) are especially simple and are analogous to the corresponding forms for uniform transmission lines.

All of the foregoing relationships are given in terms of fields or wave impedances. Usually current, voltage, and total impedance are desired. The relations are

$$V = -E_z d; \qquad I = 2\pi r H_\phi \qquad (17)$$

$$Z_{\text{total}} = \mp \frac{d}{2\pi r}\left(\frac{E_z}{H_\phi}\right). \qquad (18)$$

The sign convention defines higher voltage in the upper plate and outward current in the upper plate as positive. The upper sign in (18) is for input radius less than that of the load, $r_i < r_L$, and the lower sign for the reverse, $r_i > r_L$, since in this case the convention for positive current would be the opposite of (17).

Problems

8.12a For a TM_{01} wave in a circular waveguide it is desired to insert a blocking impedance for a given frequency. To do this, a section of shorted radial line (Fig. 8.11d) is inserted in the guide, its outer radius a chosen so that with the guide radius b given, the impedance looking into the radial line is infinite at the given frequency. Suppose that the radius b is 1.25 times greater than cutoff radius at this frequency for the TM_{01} wave and find the radius a.

8.12b It is sometimes required to break the outer conductor of a coaxial line for insulation purposes, without interrupting the r-f current flow. This may be accomplished by the radial line as shown (Fig. 8.12e) in which a is chosen so that with b and the operating wavelength specified, the radial line has zero input impedance seen from the line. Find the value of a, assuming that end effects are negligible, and that

$$\frac{2\pi b}{\lambda} = 1.$$

8.12c Find the voltage at the radius a in terms of the coaxial line's current flowing into the radial line at radius b (Fig. 8.12e).

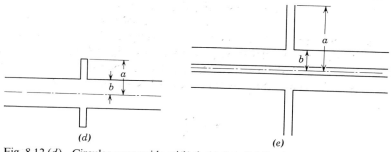

Fig. 8.12 (d) Circular waveguide with shorted radial line in series with cylinder wall. (e) Coaxial line with open radial line in series with outer conductor.

8.12d Taking the classical transmission line equations with distributed inductance and capacitance varying with radius as appropriate to the radial line,

$$L = \frac{\mu d}{2\pi r} \quad \text{and} \quad C = \frac{2\pi \epsilon r}{d},$$

show that the equation for voltage as a function of radius is a Bessel equation, and that the solutions for voltage and current obtained in this manner are consistent with (1) and (2).

8.12e Derive forms similar to (12) and (13) if E_a is specified at r_a, E_b at r_b. Repeat for H_a specified at r_a, H_b at r_b.

8.13 Circumferential Modes in Radial Lines; Sectoral Horns

There are many higher-order modes in the radial transmission lines studied in the last article. All those with z variations require a spacing between plates greater than a half-wavelength for radial propagation of energy. More interesting are those modes having circumferential variations but no z variations. The field components may be written

$$E_z = A_\nu Z_\nu(kr) \sin \nu\phi \tag{1}$$

$$H_\phi = -\frac{j}{\eta} A_\nu Z_\nu'(kr) \sin \nu\phi \tag{2}$$

$$H_r = \frac{j\nu A_\nu}{k\eta r} Z_\nu(kr) \cos \nu\phi. \tag{3}$$

In the foregoing equations, Z_ν denotes any solution of the ordinary νth order Bessel equation. For example, to stress the concept of radially propagating waves it may again be convenient to utilize Hankel functions.

$$Z_\nu(kr) = H_\nu^{(1)}(kr) + c_\nu H_\nu^{(2)}(kr). \tag{4}$$

These circumferential modes may be important as disturbing effects excited by asymmetries in radial lines intended for use with the symmetrical mode studied in the preceding article, Figs. 8.12a, b. In this case ν must be an integer, n, since the wave must have the same value at $\phi = 0$ and $\phi = 2\pi$. Waves of the form (1) to (3) may also be supported in a wedge-shaped guide with conducting planes at $\phi = 0$ and $\phi = \phi_0$ as well as at $z = 0$, d (Fig. 8.13a). The latter case is important as a sectoral electromagnetic horn[11] used for radiation. In this case, since E_z must be zero at $\phi = 0$, ϕ_0,

$$\nu = \frac{m\pi}{\phi_0}. \tag{5}$$

[11] W. L. Barrow and L. J. Chu, "Sectoral Electromagnetic Horns," *Proc. I.R.E.*, **27**, 51–64 (January 1939).

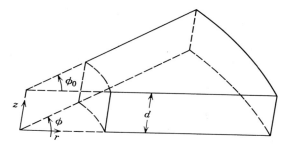

Fig. 8.13a   Wedge-shaped guide or sectoral horn.

The waves discussed here are interesting in one respect especially. If we think of the lowest order mode ($m = 1$) propagating radially inward in the pie-shaped guide of Fig. 8.13a, it would be quite similar to the TE_{10} mode of the rectangular guide, although modified by the convergence of the sides. We would consequently expect a cutoff phenomenon at such a radius r_c that the width $r_c\phi_0$ becomes a half-wavelength. Similarly, for the nth order circumferential mode in the radial line of Figs. 8.12a, b, we would expect a cutoff at such a radius that circumference is n wavelengths.

$$2\pi r_c = n\lambda \text{ for radial line} \qquad \phi_0 r_c = \lambda/2 \text{ for sectoral horn.} \qquad (6)$$

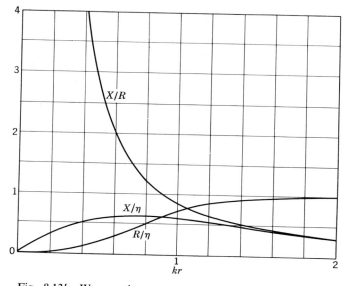

Fig. 8.13b   Wave resistance and reactance for circumferential mode in radial line for $\nu = 1$.

A casual inspection of Eqs. (1) to (3) would not reveal this cutoff since there is no sudden change of mathematical form as there was in the rectangular guide at cutoff. However, a more detailed study would reveal that there is a very effective cutoff phenomenon at about the radius predicted by (6) in that the reactive energy for a given power transfer becomes very great for radii less than this. For example, the radial field impedance for an outward-traveling wave is

$$\left(\frac{E_z}{H_\phi}\right)_+ = j\eta \, \frac{H_v^{(2)}(kr)}{H_v^{(2)\prime}(kr)} = R_v + jX_v. \tag{7}$$

The field impedance for the inward-traveling wave is just the conjugate of (7). These impedances become predominantly reactive at a value $kr \approx v$, which is compatible with (6). This is illustrated in Fig. 8.13b, which shows real and imaginary parts of the wave impedances versus kr for $v = 1$. If the radial modes are undesired, particular caution must be taken to guard against them for radial lines with circumferences greater than a wavelength.

Problems

8.13a Sketch lines of current flow for a circumferential mode with $v = 1$ in a radial line. (Take $Z_n = J_n$ for this purpose.) Suggest methods of suppressing this mode by judicious cuts without disturbing the symmetrical mode.

8.13b A section of the wedge-shaped guide as in Fig. 8.13a may be used to join two waveguides of the same height but different width, both propagating the TE_{10} mode, and a good degree of match is obtained by the process so long as the transition is gradual. Discuss qualitatively the transition between the fields of the waveguide and those of the sectoral guide.

8.14 Duality; Propagation between Inclined Planes

Given certain solutions of Maxwell's equations, we may obtain other useful ones by making use of the simple but important principle of duality. This principle follows from the symmetry of the field equations for charge-free regions,

$$\nabla \times \bar{E} = -j\omega\mu\bar{H} \tag{1}$$

$$\nabla \times \bar{H} = j\omega\epsilon\bar{E}. \tag{2}$$

It is evident that, if $\bar{E}$ is replaced by $\bar{H}$, $\bar{H}$ by $-\bar{E}$, μ by ϵ, and ϵ by μ, the original equations are again obtained. It follows that, if we are given any solution for such a dielectric, another may be obtained by interchanging components as stated. It may be difficult to supply appropriate boundary conditions for the new solution since the magnetic equivalent of the perfect conductor is not known at high frequencies, so the new solution is not always of practical importance.

One example in which the principle of duality may be utilized to save work in a practical problem is that of the principal mode in the wedge-shaped dielectric region between inclined plane conductors (Fig. 8.14). This mode has electric field E_ϕ representing a radial flow of current in the

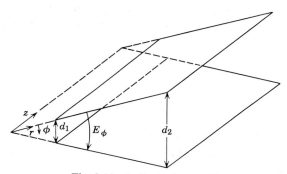

Fig. 8.14 Inclined-plane guide.

planes and magnetic field H_z. If there are no variations with ϕ or z, it is evident that the field distributions can be obtained from those of the radial transmission line mode, Art. 8.12, through the foregoing principle of duality. Replacing $\bar{E}$ by $\bar{H}$, $\bar{H}$ by $-\bar{E}$, μ by ϵ, and ϵ by μ in Eqs. 8.12(1) to (2),

$$H_z = AH_0^{(1)}(kr) + BH_0^{(2)}(kr) \tag{3}$$

$$E_\phi = -j\sqrt{\mu/\epsilon}\,[AH_1^{(1)}(kr) + BH_1^{(2)}(kr)]. \tag{4}$$

The real advantage is that all the derived expressions 8.12(9) to (16) may be used without rederivation, as well as the curves of Fig. 8.12c, with the interchange of quantities as above. Admittance should be read in place of impedance, and the numerical scale of $Z_0\sqrt{\epsilon_r}$ in ohms (Fig. 8.12c) should be divided by $(377)^2$ to give the characteristic admittance $Y_0/\sqrt{\epsilon_r}$ in mhos. Total admittance is obtained from the field admittance as follows:

$$Y_{\text{total}} = \mp\frac{l}{r\phi_0}\left[-\frac{H_z}{E_\phi}\right], \tag{5}$$

where the upper sign is for $r_i < r_L$, the lower for $r_i > r_L$.

One application of this line might be in impedance matching between parallel-plate transmission lines of different spacings, d_1 and d_2 (Fig. 8.14). It is known from practical experience that such transitions, if gradual enough, supply a good impedance match over a wide band of frequencies (unlike schemes studied in Prob. 1.18b, which depend upon quarter-wavelengths of line). It is seen from Fig. 8.12c that for both kr_i and kr_L large (say greater than 5) the characteristic admittance Y_0 is nearly $1/\eta$ and θ and ψ are nearly equal (i.e., $\theta_i \approx \psi_i$, $\theta_L \approx \psi_L$). If the parallel-plane line to the right is matched, its characteristic wave admittance is that of a plane wave, $1/\eta$. Equation 8.12(16) then shows that with the above approximations the input wave admittance is also approximately $1/\eta$, so that the parallel-plane line to the left is also nearly matched. This gives some quantitative support to the matching phenomenon mentioned.

Problems

8.14a In the use of the inclined plane line for matching as discussed in the last paragraph, suppose that $f = 3000$ Mc/sec, $d_1 = 1$ cm, $d_2 = 2$ cm, $kr_1 = 2.5$, and the dielectric is air. If the line to the right is perfectly matched, obtain the approximate standing-wave ratio in the line to the left. Compare with that which would exist with a sudden transition, considering only the impedance discontinuity.

8.14b Discuss the approximation in the procedure of the last paragraph of Art. 8.14. at the junctions in view of the curved wave fronts in the tapered line and the plane wave fronts in the parallel-plane line.

8.14c Apply the principle of duality to the TE_{11}, TE_{01}, and TM_{01} modes in circular cylindrical waveguides to obtain qualitatively the fields of the "dual" modes. For which of these might boundary conditions be supplied, allowing changes in the conductor position or shape from those of the original mode?

8.14d A wedge-shaped dielectric region is bounded by conducting planes at $\phi = 0$ and ϕ_0, $z = 0$ and d. Find the field components of the lowest-order mode with E_ϕ, H_r, and H_z. Is this the dual of the mode discussed for sectoral horns in Art. 8.13?

8.14e Discuss the application of the mode of Prob. 8.14d to the matching between rectangular waveguides of different height, both propagating the TE_{10} mode.

8.15 Waves Guided by Conical Systems

The problem of waves guided by conical systems (Fig. 8.15) is important to a basic understanding of waves along dipole antennas and in certain classes of cavity resonators. In particular, one very important wave propagates along the cones with the velocity of light and has no field components in the radial direction, and so is analogous to the transmission line wave on cylindrical systems. This basic wave is symmetric about the axis of the guiding cones, so that, if the two curl relations of Maxwell's

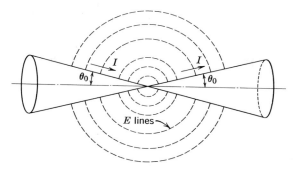

Fig. 8.15   Biconical guide.

equations are written in spherical coordinates with all ϕ variation eliminated, it is seen that there is one independent set containing E_θ, H_ϕ, and
E_r only:

$$\frac{1}{r}\frac{\partial(rE_\theta)}{\partial r} - \frac{1}{r}\frac{\partial E_r}{\partial \theta} + j\omega\mu H_\phi = 0 \qquad (1)$$

$$\frac{1}{r\sin\theta}\left[\frac{\partial}{\partial\theta}(\sin\theta H_\phi)\right] - j\omega\epsilon E_r = 0 \qquad (2)$$

$$-\frac{1}{r}\frac{\partial(rH_\phi)}{\partial r} - j\omega\epsilon E_\theta = 0. \qquad (3)$$

Although we might proceed to a direct attack on these equations, it can
be checked by substitution that the following solution does satisfy the
three equations.

$$E_r = 0 \qquad (4)$$

$$rE_\theta = \frac{\eta}{\sin\theta}[Ae^{j(\omega t - kr)} + Be^{j(\omega t + kr)}] \qquad (5)$$

$$rH_\phi = \frac{1}{\sin\theta}[Ae^{j(\omega t - kr)} - Be^{j(\omega t + kr)}]. \qquad (6)$$

These equations show the now familiar propagation behavior, the first
term representing a wave traveling radially outward with the velocity of
light in the dielectric material surrounding the cones, the second term
representing a radially inward traveling wave of the same velocity. The
ratio of electric to magnetic field is given by $+\eta$ for the positively traveling
wave, by $-\eta$ for the negatively traveling wave. There is no field component in the radial direction, which is the direction of propagation.

The above wave looks much like the ordinary transmission line waves of uniform cylindrical systems. This resemblance is stressed if we note that the E_θ corresponds to a voltage difference between the two cones,

$$V = -\int_{\theta_0}^{\pi-\theta_0} E_\theta r\, d\theta = -\eta \int_{\theta_0}^{\pi-\theta_0} \frac{d\theta}{\sin\theta}\, [Ae^{j(\omega t - kr)} + Be^{j(\omega t + kr)}]$$

$$= 2\eta \ln \cot \frac{\theta_0}{2}\, [Ae^{j(\omega t - kr)} + Be^{j(\omega t + kr)}], \tag{7}$$

where the case treated is that of equal angle cones (Fig. 8.15). This is a voltage which is independent of r, except through the propagation term, $e^{\pm jkr}$. Similarly the azimuthal magnetic field corresponds to a current flow in the cones,

$$I = 2\pi r H_\phi \sin \theta$$

$$= 2\pi [Ae^{j(\omega t - kr)} - Be^{j(\omega t + kr)}]. \tag{8}$$

This current is also independent of radius, except through the propagation term. A study of the sign relations shows that it is in opposite radial directions in the two cones at any given radius.

The ratio of voltage to current in a single outward-traveling wave, a quantity which we call characteristic impedance in an ordinary transmission line, is obtained by setting $B = 0$ in (7) and (8):

$$Z_0 = \frac{\eta \ln \cot \theta_0/2}{\pi}. \tag{9}$$

For a negatively traveling wave, the ratio of voltage to current is the negative of this quantity. This value of impedance is a constant, independent of radius, unlike those ratios defined for a radial transmission line in Art. 8.12. We might have guessed this had we started from the familiar concept of Z_0 as $\sqrt{L/C}$, since inductance and capacitance between cones per unit radial length are independent of radius. This comes about since surface area increases proportionally to radius, and distance separating the cone, along the path of the electric field, also increases proportionally to radius.

So far as this wave is concerned, the system arising from two ideal coaxial conical conductors can be considered a uniform transmission line. All the familiar formulas for input impedances and voltage and current along the line hold directly with Z_0 given by (9) and phase constant corresponding to velocity of light in the dielectric,

$$\beta = \frac{2\pi}{\lambda} = \omega\sqrt{\mu\epsilon}. \tag{10}$$

If the conducting cones have resistance, there is a departure from uniformity due to this resistance term, but this is usually not serious in any practical cases where such conical systems are used.

Of course a large number of higher-order waves may exist in this conical system and in similar systems. These will in general have field components in the radial direction and will not propagate at the velocity of light. We shall consider such general wave types for spherical coordinates later.

Problems

8.15a It has been seen that along cones, cylinders, planes, etc., a principal wave can exist in which, at least for perfect conductors, it is possible to analyze the problem correctly by dealing with distributed L's and C's per unit length, these distributed constants being computed from static field distributions. It is not always true that the electric and magnetic field lines over the cross section of the wave, for the principal wave, will be as in the static case. This does not mean that the distributed constant technique fails for such lines, but it does mean that it is no longer exact to use L and C as computed from the static field equations. Illustrate the above statement by considering waves propagating symmetrically between concentric spheres in the θ direction ($\partial/\partial\phi = 0$). Show that no wave can exist containing only E_r and H_ϕ; E_θ must also be present. Show also that, if the distance between spheres is small compared with wavelength, the presence of E_θ has a negligible effect on the wave distribution and distributed L and C (computed from statics) may be used for good approximate results.

8.15b Derive the basic characteristics of the principal waves on a transmission line consisting of two coaxial, common-apex cones of unequal angles.

8.15c Write the dual of the mode studied in this article. Can it be supported by physical boundaries using perfect conductors?

8.16 Ridge Waveguide

Of the miscellaneous shapes of cylindrical guides that have been utilized, one rather important one is the ridge waveguide, which has a central ridge added either to the top or botton or both of a rectangular section, Fig. 8.16a. It is interesting from an electromagnetic point of view since the cutoff frequency is lowered because of the capacitive effect at the center, and could in principle be made as low as desired by decreasing the gap width g sufficiently. Of course, the effective impedance of the guide also decreases as g is made smaller. One of the important applications is as a nonuniform transmission system for matching purposes (see Art. 8.14) obtained by varying the depth of ridge as one progresses along the guide.

The calculation of cutoff frequency, which has been found to be one of the very important parameters for any shape of guide, also illustrates an interesting approach that may be applied to many guide shapes which cannot be solved exactly. At cutoff, there is no variation in the z direction ($\gamma = 0$), so one may think of this as the condition for waves propagating

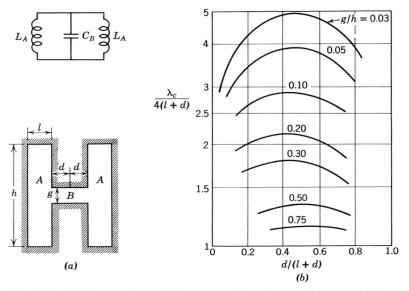

(a)

(b)

Fig. 8.16 (a) Cross section of ridge waveguide and approximate equivalent circuit for cutoff calculation. (b) Curves giving cutoff wavelength for a ridge waveguide as in Fig. a. Data from Cohn.[12]

only transversely in the given cross section, according to the desired mode. For example, the TE_{10} wave in a rectangular guide has a cutoff frequency equal to the resonant frequency for a plane wave propagating only in the x direction across the guide, thus corresponding to a half-wavelength in the x direction. A very approximate calculation of cutoff frequency for the ridge guide might then be made as in Fig. 8.16a by considering the gap a capacitance and the side sections inductances, and writing the condition for resonance.

$$f_c = \frac{1}{2\pi}\left(C_B \frac{L_A}{2}\right)^{-\frac{1}{2}} = \frac{1}{2\pi}\left(\frac{2d\epsilon}{g}\right)^{-\frac{1}{2}}\left(\frac{\mu lh}{2}\right)^{-\frac{1}{2}} = \frac{1}{2\pi}\left(\frac{g}{\mu\epsilon lhd}\right)^{\frac{1}{2}}. \quad (1)$$

A better equivalent circuit for calculation of the transverse resonance is one in which the two sections A and B are considered parallel-plane transmission lines with a discontinuity capacitance C_d placed at the junction between them. (This junction effect will be discussed in Chapter 11.) Curves of cutoff frequency and a total impedance for the guide have been calculated in this manner by Cohn.[12] Some results are shown in Fig. 8.16b. Definitions of total impedance of waveguides are also discussed in Chapter 11.

Problems

8.16a Demonstrate that the cutoff frequency of a TM_{01} mode in circular guide may be found by considering transverse resonance of a radial line mode.

8.16b Calculate by the approximate formula (1) the cutoff frequency of some of the ridge waveguides for which better results may be obtained from Fig. 8.16b, and make comparisons. Choose at least one with a small gap and at least one with a wide one.

8.17 The Idealized Helix and Other Slow-Wave Structures

A wire wound in the form of a helix (Fig. 8.17a) makes a type of guide that has been found useful for antennas[13] and as slow-wave structures in traveling-wave tubes.[14] It is interesting as an example of a general class of structures which possess waves with a phase velocity along the axis much less than the velocity of light, as contrasted to most of the waves so far studied, which have phase velocities greater than the velocity of light. A rough picture would convince one that the wave should follow the wire with about the velocity of light, so that its rate of progress along the axis should correspond to a phase velocity

$$v_p \approx c \sin \psi, \qquad (1)$$

where ψ is the pitch angle. It is rather surprising that this represents a good approximation over a wide range of parameters. It is also interesting to find that a useful analysis can be made by considering an idealization of the actual helix.

The idealization commonly analyzed,[14] referred to as the *helical sheet*, is a cylindrical surface in which the component of electric field along the direction of ψ is assumed to be zero *at all points of the sheet* (Fig. 8.17b). Moreover, the component of electric field lying in the cylindrical surface normal to the direction of ψ is assumed to be continuous through the surface, as is the component of magnetic field along ψ (the latter because

[12] S. B. Cohn, *Proc. I.R.E.*, **35**, 783–788 (Aug. 1947).
[13] J. D. Kraus, *Antennas*, McGraw-Hill, New York, 1950, Chapter 7.
[14] J. R. Pierce, *Traveling-Wave Tubes*, Van Nostrand, Princeton, N.J., 1950, Chapter III and Appendix II.

there is to be no current flow normal to the direction of ψ). Since the
idealization takes these conditions to be the same over all the sheet, it
would be expected to give best results for fine-wire helices of small pitch
angle or for multifilar helices with fine wires close together.

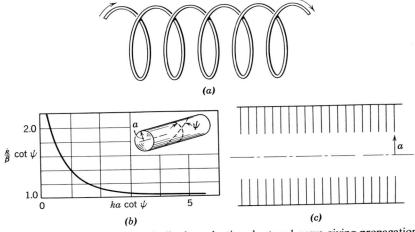

(a)

(b)

(c)

Fig. 8.17   (a) Wire helix. (b) Idealized conducting sheet and curve giving propagation
constant.[14]   (c) Section of disk-loaded waveguide.

The solutions inside and outside the surface are taken with no ϕ variations. They require both TM and TE modes and may be written

$$r < a \qquad\qquad\qquad r > a$$

$$E_{z1} = A_1 I_0(\tau r) \qquad\qquad E_{z2} = A_2 K_0(\tau r) \tag{2}$$

$$E_{r1} = \frac{j\beta}{\tau} A_1 I_1(\tau r) \qquad\qquad E_{r2} = -\frac{j\beta}{\tau} A_2 K_1(\tau r) \tag{3}$$

$$H_{\phi 1} = \frac{j\omega\epsilon}{\tau} A_1 I_1(\tau r) \qquad\qquad H_{\phi 2} = -\frac{j\omega\epsilon}{\tau} A_2 K_1(\tau r) \tag{4}$$

$$H_{z1} = B_1 I_0(\tau r) \qquad\qquad H_{z2} = B_2 K_0(\tau r) \tag{5}$$

$$H_{r1} = \frac{j\beta}{\tau} B_1 I_1(\tau r) \qquad\qquad H_{r2} = -\frac{j\beta}{\tau} B_2 K_1(\tau r) \tag{6}$$

$$E_{\phi 1} = -\frac{j\omega\mu}{\tau} B_1 I_1(\tau r) \qquad E_{\phi 2} = \frac{j\omega\mu}{\tau} B_2 K_1(\tau r) \tag{7}$$

where all variations have been taken as $e^{j(\omega t - \beta z)}$ and

$$\tau^2 = -(\gamma^2 + k^2) = \beta^2 - k^2. \tag{8}$$

The idealized boundary conditions first described are

$$E_{z1} \sin \psi + E_{\phi1} \cos \psi = 0 \tag{9}$$
$$E_{z2} \sin \psi + E_{\phi2} \cos \psi = 0 \tag{10}$$
$$E_{z1} \cos \psi - E_{\phi1} \sin \psi = E_{z2} \cos \psi - E_{\phi2} \sin \psi \tag{11}$$
$$H_{z1} \sin \psi + H_{\phi1} \cos \psi = H_{z2} \sin \psi + H_{\phi2} \cos \psi. \tag{12}$$

Application of (9) through (12) to (2) through (7) yields the equation

$$(\tau a)^2 \frac{I_0(\tau a)K_0(\tau a)}{I_1(\tau a)K_1(\tau a)} = (ka \cot \psi)^2. \tag{13}$$

A solution of this taken from Pierce[14] is shown in Fig. 8.17b. It is seen that, for $ka \cot \psi > 4$, the approximation (1) gives good results.

Some general comments about slow-wave structures are in order. In these we will neglect attenuation, assuming $\gamma = j\beta$. If it is desired to produce an electric field along the axis propagating with a phase velocity less than that of light (as in a traveling-wave tube where the phase velocity should be of the order of the beam velocity for efficient interaction with the electrons), we see that the combination $\gamma^2 + k^2$, which we have called k_c^2 in Chapter 7, will be negative, since $\beta > k$.

$$\tau^2 = -k_c^2 = \beta^2 - k^2 \tag{14}$$

$$\tau = \beta\left(1 - \frac{v_p^2}{c^2}\right)^{1/2}. \tag{15}$$

It is consequently necessary in a cylindrically symmetric system that the Bessel function solutions (Art. 7.16) have imaginary arguments, and they may therefore be written as modified Bessel functions. For a TM wave,

$$E_z = AI_0(\tau r) \tag{16}$$

$$H_\phi = \frac{\omega\epsilon}{\beta} E_r = \frac{j\omega\epsilon}{\tau} I_1(\tau r). \tag{17}$$

If we ask about the boundary conditions that might be supplied at a cylindrical surface $r = a$ in order to support such waves, we see that, if uniform, it should be of the nature of a reactive sheet with

$$jX = -\left.\frac{E_z}{H_\phi}\right|_{r=a} = j\eta \frac{\tau}{k} \frac{I_0(\tau a)}{I_1(\tau a)}. \tag{18}$$

The helical sheet studied earlier may be considered as supplying this required reactance through the interaction with the TE waves and external fields caused by the helical cuts. The short-circuited sections of radial lines of a disk-loaded waveguide (Fig. 8.17c) may also be considered as supplying an approximation to the above required uniform reactance at $r = a$, and will therefore support a slow wave also. The approximate reactance supplied by this structure is

$$X = \eta \left[\frac{J_0(ka)N_0(kb) - J_0(kb)N_0(ka)}{J_1(ka)N_0(kb) - J_0(kb)N_0(ka)} \right]. \tag{19}$$

Note that, if $(v_p/c)^2 \ll 1$, τ is substantially equal to β. By the nature of the I_0 functions (Fig. 3.26c), the field on the axis of such slow-wave structures is much less than that on the boundary when βa is large. This is of course undesirable when it is the field on the axis that is to act on electrons as in a traveling-wave tube. Of course the presence of electron space charge will modify the forms of solution somewhat.

Problems

8.17a Imagine a parallel-plane transmission line of spacing $2a$ in which both upper and lower planes are cut with many fine cuts at angle ψ from the y direction (coordinate system as in Fig. 7.04). Assume no variations with y, and apply approximations as utilized in the helical sheet analysis, obtaining the field components for propagation in the z direction, the complete equation determining β, and the approximate solution of this for $ka \cot \psi \gg 1$.

8.17b Assuming $(v_p/c)^2 \ll 1$, plot kaX/η vs. βa for a slow-wave structure. State the requirements on the reactance in order that there may be any slow-wave solution of this type. What should X/η be for βa large?

8.17c Show that a reactance sheet might be used as the boundary condition on fast waves of the TM_{01} type studied in Art. 8.04. Plot the required value of kaX/η as a function of $k_c a$. Under what conditions might there be a slow wave and a series of fast waves in a given guide of this type?

8.18 Surface Guiding

The result of Art. 8.17 suggests a localization of fields near a surface which possesses a reactive surface impedance. This concept appeared there in an interior region, but may be useful when the fields are in the external region also. Because of the surface guiding principle the energy is maintained near the surface so that it is not radiated or coupled seriously to nearby objects. Thus the external region corresponding to Fig. 8.17c would be as shown in Fig. 8.18a. The proper solutions for the external cylindrical region for a TM wave are the same as Eqs. 8.17(2) to (4) for $r > a$. For E_z and H_ϕ,

$$E_z = A K_0(\tau r) \tag{1}$$

$$H_\phi = \frac{j\omega\epsilon}{\tau} A K_1(\tau r). \tag{2}$$

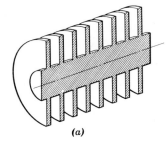

(a)

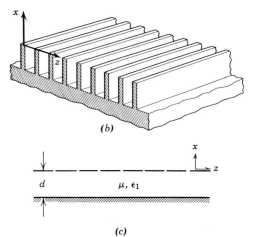

(b)

(c)

Fig. 8.18 (a) Rod with periodic radius variations capable of propagating a slow wave. (b) Planar equivalent of a. (c) Dielectric-coated conducting surface.

The field reactance at $r = a$ necessary to support such a wave is then

$$jX = \frac{E_z}{H_\phi}\bigg|_{r=a} = j\eta\,\frac{\tau}{k}\frac{K_0(\tau r)}{K_1(\tau r)}. \tag{3}$$

Equation (3) again represents a positive or inductive reactance as did Eq. 8.17(18), and the solutions (1) and (2) die off for large r. Phase velocity is less than the velocity of light in the external dielectric in order to maintain τ real, as in Eq. 8.17(14),

$$\tau^2 = \beta^2 - k^2. \tag{4}$$

This concept is perhaps more easily visualized for a plane sheet, as pictured in Fig. 8.18b. Substitution in Eqs. 7.02(1) to (6) easily verify that the following are solutions of Maxwell's equations, using the definition (4), and $e^{j(\omega t - \beta z)}$ understood in all terms.

$$E_z = Ce^{-\tau x} \tag{5}$$

$$H_y = -\frac{j\omega\epsilon C}{\tau} e^{-\tau x} \tag{6}$$

$$E_x = \frac{j\beta C}{\tau} e^{-\tau x}. \tag{7}$$

A surface wave impedance defined for this example is then

$$jX = \frac{E_z}{H_y}\bigg|_{x=0} = \frac{j\tau}{\omega\epsilon}. \tag{8}$$

Again we see that the impedance sheet should be inductive for surface guiding of this TM wave (but see Prob. 8.18a), and that the value of β must be greater than k if the wave is to die away with increasing x. Therefore phase velocity is less than the velocity of light in the dielectric. The spaces between the conducting fins may be considered to be shorted parallel plane transmission lines and the field impedance at the ends of the fins can be found from Chapter 7 as

$$\frac{E_z}{H_y} = j\eta \tan kd$$

where d is the height of the fins. It is clear that if $kd < \pi/2$, the surface appears as an inductive reactance.

Figure 8.18b illustrates the use of slots or corrugations to obtain the reactance. Another important way of obtaining the surface impedance sheet is by coating a conductor with a thin layer of dielectric, as illustrated in Fig. 8.18c. The following TM solutions for the region 1 can be verified by substitution in Eqs. 7.02(1) to (6). The conductor is assumed perfect and the argument of the sine is selected to make E_z zero at the conductor surface, $x = -d$.

$$E_z = D \sin k_x(x + d) \tag{9}$$

$$H_y = -\frac{j\omega\epsilon_1 D}{k_x} \cos k_x(x + d) \tag{10}$$

$$E_x = -\frac{j\beta D}{k_x} \cos k_x(x + d) \tag{11}$$

$$k_x^2 = k_1^2 - \beta^2. \tag{12}$$

From (9) and (10) a field impedance at $x = 0$ can be found as follows:

$$jX = \left. \frac{E_z}{H_y} \right|_{x=0} = \frac{jk_x}{\omega\epsilon_1} \tan k_x d. \tag{13}$$

This is inductive as required for guiding TM waves, and if equated to (8) will define the β of the desired surface wave. For small thicknesses, $k_x d \ll 1$, (13) becomes

$$jX \approx \frac{jk_x^2 d}{\omega\epsilon_1}. \tag{14}$$

In this example we note that the phase velocity in the z direction is between the velocity of light in the external dielectric and that in the coating, as might be expected.

The principle is also applicable to lossy dielectrics and/or conductors, for which a finite but relatively small attenuation in the z direction is obtained. Zenneck[15] and Sommerfeld[16] provided the early classical analyses of this phenomenon; Goubau[17] illustrated its usefulness as a practical waveguiding means by using either thin dielectric coatings or corrugations on round wires; a modern and thorough treatment is given by Collin.[18] It is clear that the problem treated in Eqs. (9) to (12) (Fig. 8.18c) is just the upper half of the solution for the dielectric slab waveguide, Fig. 8.11a and Eqs. 8.11(1) to (5), so surface guiding and dielectric waveguiding are closely related phenomena.

Problems

8.18a Analyze a TE surface wave over a plane with no variations in y and show that a capacitive reactance is necessary to produce an exponential decay with x.

8.18b For the TM surface wave established by the thin dielectric coating on a perfect conductor, Eqs. (9) to (12), find the average power transfer in the z direction.

8.18c Utilizing the result of Prob. *b*, find the approximate attenuation if the conductor at $x = -d$ has surface resistivity R_s.

8.18d Repeat Prob. *c*, but assume conductor perfect and dielectric with a small lossy part, $\epsilon_1 = \epsilon_1' - j\epsilon_1''$ with $\epsilon_1'' \ll \epsilon_1'$.

[15] J. Zenneck, *Ann. Phys.* **23**, 846 (1907).

[16] A. Sommerfeld, *Ann. Phys. u. Chemie* **67**, 233 (1899). Described in Stratton, *op. cit.* p. 527.

[17] G. Goubau, *Proc. I.R.E.* **39**, 619–624 (1951); *J. Appl. Phys.* **21**, 1119–1128 (1950).

[18] R. Collin, *Field Theory of Guided Waves*, McGraw-Hill, New York, 1960; Chapter 11.

8.19 Periodic Structures and Space Harmonics

The corrugated surfaces used as illustrations of reactance walls in the two preceding articles are actually special examples of periodic systems if the spacing between corrugations is uniform. Periodic systems have interesting properties and important applications, so will be examined more carefully in this article. We recognize that the treatment as a smooth reactance wall, used in Arts. 8.17 and 8.18, is only an approximation since the grooves will cause field disturbances not accounted for by this "smoothed out" approximation.

Let us begin by consideration of a specific example, the parallel-plane transmission line with periodic troughs in one plate, as illustrated in Fig. 8.19a. If the grooves are relatively narrow, the troughs will act to waves with z-directed currents in the bottom plate as shorted transmission lines in series with the conductor. These lines will produce values of E_z and H_y at $x = 0$, which are essentially constant over the gap width w. Thus the boundary condition for E_z at $x = 0$ is as shown in Fig. 8.19b, a phase shift of $\beta_0 d$ being allowed over each period, since we will stress propagating waves. The square waves shown neglect higher-order fringing fields at the corners, but are better approximations than the complete smoothing out of the effect (as in Art. 8.18) and are sufficient to illustrate the basic properties of periodic structures.

To fulfill the boundary condition at $x = 0$, we might expect to add solutions of Maxwell's equations just as we added solutions of Laplace's equation in Chapter 3 to satisfy boundary conditions not satisfied by a single solution.

For the present problem let us take $\partial/\partial y = 0$ and consider waves with E_x, E_z, and H_y only. Thus a sum of solutions satisfying Maxwell's equations and the boundary condition of $E_z = 0$ at $x = a$ may be written by adding waves of the TM form, the TEM component being included if the sum includes $n = 0$.

$$E_z(x, z) = \sum_{n=-\infty}^{\infty} A_n \sin K_n(a - x)e^{-j\beta_n z} \tag{1}$$

$$E_x(x, z) = \sum_{n=-\infty}^{\infty} \frac{-j\beta_n}{K_n} A_n \cos K_n(a - x)e^{-j\beta_n z} \tag{2}$$

$$H_y(x, z) = \sum_{n=-\infty}^{\infty} \frac{-j\omega\epsilon}{K_n} A_n \cos K_n(a - x)e^{-j\beta_n z} \tag{3}$$

where
$$K_n{}^2 = \omega^2\mu\epsilon - \beta_n{}^2 = k^2 - \beta_n{}^2. \tag{4}$$

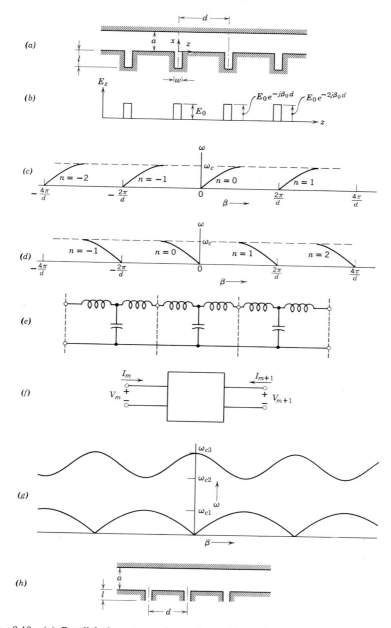

Fig. 8.19 (a) Parallel-plane transmission line with periodic short-circuited troughs. (b) Idealized variations of E_z along the lower plate in the structure of a. (c) $\omega - \beta$ relation for space harmonics of wave with fundamental traveling in $+z$ direction. (d) $\omega - \beta$ relation for space harmonics of wave with fundamental traveling in $-z$ direction. (e) Low-frequency equivalent circuit for fundamental space harmonic of structure in Fig. a. (f) General network showing sign conventions. (g) Composite $\omega - \beta$ diagram including pass band at higher frequency. (h) Line with open-circuited troughs.

The boundary condition illustrated by Fig. 8.19b will be a periodic function of z if the phase factor is taken out separately. If we expand the resulting periodic function in the complex form of the Fourier series (Art. 1.10), we may write for the boundary condition

$$E_z(0, z) = e^{-j\beta_0 z} \sum_{n=-\infty}^{\infty} C_n e^{-(j2\pi nz/d)} \qquad (5)$$

where $\quad C_n = \dfrac{1}{d} \displaystyle\int_{-d/2}^{d/2} E_z(0, z)e^{+j(2\pi nz/d)} \, dz = \dfrac{1}{d} \displaystyle\int_{-w/2}^{w/2} E_0 e^{+j(2\pi nz/d)} \, dz$

$$= \frac{E_0}{\pi n} \sin\left(\frac{n\pi w}{d}\right). \qquad (6)$$

By comparing (5) with (1) evaluated at $x = 0$, we can now identify A_n and β_n

$$A_n = \frac{C_n}{\sin K_n a} = \frac{E_0}{\pi n} \frac{\sin\left(\dfrac{n\pi w}{d}\right)}{\sin K_n a} \qquad (7)$$

$$\beta_n = \beta_0 + \frac{2\pi n}{d}. \qquad (8)$$

A wave solution is thus determined for this problem with the approximations described.

We wish first to stress the different role of the *TM* solutions in this problem compared with that considered previously. In earlier articles *TM* solutions have been considered as "modes" with the inference that they may be excited independently. Here they are coupled by the periodic boundary condition and must exist in the proper relationship to satisfy this boundary condition. In this capacity they are known as "space harmonics," a natural extension of the harmonic character of the Fourier series to the periodic system in space. We note especially from (8) that determination of β for any space harmonic automatically determines the value for all others. Thus the ω-β diagram (Art. 1.25) is periodic in β with repetition at intervals of $2\pi/d$ as illustrated in Figs. 8.19c and d.

Determination of the shape of one period of this plot (say β_0) requires study of the boundary conditions on two field components. We have already considered E_z and now choose H_y as the second component for this example. If the solution for the troughs is well approximated by the shorted transmission line behavior, the value of H_y at $x = 0$, $z = 0$ for the shorted lines is given by

$$H_y = \frac{-jE_0}{\eta} \cot kl.$$

Thus one might equate this to (3) evaluated at $x = 0$, with A_n substituted from (7):

$$\frac{1}{\eta} \cot kl = \sum_{n=-\infty}^{\infty} \frac{-j\omega\epsilon}{\pi n K_n} \sin \frac{\pi n w}{d} \cot K_n a. \tag{9}$$

This with (4) and (8) determines β_0 in principle, although general solution may be difficult.

For the special case of $kl \ll 1$ and $\beta_0 d \ll 1$, lumped element approximations may be used. The fundamental harmonic solution of the corresponding low-pass filter then gives the characteristics of the fundamental, and from that, the values of β for other space harmonics. The filter corresponding to the line used in the above example is shown in Fig. 8.19e. The capacitance is the low-frequency effect of the parallel-plate section between grooves and the inductances represent the effect of the grooves. Each T-section of the filter corresponds to the guide between planes bisecting the grooves so the inductances have one-half the value given by the shorted transmission-line formula.

For a general linear reciprocal network section as shown in Fig. 8.19f, we may write

$$\begin{aligned} I_m &= Y_{11} V_m + Y_{12} V_{m+1} \\ I_{m+1} &= Y_{21} V_m + Y_{22} V_{m+1} \end{aligned} \tag{10}$$

where $Y_{12} = Y_{21}$. Assuming $I_{m+1} = -I_m e^{-j\beta_0 d}$ and $V_{m+1} = V_m e^{-j\beta_0 d}$ we can show (see Prob. 8.19a) that

$$\cos \beta_0 d = -\frac{Y_{11} + Y_{22}}{2Y_{12}}. \tag{11}$$

In terms of a symmetrical T-network, this becomes

$$\cos \beta_0 d = 1 + \frac{Y_2}{Y_1}, \tag{12}$$

where Y_1 and Y_2 are the series and shunt admittances, respectively. The low-frequency and small-β portion of the ω-β curve, where the conditions $kl \ll 1$ and $\beta_0 d \ll 1$ are satisfied, can be found from (11) and (12). We restrict our attention here to the case where the filter elements are purely reactive; the line is lossless. We see from (12) that real values of β_0 exist only where

$$-2 \leqslant \frac{Y_2}{Y_1} \leqslant 0. \tag{13}$$

Outside this range, β_0 takes imaginary values and the filter is cut off. There are ranges of frequency for which waves do not propagate in periodic systems.

Although illustrated for a particular example to provide concreteness, the periodic character of the ω-β diagram, and the relation (8) for phase constant of a space harmonic, apply to any structure of period d. Other important properties are as follows:

1. The group velocity of all space harmonics of a given wave are equal. This would be expected so that the wave would stay together, but may be noted either from the ω-β diagrams, or by differentiating (8),

$$\frac{1}{v_{gn}} = \frac{d\beta_n}{d\omega} = \frac{d\beta_0}{d\omega}.$$

2. Of the infinite number of space harmonics, half are backward waves (Art. 1.25) with phase and group velocities in the opposite directions. Thus the $n = 0, 1, 2$, etc. of Fig. 8.19c are forward waves whereas $n = -1$, -2, etc. are backward waves, as is seen by comparing the signs of ω/β and $d\omega/d\beta$ for the various portions of the figure. If the phase velocity of the fundamental space harmonic is negative, the harmonics are as shown in Fig. 8.19d. Here the $n = 0, -1, -2$, etc. have both phase and group velocities in the negative direction and are not backward waves, whereas the $n = 1, 2$, etc. are backward waves with positive phase velocities and negative group velocities. The structure of Fig. 8.19a has a fundamental forward wave, but other periodic structures may have fundamental backward waves.

3. The field distribution at any plane $z = md$ (m an integer) is the same as at $z = 0$ except for multiplication by the phase factor $e^{-j\beta_0 md}$. This important property is related to Floquet's theorem,[19] and is often taken as the fundamental starting point for the study of periodic systems. For the particular example used in this article, (1) with (8) yields

$$E_z(x, md) = \sum_{n=-\infty}^{\infty} A_n \sin K_n(a - x)e^{-j\beta_0 md}e^{-j2\pi mn}$$

$$= e^{-j\beta_0 md} \sum_{n=-\infty}^{\infty} A_n \sin K_n(a - x) = e^{-j\beta_0 md}E_z(x, 0), \quad (14)$$

and similarly for the other field components.

4. The wave is cut off where group velocity becomes zero, shown as ω_c in Figs. 8.19c and d. Above this frequency there is a region of reactive attenuation, typical of filters in the attenuating region. As frequency is increased, however, other pass bands will be found with propagating waves, as illustrated in Fig. 8.19g. Each of these waves has space harmonics, just as the low-pass wave studied. The Pierce coupled-mode theory[20] is

[19] L. Brillouin, *Wave Propagation in Periodic Structures*; Dover, New York, 1953.
[20] D. A. Watkins, *Topics in Electromagnetic Theory*; John Wiley and Sons, New York, 1958.

especially powerful in giving a picture of the entire ω-β diagram in a structure with relatively small periodic perturbations if the phase constants of the unperturbed system are known.

As has been noted, the transmission line approximation may be useful in finding the behavior of the fundamental of the lowest order wave. The problem is then one-dimensional. The nonuniform line with a sinusoidal variation of C, for example, would give [Eq. 1.26(4)]

$$\frac{d^2V}{dz^2} - \omega^2 L_0(C_0 + C_1 \cos \beta_c z)V = 0. \tag{15}$$

This is Mathieu's equation, and has known solutions,[21] and it has also received special attention with respect to the regions of stability and instability.

Problems

8.19a Derive Eqs. 8.19(11) and (12) which give the relations between ω and β for the filter line.

8.19b Making the assumptions that $kl \ll 1$ and $\beta_0 d \ll 1$, plot the lowest-frequency pass band for the structure of Fig. 8.19a. Plot the curve for all β and state your reasoning.

8.19c Take the same approximations as in Prob. *b*, but assume the "troughs" are open circuited as in Fig. 8.18*h*. Find the equivalent lumped-element circuit, the propagation constant of the fundamental, and sketch the ω-β diagram of this wave. Note the fact that the cutoff region includes $\omega = 0$ and frequencies up to some lower cutoff frequency.

8.19d Find the low-frequency portion of the ω-β diagram for a periodic transmission system composed of a series of parallel inductively coupled resonant circuits. Note that the fundamental space harmonic is a backward wave.

8.19e The example used in this article was a closed line. Consider an open region, such as those studied in Art. 8.18 for surface-wave propagation. What regions of the ω-β plot will represent nonradiating or guided surface waves?

8.19f Illustrate Prob. *e* by solving a problem with the structure at $x = 0$ as in Fig. 8.19a, but with the top plate removed so that the region extends to infinity.

8.20 Periodic Systems of Lenses

The special periodic system made up of equally spaced thin lenses, which can be treated by geometrical optics, is interesting in that it is useful for transmission of light beams, as a way of looking at optical resonators

---

[21] N. W. McLachlan, *Theory and Application of Mathieu Functions*, Oxford University Press, London, 1947.

(Art. 10.16), and for periodic focusing of electron beams where the lenses are electrostatic or magnetostatic lenses.[22] The method of analysis to be used is also an excellent tie between that of the last article and that for periodic networks to be considered in Chapter 11. It is essentially that given by Pierce.[23]

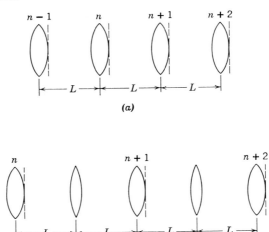

Fig. 8.20 (a) Periodic system of identical lenses. (b) Periodic system of lenses with alternating focal lengths.

Consider the periodic system of thin lenses of focal length f pictured in Fig. 8.20a. The radius of a ray at a plane following lens $(n + 1)$ is given by values at the corresponding plane following lens n and constants which contain the spacing and lens focal length. Thus

$$r_{n+1} = r_n + Lr'_n \tag{1}$$

$$r'_{n+1} = r'_n - \frac{r_{n+1}}{f} = -\frac{r_n}{f} + \left(1 - \frac{L}{f}\right)r'_n. \tag{2}$$

The last form in (2) comes from substituting r_{n+1} from (1). A single difference equation may be found by solving (1) for r'_n,

$$r'_n = \frac{1}{L}(r_{n+1} - r_n). \tag{3}$$

[22] J. R. Pierce, *Theory and Design of Electron Beams*, 2nd Ed. Van Nostrand, Princeton, N.J., 1954, Chapter VII.
[23] *Ibid.*, Chapter XI.

A similar form must apply between lens $(n + 2)$ and lens $(n + 1)$,

$$r'_{n+1} = \frac{1}{L}(r_{n+2} - r_{n+1}). \tag{4}$$

Substitution of (2) then yields the difference equation

$$r_{n+2} - 2br_{n+1} + r_n = 0 \tag{5}$$

where

$$b = \left(1 - \frac{L}{2f}\right). \tag{6}$$

Following the arguments of the preceding article, let us assume that a solution is given by the following form:

$$r_n = r_0 e^{jn\theta} \tag{7}$$

Substitution in (5) yields

$$e^{2j\theta} - 2be^{j\theta} + 1 = 0. \tag{8}$$

This is a quadratic in $e^{j\theta}$ and has a solution

$$e^{j\theta} = b \pm \sqrt{b^2 - 1} = b \pm j\sqrt{1 - b^2}, \tag{9}$$

which, by inspection, is satisfied if

$$\theta = \pm\cos^{-1} b. \tag{10}$$

This system then gives an interesting physical view of the condition for a stable periodic solution. If b, given by (6), has a magnitude less than unity, values for θ are real and the solution is periodic, meaning that the rays will remain within the lens system. However if $|b| > 1$, θ is imaginary so that (7) has solutions in exponentials. The solution is not periodic; the rays eventually leave the lens system, and the system cannot continue to "guide" the ray.

A useful extension is that pictured in Fig. 8.20b in which the system repeats after a sequence of two different lenses, the first having focal length f_1 and the second focal length f_2. The spacings in this case are assumed the same. Repetition of the equations (1) and (2) through the second lens give the relations between values of the new $(n + 1)$ plane and the nth plane:

$$r_{n+1} = \left(1 - \frac{L}{f_2}\right)r_n + L\left(2 - \frac{L}{f_2}\right)r'_n \tag{11}$$

$$r'_{n+1} = -\left[\frac{1}{f_1} + \frac{1}{f_2}\left(1 - \frac{L}{f_1}\right)\right]r_n - \left[\frac{L}{f_1} - \left(1 - \frac{L}{f_1}\right)\left(1 - \frac{L}{f_2}\right)\right]r'_{n+1}. \tag{12}$$

The difference equation is then exactly as (5) with

$$b = 1 - \frac{L}{f_1} - \frac{L}{f_2} + \frac{L^2}{f_1 f_2}. \tag{13}$$

The solution is then of the form (7) and (10), with stable solutions again for $|b| < 1$. A most interesting application of this extension is for the case of alternate converging and diverging lenses of like focal length. Thus if $f_1 = -f_2$, the condition for stability of a periodic solution is

$$|b| = \left| 1 - \frac{L^2}{f_1^2} \right| < 1. \tag{14}$$

It might be thought that no focusing would be possible with the alternating lenses of equal strength, but the net focusing arises in that the ray passes through the converging lens at a larger radius, so that the r/f term in (2) is larger and focuses stronger for the converging than for the diverging lens.

The example of repetition after two lenses will also be utilized in the discussion of optical resonators in Chapter 10.

Problems

8.20a Show that an alternative solution to (7) may be written

$$r_n = A \cos n\theta + B \sin n\theta.$$

8.20b Consider a system as shown in Fig. 8.20a with $L/f = 5$. By the condition found, this should result in an unstable solution. To demonstrate, sketch the behavior of a ray entering one lens with zero slope at a radius $r = 10^{-2}f$, and passing through a few lenses each of radius $R = 0.2\,f$.

8.20c Repeat Prob. b for the stable case of $L/f = 1$.

8.20d Derive equations similar to (11) to (13) for a system like Fig. 8.20b but with different spacings L_1 and L_2 between lenses along with the two different focal lengths. Show that these reduce to (11) to (13) if $L_1 = L_2$.

8.20e Repeat Prob. c for the alternate converging-diverging system with $L/f_1 = -L/f_2 = 1$. Note the significance of any differences with respect to the solution of Prob. c.

8.21 Waves in Inhomogeneous Materials

If μ, ϵ, and σ are scalar functions of space we must return to Maxwell's equations in their original form and recognize that the waves derived in this chapter and the preceding one do not generally apply. Maxwell's equations for the time-periodic case are

$$\nabla \cdot (\epsilon \bar{E}) = \rho \tag{1}$$

$$\nabla \cdot (\mu \bar{H}) = 0 \tag{2}$$

$$\nabla \times \bar{E} = -j\omega\mu\bar{H} \tag{3}$$

$$\nabla \times \bar{H} = (\sigma + j\omega\epsilon)\bar{E}, \tag{4}$$

where $\epsilon = \epsilon(x, y, z)$, $\mu = \mu(x, y, z)$, $\sigma = \sigma(x, y, z)$. The system may be differentiated to yield modified forms of the wave equation for $\bar{E}$ or $\bar{H}$, but the space derivatives of μ, ϵ, and σ yield extra terms and the resulting equations are cumbersome (Prob. 8.21a). An alternative approach for general space variations is through numerical solution of (1) to (4) directly, but computing times are impractical even with modern high-speed computers unless some field components, source terms, or directions of space variation are negligible.

To specialize somewhat, note first that for a charge-free, loss-free problem with $\rho = 0$, $\sigma = 0$, equations (1) and (2) follow from (3) and (4) by taking the divergence of $(\mu\bar{H})$ and $(\epsilon\bar{E})$ in the last two equations. Thus for such cases, just as in the case of homogeneous dielectrics, only the curl equations need be solved.

One simple and useful situation reduces to the nonuniform transmission-line problem. Thus consider waves with E_x and H_y only, ρ and σ zero as above, and no variations of either fields or μ and ϵ in the plane transverse to the z direction. Equations (3) and (4) then yield

$$\frac{dE_x}{dz} = -j\omega\mu(z)H_y \tag{5}$$

$$\frac{dH_y}{dz} = -j\omega\epsilon(z)E_x. \tag{6}$$

These are identical in form to the nonuniform transmission-line equations of Art. 1.26, with E_x analogous to voltage, H_y to current, μ to distributed inductance of the line, and ϵ to distributed capacitance. Solutions may then be written at once for the four nonuniform line problems we have treated in this text:

1. Exponential variation of μ and ϵ (Art. 1.26).
2. "Radial line" solution with $\epsilon = 1/\mu v^2 = K_1 z$ (Art. 8.12).
3. The dual of 2 with $\mu = 1/\epsilon v^2 = K_2 z$ (Art. 8.14).
4. Periodic variation of μ and ϵ with z (Art. 8.19).

Numerical solution of the set (5) and (6) is also very practical for more general functions $\mu(z)$ and $\epsilon(z)$.

The nonuniform line solutions can also be used for the slightly more general case of a TM wave with no variations in y, exponential variations in x, and only z variations of μ and ϵ. Let

$$E_x = V(z)e^{-jk_x x} \tag{7}$$

$$H_y = I(z)e^{-jk_x x} \tag{8}$$

$$E_z = A(z)e^{-jk_x x}. \tag{9}$$

Substitution into the y component of (3) and the x and z components of
(4) gives

$$-I' = j\omega\epsilon V \tag{10}$$

$$V' + jk_x A = -j\omega\mu I \tag{11}$$

$$-jk_x I = j\omega\epsilon A. \tag{12}$$

Elimination of A from (11) and (12) yields

$$V' = -j\left(\omega\mu - \frac{k_x^{\,2}}{\omega\epsilon}\right)I. \tag{13}$$

Equations (10) and (13) are again of the form of the nonuniform line
equations if

$$C(z) = \epsilon(z) \tag{14}$$

$$L(z) = \mu(z)\left(1 - \frac{k_x^{\,2}}{\omega^2\mu\epsilon}\right). \tag{15}$$

Likewise *TE* solutions under similar conditions may be obtained.

The final inhomogeneous problem to be considered here is the path of a
ray in geometrical optics (Art. 6.17). This is a most important problem in
tracing the propagation path of a radio wave in the ionosphere, or a light
wave in a material with varying index of refraction, when the approximations for geometrical optics apply. Considering Fig. 8.21, we may apply

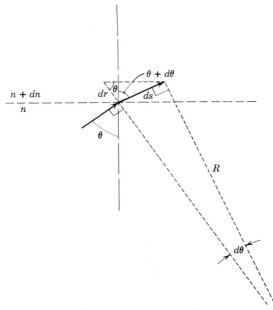

Fig. 8.21 Construction for calculation of refraction
of ray through inhomogeneous medium.

Snell's law to the passage of the ray from a medium with index of refraction n to one with $n + dn$,

$$\frac{n}{n + dn} = \frac{\sin(\theta + d\theta)}{\sin \theta} = \frac{\sin \theta + d\theta \cos \theta}{\sin \theta}$$

or

$$\cot \theta \, d\theta = -\frac{dn}{n},$$

which yields the following radius of curvature:

$$\frac{1}{R} = \frac{d\theta}{ds} = \frac{d\theta \cot \theta}{dr} = -\frac{1}{n}\frac{dn}{dr}. \tag{16}$$

This may also be written in the form

$$\frac{1}{R} = -\bar{a}_r \cdot \nabla[\ln n]. \tag{17}$$

Thus as index of refraction varies from point to point, a radius of curvature may be calculated for each point and the ray traced by joining the corresponding arcs at suitably small intervals.

Problems

8.21a By taking the curl of (3) and suitable use of vector identities, obtain a differential equation relating $\bar{E}$ to ρ and the variations of μ, ϵ, and σ. Derive the corresponding equation for $\bar{H}$. Show that these reduce to the common wave equation for homogeneous materials with $\rho = 0$.

8.21b Write the solutions for E_x and H_y for (5) and (6) for the four cases described in (1) to (4) where nonuniform line solutions may be directly applied.

8.21c Show the applicability of the nonuniform line solutions for a *TE* wave with $\partial/\partial y = 0$ and exponential variations in the x direction. Give the values to be used for $C(z)$ and $L(z)$.

8.21d Suppose ϵ and μ are functions only of the radius in circular cylindrical coordinates ($\rho = 0$ and $\sigma = 0$). Give conditions under which simple solutions may be found.

8.21e Repeat Prob. *d* for ϵ and μ varying only with the radius in spherical coordinates.

8.21f Utilizing the formulas (16) or (17), check the approximate equation for focal length f of the lens described in Art. 6.17 in which an inhomogeneous medium of width w small compared with f has index of refraction varying parabolically with radius from the axis.

9 WAVE PROPAGATION IN ANISOTROPIC MEDIA

9.01 Introduction

A number of important applications of anisotropic media in the field of electromagnetic waves have recently come to the forefront. Prominent among these are wave propagation effects in plasmas, ferrite devices, traveling wave tubes, and maser systems at microwave and light frequencies. Up to this point in the text we have concentrated our attention on the broad range of situations in which the media are isotropic. Hints of the necessity of a somewhat different formalism for anisotropic problems have been given. It is convenient to treat in one place, as in this chapter, a variety of anisotropic problems in order to see the essential unity in the required formalism.

Anisotropic materials may be divided into two classes, depending on whether the natural modes of propagation are linearly polarized or circularly polarized waves. In the former, the permittivity and permeability components discussed in Art. 2.44 are symmetric; that is, $\epsilon_{ij} = \epsilon_{ji}$ and $\mu_{ij} = \mu_{ji}$. For the latter, called *gyrotropic* media, the permittivity or permeability components for loss-free media are antisymmetric, having $\epsilon_{ij} = -\epsilon_{ji}$ or $\mu_{ij} = -\mu_{ji}$. Gyrotropic behavior results from the application of a finite magnetic field to a plasma, to a ferrite, and to some dielectric crystals. The physical reason for the off-diagonal terms in permittivity of a plasma, for example, is easy to see. The dielectric behavior of a plasma depends on the movement of the charged particles. If an electron is forced by the electric field of a wave to move with a velocity component normal to the applied magnetic field, a component of velocity in another direction arises from the $\bar{v} \times \bar{B}$ force. The off-diagonal terms represent this coupling. The source of the signs will appear in the analysis.

We shall first study wave propagation in dielectric crystals, a simple example of anisotropy. The subject is of special interest because of the recent emergence of coherent light systems in electrical engineering. The anisotropic electro-optic effects which can be used to modulate light at very high frequencies will also be mentioned. We then present shorter notation for the anisotropic equations, and consider some general properties of waves in anisotropic media.

Some of the many interesting types of waves which can propagate in a plasma with a steady applied magnetic field will be studied. These waves have considerable practical importance. A drifting plasma passing through a helix is used as a model for a microwave, electron-beam amplifier. The propagation of a plane wave through a plasma in a magnetic field is an appropriate model for propagation of waves through the ionosphere and through some laboratory plasmas. The plasma with a finite magnetic field has the property that the fields of a linearly polarized wave are rotated as it travels. This rotation of the field vectors is called Faraday rotation. The same phenomenon will also be shown to occur in ferrites, subjected to a finite magnetic field, in a form more useful than in plasmas for applications in laboratory devices. In the course of these studies we will derive permittivity and permeability components from the basic physical natures of the various media.

MATERIALS WITH PRINCIPAL AXES FOR PERMITTIVITY OR PERMEABILITY

9.02 Waves in Anisotropic Liquids and Crystals: Electro-Optic Effects

Let us first consider media, such as crystals or a liquid with an applied electric field to orient the molecules, for which proper orientation of the coordinate system leads to only three components of permittivity (see Art. 2.44). We may then write, as in Eq. 2.44(4),

$$D_x = \epsilon_{11}E_x, \qquad D_y = \epsilon_{22}E_y, \qquad D_z = \epsilon_{33}E_z. \tag{1}$$

Maxwell's curl equations should then be written as

$$\nabla \times \bar{H} = j\omega\bar{D} = j\omega(\bar{a}_x\epsilon_{11}E_x + \bar{a}_y\epsilon_{22}E_y + \bar{a}_z\epsilon_{33}E_z) \tag{2}$$

$$\nabla \times \bar{E} = -j\omega\mu_0\bar{H}, \tag{3}$$

where we assume that the deviation of the permeability from that of free space is negligible. Let us consider a wave with only E_x and H_y field components, no variations with x or y, and z propagation as $e^{-\gamma z}$. The x component of (2) is then

$$\gamma H_y = j\omega\epsilon_{11}E_x, \tag{4}$$

and the y component of (3) is

$$\gamma E_x = j\omega\mu_0 H_y. \tag{5}$$

Combining (4) and (5), we have

$$\gamma^2 = -\omega^2\mu_0\epsilon_{11} \tag{6}$$

$$\beta^{(x)} = \omega\sqrt{\mu_0\epsilon_{11}}, \tag{7}$$

where the superscript (x) indicates that $\bar{E} = \bar{a}_x E_x$. In a corresponding way for $\bar{E} = \bar{a}_y E_y$ we find

$$\beta^{(y)} = \omega\sqrt{\mu_0\epsilon_{22}}. \tag{8}$$

Thus we see that propagation depends on the orientation of the electric field vector.

If the boundary condition on the plane $z = 0$ on a crystal with diagonal representation is a field of the form

$$\bar{E}(0) = \bar{a}_x E_x(0) + \bar{a}_y E_y(0), \tag{9}$$

each component can be considered to propagate separately according to the relations (7) and (8), assuming the medium to be linear. The polarization of total $\bar{E}$ changes with distance through the medium. We can write

$$\bar{E}(z) = \bar{a}_x E_x(0)e^{-j\beta^{(x)}z} + \bar{a}_y E_y(0)e^{-j\beta^{(y)}z}, \tag{10}$$

or by defining

$$\Delta\beta = \beta^{(y)} - \beta^{(x)} \tag{11}$$

$$\bar{E}(z) = [\bar{a}_x E_x(0) + \bar{a}_y E_y(0)e^{-j\Delta\beta z}]e^{-j\beta^{(x)}z}. \tag{12}$$

At the planes where $\Delta\beta z = \pi/2$, the x and y components are 90° out of phase. As we saw in Art. 6.03 this is the condition for elliptic polarization. The wave returns to linear polarization but rotated by 90° in space at planes where $\Delta\beta z = \pi$. The polarization continues to alternate between linear and elliptic. The change of polarization is illustrated in Fig. 9.02a. The result in this simple case is just what might have been expected. There are two separable solutions corresponding to the two directions of plane polarization. The wave having E_x propagates with a phase constant like that in an isotropic dielectric, except that the permittivity coefficient ϵ_{11} appropriate to the x direction enters the relation. For the wave with E_y, ϵ_{22} applies.

Although the above described anisotropy occurs naturally in certain crystals, perhaps more important are similar anisotropic effects at optical frequencies arising because of polarizations in asymmetric molecules of certain materials when d-c or r-f electric fields are applied. These are called *electro-optic* effects, and as with natural optical activity, have been known for many years.[1] One well-known example is the *Kerr effect*, which occurs in liquids such as nitrobenzene and in a few solids, and yields a phase shift in (11) proportional to the square of electric field when this is

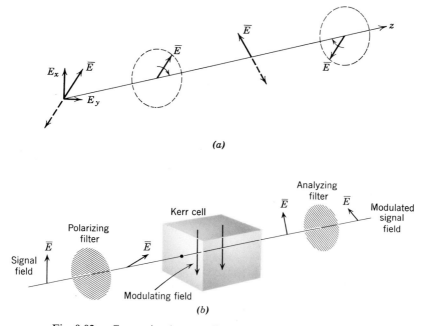

(a)

(b)

Fig. 9.02a   Conversion between linear and elliptic polarization in an anisotropic crystal. (b) System for modulation of light.

applied normal to the direction of propagation. The *Pockels effect* occurs in certain crystals such as KDP(KH_2PO_4), ADP($NH_4H_2PO_4$), and some semiconducting compounds such as GaAs and GaP. This effect depends on the orientation of the crystal as well as on the direction of applied field, and yields a phase shift in (11) directly proportional to electric field. Electro-optic effects are important in modern optics because of their possible use in modulation, switching, or deflection of light beams. Because of this there is currently much effort on materials with still larger electro-optic coefficients.[2]

[1] R. W. Ditchburn, *Light*, Interscience—Wiley, New York, 1963, Chapter XVI.
[2] Note for example the material KTN. See F. S. Chen *et al.*, *Proc. IEEE*, **52**, 1258 (October, 1964).

Although it is not the purpose of this book to develop applications in any detail, it is interesting to note the matter of modulation. If the phase shift in (11) varies with applied field, phase or frequency modulation can be had directly. "Discriminators" to convert the phase variation to amplitude variation at the detector may be made at optical frequencies by combining waves traveling over different path lengths, or by using the frequency response resulting from atomic resonances as illustrated in Fig. 6.04a. However, the classical electro-optic modulator or shutter utilizes the rotation of the wave polarization described by (12). As pictured in Fig. 9.02b, the unpolarized light is first passed through a polarizing filter which transmits light having $\bar{E}$ vectors in one direction only. This direction is chosen to make an angle of 45° with the field used to orient the molecules in the electro-optic material. If no modulating field is applied to the electro-optic material, there is no rotation. The polarized light then cannot pass through the analysis filter which is rotated 90° from the polarizing filter. A field applied to the material causes the permittivity elements ϵ_{11} and ϵ_{22} to differ and $\Delta\beta$ in (11) assumes a non-zero value. The value of the component of the field in the direction which is passed by the analyzing filter increases with the strength of the modulating field up to the point where $\Delta\beta l = \pi$, where l is the length of the modulating material.

Problems

9.02a   Consider modulation of light of wavelength 5560 Å(1 Å $= 10^{-10}$ meter) by an electro-optic crystal ($NH_4H_2PO_4$) with indices of refraction $n_0 = 1.48$ in the x and y directions before application of a modulating field E_{mz}. These become

$$n_x = n_0 + \tfrac{1}{2}n_0{}^3 r_p E_{mz}; \quad n_y = n_0 - \tfrac{1}{2}n_0{}^3 r_p E_{mz}$$

where r_p is the electro-optic coefficient (-8.3×10^{-12} meter/volt) when the modulating field is applied. The permeability of the crystal is essentially the same as for free space. Plot light transmitted by analyzer (fraction of maximum possible) as a function of the product of E_{mz} and the length of the crystal. Assume transmission coefficients at all surfaces to be unity for simplicity.

9.02b   Assume a spectrum of light of uniform intensity with wavelengths in the range 4000 Å $\leqslant \lambda \leqslant$ 7000 Å to be passed through the modulator of Prob. *a*. Find the modulator voltage for maximum transfer of light and find the fraction of incident light flux transferred. Assume transmission coefficients at all surfaces to be unity for simplicity.

9.02c   Assume a voltage applied to the ADP crystal of Prob. *a* sufficient to give $\Delta\beta z = \pi/2$. A light wave of $\lambda = 5560$ Å polarized at 45° from the x and y axes is incident on the crystal from air and passes again into air on the other end. Find the dependence of polarization beyond the crystal on the length of the crystal, taking into account reflections from end surfaces.

9.03   Fundamental Relations for Anisotropic Media

Now that we have seen a simple example of wave propagation in anisotropic materials, let us lay some general groundwork for the remainder of
the chapter.   For this, we return to the full set of equations for anisotropic
dielectrics, Eq. 2.44(2):

$$D_x = \epsilon_{11}E_x + \epsilon_{12}E_y + \epsilon_{13}E_z$$
$$D_y = \epsilon_{21}E_x + \epsilon_{22}E_y + \epsilon_{23}E_z \tag{1}$$
$$D_z = \epsilon_{31}E_x + \epsilon_{32}E_y + \epsilon_{33}E_z.$$

It is convenient to write (1) as an array or matrix, as follows:

$$\begin{bmatrix} D_x \\ D_y \\ D_z \end{bmatrix} = \begin{bmatrix} \epsilon_{11} & \epsilon_{12} & \epsilon_{13} \\ \epsilon_{21} & \epsilon_{22} & \epsilon_{23} \\ \epsilon_{31} & \epsilon_{32} & \epsilon_{33} \end{bmatrix} \begin{bmatrix} E_x \\ E_y \\ E_z \end{bmatrix}. \tag{2}$$

In the text, little matrix algebra will be needed, but the terminology and
notation is useful for compactness in handling sets of linear equations
such as (1).   The form (2) is equivalent to the set of equations (1) because
of the law of multiplication of matrices, which states that if matrix A
multiplies matrix B, there results a matrix C whose term in the ith row
and jth column is

$$C_{ij} = \sum_{n=1}^{N} A_{in}B_{nj}. \tag{3}$$

In (2), the components of D have only one column, so the D matrix is
called a column matrix, and likewise for E.   (Note that this is an alternative
way of displaying the components of a vector over that utilizing unit
vectors.)   The matrix for ϵ is a square matrix.   Hence (3) reduces to

$$D_i = \sum_{n=1}^{3} \epsilon_{in}E_n \tag{4}$$

and is equivalent to (2).

We may shorten our notation still further by denoting each of the
matrices by a symbol.   One way is

$$[D] = [\epsilon][E], \tag{5}$$

or alternatively we may keep the vector notation for $\bar{D}$ and $\bar{E}$, and write

$$\bar{D} = \hat{\epsilon}\bar{E}. \tag{6}$$

We will adopt this latter notation when dealing with vectors. Although the quantities may be treated by matrix algebra, they are more properly called tensors since $\bar{D}$ and $\bar{E}$ are physical vectors which must remain the same regardless of the coordinate system used to express them, and so must transform with rotation of coordinates so that this happens. Similarly $\hat{\epsilon}$ has restrictions under coordinate transformation. Vectors are tensors of rank one and the square matrix with proper transformation properties is a tensor of rank two. Thus we will occasionally speak of *tensor permittivity* and *tensor permeability* in anisotropic materials, although we will actually need no special knowledge of tensor analysis, and only the elementary operations of matrix algebra defined here.

The addition rule for matrices or tensors gives

$$C_{ij} = A_{ij} + B_{ij} \tag{7}$$

if $\hat{C} = \hat{A} + \hat{B}$. Thus we may write the set of equations 2.44(3) as

$$\hat{\epsilon} = \epsilon_0[\hat{I} + \hat{\chi}_e], \tag{8}$$

where $\hat{I}$ is the unit matrix,

$$\hat{I} = \begin{bmatrix} 1 & 0 & 0 \\ 0 & 1 & 0 \\ 0 & 0 & 1 \end{bmatrix}. \tag{9}$$

For real anisotropic dielectrics, it can be shown that $\hat{\epsilon}$ is symmetric,[3] so that $\epsilon_{ij} = \epsilon_{ji}$. A particularly important transformation of coordinates is then possible since every symmetrical tensor of rank two can be transformed, by rotation of the coordinate system, to a diagonal form.[4] This form is one with no terms except those on the diagonal of the matrix. Thus for particular coordinates in a given medium, $\hat{\epsilon}$ has the form

$$\hat{\epsilon} = \begin{bmatrix} \epsilon_{11} & 0 & 0 \\ 0 & \epsilon_{22} & 0 \\ 0 & 0 & \epsilon_{33} \end{bmatrix}. \tag{10}$$

When the coordinate system is chosen to have $\hat{\epsilon}$ in the diagonal form (10), the axes of the coordinate system are said to be the *principal axes* of the medium. The example of the preceding article assumed this form.

[3] See for example L. D. Landau and E. M. Lifshitz, *Electrodynamics of Continuous Media*, Addison-Wesley, Reading, Mass., 1960, p. 58. An exception occurs when a steady magnetic field is applied to the dielectric, as is illustrated by an example later in this chapter.

[4] I. S. Sokolnikoff, *Tensor Analysis*, John Wiley and Sons, New York, 1951.

A similar formulation applies to magnetic properties. That is, when the magnetization $\bar{M}$ resulting from an applied field $\bar{H}$ depends on the orientation of $\bar{H}$, we may write the relation in Eq. 2.22(3) as

$$\bar{B} = \hat{\mu}\bar{H} \tag{11}$$

and Eq. 2.38(4) as

$$\hat{\mu} = \mu_0[\hat{I} + \hat{\chi}_m]. \tag{12}$$

In these $\hat{\mu}$ and $\hat{\chi}_m$ are tensor or matrix permeability and magnetic susceptibility, respectively, and $\hat{I}$ is the unit matrix. The tensor permeability, in the presence of an applied field, is not always symmetrical, as we shall see when we study gyrotropic media.

With the notation introduced in (6) and (11), Maxwell's equations take the form

$$\nabla \times \bar{E} = -j\omega\hat{\mu}\bar{H} \tag{13}$$
$$\nabla \times \bar{H} = j\omega\hat{\epsilon}\bar{E}. \tag{14}$$

Technically important materials sometimes have tensor permittivities or permeabilities, but seldom both. Therefore, in considering wave propagation in any anisotropic material we will assume that either permeability or permittivity is a scalar and the other is a tensor.

In the first class of media to be considered, permeability is a scalar and permittivity is a tensor. The equation basic to consideration of wave propagation for this class may be obtained by taking the curl of (13) with μ considered as a scalar. Substituting (14), we see that

$$\nabla \times \nabla \times \bar{E} = \omega^2\mu\hat{\epsilon}\bar{E}. \tag{15}$$

We may expand the left side of (15) by using a vector identity as we did to obtain the wave equation for isotropic media. The result is

$$\nabla^2\bar{E} - \nabla(\nabla \cdot \bar{E}) + \omega^2\mu\hat{\epsilon}\bar{E} = 0. \tag{16}$$

We will see that (16) can be reduced to a wave equation for $\bar{E}$ in certain circumstances where it is possible to handle the second term appropriately.

Where permittivity is a scalar and permeability is a tensor, an analogous derivation yields

$$\nabla^2\bar{H} - \nabla(\nabla \cdot \bar{H}) + \omega^2\epsilon\hat{\mu}\bar{H} = 0. \tag{17}$$

Again, the obtaining of a wave equation in $\bar{H}$ alone depends on appropriate treatment of the second term. In the case for which we will use (17), the divergence of $\bar{H}$ vanishes. In some problems it is not possible to get a wave equation in $\bar{E}$ or $\bar{H}$ only. In those cases it is just as well to work directly with Maxwell's equations as is discussed in Art. 9.15.

Problems

9.03a As a simple example of the idea of diagonalizing tensors by coordinate transformations, consider a two-dimensional system where

$$\begin{bmatrix} D_x \\ D_y \end{bmatrix} = \epsilon_0 \begin{bmatrix} 1.75 & 0.433 \\ 0.433 & 1.25 \end{bmatrix} \begin{bmatrix} E_x \\ E_y \end{bmatrix}.$$

Write expressions for $\bar{D}$ and $\bar{E}$ in a coordinate system rotated by an angle θ from the unprimed system. By combining these with the given relation between $\bar{D}$ and $\bar{E}$, find the amount of rotation necessary to put $\hat{\epsilon}$ in the diagonal form

$$\hat{\epsilon} = \epsilon_0 \begin{bmatrix} 1 & 0 \\ 0 & 2 \end{bmatrix}.$$

9.03b A plane wave propagating in an arbitrary direction $\bar{r} = \bar{a}_x x + \bar{a}_y y + \bar{a}_z z$ with a propagation constant $\bar{\gamma} = \bar{a}_x \gamma_x + \bar{a}_y \gamma_y + \bar{a}_z \gamma_z$ has a spatial variation of the form $e^{-\bar{\gamma} \cdot \bar{r}}$. Show that Eq. 9.03(15) can then be put in the form

$$\bar{\gamma} \times \bar{\gamma} \times \bar{E} = \omega^2 \mu \hat{\epsilon} \bar{E}.$$

This form is frequently used for the study of plane wave propagation in anisotropic media.

9.03c Characteristic vectors (eigenvectors) of a tensor are those vectors which when operated on by the tensor yield the original vector multiplied by a constant (characteristic value or eigenvalue). Discuss the application of (15) to the eigenvectors of $\hat{\epsilon}$ with particular reference to the relation between the propagation constant and the eigenvalues of $\hat{\epsilon}$.

9.03d Assuming $\mu = \mu_0$ for the dielectric of Prob. a, find the two field eigenvectors for uniform plane waves propagating in the z direction, and the corresponding propagation constants.

9.03e Demonstrate that the eigenvalues of a matrix (using a 2×2 matrix with symbolic coefficients as an example) are real if $A_{ij} = A_{ji}$ (symmetric matrix) and also if $A_{ij} = A_{ji}^*$ (Hermitian matrix). Discuss the implications with regard to propagation constants.

9.04 Double Refraction in Uniaxial Dielectrics

An important special case of dielectrics with diagonal permittivity tensors is that in which the components along two of the principal axes are equal and the third is different. Such a dielectric is called *uniaxial* and is exemplified by crystals having rhombohedral, tetragonal, and hexagonal structures, by the Kerr cell mentioned in Art. 9.02, and by the plasma with an infinite steady magnetic field to be described in Art. 9.05. The direction to which the one different permittivity element applies is called the *optical axis*.

It is convenient to introduce here the expression for a wave with a plane phase front oriented in an arbitrary direction. The physical quantities of the wave may be assumed to vary as $e^{-j\bar{\beta}\cdot\bar{r}}$ where

$$\bar{\beta} = \bar{a}_x\beta_x + \bar{a}_y\beta_y + \bar{a}_z\beta_z$$

is a vector phase factor and

$$\bar{r} = \bar{a}_x x + \bar{a}_y y + \bar{a}_z z \tag{1}$$

is the vector distance from an arbitrary origin. Thus we may write

$$\bar{E} = \bar{E}_0 e^{-j\bar{\beta}\cdot\bar{r}}; \quad \bar{D} = \bar{D}_0 e^{-j\bar{\beta}\cdot\bar{r}}; \quad \bar{H} = \bar{H}_0 e^{-j\bar{\beta}\cdot\bar{r}} \tag{2}$$

where $\bar{E}_0$, $\bar{D}_0$, and $\bar{H}_0$ are the constant complex vectors representing the electric field intensity, electric flux density, and magnetic field intensity with all spatial dependence removed. Constant phase surfaces are those for which $\bar{\beta} \cdot \bar{r} = \beta r \cos\theta = $ constant, where θ is the angle between $\bar{\beta}$ and $\bar{r}$. It is evident from Fig. 9.04a that the constant phase surfaces are planes.

Let us substitute $\bar{D}$ and $\bar{H}$ in the form (2) into Maxwell's equation

$$\nabla \times \bar{H} = j\omega\bar{D}$$

and apply the vector identity

$$\nabla \times (\Phi\bar{A}) = \nabla\Phi \times \bar{A} + \Phi\nabla \times \bar{A},$$

where Φ is a scalar and $\bar{A}$ is an arbitrary vector. The result is

$$(-j\bar{\beta} \times \bar{H}_0)e^{-j\bar{\beta}\cdot\bar{r}} + e^{-j\bar{\beta}\cdot\bar{r}}\nabla \times \bar{H}_0 = j\omega\bar{D}_0 e^{-j\bar{\beta}\cdot\bar{r}}.$$

Noting that $\nabla \times \bar{H}_0 = 0$ since $\bar{H}_0$ is spatially invariant, we obtain

$$-\bar{\beta} \times \bar{H} = \omega\bar{D}. \tag{3}$$

Application of the same operations to the other of Maxwell's curl equations, $\nabla \times \bar{E} = -j\omega\mu\bar{H}$, yields

$$\bar{\beta} \times \bar{E} = \omega\mu\bar{H}. \tag{4}$$

Since the vector product is normal to both terms in the product, (3) shows that $\bar{\beta}$ is perpendicular to $\bar{D}$. Similarly, (4) shows that $\bar{\beta}$ is also normal to $\bar{H}$. Therefore $\bar{\beta}$ is normal to the direction defined by $\bar{D}$ and $\bar{H}$ which means that constant phase surfaces contain $\bar{D}$ and $\bar{H}$.

Another important direction of wave propagation is the direction of power flow. This is defined by the Poynting vector

$$\bar{P} = \bar{E} \times \bar{H}. \tag{5}$$

In optics the unit vector in the direction of $\bar{P}$ is called the *ray vector*. For situations in which $\bar{D}$ and $\bar{E}$ are parallel, the energy flow is normal to the phase front and therefore in the direction of the phase velocity. This is

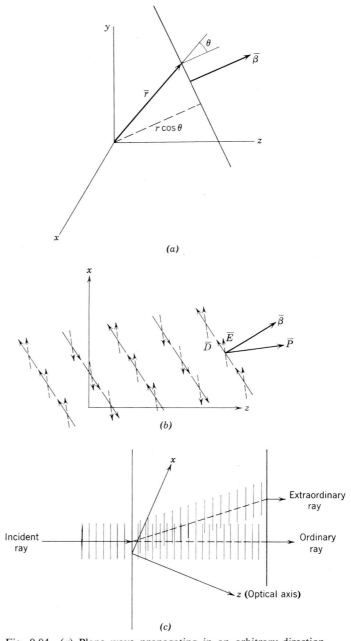

Fig. 9.04 (a) Plane wave propagating in an arbitrary direction.
(b) Vector relations in an extraordinary wave. (c) Double refraction.

the same as the behavior of waves in isotropic media. Since $\bar{P} = \bar{E} \times \bar{H}$ and $\bar{\beta}$ is in the direction of $\bar{D} \times \bar{H}$, the angle between $\bar{P}$ and $\bar{\beta}$ is the same as between $\bar{E}$ and $\bar{D}$ as seen in Fig. 9.04b.

The relation between $\bar{D}$ and $\bar{E}$ for a uniaxial crystal with optical axis in the z direction has the form

$$\begin{bmatrix} D_x \\ D_y \\ D_z \end{bmatrix} = \begin{bmatrix} \epsilon_1 & 0 & 0 \\ 0 & \epsilon_1 & 0 \\ 0 & 0 & \epsilon_2 \end{bmatrix} \begin{bmatrix} E_x \\ E_y \\ E_z \end{bmatrix} \tag{6}$$

where $\epsilon_1 \neq \epsilon_2$. From (6) we see that if the electric field vector has E_x and E_y components only, $\bar{D}$ and $\bar{E}$ are parallel and therefore power flow is along the wave normal $\bar{\beta}$. Thus the wave propagates as though in an isotropic medium and is called an *ordinary* wave. The electric field is normal to both $\bar{\beta}$ and the optical axis (z) and, therefore, to the plane containing them, which is called the *principal section*. A second type of wave having fields in the principal section may have components in the direction of the optical axis (z) and in the x and y directions. It is then clear from (6) that $\bar{D}$ and $\bar{E}$ are not parallel. Therefore the power flow is not in the direction of the wave normal, as is evident in Fig. 9.04b. This wave is called the *extraordinary* wave. If $\bar{\beta}$ is parallel with the optical axis, there is no extraordinary wave. If $\bar{\beta}$ is normal to the optical axis, the two waves have different $|\beta|$ but each has $\bar{D}$ parallel with $\bar{E}$ and, therefore, $\bar{P}$ parallel with $\bar{\beta}$. In general, however, there will be the two separate waves with energy propagation in different directions with different velocities.

The detailed study of reflection and refraction at surfaces of anisotropic media, in general, is beyond the scope of the present treatment. It is of interest, however, to see the qualitative behavior of a case which differs markedly from the familiar results for isotropic media. Consider a crystal face cut at an angle oblique to the optical axis as shown in Fig. 9.04c. The y axis is normal outward from the page. It is assumed that the normally incident ray has tangential electric field vectors both in the plane of the page and normal to it. Both ordinary and extraordinary waves are excited in the crystal. The ordinary wave has its electric field oriented in the y direction and, therefore, its $\bar{D}$ and $\bar{E}$ are parallel. Thus $\bar{P}$ and $\bar{\beta}$ are parallel as is indicated in Fig. 9.04c by having the path of the ray normal to the constant phase surfaces. The remaining component of the incident electric field lies in the plane of the page and is responsible for excitation of the extraordinary wave. Since the angle of incidence was taken to be zero, the boundary is a constant-phase plane. We have argued previously in connection with (3) and (4) that $\bar{D}$ lies in the planes of constant phase; therefore, it must be parallel with the surface of the crystal. But, because

$\bar{D}$ and $\bar{E}$ are not parallel within the crystal, the energy propagates at an angle oblique to the surface as shown in Fig. 9.04c. This splitting of the refracted waves is called *double refraction* or *birefringence*. Note that the two rays upon emergence from the planar slab are again parallel (Fig. 9.04c). This is because continuity conditions at the boundary surfaces are in terms of phase velocities, and these have the same direction for ordinary and extraordinary rays.

This article has been concerned with uniaxial crystals (and other media with the same form of dielectric tensor) and it is of interest to note here the dielectric behavior of the remaining types of crystals. All three elements of the tensor are identical for crystals with cubic symmetry and these behave as isotropic materials. All other crystal symmetries lead to tensors in which no two elements are identical and in this case the wave propagation becomes more complicated.

Problems

9.04a Suppose a beam of light is normally incident on a surface of a calcite ($CaCO_3$) crystal as shown in Fig. 9.04c. The optical axis is at an angle of 29° from the inward surface normal. Take $\epsilon_1 = 2.7$ and $\epsilon_2 = 2.2$ in Eq. 9.04(6). Treat the incident light as an unpolarized *TEM* wave over the cross section of the beam. Find the spatial separation of ordinary and extraordinary rays at the opposite (parallel) crystal surface 1 cm away.

9.04b For a ray incident at an angle upon a planar slab of double refracting (birefringent) material, show that the two emergent rays are parallel, based on the continuity of phase velocity argued in Art. 9.04.

9.04c Derive an expression for the angle between $\bar{P}$ and $\bar{\beta}$ assuming $\mu = \mu_0$. Evaluate the result for uniaxial dielectrics for the ordinary and extraordinary waves in terms of the angle between $\bar{D}$ and the optical axis.

9.04d Use the formula in Prob. 9.03b to find the propagation constants of the ordinary and extraordinary waves for the conditions of Prob. *a*.

9.05 Permittivity Tensor for a Plasma or Neutralized Electron Stream in an Infinite Magnetic Field

The aim of this article is to study the convection currents arising by virtue of the movement of the electrons in a highly ionized gas or plasma and to derive an equivalent permittivity in tensor form. The special, but important, case in which the magnetic field may be considered uniform in space and infinite in magnitude is studied. The ions are assumed immobile for simplicity. The results of this section are applicable for studies of waves in plasmas as well as for studies of waves in electron streams for which the presence of ions is simply a means for avoiding consideration of the static electric fields.

The convection current is given by Eq. 4.06(7) as

$$\bar{i} = \rho\bar{v},\tag{1}$$

where ρ is the charge density. The reader will recall from elementary particle dynamics that electrons, given velocities transverse to a finite magnetic field, spiral around the field lines. The radius of curvature of the electron path is inversely proportional to the magnetic field strength B_0; raising B_0 to infinity reduces the radius to zero. Therefore, all transverse motion is precluded and the electrons can move only in the z direction and (1) may be written in scalar form

$$i_z = \rho v_z.\tag{2}$$

To expand the utility of the resulting expressions, the possibility of an average drift v_{0z} of the electrons in the z direction will be included. Then (2) may be written for the electrons as

$$I_0 + i_z = (\rho_0 + \rho_1)(v_{0z} + v_{1z}),\tag{3}$$

where I_0 is the average current, i_z is the a-c current, ρ_0 is the average electron charge density (equal to the ion density), ρ_1 is the a-c charge density resulting from bunching of electrons, and v_{1z} is the a-c electron velocity. This may be simplified to

$$i_z = \rho_0 v_{1z} + \rho_1 v_{0z}\tag{4}$$

by using $I_0 = \rho_0 v_{0z}$ and assuming that the product of the a-c quantities $\rho_1 v_{1z}$ is small compared with the remaining terms.

The Lorentz force equation [Eq. 4.06(5)] for the z component of velocity of an electron with charge $-e$ and mass m is

$$\frac{dv_z}{dt} = -\frac{e}{m} E_z.\tag{5}$$

The magnetic force term is zero since the d-c magnetic field is in the z direction and effects of a-c magnetic fields are neglected as discussed in Art. 6.06. From the total derivative as expanded in Eq. 6.06(3), we note that, for this case,

$$\frac{dv_z}{dt} = \frac{\partial v_z}{\partial t} + \frac{\partial v_z}{\partial z} v_z.\tag{6}$$

The results can be put into a convenient form if we choose the variations of a-c quantities in the z direction to be given by $e^{-\gamma_z z}$. By letting $v_z = v_{0z} + v_{1z}$, (6) becomes

$$\frac{dv_z}{dt} = j\omega v_{1z}e^{j\omega t - \gamma_z z} - (v_{0z} + v_{1z})\gamma_z v_{1z}e^{j\omega t - \gamma_z z}.\tag{7}$$

There may be variations in the x and y directions, but these do not enter explicitly in (7); if $v_{0z} \gg v_{1z}$, this expression may be considered linear in v_{1z} by neglecting v_{1z} in the parenthesis of the last term. Combining (5) and (7), with the foregoing stipulation, we obtain

$$(j\omega - \gamma_z v_{0z})v_{1z} = -\frac{e}{m}E_z, \tag{8}$$

where $e^{j\omega t - \gamma_z z}$ variations are implicit.

The a-c charge density may be found in terms of the current by use of the continuity equation, Eq. 4.03(5)

$$\nabla \cdot \bar{i} = -\frac{\partial \rho}{\partial t}. \tag{9}$$

With the foregoing assumptions regarding direction of current and form of variations, (9) becomes

$$\gamma_z i_z = j\omega \rho_1. \tag{10}$$

Substituting v_{1z} from (8) and ρ_1 from (10) in (4), one obtains

$$i_z = -j\omega \frac{\rho_0(e/m)}{(j\omega - \gamma_z v_{0z})^2} E_z. \tag{11}$$

Introducing the plasma frequency, $\omega_p = (Ne^2/\epsilon_0 m)^{1/2}$, where N is the electron number density, we have

$$i_z = j\omega\epsilon_0 \frac{\omega_p{}^2}{(j\omega - \gamma_z v_{0z})^2} E_z. \tag{12}$$

The equivalent permittivity tensor may then be found from

$$\nabla \times \bar{H} = j\omega\epsilon_0 \bar{E} + \bar{i} = j\omega\hat{\epsilon}\bar{E}, \tag{13}$$

where

$$\hat{\epsilon} = \begin{bmatrix} \epsilon_0 & 0 & 0 \\ 0 & \epsilon_0 & 0 \\ 0 & 0 & \epsilon_{33} \end{bmatrix} \tag{14}$$

and

$$\epsilon_{33} = \epsilon_0\left[1 - \frac{\omega_p{}^2}{(\omega + j\gamma_z v_{0z})^2}\right].$$

We see that the permittivity tensor has the same form as for a uniaxial crystal. The situation here is complicated, however, by the dependence of ϵ_{33} on the propagation constant.

We note, in review, that by means of certain assumptions, an expression for the permittivity has been found in a form independent of the field magnitudes. This linearization will permit the writing of linear wave equations, thus facilitating solution and allowing the use of superposition. The assumptions used were $\rho_1 \ll \rho_0$ and $v_{1z} \ll v_{0z}$. Let us examine the validity of the equations for a stationary plasma, $v_{0z} = 0$. Here the second term on the right side of (4) vanishes and $\rho_1 v_{1z}$ is still small compared with the remaining terms. In (8) we assumed $v_{1z} \ll v_{0z}$. If v_{0z} is zero, the effect of keeping v_{1z} must be considered. Dividing (7) by γ_z and assuming pure propagation $(\gamma_z = j\beta_z)$, we see we must compare ω/β_z and the neglected v_{1z}. The first of these is the phase velocity of the wave in the z direction. Then, in order to use (14), with v_{0z} set to zero, as the permittivity tensor for the stationary plasma, we must require the signal levels to be small enough that $v_{1z} \ll v_p$.

Problems

9.05a Repeat the derivation of this article to find the permittivity tensor taking into account the a-c motion of ions as well as electrons.

9.05b Repeat the derivation of this article taking into account the effect of collisions in the manner of Art. 6.06, considering movement of electrons only.

9.06 TEM Waves on a Plasma with Infinite Magnetic Field

In the special cases of *TEM* waves propagating parallel or perpendicular to an infinite magnetic field in a plasma as indicated in Figs. 9.06a and 9.06b, the wave behavior is the same as for an anisotropic crystal, discussed

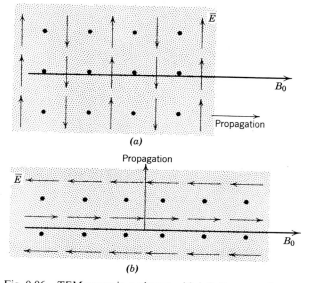

Fig. 9.06 *TEM* waves in a plasma with infinite magnetic field. Wave propagation (a) parallel with magnetic field; (b) perpendicular to magnetic field.

in Arts. 9.02 and 9.04. Here we will use the permittivity tensor developed in the previous article; the infinite magnetic field is in the z direction. For the cases to be considered here, $\nabla \cdot \bar{E} = 0$ in the second term of 9.03(16) since either the field or its partial derivative is zero in every direction. The more complicated problem of propagation of *TEM* waves at an arbitrary angle involves a nonvanishing $\nabla \cdot \bar{E}$ and will not be treated here. A method of treating a finite $\nabla \cdot \bar{E}$ is examined in the next article. Since μ can be assumed to have its free-space value, μ_0, Eq. 9.03(16) becomes

$$\nabla^2 \bar{E} + \omega^2 \mu_0 \hat{\epsilon} \bar{E} = 0. \tag{1}$$

If the *TEM* wave is propagating in the z direction as $e^{-\gamma z}$, the field $\bar{E}$ may have x and y components only. Separating (1) and using the assumed $e^{-\gamma z}$ variation and the dielectric tensor, Eq. 9.05(14), we obtain

$$(\gamma^2 + \omega^2 \mu_0 \epsilon_0) E_x = 0 \tag{2}$$

and the same form for E_y. Thus we see that such a wave propagates as though it were in free space, as would be expected on the basis that no electron motion can be induced normal to the infinite magnetic field.

Now consider a *TEM* wave propagating in the x direction. Note that here $\gamma_z = 0$. For a wave with $\bar{E} = \bar{a}_y E_y$, (1) may be separated to give

$$(\gamma^2 + \omega^2 \mu_0 \epsilon_0) E_y = 0, \tag{3}$$

which is again a wave propagating as though in free space. But, for a wave with $\bar{E} = \bar{a}_z E_z$ we have from Eq. 9.05(14) with $\gamma_z = 0$,

$$(\gamma^2 + \omega^2 \mu_0 \epsilon_{33}) E_z = 0, \tag{4}$$

where
$$\epsilon_{33} = \epsilon_0 \left[1 - \frac{\omega_p^2}{\omega^2} \right]. \tag{5}$$

We see that if a wave propagates normal to an infinite magnetic field with the electric field directed along the d-c magnetic field, the propagation is the same as for a transverse wave propagating through a plasma without a magnetic field. That is, the phase factor

$$\beta = \omega \sqrt{\mu_0 \epsilon_{33}} \tag{6}$$

goes to zero as the wave frequency approaches the plasma frequency, and for lower frequencies the wave does not propagate; where electric forces are parallel with the magnetic field, it is to be expected that the latter will have no effect.

A plane wave having both E_z and E_y components propagating in the x direction can be treated as two separate waves having different phase velocities, as was done with the anisotropic crystal. Thus the plasma will act to convert linear polarization to elliptic polarization above the cutoff frequency $\omega = \omega_p$.

Problems

9.06a A linearly polarized plane wave with equal y and z components of electric field is launched in the x direction in a neutral plasma with infinite magnetic field in the z direction. The frequency is 4000 Mc and the number density of electrons is 10^{17} per cubic meter. Find the distance in which the linearly polarized wave becomes circularly polarized.

9.06b Consider a periodic series of infinite parallel sheets of stationary plasma normal to the x axis, each having thickness t and center-to-center spacing d. Assume infinite magnetic field in the z direction and plasma frequency $\omega_p = \sqrt{2}\,\omega$. Plane waves propagate in the x direction with electric field in the z direction. Find the coefficients of an admittance matrix, Eq. 8.19(10), for one period using the transmission-line analogy of Art. 6.08. Sketch the ω-β diagram.

9.07 Space-Charge Waves on a Plasma with Infinite Magnetic Field

In Art. 9.06 we considered waves having no electric field component in the direction of propagation. Let us now examine the case of waves where a component of $\bar{E}$ is considered to exist in the direction of propagation. These waves, called *space-charge waves*, will be seen to have phase velocities approximately equal to the drift velocity of the plasma. They play the central role in the amplification of microwaves in electron-beam devices. A moving plasma has the essential features of an electron stream except for the static electric fields. The neglect of the d-c electric fields typically causes little difference in the results.

Only waves propagating in the direction of the z-directed magnetic field, as shown in Fig. 9.07, will be considered. Using Gauss's law and assumed $e^{-\gamma z}$ form of variations, the z component of Eq. 9.03(16) may be written as

$$\nabla_t^2 E_z + \gamma^2 E_z + \gamma \frac{\rho_1}{\epsilon_0} + \omega^2 \mu_0 \epsilon_{33} E_z = 0 \tag{1}$$

where $\nabla_t^2 E_z$ contains partial derivatives transverse to the z direction. Combining Eqs. 9.05(10) and (12) and taking account of the fact that $\gamma_z = \gamma$, we find

$$\rho_1 = - \frac{\epsilon_0 \omega_p^2 \gamma}{(\omega + j\gamma v_{0z})^2} E_z. \tag{2}$$

Then combining (1) and (2) and using the value of ϵ_{33} from Eq. 9.05(14), we obtain the desired wave equation

$$\nabla_t^2 E_z + (\gamma^2 + \omega^2 \mu_0 \epsilon_0)\left[1 - \frac{\omega_p^2}{(\omega + j\gamma v_{0z})^2}\right] E_z = 0. \tag{3}$$

We will restrict our attention in this article to uniform plane longitudinal waves; that is, waves with electric fields along the direction of propagation

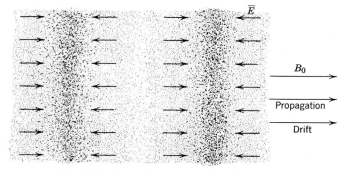

Fig. 9.07 Space-charge waves in a plasma.

and no transverse variations. Therefore the first term of (3) vanishes. Also the bracketed term must vanish since, from Eq. 9.05(13) and (14), it equals, when multiplied by $\bar{E}$ the z component of $\nabla \times \bar{H}$, which must be zero for a uniform wave. Thus,

$$1 - \frac{\omega_p^2}{(\omega + j\gamma v_{0z})^2} = 0. \tag{4}$$

This leads to two possible waves with propagation constants

$$\gamma_{1,2} = j\beta_{1,2} = j\,\frac{\omega \pm \omega_p}{v_{0z}}. \tag{5}$$

Since γ must be given by (5) to assure uniformity of the wave $[(\nabla \times \bar{H})_z = 0]$ for the longitudinal waves, the term $\gamma^2 + \omega^2 \mu_0 \epsilon_0$ yields only the usual *TEM field waves* with zero E_z for the infinitely broad stream. The waves with propagation constants given by (5) are called *space-charge waves*.[5] Typically, $\omega_p \ll \omega$, and we may use the binomial expansion to obtain the phase velocities in the form

$$(v_p)_{1,2} \equiv \frac{\omega}{\beta_{1,2}} \simeq v_{0z}\left(1 \mp \frac{\omega_p}{\omega}\right), \tag{6}$$

[5] S. Ramo, "Space charge and field waves in electron beams," *Phys. Rev.* **56** (1939) 276; the concept was first usefully applied to electron devices by W. C. Hahn, "Small signal theory of velocity modulated electron beams," *Gen. Elect. Rev.* **42** (1939) 258; 497.

the values of which are seen to be somewhat greater and somewhat less than the drift velocity v_{0z}. The group velocity is

$$v_g = \frac{\partial \omega}{\partial \beta} = v_{0z} \tag{7}$$

for both space-charge waves. With the plasma drift v_{0z} reduced to zero, a perturbation of the electron charge density leads to a local oscillation at a frequency $\omega = \omega_p$ but the effect does not propagate.

In Art. 9.08 we shall study the case of a plasma of finite cross section in which the first term of (3) does not vanish and the foregoing conclusions are modified.

Problem

9.07 Evaluate the propagation constants in Eq. 9.07(5) for a beam of electrons which has been accelerated to an energy of 2000 volts. The current density is 10^5 amperes per square meter. Plot an ω-β diagram for the space-charge waves. For convenience use $\omega \sqrt{\mu_0 \epsilon_0}$ as the ordinate.

9.08   Space-Charge Waves in Cylindrical Waveguides

In this article we will examine the effect on space-charge waves when a moving plasma is confined within a perfectly conducting waveguide of circular cross section. The guide of radius a will be assumed to be filled with the plasma having electrons with drift velocity v_{0z} along the infinite magnetic field lying parallel with the axis of the cylinder. The model for the electron dynamics is the same as that used in the preceding articles. The appropriate differential equation for this situation is Eq. 7.16(1) with the constant k_c^2 replaced by the coefficient of the second term of Eq. 9.07(3):

$$\frac{\partial^2 E_z}{\partial r^2} + \frac{1}{r}\frac{\partial E_z}{\partial r} + \frac{1}{r^2}\frac{\partial^2 E_z}{\partial \phi^2} = -(\gamma^2 + \omega^2 \mu_0 \epsilon_0)\left[1 - \frac{\omega_p^2}{(\omega + j\gamma v_{0z})^2}\right]E_z. \tag{1}$$

Since the form is the same as Eq. 7.16(1), the solutions are those given as Eqs. 7.16(4) to (7). The wave we are considering is a transverse magnetic or E wave with finite E_z. (The transverse electric waves have electric field components only in directions in which the electrons are prohibited from moving by the infinite magnetic field; the solutions are those given for an empty guide in Art. 8.04.) Since the boundary conditions require the electric field E_z to be zero at a finite radius a and finite on the axis, the appropriate solution has the form

$$E_z = A J_n(k_c r)\begin{cases}\sin n\phi \\ \cos n\phi\end{cases}, \tag{2}$$

where the choice between the cosine and sine functions depends on orientation of the coordinate system.

The boundary condition to be satisfied is $E_z(a) = 0$, so

$$J_n(k_c a) = 0. \tag{3}$$

This condition is satisfied where

$$k_c = \frac{p_{nl}}{a} \tag{4}$$

where p_{nl} is one of a doubly infinite set of roots of the Bessel function $J_n(x)$. For each root there is a different mode of propagation having a different distribution in the transverse plane ($z = $ constant). The modes which are actually excited in a plasma depend on the boundary conditions required on a transverse plane. The relation between the propagation constant and frequency is found by equating the group of constants in (1) defined as k_c^2 with the value of k_c^2 imposed by the boundary condition (4):

$$(\gamma^2 + \omega^2 \mu_0 \epsilon_0) \left[1 - \frac{\omega_p^2}{(\omega + j\gamma v_{0z})^2} \right] = \left(\frac{p_{nl}}{a} \right)^2. \tag{5}$$

Equation (5) is quartic, having two solutions which are perturbed waveguide (or *field*) modes. The ω-β curve of the perturbed field mode is compared in Fig. 9.08a with the ω-β curve for the corresponding empty guide mode. The two remaining roots of (5) give the relation between γ (and hence, β) and ω for space-charge waves which are perturbed by the guide. These are compared in Fig. 9.08b with the ω-β relation for the corresponding infinite plasma. It is seen that at high frequencies the effect of the walls is reduced and the space-charge waves propagate as in an infinite plasma. The space-charge modes are seen to have no cutoff frequency.

The cutoff frequency for a field mode may be found by setting $\gamma = 0$ in (5). Thus

$$\omega_c^2 \mu_0 \epsilon_0 \left(1 - \frac{\omega_p^2}{\omega^2} \right) = \left(\frac{p_{ni}}{a} \right)^2 \tag{6}$$

or

$$f_c = \frac{1}{2\pi \sqrt{\mu_0 \epsilon_0}} \left[\left(\frac{p_{nl}}{a} \right)^2 + \mu_0 \epsilon_0 \omega_p^2 \right]^{1/2}. \tag{7}$$

By reference to Eq. 9.06(6) we see that the left side of (6) is the square of the phase factor for a wave with zero z variations, propagating perpendicular to the magnetic field. The free-space wavelength and its relation to the size of the guide was stated as a cutoff condition for the guides of Chapter 8. Here again, the same picture of a standing-wave pattern in the transverse direction at cutoff applies. However, the significant wavelength includes the effect of the plasma in this case.

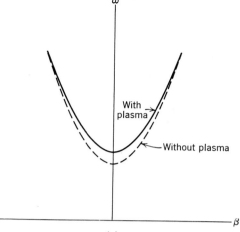

(a)

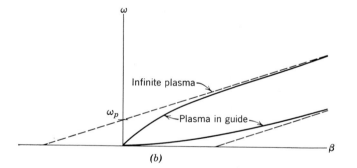

(b)

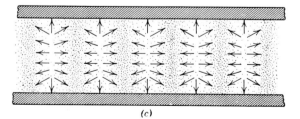

(c)

Fig. 9.08 (a) Modification $\omega - \beta$ diagram of a waveguide mode by plasma. (b) Comparison of $\omega - \beta$ curves for space-charge waves in infinite and bounded plasmas. (c) Modification of the fields of space-charge waves by conducting boundary.

The presence of the finite boundaries reduces the effect of space charge in an electron stream or moving plasma because some of the a-c flux leaks outside the stream as shown in Fig. 9.08c. For many purposes it is useful to assume axial symmetry and introduce the effect of the boundary by defining a *reduced plasma frequency* ω_q

$$\omega_q = F\omega_p,$$

where F is the reduction factor. Then the propagation constants are written in the same form as for the finite stream but with ω_p replaced by ω_q:

$$\beta_{1,2} = \frac{\omega \pm \omega_q}{v_{0z}}. \tag{8}$$

For space-charge waves, $\omega^2\mu_0\epsilon_0 \ll \gamma^2$ (phase velocity much less than speed of light). Making this simplification, substituting (8) in (5), using the definition of F, and making the assumption that space charge is not very high and frequency not very low so that $F\omega_p \ll \omega$, one can find

$$F^2 = \frac{1}{1 + \left(\dfrac{p_{01}}{a}\dfrac{v_{0z}}{\omega}\right)^2}. \tag{9}$$

We can consider F to be a measure of the leakage of the flux outside the stream. It is seen that F decreases for higher-order modes and smaller ratios of radius a to wavelength $\lambda = 2\pi v_{0z}/\omega$, as is to be expected from flux leakage considerations. An analysis similar to that described above but for a plasma partially filling the guide can be carried through. Curves of the reduction factor as a function of the beam radius with the ratio of waveguide radius to beam radius as a parameter may be found in several texts.[6]

Problems

9.08a Plot a curve of reduction factor F as a function of $\omega a/v_{0z}$ for the lowest-order mode for the case of the electron stream filling the guide.

9.08b Suppose the fast and slow, lowest-order, axially symmetric, space-charge waves are equally excited at $z = 0$ in a 50 ma electron stream filling a cylinder of radius 0.050 inch. Take frequency to be 3000 Mc and drift velocity 10^7 meters per second. Assume ion neutralization of static space-charge fields and find the value of z at the first minimum of the standing wave pattern, using the results of Prob. *a*.

9.08c Sketch field lines as in Fig. 9.08c for a cylindrical plasma of smaller radius than the concentric waveguide. Discuss the physical meaning of the plasma-frequency reduction factor for this case.

[6] See, for example, *Space Charge Waves*, A. H. W. Beck, Pergamon Press, New York, 1958, Chapter 4.

9.09   Space-Charge Waves in a Helix

Here we examine the very interesting example of an electron stream (or moving plasma) passing through a helix. For simplicity, the stream will be assumed to fill the helix and to be guided by an infinite magnetic field parallel with the axis. In an actual helix, the electrons are prevented from grazing the metal surface for practical reasons; in our idealization the infinite magnetic field permits having the stream pass arbitrarily close to the helix without touching it. Although in practical physical systems there is usually an appreciable space between the beam and the helix, an analysis based on a filled helix gives the correct form of the behavior, and is a good quantitative approximation for beams closely coupled to the helix. As in Art. 8.17 the helix is replaced by a so-called *sheath helix*, a cylindrical sheet which is perfectly conducting, but only in the direction of the conductors of the helix. Axial symmetry is assumed.

The presence of the electron stream affects only the transverse magnetic modes inside the helix since the fields can accelerate the electrons only parallel to the infinite magnetic field (z direction). The transverse electric waves have no components of electric field in the only allowed direction of motion of the electrons and therefore satisfy the charge-free wave equation. Obviously, the differential equation applicable outside the helix is unmodified by the presence of the electrons inside. The wave equation which must be applied for the E modes inside is Eq. 9.08(1), with the ϕ variation set to zero since axial symmetry has been assumed. The form is the same as the free-space wave equation but with $\tau^2 = -(\gamma^2 + \omega^2 \mu_0 \epsilon_0)$ replaced by the coefficient

$$p^2 = -(\gamma^2 + \omega^2 \mu_0 \epsilon_0)\left[1 - \frac{\omega_p^2}{(\omega + j\gamma v_{0z})^2}\right]. \tag{1}$$

The restrictions at $r = 0$ and $r = \infty$ are as in Art. 8.17 (E_z and H_z finite at $r = 0$ and zero at $r = \infty$). Thus, the forms of the components of the *TE* modes are identical with Eqs. 8.17(5) to (7). The components of the *TM* modes are as in Eqs. 8.17(2) to (4) but with τ replaced by p for $r < a$. The boundary conditions at the helix are those given by Eqs. 8.17(9) to (12). Substitution of the field components into Eqs. 8.17(9) to (12) gives a homogeneous set of equations with field amplitudes as dependent variables. A nontrivial solution requires that the determinant of the set be zero, from which it follows that

$$\frac{pI_1(pa)}{I_0(pa)} = -\frac{\tau K_1(\tau a)}{K_0(\tau a)} + \frac{\tau^3 \tan^2 \psi}{\omega^2 \mu_0 \epsilon_0}\left[\frac{I_0(\tau a)}{I_1(\tau a)} + \frac{K_0(\tau a)}{K_1(\tau a)}\right]. \tag{2}$$

This relation contains implicitly the relation between the propagation constant γ and frequency ω for the various possible modes of propagation.

The most useful of these modes has a phase velocity near that of the free helix $v_p \simeq c \tan \psi$. Typically, it can be assumed with reasonable accuracy that $\tau a \gg 1$ and $pa \gg 1$, that is, the radius of the helix is of the order of a space-charge wavelength at the operating frequency. The ratios of Bessel functions in (2) tend to unity with this approximation. Then

$$p = -\tau\left(1 - \frac{2\tau^2}{\omega^2\mu_0\epsilon_0}\cot^2\psi\right). \tag{3}$$

Let us further require that the drift velocity of the electrons be equal to the approximate value of the phase velocity on the free helix. That is,

$$\frac{\omega}{v_{0z}} = \frac{\omega}{c\tan\psi} = \omega\sqrt{\mu_0\epsilon_0}\cot\psi. \tag{4}$$

Substituting (4) into (3) and equating (3) with the square root of (1), one obtains

$$1 - \frac{\omega_p{}^2}{(\omega + j\gamma v_{0z})^2} = 1 + \frac{2\gamma^2}{(\omega/v_{0z})^2}, \tag{5}$$

where τ^2 has been replaced by its approximate value $-\gamma^2$. To find values for γ it is convenient to make use of the approximation $\gamma \simeq j(\omega/v_{0z})$. Let

$$\gamma = j\frac{\omega}{v_{0z}}(1 + \delta), \tag{6}$$

where δ is a small dimensionless quantity. Substituting (6) in (5) gives a relation for δ having third and higher powers. If the higher powers are neglected, there remains

$$\delta^3 = -C_1{}^3 \tag{7}$$

where $C_1{}^3 = \omega_p{}^2/8\omega^2$. Taking the cube root of (7) we have the three roots

$$\delta_1 = -C_1; \quad \delta_2 = \frac{C_1}{2}(1 + j\sqrt{3}); \quad \delta_3 = \frac{C_1}{2}(1 - j\sqrt{3}) \tag{8}$$

and the corresponding values of γ are

$$\gamma_1 = j\frac{\omega}{v_{0z}}(1 - C_1) \tag{9}$$

$$\gamma_2 = -\frac{\sqrt{3}}{2}\frac{\omega C_1}{v_{0z}} + j\frac{\omega}{v_{0z}}\left(1 + \frac{C_1}{2}\right) \tag{10}$$

$$\gamma_3 = \frac{\sqrt{3}}{2}\frac{\omega C_1}{v_{0z}} + j\frac{\omega}{v_{0z}}\left(1 + \frac{C_1}{2}\right). \tag{11}$$

Thus we see that the modes which can propagate with phase velocity near the electron velocity include one wave of constant amplitude, one that decays, and one that grows. The existence of a growing wave in such a system forms the basis of operation of electron-beam, traveling wave amplifiers.[7] The r-f power increase with distance associated with the growing wave is derived from the kinetic energy of the electrons.

Problems

9.09a Use relations of Art. 9.05 relating the a-c current and velocity to electric field for a single mode to write a set of linear equations giving total a-c current, total a-c velocity, and total electric field E_{zT} in terms of the fields of the individual modes of this article [Eqs. (9), (10), (11)]. Assume total a-c current and a-c velocity to be zero at $z = 0$ and solve the equations to show that the electric fields of each wave is one third of the total field.

9.09b Suppose a 1000-volt beam of electrons filling a one-centimeter diameter helix and moving at the phase velocity of the empty helix carries a current of 10 milliamperes. A signal at 3000 megacycles applied to the helix at $z = 0$ excites all three waves to the same magnitude. Find the value of z beyond which the growing wave exceeds either of the other two by a factor of 10.

9.09c For the situation where $v_z = i_z = 0$ at beginning of the helix and the length L of the helix-beam system is large enough that the growing wave dominates, as in Prob. *b*, show that the gain in decibels can be expressed by

$$G(db) = 10 \log \left| \frac{E_z(L)}{E_z(0)} \right|^2 = -9.54 + 47.3 C_1 N,$$

where C_1 is the parameter in Art. 9.09 and N is the number of space-charge wavelengths in the length L. (A space-charge wavelength is $\lambda_{sc} \equiv 2\pi v_{0z}/\omega_p$.) This is the gain expression for a traveling-wave amplifier given by Pierce.[7]

9.09d Review the assumptions made in Probs. *a* to *c* and in the appropriate parts of the text to define the model to which the results of Prob. *c* apply.

GYROTROPIC MEDIA

9.10 Stationary Plasma in Finite Magnetic Field

The permittivity tensor for a plasma is somewhat more complicated if the magnetic field is not infinite. An electric field component transverse to the magnetic field can give rise to transverse electron motion, whereas with infinite magnetic field (cf. Arts. 9.05 to 9.09) all transverse motion is

[7] J. R. Pierce, *Traveling Wave Tubes*, Van Nostrand, Princeton, N.J., 1950; a shorter treatment is given, for example, in Ref. 6, Chapter 7.

precluded. One transverse velocity interacts with the magnetic field to produce motion in the orthogonal transverse direction. Thus, if the magnetic field is z-directed, an electric field in the x direction causes motion in both the x and y directions. As a result, off-diagonal terms appear in the matrix relating current to electric field and therefore also appear in the permittivity tensor. We will find, in the course of the derivation, that the nature of the magnetic forces is such that an antisymmetric permittivity tensor ($\epsilon_{ij} = -\epsilon_{ji}$; $i \neq j$) is obtained for the model chosen. Thus this is a simple example of a gyrotropic medium as defined in Art. 9.01. It will be shown in the following article that the natural waves here are circularly polarized.

The plasma will be considered stationary in the first part of this analysis. A steady drift of the electrons is included at the end of the article. As in the previous articles it is assumed that the ions play no role in the a-c phenomena. They are considered to serve only to neutralize the d-c fields of the electrons. The effect of collisions and thermal velocities will be neglected here. The forces resulting from the magnetic component of the wave are neglected following the argument of Art. 6.06. The steady magnetic field is chosen to be spatially uniform and z-directed.

As in the previous sections, the first step is to find the convection current in the plasma. Equation 9.05(1) may be written as

$$\bar{I}_0 + \bar{i}_1 = (\rho_0 + \rho_1)(\bar{v}_0 + \bar{v}_1). \tag{1}$$

Here $\bar{v}_0$ and $\bar{I}_0$ are equal to zero since the plasma is assumed stationary. Thus, neglecting products of a-c terms as in Art. 9.05, we see that

$$\bar{i}_1 = \rho_0 \bar{v}_1. \tag{2}$$

The velocity $\bar{v}_1$ is found from the Lorentz equation [Eq. 4.06(5)]

$$\frac{d\bar{v}_1}{dt} = -\frac{e}{m}(\bar{E} + \bar{v}_1 \times \bar{B}). \tag{3}$$

To find the conditions required for linearization of the equations, let us consider a plane wave having arbitrary direction of propagation, such that the a-c spatial variations may be expressed by

$$e^{\bar{\gamma} \cdot \bar{r}} = e^{-(\gamma_x x + \gamma_y y + \gamma_z z)}. \tag{4}$$

More complicated fields can be considered to be a superposition of plane waves as was shown for a waveguide mode in Art. 7.08.

The left side of (3), expanded in partial derivatives as in Eq. 6.06(3) and evaluated using (4), becomes

$$\frac{d\bar{v}_1}{dt} = (j\omega - \gamma_x v_{1x} - \gamma_y v_{1y} - \gamma_z v_{1z})\bar{v}_1. \tag{5}$$

Consider the situation where $\bar{\gamma} = j\bar{\beta}$. If the a-c velocity is assumed to be small compared with any possible phase velocities, (5) reduces to

$$\frac{d\bar{v}_1}{dt} \simeq j\omega\bar{v}_1. \tag{6}$$

Writing (3) in component form using (6), we have

$$j\omega v_{1x} = -\frac{e}{m} E_{1x} - \frac{e}{m} B_z v_{1y}$$

$$j\omega v_{1y} = -\frac{e}{m} E_{1y} + \frac{e}{m} B_z v_{1x} \tag{7}$$

$$j\omega v_{1z} = -\frac{e}{m} E_{1z}.$$

Equations (7) may be solved for velocity components in terms of the fields with the result

$$v_{1x} = \frac{-j\omega(e/m)E_{1x} + (e/m)\omega_c E_{1y}}{\omega_c^2 - \omega^2}$$

$$v_{1y} = \frac{-(e/m)\omega_c E_{1x} - j\omega(e/m)E_{1y}}{\omega_c^2 - \omega^2} \tag{8}$$

$$v_{1z} = \frac{j(e/m)}{\omega} E_{1z}$$

where $\omega_c = (e/m)B_z$ is called the *angular cyclotron frequency*.

Substituting (8) into (2) and proceeding as in Eqs. 9.05(13) and (14), we find the permittivity tensor as

$$\hat{\epsilon} = \begin{bmatrix} \epsilon_{11} & \epsilon_{12} & 0 \\ \epsilon_{21} & \epsilon_{22} & 0 \\ 0 & 0 & \epsilon_{33} \end{bmatrix} \tag{9}$$

where

$$\epsilon_{11} = \epsilon_{22} = \epsilon_0 \left[1 + \frac{\omega_p^2}{\omega_c^2 - \omega^2} \right]$$

$$\epsilon_{12} = -\epsilon_{21} = \frac{j\omega_p^2(\omega_c/\omega)\epsilon_0}{\omega_c^2 - \omega^2} \tag{10}$$

$$\epsilon_{33} = \epsilon_0 \left[1 - \frac{\omega_p^2}{\omega^2} \right].$$

For plane waves in a plasma without a magnetic field, ω_p was observed to be a characteristic frequency in that no propagation occurs for $\omega < \omega_p$. It is clear from the form of (10) that the cyclotron frequency ω_c is also a characteristic frequency in this case. The singularity at ω_c is seen from (8) to result from the singularity in the velocities produced by the wave. A moving electron in a magnetic field without an electric field rotates at an angular frequency ω_c. If the applied alternating electric field oscillates at ω_c, it is so phased on each cycle that it continually pumps the electron to higher and higher velocities. This leads to the infinite response for the continuous-wave case in the model, although collisions would limit excursions in practice. Propagation through the ionosphere[8] is influenced by the earth's magnetic field, and leads to ordinary and extraordinary rays following different paths, somewhat as in Art. 9.04.

The permittivity tensor (9)–(10) is also applicable to a plasma drifting at a finite velocity if much less than the speed of light. All motions are with respect to the reference frame moving in the z direction with the plasma at its drift velocity. The permittivity tensor can be transformed to a stationary reference frame $z' = z + v_{0z}t$ where z is the coordinate in the drifting frame and t is time. This is known as a Galilean transformation[9] and is applicable for nonrelativistic translations. The coefficient values given in (10) are modified for the drifting plasma by simply replacing ω by $(\omega - v_{0z}\beta_z)$. The reader will recall this to be the expression for the Doppler-shifted frequency. It is not hard to see the reason for this transformation. Each of the electrons experiences an oscillating force resulting from the alternating electric field. If the electron is drifting at a velocity v_{0z}, it experiences an alternation of force at the rate of the Doppler-shifted frequency, rather than the actual field frequency.

Problem

9.10 Discuss the implications of Prob. 9.03e with respect to propagation constants for uniform plane waves in a plasma with finite magnetic field. Consider waves traveling along x, y, and z coordinates with various polarizations.

9.11   *TEM* Waves on a Plasma in a Finite Magnetic Field

The general study of waves on a plasma in a finite magnetic field reveals many interesting wave types including modifications of the space-charge

[8] E. C. Jordon, *Electromagnetic Waves and Radiating Systems*, Prentice-Hall, Englewood Cliffs, N.J., 1950.

[9] H. Goldstein, *Classical Mechanics*, Addison-Wesley, Cambridge, Mass., 1953.

waves found in Art. 9.07 to 9.09. Analysis reveals that a *TEM* wave can propagate (in an unbounded region), but that no pure *TE* or *TM* modes can exist. The actual hybrid modes have both E_z and H_z. Since the same phenomenon occurs in magnetized ferrites, we will postpone consideration of hybrid modes until Art. 9.15. The analysis of the waves similar to space-charge waves can be simplified by recognizing that the electric field can be found, approximately, as the gradient of a scalar potential for a useful range of conditions. A pure *TM* wave is found in this so-called *quasistatic* approximation. We will examine here only the simple *TEM* wave. The reader is referred to books on plasma waves for the details of the other types.[10]

We restrict our attention here to the very important case of *TEM* waves propagating in the z direction parallel with the applied steady magnetic field. Since we will use the phasor form of the wave equation, the appropriate form of z dependence is $e^{\mp \gamma z}$. Since the *TEM* wave has no E_z component and no variations of fields with respect to transverse coordinates, the $\nabla \cdot \bar{E} = 0$ and Eq. 9.03(16) may be written in matrix form as

$$
\frac{\partial^2}{\partial z^2}
\begin{bmatrix} E_x \\ E_y \\ E_z \end{bmatrix}
+ \omega^2 \mu_0
\begin{bmatrix} \epsilon_{11} & \epsilon_{12} & 0 \\ \epsilon_{21} & \epsilon_{22} & 0 \\ 0 & 0 & \epsilon_{33} \end{bmatrix}
\begin{bmatrix} E_x \\ E_y \\ E_z \end{bmatrix} = 0. \tag{1}
$$

Here we have made use of the form of the permittivity found in the previous article and the fact that μ differs negligibly from μ_0.

Previously, our wave solutions were taken to be linearly polarized waves which, by suitable orientation of the coordinate system, might have one component only (e.g., $\bar{E} = \bar{a}_x E_x$). If we substitute such an assumed form of solution in (1), we find a vector with only an x component in the first term whereas the vector in the second term has both x and y components. For the sum of two vectors to be zero, their components must individually add to zero. Therefore, the magnitude of the y component must be zero. This is possible only if either ϵ_{21} or E_x is zero. We know from Art. 9.10 that ϵ_{21} is not zero, and if E_x is zero, there is no wave. Thus we must conclude that a linearly polarized wave is not a possible solution; that is, it is not a *normal mode* of propagation for the medium.

Let us now consider the possibility of a solution in the form of a circularly polarized wave. For a clockwise polarized wave (field vectors

[10] T. Stix, *Theory of Plasma Waves*, McGraw-Hill, New York, 1963; or W. P. Allis, S. T. Buchsbaum, and A. Bers, *Waves in Anisotropic Plasmas*, MIT Press, Cambridge, Mass., 1963.

rotate clockwise as a function of time at a fixed plane in space, looking in the direction of propagation), the field has the form

$$\bar{E}_+^{cw} = E_+^{cw}(\bar{a}_x - j\bar{a}_y). \tag{2}$$

Substituting (2) in (1) and making use of Eqs. 9.10(9) and (10), we find

$$(\gamma_+^{cw})^2 = -\omega^2\mu_0(\epsilon_{11} - j\epsilon_{12})$$

$$= -\omega^2\mu_0\epsilon_0\left(1 + \frac{\omega_p^2/\omega}{\omega_c - \omega}\right). \tag{3}$$

We see that the circularly polarized wave is a possible solution or *normal mode* of propagation. For the forward wave we use the form $e^{-\gamma z}$ so we choose the positive square root of (3):

$$\gamma_+^{cw} = j\omega\sqrt{\mu_0\epsilon_0}\left(1 + \frac{\omega_p^2/\omega}{\omega_c - \omega}\right)^{\frac{1}{2}}. \tag{4}$$

The propagation constant for a wave propagating in the negative z direction with $e^{\gamma z}$ spatial variations and having counterclockwise rotation has an electric field of the same form as (2):

$$\bar{E}_-^{ccw} = E_-^{ccw}(\bar{a}_x - j\bar{a}_y). \tag{5}$$

Therefore, the corresponding γ_-^{ccw} is identical with (4). This follows directly from the equations but might also be expected physically since the rotation of the forces on the electrons is in the same direction relative to the magnetic field.

For a wave propagating in the positive z direction with counterclockwise polarization, the electric field may be represented by

$$\bar{E}_+^{ccw} = E_+^{ccw}(\bar{a}_x + j\bar{a}_y). \tag{6}$$

Using the assumed form $e^{-\gamma z}$ and proceeding as above, we find

$$\gamma_+^{ccw} = j\omega\sqrt{\mu_0\epsilon_0}\left(1 - \frac{\omega_p^2/\omega}{\omega_c + \omega}\right)^{\frac{1}{2}}. \tag{7}$$

The field vector $\bar{E}_-^{cw}$ for the clockwise polarized negatively traveling wave has the same form as (6) and therefore $\gamma_-^{cw} = \gamma_+^{ccw}$ given by (7).

The transmission-line analogy may be used to solve reflection and transmission problems with circularly polarized waves. It is therefore useful to define characteristic impedances for the various wave types. If we substitute $\bar{E}_+^{cw}$ from (2) into Maxwell's curl $\bar{E}$ equation, we find the conditions

$$\gamma_+^{cw} E_+^{cw} = \omega\mu_0 H_x \tag{8}$$

and

$$\gamma_+^{cw} E_+^{cw} = j\omega\mu_0 H_y. \tag{9}$$

From (8) and (9) we see that $H_x = jH_y$ or

$$\bar{H}_+^{cw} = (j\bar{a}_x + \bar{a}_y)H_+^{cw} \tag{10}$$

and

$$\eta_+^{cw} = \frac{E_+^{cw}}{H_+^{cw}} = \frac{j\omega\mu_0}{\gamma_+^{cw}} = \sqrt{\mu_0/(\epsilon_{11} - j\epsilon_{12})}. \tag{11}$$

The characteristic impedance for the negatively traveling, counterclockwise polarized wave is just the negative of (11),

$$\eta_-^{ccw} = \frac{E_-^{ccw}}{H_-^{ccw}} = -\eta_+^{cw} \tag{12}$$

and the form (10) applies.

By substituting (6) in the curl $\bar{E}$ equation and using the $e^{-\gamma z}$ form of variation with z, we find

$$\bar{H}_+^{ccw} = (-j\bar{a}_x + \bar{a}_y)H_+^{ccw} \tag{13}$$

and

$$\eta_+^{ccw} = \frac{E_+^{ccw}}{H_+^{ccw}} = \sqrt{\mu_0/(\epsilon_{11} + j\epsilon_{12})}. \tag{14}$$

The corresponding wave is that with field $\bar{E}_-^{cw}$ having the same form as (6). As a result of the difference of sign of γ in the exponential z dependence,

$$\eta_-^{cw} = -\eta_+^{ccw}. \tag{15}$$

In satisfying boundary conditions on fields at an interface lying in a $z = $ constant plane between two media for circularly polarized waves, we must sum all fields with the same direction of rotation in the x-y plane. Thus for waves having fields rotating clockwise about the $+z$ axis, we may write expressions for the magnitude of $\bar{E}$ and $\bar{H}$, using (11) and (12), as

$$E = E_+^{cw}e^{-\gamma z} + E_-^{ccw}e^{\gamma z} \tag{16}$$

$$H = \frac{1}{\eta_+^{cw}}(E_+^{cw}e^{-\gamma z} - E_-^{ccw}e^{\gamma z}), \tag{17}$$

where

$$\gamma = \gamma_+^{cw} = \gamma_-^{ccw}.$$

Comparing (16) and (17) with Eqs. 6.08(1) and (2), we see that these are in the transmission-line form and all of the formalism used in Art. 6.08 may be applied here for waves propagating parallel with the z axis.

Problems

9.11a Verify Eqs. 9.11 (13) and (14).

9.11b Suppose a stationary plasma filling the half-space $z > 0$ in a magnetic field in the $+z$ direction. The other half-space $z < 0$ has only vacuum. Take the number density of electrons to be 10^{17} per cubic meter and the magnetic field to be 1000 gauss. A clockwise polarized plane wave of frequency 3000 megacycles propagating in the $+z$ direction is incident on the plasma. What is the value of the field of the wave propagating in the plasma as a fraction of the field in the incident wave?

9.11c Find expressions for cutoff frequencies of clockwise and counterclockwise polarized waves propagating along the $+z$ axis.

9.12 Faraday Rotation

In this article we shall see how the difference of propagation constants between clockwise and counterclockwise polarized waves can be used to show that a linearly polarized wave is rotated when it passes through a gyrotropic medium. Let us first consider a linearly polarized wave propagating in the $+z$ direction with the $\bar{E}$ vector in the x direction at the plane $z = 0$ in the plasma of Art. 9.11. This field may be decomposed into circularly polarized modes of propagation

$$\bar{E}^{cw} = (\bar{a}_x - j\bar{a}_y) \frac{E}{2} e^{-j\beta^{cw}z} \tag{1}$$

and

$$\bar{E}^{ccw} = (\bar{a}_x + j\bar{a}_y) \frac{E}{2} e^{-j\beta^{ccw}z} \tag{2}$$

since the sum of (1) and (2) at $z = 0$ is

$$\bar{E} = \bar{a}_x E.$$

This can be thought of as finding magnitudes of the natural modes of the system necessary to match the given boundary condition at $z = 0$. It is convenient in this analysis to replace the γ of Art. 9.11 by $j\beta$, assuming zero attenuation or that any existing attenuation may be included in $j\beta$.

The field at any other plane, $z = $ constant, is found by adding (1) and (2):

$$\bar{E} = \frac{E}{2} [\bar{a}_x(e^{-j\beta^{ccw}z} + e^{-j\beta^{cw}z}) + \bar{a}_y(e^{-j\beta^{ccw}z} - e^{-j\beta^{cw}z})] \tag{3}$$

which can be cast into the form

$$\bar{E} = E e^{-(j/2)(\beta^{cw}+\beta^{ccw})z} \left[\bar{a}_x \cos\left(\frac{\beta^{cw} - \beta^{ccw}}{2}\right)z - \bar{a}_y \sin\left(\frac{\beta^{cw} - \beta^{ccw}}{2}\right)z\right]. \tag{4}$$

The sum wave (4) is seen to have field vectors in a fixed direction at each value of z since there is no phase difference between the x and y components. The direction of the field vector relative to that at $z = 0$ is, as seen in Fig. 9.12, given by

$$\tan \theta = \frac{E_y}{E_x} = -\tan \left(\frac{\beta^{cw} - \beta^{ccw}}{2} \right) z \quad (5)$$

$$\text{or} \quad \theta = \left(\frac{\beta^{ccw} - \beta^{cw}}{2} \right) z. \quad (6)$$

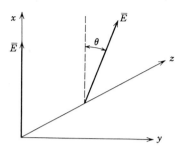

Fig. 9.12 Rotation of a linearly polarized wave in a gyrotropic medium.

The sign of the angle θ is positive for clockwise rotation about the positive z axis. Thus we see that the linearly polarized wave rotates upon passing along the gyrotropic axis (z axis) and has a propagation constant which is the average of those of the clockwise and counterclockwise modes.

It is of special interest to note that the direction of rotation about the *positive* z axis is the same for waves traveling in the positive and negative z directions. In Art. 9.15 we will see applications of this phenomenon.

Problems

9.12a Verify relation (4) for the rotating linearly polarized wave and draw a sketch of the instantaneous field distribution at $t = 0$ for various values of z.

9.12b For the plasma with electron density of 10^{18} per cubic meter, plot the angle of rotation per meter of a linearly polarized wave at $f = 3000$ megacycles as a function of magnetic field from $B = 0$ to $B = 1000$ gauss.

9.12c Discuss the comparison between Faraday rotation and the effect described in Art. 9.02.

9.12d Some materials possess a property called *natural optical rotation* whereby the plane of polarization of a wave passing through them is rotated without the application of electric or magnetic fields. This is explained by the "screw-like" nature of individual molecules. For example, a 10 cm column of a cane sugar solution (0.1 gm per cc) produces about 6.7° of rotation. Assuming the individual molecules to be represented crudely by right-hand screws, explain why there remains a net effect in a solution where these molecules are randomly oriented. Explain also why the reflected wave returns to its original polarization, in contradistinction to the Faraday effect where the reflected wave rotates through an additional angle. What should be the rotation per meter of a 0.05 gm per cc solution of sugar?

9.13   Tensor Permeability for Ferrites

There exists a group of materials, called ferrites, having the important characteristics of low loss and strong magnetic effects at microwave frequencies. These are solids with a particular type of crystal structure made up of atoms of oxygen, iron, and another element which might be lithium, magnesium, zinc, or any of a number of others. The details of the ferrite structure are beyond the scope of this treatment and are described in other books.[11,12] The important factors in the study of wave propagation in ferrites are that the losses at microwave frequencies are small, the dielectric constants are relatively high (within a factor of about two of $\epsilon_r = 15$), and anisotropic behavior results when the ferrite is subjected to a steady magnetic field.

A complete statement of the energy state of an atom requires, in addition to the specification of the orbits of the electrons, a specification of their spins. In the language of quantum mechanics, there are orbital and spin quantum numbers, both of which must be stated to define the energy state of an atom. A strong magnetic moment is associated with the electron spin. In paramagnetic substances these magnetic moments are randomly oriented with respect to those in neighboring atoms but in ferromagnetic, antiferromagnetic, or ferrimagnetic (ferrites) materials there exists a strong coupling between spin magnetic moments of neighboring atoms, causing parallel or antiparallel alignment as discussed in Art. 2.43. We will study the situation in which all the domains are aligned in one direction by a strong applied steady field; the material is saturated. An equation of motion for the spin magnetic moments will be found. By assuming small perturbations of the magnetic field quantities about the large steady values, a permeability tensor for the perturbations will be derived.

The model of the spinning electron used in the derivation is shown diagrammatically in Fig. 9.13a. The analogy between the spinning electron and a gyroscope is evident. For any rotating body the rate of change of the angular momentum $\bar{J}$ equals the applied torque $\bar{T}$:

$$\frac{d\bar{J}}{dt} = \bar{T}. \tag{1}$$

Note as an example the gyroscope shown in Fig. 9.13b. The earth's gravitational attraction applies a force or torque to the gyroscope in the

[11] B. Lax and K. J. Button, *Microwave Ferrites and Ferrimagnetics*, McGraw-Hill, New York, 1962.
[12] R. F. Soohoo, *Theory and Applications of Ferrites*, Prentice-Hall, Englewood Cliffs, N.J., 1960.

direction shown, and the angular momentum vector along the axis of the gyroscope rotates slowly about a vertical line through the pivot. This rotation, called precession, is at a rate sufficient to conserve the initial

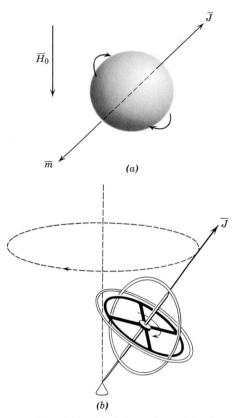

Fig. 9.13 (a) Spherical model of spinning electron in magnetic field.
(b) Precession of a gyroscope.

angular momentum. We may also relate the magnetic moment $\bar{m}$ to the applied torque since

$$\bar{m} = \gamma \bar{J}, \tag{2}$$

where γ is called the gyromagnetic ratio.[13] If the electron is considered to be a uniform charge distribution in a spherical volume and γ is found by

[13] The γ of this article is not to be confused with propagation constant, which has the same symbol in other parts of the book.

classical calculations of $\bar{m}$ and $\bar{J}$, the result is in error by a factor of almost exactly 2. The correct value of γ which is approximately -1.759×10^{11} rad/(sec) (Webers/m²) must be found from quantum mechanics.

The torque resulting from subjecting a magnetic moment $\bar{m}$ to a magnetic field $\bar{B}_i$ is

$$\bar{T} = \bar{m} \times \bar{B}_i \tag{3}$$

as shown in Prob. 2.31. There are also torques resulting from loss mechanisms but these will be neglected here. We may combine (1) to (3) to get

$$\frac{d\bar{m}}{dt} = \gamma(\bar{m} \times \bar{B}_i) \tag{4}$$

where $\bar{B}_i$ is the total field to which the spinning charges are subjected. As is pointed out in Appendix III the total magnetic field acting on a molecule in a magnetic material can be adequately represented by

$$\bar{B}_i = \mu_0 \bar{H} + \kappa\mu_0 \bar{M}. \tag{5}$$

The magnetization vector (or magnetic dipole density) $\bar{M}$ is $N_0\bar{m}$ where N_0 is the effective number density since all spins in a saturated material act in concert. The magnetic intensity $\bar{H}$ is the value averaged over the space of many molecules within the material. The relation between $\bar{H}$ and the external applied field depends on the shape of the ferrite body.[14] The importance of shape factors was discussed in Chapter 2.

Then combining (4) and (5) and noting that $\bar{M} \times \bar{M} = 0$, we find

$$\frac{d\bar{M}}{dt} = \gamma\mu_0(\bar{M} \times \bar{H}). \tag{6}$$

Equation (6) may be written in phasor component form taking note of the fact that, since the electrons are bound, the total time derivative equals the partial time derivative:

$$\begin{aligned} j\omega M_x &= \gamma\mu_0(M_y H_z - M_z H_y) \\ j\omega M_y &= \gamma\mu_0(M_z H_x - M_x H_z) \\ j\omega M_z &= \gamma\mu_0(M_x H_y - M_y H_x). \end{aligned} \tag{7}$$

Now consider the applied magnetic field in the form of a sum of d-c and a-c terms

$$\bar{H} = \bar{a}_z H_0 + \bar{H}_1 e^{j\omega t}. \tag{8}$$

The material is, by previous statement, saturated so the magnetization vector must have the form

$$\bar{M} = \bar{a}_z M_0 + \bar{M}_1 e^{j\omega t}, \tag{9}$$

[14] *Op. cit.*, Lax and Button, Chapter 4.

where M_0 is the saturation magnetization. The expressions (8) and (9) are substituted, in phasor component form, in (7), and all products of a-c terms are considered to be negligible compared with products involving one steady term and one alternating term. The result is

$$j\omega M_x = \gamma \mu_0 (M_y H_0 - M_0 H_y)$$
$$j\omega M_y = \gamma \mu_0 (M_0 H_x - M_x H_0) \qquad (10)$$
$$j\omega M_z = 0$$

where the subscript 1 is deleted from the a-c terms for simplicity. Equations (10) may be solved to give $\bar{M}$ in terms of $\bar{H}$ and the result substituted in

$$\bar{B} = \mu_0 (\bar{H} + \bar{M}) \qquad (11)$$

to obtain the result

$$\bar{B} = \hat{\mu} \bar{H} \qquad (12)$$

or

$$\begin{bmatrix} B_x \\ B_y \\ B_z \end{bmatrix} = \begin{bmatrix} \mu_{11} & \mu_{12} & 0 \\ \mu_{21} & \mu_{22} & 0 \\ 0 & 0 & \mu_0 \end{bmatrix} \begin{bmatrix} H_x \\ H_y \\ H_z \end{bmatrix} \qquad (13)$$

where

$$\mu_{11} = \mu_{22} = \mu_0 \left[1 + \frac{\mu_0^2 \gamma^2 M_0 H_0}{\mu_0^2 \gamma^2 H_0^2 - \omega^2} \right] = \mu_0 \left[1 + \frac{\omega_0 \omega_M}{\omega_0^2 - \omega^2} \right]$$

$$\mu_{12} = -\mu_{21} = j \frac{\omega \mu_0^2 \gamma M_0}{\mu_0^2 \gamma^2 H_0^2 - \omega^2} = j \frac{\mu_0 \omega \omega_M}{\omega_0^2 - \omega^2} ; \qquad (14)$$

where ω_M can be considered to be a convenient collection of parameters which characterizes the material and has the units of frequency; and where ω_0 is discussed below. We see that the permeability of a ferrite with a finite d-c magnetic field has the same form as the permittivity of the plasma with finite magnetic field [Eqs. 9.10(9) and (10)]. Note that a resonance occurs at the frequency $\omega_0 = -\gamma \mu_0 H_0 = (e/m)\mu_0 H_0$. The resonance frequency of the stationary plasma is $\omega_c = (e/m)\mu_0 H_z$. The difference between these frequencies is that the magnetic field H_0 within the ferrite differs from the applied field, as mentioned after (5), whereas the H_z within the plasma is essentially the same as the applied field. The singularity at resonance vanishes if the mechanisms responsible for damping the precession are considered in the analysis.

Problems

9.13a   Assume a model of an electron as a spinning sphere of uniform mass and charge and calculate its magnetic moment and angular momentum. Show that γ in (2) differs by a factor of two from the value given in the text.
9.13b   Verify the matrix coefficients (14) starting with (10).

9.14 TEM Wave Propagation in Ferrites

The wave equation, Eq. 9.03(17), for magnetic field intensity $\bar{H}$ in a *TEM* wave may be expressed in matrix notation as

$$\frac{d^2}{dz^2}\begin{bmatrix} H_x \\ H_y \\ 0 \end{bmatrix} + \omega^2\epsilon\begin{bmatrix} \mu_{11} & \mu_{12} & 0 \\ \mu_{21} & \mu_{22} & 0 \\ 0 & 0 & \mu_0 \end{bmatrix}\begin{bmatrix} H_x \\ H_y \\ 0 \end{bmatrix} = 0. \tag{1}$$

The vanishing of $\nabla \cdot \bar{H}$ follows from having no field in the direction of variations (z) and no variations in the directions of the field (x and y). This matrix has the same form as Eq. 9.11(1), the wave equation for a plasma in a finite magnetic field. Therefore the propagation constants found by substituting

$$\bar{H}_+^{ccw} = H_+^{cw}(\bar{a}_x - j\bar{a}_y) \tag{2}$$

and

$$\bar{H}_+^{ccw} = H_+^{ccw}(\bar{a}_x + j\bar{a}_y)$$

in (1), have the same form as those in Art. 9.11. Similar procedure applies for the negative propagating waves. We may summarize the results as

$$(\gamma_+^{cw})^2 = (\gamma_-^{ccw})^2 = -\omega^2\epsilon(\mu_{11} - j\mu_{12}) \tag{3}$$

$$(\gamma_-^{cw})^2 = (\gamma_+^{ccw})^2 = -\omega^2\epsilon(\mu_{11} + j\mu_{12}) \tag{4}$$

where μ_{11} and μ_{12} are given by Eq. 9.13(14). It is common to consider $\mu_{11} - j\mu_{12}$ and $\mu_{11} + j\mu_{12}$ as equivalent relative permeabilities. It is clear that if $\mu_{11} - j\mu_{12}$ is positive, the propagation constant for the clockwise forward wave (and counterclockwise reverse wave) is pure imaginary

$$\gamma_+^{cw} = j\beta_+^{cw} = j\omega\sqrt{\epsilon}(\mu_{11} - j\mu_{12})^{\frac{1}{2}}. \tag{5}$$

If $\mu_{11} - j\mu_{12}$ is negative, we have a purely attenuated (evanescent) wave. If losses are taken into account in the derivation of the permeability components, there are neither purely attenuating nor purely propagating regimes. We will restrict our attention to the simpler lossless case. From the forms of the matrix elements Eq. 9.13(14) it may be observed that the signs of μ_{11} and μ_{12} depend on frequency. In Figs. 9.14a and 9.14b variations of equivalent relative permeability are shown for the clockwise and counterclockwise waves, respectively. The frequency ranges of propagation and attenuation are delineated.

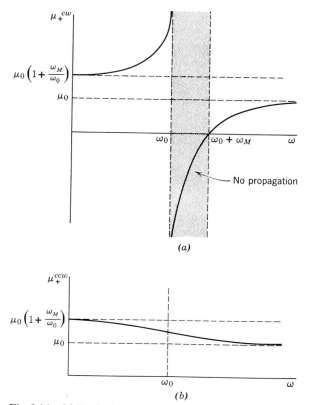

Fig. 9.14   (a) Equivalent permeability for clockwise circularly polarized wave propagating in $+z$ direction. (b) Equivalent permeability for counterclockwise circularly polarized wave propagating in $+z$ direction.

It is evident that the difference of propagation constants provides for Faraday rotation of linearly polarized waves. Several devices based on this principle have become important in microwave systems and are reviewed in Art. 9.16.

Intrinsic impedances may be defined for a ferrite as they were for the gyrotropic plasma in Art. 9.11. Substitution of (2) into Maxwell's curl $\bar{H}$ equation yields

$$\eta_+^{cw} = -\eta_-^{ccw} = \sqrt{(\mu_{11} - j\mu_{12})/\epsilon} \tag{6}$$

and

$$\eta_+^{ccw} = -\eta_-^{cw} = \sqrt{(\mu_{11} + j\mu_{12})/\epsilon}.$$

With these definitions, the transmission line formalism can be used to solve propagation problems.

Problems

9.14a Consider a 10-centimeter thick plane slab of ferrite of infinite cross section normal to the z axis. Assume a d-c z-directed magnetic field H_0 of 3×10^5 ampere turns per meter inside the ferrite. The saturation magnetization M_0 of the ferrite is 10^6 ampere turns per meter and the relative permittivity is 9.0. A linearly polarized plane wave of frequency 10^9 cycles/second moving in the $+z$ direction is incident on the slab. Find the wave on the other side of the slab in terms of the incident wave using transmission line methods.

9.14b The literature on ferrite properties usually gives saturation magnetization as $4\pi M_0$ and magnetic field H_0 in Gaussian units. Calculate the Gaussian values of $4\pi M_0$ and H_0 from the MKS values of M_0 and H_0 given in Prob. *a*. Also equate values of ω_0 for the two systems of units to show that γ in the expression $\omega_0 = \gamma H_0$ using Gaussian units has the value -1.76×10^7 radians per oersted-second.

9.15 Waveguides Containing Ferrites

In Art. 9.14 we discussed the waves which propagate through a ferrite parallel with the d-c magnetic field. It is also possible to find expressions for the propagation constants of plane waves traveling transverse to the direction of the magnetic field. The more difficult problem of waves in ferrites of bounded cross section can also be solved formally for certain special situations. Two important configurations which have been treated are shown in Fig. 9.15a and b. The ferrite in the circular guide is magnetized along the direction of propagation and that in the rectangular guide is magnetized transversely. Two methods of solution have been used. The fields may be found by directly solving the boundary value problem.[15] Solutions with arbitrary constants are obtained for the ferrite and free-space regions and, by matching fields across the boundaries, the determinantal equation for the propagation constants is obtained. A second method which has been used in some problems where the ferrite insert is small compared with the cross section of the guide finds the propagation constants as perturbations of those for the guide without the ferrite.[16]

Only a few boundary value problems have been solved and these lead to complicated transcendental relations for the propagation constants and the fields. We do not wish to go into all details of the rather complicated analyses required for this anisotropic boundary value problem. It is of interest, however, to outline the major steps of an analysis to indicate the

[15] *Op. cit.*, B. Lax and K. J. Button, Chapter 9 and R. F. Soohoo, Chapter 9.
[16] *Op. cit.*, B. Lax and K. J. Button, Chapter 8.

factors which distinguish this problem from that of the isotropic guide. The case we will examine is that for which there may be found a complete set of modes, the cylindrical guide with d-c magnetic field along the axis, as shown in Fig. 9.15a. The principal distinction from the isotropic case is that the natural modes cannot be divided into *TE* and *TM* modes; rather, they have both E_z and H_z.

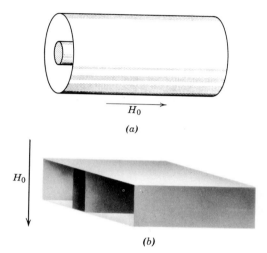

(a)

(b)

Fig. 9.15 (a) Ferrite rod in circular waveguide with longitudinal magnetic field. (b) Ferrite slab in rectangular guide with transverse magnetic field.

As was pointed out in Art. 9.03, the vector relations Eqs. 9.03(16) and (17) cannot always be reduced to scalar wave equations. In the case being examined here, where field components exist in the direction of propagation, $\nabla \cdot \bar{H} \neq 0$. It is convenient to revert to Maxwell's equations which, for the situation where $\hat{\mu}$ is a tensor and ϵ is a scalar, are

$$\nabla \times \bar{H} = j\omega\epsilon\bar{E}; \quad \nabla \times \bar{E} = -j\omega\hat{\mu}\bar{H}. \tag{1}$$

Writing these in component form for cylindrical coordinates with an assumed $e^{-\gamma z}$ variation, we find

$$\frac{1}{r}\frac{\partial H_z}{\partial \phi} + \gamma H_\phi = j\omega\epsilon E_r \tag{2}$$

$$-\gamma H_r - \frac{\partial H_z}{\partial r} = j\omega\epsilon E_\phi \tag{3}$$

$$\frac{1}{r}\frac{\partial(rH_\phi)}{\partial r} - \frac{1}{r}\frac{\partial H_r}{\partial \phi} = j\omega\epsilon E_z \tag{4}$$

$$\frac{1}{r}\frac{\partial E_z}{\partial \phi} + \gamma E_\phi = -j\omega(\mu_{11}H_r + \mu_{12}H_\phi) \tag{5}$$

$$-\gamma E_r - \frac{\partial E_z}{\partial r} = -j\omega(\mu_{21}H_r + \mu_{22}H_\phi) \tag{6}$$

$$\frac{1}{r}\frac{\partial(rE_\phi)}{\partial r} - \frac{1}{r}\frac{\partial E_r}{\partial \phi} = -j\omega\mu_0 H_z. \tag{7}$$

In writing the right side of (5) to (7), we have made use of Eq. 9.13(13), replacing the rectangular field components with the equivalent cylindrical components. The set of four equations (2), (3), (5), and (6) may be solved to find E_r, E_ϕ, H_r, and H_ϕ in terms of the derivatives of E_z and H_z. These relations have the form exemplified by

$$E_r = a\frac{\partial E_z}{\partial r} + b\frac{1}{r}\frac{\partial E_z}{\partial \phi} + c\frac{\partial H_z}{\partial r} + d\frac{1}{r}\frac{\partial H_z}{\partial \phi} \tag{8}$$

Substitution of these expressions for the transverse components into (4) and (7) yields the coupled wave equations

$$\nabla_t^2 E_z + eE_z + fH_z = 0 \tag{9}$$
$$\nabla_t^2 H_z + gH_z + hE_z = 0. \tag{10}$$

where subscript t signifies that derivatives are with respect to transverse coordinates r and ϕ. The forms of the coefficients of (8), (9), and (10) are found in texts on ferrites.[11,12] The details of the combinations of ω, ϵ, γ, and coefficients of $\hat{\mu}$ comprising them are not of immediate concern here. We are primarily interested in the fact that the equations (9) and (10) are coupled. That is, there can be no pure TE or TM modes. It is common to classify a mode by its nature at cutoff, since it can be shown that the coupling terms f and h vanish where $\gamma = 0$. The modes are called quasi-TE or quasi-TM depending on whether they have H_z only or E_z only at the cutoff frequency.

Solutions of (9) and (10) are found in terms of Bessel functions:

$$E_z = [A_n J_n(K_1 r) + B_n J_n(K_2 r)]e^{jn\phi} \tag{11}$$
$$H_z = [a_1 A_n J_n(K_1 r) + b_1 B_n J_n(K_2 r)]e^{jn\phi} \tag{12}$$

where K_1, K_2, a_1, and b_1 are rather complicated expressions involving ϵ, ω, γ, and the coefficients of the permeability tensor. In the ferrite-filled, perfectly conducting guide, $E_z = 0$ and $\partial H_z/\partial r = 0$ at the guide radius. Application of these two conditions to (11) and (12) leads to the evaluation of the ratio A_n/B_n and a transcendental determinantal equation for the propagation constant γ. Transverse field components may then be found using the relations of the form (8). For a partially filled guide, field expressions for *TE* and *TM* waves must be written for the region outside the ferrite. Then z and ϕ components of the ferrite fields are equated to those of the outside fields including both *TE* and *TM* waves at the ferrite boundary. The four resulting expressions, with the two conditions at the guide wall, constitute a set of six linear homogeneous equations in the six coefficients of the Bessel functions in the field expressions. Solution of the set yields expressions for the ratios of five of the coefficients to the sixth and also the propagation constant. These expressions are, of course, even more complicated than for the filled guide.

The results of these analyses show the effect of the dimensions on the rate of Faraday rotation. It is found that decreasing the guide radius decreases the rate of rotation. Also, decreasing the ratio of the radius of the ferrite to the radius of the guide decreases the rotation, as is to be expected from consideration of the limit.

Problems

9.15a Verify the statement after Eq. 9.15(8).

9.15b Write the equivalent of Eqs. 9.15(2) to (7) in rectangular coordinates. Follow the procedure described for (9) and (10) and find the exact form of the coupled equations for rectangular coordinates, with coefficients expressed in terms of ω, ϵ, γ, and coefficients of $\bar{\mu}$.

9.16 Ferrite Devices

One family of ferrite devices employs the phenomenon of Faraday rotation described in Art. 9.12, where it was pointed out that the rotation of a linearly polarized wave is in the same direction with respect to the direction of d-c magnetic field regardless of whether the wave propagation is in the positive or negative direction (Fig. 9.16a).

The first and simplest of the microwave devices using the Faraday rotation effect was the *gyrator*,[17] shown in Fig. 9.16b. By virtue of a twist of the waveguide, a wave coming from the left is rotated clockwise by 90° before reaching the ferrite. The magnetic field and the dimensions of the ferrite are chosen so an additional 90° clockwise rotation of the wave takes place in the ferrite region. Thus, the wave progressing toward the right is inverted, or equivalently, shifted in phase by 180°. A wave passing from right to left is rotated by 90° clockwise with respect to the *direction of the*

[17] C. L. Hogan, *Bell System Tech. Jour.*, **31** (January 1952) 1–31.

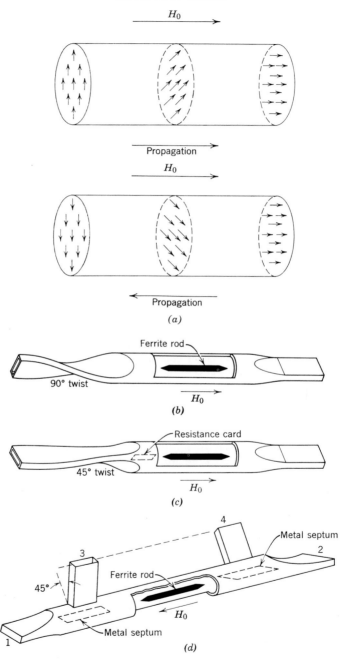

H_0

Propagation

H_0

Propagation

(a)

Ferrite rod

90° twist

H_0

(b)

Resistance card

45° twist

H_0

(c)

4

Metal septum

2

3

Ferrite rod

45°

H_0

1

Metal septum

(d)

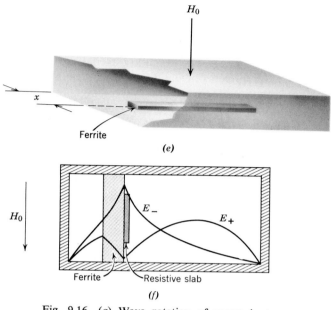

Fig. 9.16 (*a*) Wave rotation of waves in two directions in magnetized ferrite rod. (*b*) Microwave gyrator. (*c*) Microwave isolator. (*d*) Microwave circulator. (*e*) Ferrite location in resonance isolator. (*f*) Field patterns in field-displacement isolator.

magnetic field and this is cancelled by the rotation in the twisted portion of the guide to the left of the ferrite. The gyrator, therefore, serves to produce a phase shift of 180° in one direction and no shift in the opposite direction.

Another important Faraday rotation device is the *absorption isolator* shown in Fig. 9.16*c*. Here the 45° twist to the left of the ferrite rotates the wave coming from the left so that its electric field vectors are perpendicular to the thin resistance card just after the twist. With this orientation, the field suffers a minimum of conduction losses in the card. The field is then rotated back to its original orientation when it passes through the ferrite and leaves the isolator essentially unmodified. A wave traveling to the left is rotated in the ferrite in the same direction relative to the magnetic field as the wave moving to the right and is therefore oriented with its electric field vectors along the resistance card. In this way the wave traveling to the left is appreciably attenuated (typically 30 db) and the wave moving to the right suffers little loss (usually less than 0.5 db).

Another application of Faraday rotation is the *circulator* shown in Fig. 9.16*d*. The function of a circulator is to transmit a wave from guide 1 to guide 2, a wave from guide 2 to 3, 3 to 4, and 4 to 1, with all other couplings prohibited. The ferrite rod and magnetic field are chosen to give 45° rotation. The TE_{10} mode in guide 1 excites the TE_{11} mode in the circular guide. The symmetry of the TE_{11} circular mode (see Table 8.04) is such that it does not excite propagating waves in guide 3. The right half of the structure is rotated by 45° relative to guides 1 and 3 as seen in Fig. 9.16*d*. A 45° rotation of the wave coming from guide 1 places it in the same orientation with respect to 2 and 4 as it had with respect to 1 and 3 so it passes out through guide 2. A TE_{10} wave entering guide 3 excites a TE_{11} mode in the circular guide, but it is oriented at 90° from the mode excited by a wave from guide 1. It cannot excite propagating modes in 1. When rotated by 45° in the ferrite, the wave is oriented to excite waves in guide 4 but not 2. The analyses of waves entering guides 2 and 4 follow similar reasoning. The metal septums shown in the figure aid in preventing unwanted couplings. The circulator can also be used as a switch or for modulation by controlling the field which magnetizes the ferrite.

The choice of diameter and shape of the ferrite rods used in Faraday rotation devices is made to minimize reflections and maximize power handling capability while achieving the required rotation with reasonable magnetic fields. Because power is dissipated in the small rod isolated from the walls, a Faraday rotation device is useful only for low power. Some of the following devices have the ferrite connected to the metal wall and can carry higher power fields.

The functions just described can also be achieved in *resonance* and *field-displacement* devices which employ magnetic fields transverse to the guide. Analyses of some waveguide situations have been performed for transverse magnetization along the general lines of the analysis of Art. 9.15. It is sufficient for our purposes to see the nature of the effects qualitatively. Let us consider, for a rectangular waveguide with a TE_{10} mode (Art. 8.03), the r-f magnetic fields in the planes perpendicular to the d-c magnetization. The vector sum of H_x and H_z of Eqs. 8.03(2) and (3) is

$$\bar{H}_{xz} = \left[\bar{a}_x - j\left(\frac{\lambda}{2a}\right)\frac{Z_{TE}}{\eta}\left(\cot\frac{\pi x}{a}\right)\bar{a}_z\right]H_0\sin\frac{\pi x}{a}, \qquad (1)$$

where Z_{TE} is positive for a wave in the $+z$ direction and negative for the reverse wave. It is clear from (1) that at the value of x in the guide such that

$$\left|\left(\frac{\lambda}{2a}\right)\frac{Z_{TE}}{\eta}\cot\frac{\pi x}{a}\right| = 1 \qquad (2)$$

the field $\bar{H}_{xz}$ is circularly polarized. The direction of polarization depends on the sign of Z_{TE}.

If a piece of ferrite is placed on the top or bottom of the guide at the value of x given by (2) a shown in Fig. 9.16e the precessing electron-spin moments will be subjected to a circularly polarized field which either enhances the precession or is very little coupled to it, depending on the direction of the circular polarization. By appropriate choice of polarity of the d-c magnetic field, the direction of spin precession can be made opposite to the direction of rotation of the field vectors of the forward wave. In this case the forward wave is little affected. The backward wave, having an opposite polarization of $\bar{H}_{xz}$, pumps the precessing spins and loses energy in the process. This energy is transferred from the electrons to the lattice of the ferrite by microscopic damping mechanisms. If the magnetic field is adjusted to set the resonance frequency equal to the field frequency $(\omega = -\gamma\mu_0 H_0)$, the reverse loss is maximum. This device, used as an isolator, requires more d-c field than the Faraday rotation isolator described previously, since it must operate at resonance. It has the advantage, however, of allowing convenient cooling of the ferrite. The same mechanism can be used to modulate a wave.

There is a third class of devices utilizing the nonreciprocal properties of magnetized ferrites. These also use transverse magnetization but make use of the fact that forward and reverse waves may be displaced differently in a guide by the ferrite. Therefore, they are called *field-displacement* devices. If a slab of ferrite is appropriately located and magnetized, an approximate null of electric field can be made to exist at its edge for the forward wave but not for the reverse wave. This is shown schematically in Fig. 9.16f. A resistive strip attached to the side of the ferrite then attenuates the reverse wave but does not affect the forward wave. As with Faraday rotation devices, the field-displacement scheme is limited to low-power application.

These examples are given only to show applicability of the principles. For a detailed analysis of these and other devices, the references should be consulted.[11,12]

10 RESONANT CAVITIES

10.01 Introduction

At extremely high frequencies (wavelengths, say, below 1 meter) ordinary lumped-circuit elements are hardly suitable for practical use. As was seen in Chapter 5, a conventional circuit with dimensions comparable to wavelength may lose energy by radiation. It was found that resistance of ordinary wire circuits may become high because of skin effect behavior. Both of these phenomena give rise to definite modifications in elements that are to serve as efficient circuits for ultra-high frequencies. It is immediately suggested that the circuit region should be shielded, completely surrounded by a good conductor, to prevent radiation. It is also suggested that the current paths be made with as large area as possible. The result was a hollow conducting box with the electromagnetic energy confined on the inside.[1] The conducting walls act effectively as perfect shields, so that this inner region is perfectly shielded from the outside, and no radiation is possible. Since the inner walls of the box serve as current paths, the desired large area for current flow is provided and losses are extremely small. The resulting element is known as a cavity resonator.

In this chapter we shall study electromagnetic waves in regions closed by conductors, with particular application to such cavity resonators. It will first be observed that such high-frequency elements might be arrived at by extension of conventional transmission line and circuit ideas. Exact analyses will be made of certain of the simpler shapes of cavity resonators, and at least approximate analyses will be made of some of the more complex shapes of such resonators. All mathematical analyses are based on the solution of Maxwell's equations subject to the boundary conditions, and in general follow directly from the results of the last several chapters on propagating waves, since the waves inside the conducting boxes may be considered standing wave patterns arising from reflections of the appropriate

[1] W. W. Hansen, *J. Appl. Phys.*, **9**, 654–663 (Oct. 1938).

traveling waves from the walls of the enclosure. Certain circuit ideas useful in the discussion of cavity resonators, especially that of Q, are treated in this chapter, but the more detailed circuit analysis for such resonators are left for the following chapter.

Resonators for use in the optical range are also described. These differ from typical ones for the microwave range in that wavelength is small, and reasonable dimensions require sizes very large in comparison with wavelength. Such systems may have many modes, and partly to reduce the number, the resonators are usually open to space. Thus losses come from diffraction (radiation) into space in addition to the losses from imperfect reflection. Although there are important differences between the optical resonators and those for microwave frequencies, such parameters as quality factor Q will remain useful for these also.

ELEMENTAL CONCEPTS OF CAVITY RESONATORS

10.02 The Resonant Transmission Line as a Cavity Resonator

Before the solution of the wave equation inside regions closed by conductors is attempted, there are several physical analogies that should make the concept of such wave regions more meaningful, particularly in their function as "circuits" at ultra-high frequencies.

For the first analogy, let us consider something which is not ordinarily thought of as a cavity resonator, but which certainly may be. This is a section of coaxial transmission line shorted at both ends. From the transmission line analysis of Chapter 1, it is known that such a shorted line may support a standing wave of frequency such that the length of line is exactly a half-wave. The line may be thought of as resonant at that frequency, since the standing wave pattern set up has constant total energy in that section of line, that energy oscillating between the electric and magnetic fields of the line. Thus, as in Fig. 10.02, the standing wave of voltage has a zero at each end and a maximum at the center. The standing wave of current is 90° out of time phase with the voltage wave, has maxima at the two ends, and a zero at the center. These waves may exist inside this completely enclosed region without interference from, or radiation to, the outside. The shielding is complete if conductors are perfect, and practically so for any practical conductors at ultra-high frequencies. This viewpoint is verified by the previous analyses (Chapter 4) of skin effect phenomena, where it was found that depth of penetration at high frequencies is so small (of the order of 10^{-4} inch for copper at 3000 megacycles per second) that almost any practical thickness acts essentially as an infinite thickness. Fields applied on the inside of a conducting wall die out to a completely negligible value at the outside of the conductor.

Since the inside of the region is completely shielded from the outside, it will be necessary to excite the waves by some source, such as the small loop *A* (Fig. 10.02), designed to excite the magnetic field of the line at its

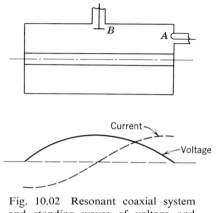

Fig. 10.02 Resonant coaxial system and standing waves of voltage and current.

maximum value, or the small probe *B* introduced at the maximum of electric field. If one of these means is used to stimulate the line exactly at its resonant frequency, the oscillations may build up to a large value. In the steady-state limit, the exciting source need supply only the relatively small amount of energy lost to the finite conductivity of the walls, the relatively large stored energy being essentially constant and passing back and forth between electric and magnetic fields. If the source excites the line at a frequency somewhat off resonance, the energies in electric and magnetic fields do not balance. Some extra energy must be supplied over one part of the cycle which is given back to the source over another part of the cycle, and the line acts as a reactive load on the exciting source in addition to its small loss component. The similarity to ordinary tuned circuit operation is evident, and it seems likely that many of the same considerations concerning effect of losses on bandwidth, expressed in terms of a Q, will hold, at least qualitatively.

This simple example essentially requires only a knowledge of transmission line theory, yet it holds all the fundamental characteristics of cavity resonators, and differs from others only in the types of waves that are utilized.

10.03 Cavity Resonators as Extensions of Lumped Resonant Circuits

Since closed resonant cavities take the place of lumped L-C circuits at high frequencies, we shall see as a next example how a closed cavity might be considered the logical evolution of such a circuit as it is extended to these frequencies. If a parallel resonant circuit with lumped L and C, such as that of Fig. 10.03, is to be extended to high frequencies, a decrease must be made in the magnitudes of C and L. Capacitance may be decreased simply by moving the plates of the condenser farther apart. To

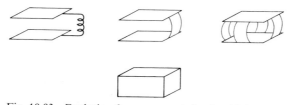

Fig. 10.03 Evolution from resonant circuit with lumped elements to a closed cavity.

decrease inductance, fewer and fewer turns might be used in the inductance until this has degenerated to a single straight wire. Next, to eliminate stray lead inductances, this might be moved to the condenser plates and connected directly between them at the edges. The final step suggested is the paralleling of many of these single-wire inductances about the outside of the plates, until in the limit the two plates are connected by a solid conducting wall. We are now left with a hollow cylindrical conducting box, completely enclosed, or in other words, another example of a cavity resonator.

This example is, of course, not exactly rigorous. It is significant in demonstrating a logical evolution from lumped-circuit ideas to the concept of cavity resonators, but if only a knowledge of lumped circuits without any background in wave phenomena were available, there would be reason to doubt that the system arrived at in the limit would even work. Certainly there is a point in the evolution where one realizes that the fields of the capacity and the inductances are becoming intimately related, and at best it is a problem with distributed rather than lumped constants with perhaps mutual impedances also present. It would appear safe to conclude that the condenser plates have actually been shorted in the limit, so that, if any voltage can exist between them, it can only exist at the center and must form a standing wave pattern inside the box, falling to zero at the shorting walls, and so requiring that the box have a diameter at least comparable to wavelength. Here it may be protested that the side walls have been imagined to act as an inductance. How can there be always zero voltage across these walls then, since there is a voltage drop across an inductance whose current is changing? The answer involves recognizing that we are speaking of total voltage, and that total voltage across any inductance made of a perfect conductor must be zero, the applied voltage being exactly balanced by that induced from the changing magnetic fields of the inductance. But these are all tentative and preliminary pictures. We will not try to press further conclusions from the present analogy, since it is realized that the wave picture is in reality the correct one and will determine whether any particular result or physical picture is legitimate. It will prove useful, however, to recall this analogy from time to time in seeking circuit ideas that may be employed in discussing resonator behavior.

10.04 Cavity Resonators from the Point of View of Wave Reflections

A picture which is in fact an exact one and one which we will utilize in following sections, considers the resonant standing wave pattern of electromagnetic fields in the resonator as the interference pattern produced by the superposition of various waves reflected from the walls of the resonator. Thus, for cylindrical resonators of any section, one may consider the standing wave produced by any of the waveguide modes appropriate to that cross section as resonant if the length between conducting end plates (shorts) is a multiple of a half guide wavelength for that mode. An example is given in Fig. 10.04a, in which fields are indicated for a circular cylindrical resonator which is one half guide wavelength for the TM_{01} mode. It is evident from this picture that a particular cavity of fixed shape and size will have many different modes (actually an infinite number) corresponding to all the wave types that may exist in the corresponding waveguide, and to different numbers of half-waves between shorting ends. This picture is pursued in detail for cylindrical resonators of circular and square section in the following articles.

One may go farther, analyzing the standing wave pattern in a resonator into component plane waves reflected from the walls of the enclosure. It is evident that in the general case these will be reflected continuously from the walls of the box. Certain conditions of dimensions proper compared with wavelength may exist such that standing wave patterns may be set up inside the box with constant total energy, this energy passing naturally between the electric and magnetic fields of the box. The simplest example of this may be found in a rectangular box with a plane wave bouncing between only four of the walls, as pictured in Fig. 10.04*b*. For the simplest case, this wave may be polarized with electric vector in the vertical or *y* direction and with no variations in that direction. If the path

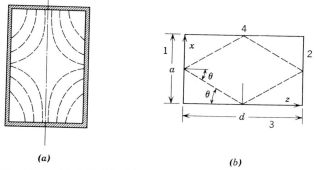

(*a*)   (*b*)

Fig. 10.04   (*a*) Cylindrical cavity and electric field pattern on a longitudinal section plane. (*b*) Paths of component uniform plane waves in a closed resonant box.

of the plane wave makes an angle θ with the normal to side 1, as shown, some general conclusions may be drawn at once from the concepts of Chapter 6 without a detailed study of the wave paths. It would be expected, for example, that since the vertical electric field should be zero at the conducting sides 1 and 2, the dimension *d* should be a half-wavelength *measured at the phase velocity in the z direction.*

$$d = \frac{1}{2f\sqrt{\mu\epsilon}\cos\theta}, \tag{1}$$

where μ and ϵ are the constants for the dielectric filling the guide. Similarly, the dimension *a* should be a half-wavelength measured at the phase velocity in the *x* direction, so that the vertical electric field may be zero at the two conducting sides 3 and 4.

$$a = \frac{1}{2f\sqrt{\mu\epsilon}\sin\theta}. \tag{2}$$

The top and bottom raise no problem, since the only electric field component is vertical and so ends on top and bottom normally as required, no matter how far apart these are placed. The two conditions (1) and (2) might be combined to eliminate θ, giving

$$\omega^2\mu\epsilon = \left(\frac{\pi}{a}\right)^2 + \left(\frac{\pi}{d}\right)^2. \tag{3}$$

This expression shows that the natural frequency necessary to set up the assumed standing wave pattern is fixed by the dimensions a and d, and by the dielectric material filling the box. This expression is derived in other ways in later articles, where it will be studied more completely. For the moment, it should be noted that (3) has been derived from wave solutions to Maxwell's equations and is therefore completely correct.

A final analogy that should not be overlooked comes from another branch of science. In the study of sound, one finds resonators for the sound waves which are quite similar to the cavity resonators for electromagnetic waves. This analogy may be appreciated from the pictures of the standing waves arising because of reflections of waves from the box walls. The phenomena of reflections and standing wave patterns obviously occur also for sound waves. The analogy is exact for certain modes so far as resonant frequency is concerned, and may be practically useful for predicting resonant frequencies by model studies. The velocity and pressure fields of a sound wave may be derived, however, from a scalar potential, and we have seen that a general electromagnetic field requires a vector potential also (Chapter 4), so the analogy is not always complete.

Each of the several analogies discussed supplies background for understanding electromagnetic energy storage inside a hollow closed conducting box of practically any shape and for appreciating the usefulness of this arrangement in place of the usual tuned circuit of low frequencies. It should be recognized that, except for extraneous holes or leaks that may be added in constructing the cavity practically, the region is perfectly shielded from the outside, so that there is no radiation to or interference from the outside. The behavior of the cavity for frequencies on and near resonance will be similar to that of lumped circuits with, as we shall see later, extremely high values of Q. A given cavity should have many possible modes (actually an infinite number), and for each mode the resonant frequency is determined by the mode, the cavity dimensions, and the constants of the dielectric filling the cavity. Coupling to the cavity may be either to the electric or the magnetic fields of the mode it is desired to excite, or to both.

Problem

10.04 Considering plane wave reflections in three dimensions within a rectangular cavity of dimensions a, b, and d, extend the formula (3) for the resonant condition for such a cavity.

RESONATORS OF SIMPLE SHAPE

10.05   Fields of Simple Rectangular Resonator

For the first mode to be studied in some detail, we shall choose that mode in a rectangular conducting box which may be considered the standing wave pattern corresponding to the TE_{10} mode in a rectangular

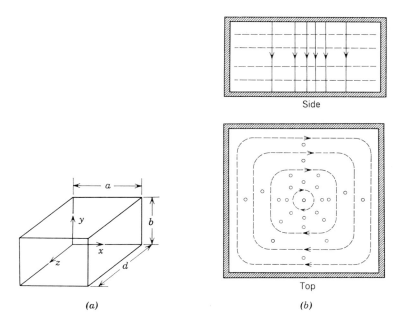

Side

Top

(a)   (b)

Fig. 10.05   (a) Rectangular cavity. (b) Electric and magnetic fields in rectangular resonator with TE_{101} mode.

guide. As was done in the study of waveguides, the conducting walls will be taken as perfect, and losses in an actual resonator will be computed approximately by taking the current flow of the ideal mode as flowing in the walls of known conductivity.

In the rectangular conducting box of Fig. 10.05a, imagine a TE_{10} waveguide mode oriented with its electric field in the y direction and propagating in the z direction. The condition that E_y shall be zero at $z = 0$ and d, as required by the perfect conductors, is satisfied if the dimension d is a half guide wavelength. Using Eq. 8.03(6)

$$d = \frac{\lambda_g}{2} = \frac{\lambda}{2\sqrt{1 - (\lambda/2a)^2}}$$

or
$$\lambda = \frac{2ad}{\sqrt{a^2 + d^2}} . \qquad (1)$$

By recalling that $\omega^2 \mu \epsilon = (2\pi/\lambda)^2$, condition (1) may be shown to be equivalent to Eq. 10.04(3), which was derived by considering plane wave reflections.

To obtain the field distributions in the dielectric interior, we add positive and negative propagating waves of the form of Eqs. 8.03(1) to (3).

$$E_y = (E_+ e^{-j\beta z} + E_- e^{j\beta z}) \sin \frac{\pi x}{a} \qquad (2)$$

$$H_x = -\frac{1}{Z_{TE}} (E_+ e^{-j\beta z} - E_- e^{j\beta z}) \sin \frac{\pi x}{a} \qquad (3)$$

$$H_z = \frac{j}{\eta}\left(\frac{\lambda}{2a}\right)(E_+ e^{-j\beta z} + E_- e^{j\beta z}) \cos \frac{\pi x}{a} . \qquad (4)$$

Since E_y must be zero at $z = 0$, $E_- = -E_+$, as we would expect, since the reflected wave from the perfectly conducting wall should be equal to the incident wave. E_y must also be zero at $z = d$, so that $\beta = \pi/d$, which may be shown to yield again the condition (1) or Eq. 10.04(3). Then (2)–(4) may be simplified, letting $E_0 = -2jE_+$:

$$E_y = E_0 \sin \frac{\pi x}{a} \sin \frac{\pi z}{d} \qquad (5)$$

$$H_x = -j\frac{E_0}{\eta}\frac{\lambda}{2d} \sin \frac{\pi x}{a} \cos \frac{\pi z}{d} \qquad (6)$$

$$H_z = j\frac{E_0}{\eta}\frac{\lambda}{2a} \cos \frac{\pi x}{a} \sin \frac{\pi z}{d} . \qquad (7)$$

In studying the foregoing expressions, we find that electric field passes vertically from top to bottom, entering top and bottom normally and becoming zero at the side walls as required by the perfect conductors. The magnetic field lines lie in horizontal (x-z) planes and surround the vertical displacement current resulting from the time rate of change of E_y. Fields are sketched roughly in Fig. 10.05b. There are equal and opposite charges on top and bottom because of the normal electric field ending there. A current flows between top and bottom, becoming vertical in the side walls. Here we are reminded of a conventional resonant circuit with the top and bottom acting as capacitor plates and the side walls as the current path between them, as in the elemental analogy of Art. 10.03.

Because the mode studied here has one half-sine variation in the x direction, none in the y direction, and one in the z direction, it is sometimes known as a TE_{101} mode. The coordinate system is of course arbitrary, but some choice must be made before the mode can be described in this manner.

Problems

10.05a Show that the mode described in Art. 10.05 (resonant condition and field expressions) would be obtained if one started with the point of view that it was a TE_{10} mode propagating in the x direction; similarly consider it a TM_{11} mode propagating in the y direction exactly at cutoff.

10.05b Find the total charge on top plate and bottom plate. Determine an equivalent capacitance that would give this charge with a voltage equal to that between top and bottom at the center of the box.

10.05c Find the total current in the side walls. Determine an equivalent inductance in terms of this current and the magnetic flux linking a vertical path at the center of the box. What resonant frequency would be given by this inductance and the equivalent capacitance of Prob. b? Compare with result of Eq. 10.05(1).

10.05d Suppose that in place of a perfect conductor at $z = d$, a "reactive wall" giving a wave reactance $E_y/H_x = jX$ is placed there. Obtain the condition for resonance. Discuss physical ways in which the reactance wall might be produced, at least as an approximation.

10.06 Energy Storage, Losses, and Q of Simple Resonator

The energy storage and energy loss in the rectangular resonator of the preceding article are of fundamental interest and will be calculated. Since the total energy passes between electric and magnetic fields, we may calculate it by finding the energy storage in electric fields at the instant when these are a maximum, for magnetic fields are then zero in the standing wave pattern of the resonator.

$$U = (U_E)_{max} = \frac{\epsilon}{2} \int_0^d \int_0^b \int_0^a |E_y|^2 \, dx \, dy \, dz.$$

Utilizing Eq. 10.05(5), we see that

$$U = \frac{\epsilon}{2} \int_0^d \int_0^b \int_0^a E_0^2 \sin^2 \frac{\pi x}{a} \sin^2 \frac{\pi z}{d} \, dx \, dy \, dz$$

$$= \frac{\epsilon E_0^2}{2} \cdot \frac{a}{2} \cdot b \cdot \frac{d}{2} = \frac{\epsilon abd}{8} E_0^2. \tag{1}$$

To obtain an approximation for power loss in the walls, we utilize the current flow in the ideal conductors as obtained from the tangential magnetic field at the surface. Referring to Fig. 10.05a,

Front: $J_y = -H_x\big|_{z=d}$ Back: $J_y = H_x\big|_{z=0}$

Left side: $J_y = -H_z\big|_{x=0}$ Right side: $J_y = H_z\big|_{x=a}$

Top: $J_x = -H_z, J_z = H_x$ Bottom: $J_x = H_z, J_z = -H_x.$

If the conducting walls have surface resistivity R_s, the foregoing currents will produce losses as follows:

$$W_L = \frac{R_s}{2}\left\{ 2\int_0^b\int_0^a |H_x|^2_{z=0}\ dx\,dy + 2\int_0^d\int_0^b |H_z|^2_{x=0}\ dy\,dz \right.$$
$$\left. + 2\int_0^d\int_0^a [|H_x|^2 + |H_z|^2]\ dx\,dz \right\}.$$

In this equation, the first term comes from the front and back, the second from left and right sides, and the third from top and bottom. Substituting from Eqs. 10.05(6) and (7) and evaluating the integrals,

$$W_L = \frac{R_s\lambda^2}{8\eta^2} E_0^2 \left[\frac{ab}{d^2} + \frac{bd}{a^2} + \frac{1}{2}\left(\frac{a}{d} + \frac{d}{a}\right) \right]. \tag{2}$$

A Q of the resonator may be defined from the basic definition of Eq. 1.04(6),

$$Q = \frac{\omega_0 U}{W_L}. \tag{3}$$

Substituting (1) and (2), we have

$$Q = \frac{\pi\eta}{4R_s}\left[\frac{2b(a^2 + d^2)^{3/2}}{ad(a^2 + d^2) + 2b(a^3 + d^3)} \right]. \tag{4}$$

Note that for a cube, $a = b = d$, this reduces to the expression

$$Q_{\text{cube}} = \frac{\sqrt{2}\,\pi}{6}\frac{\eta}{R_s} = 0.742\frac{\eta}{R_s}. \tag{5}$$

For an air dielectric, $\eta \approx 377$ ohms, and a copper conductor at 10,000 Mc/sec, $R_s \approx 0.0261$ ohm, the Q is about 10,730. Thus we see the very large values of Q for such resonators as compared with those for lumped circuits (order of a few hundred) or even with resonant lines (order of a few thousand). In practice, some care must be used if Q's of the order of that calculated are to be obtained, since disturbances caused by the coupling system, surface irregularities, and other perturbations will act to increase the losses. Dielectric losses and radiation from small holes, when present, may be especially serious in lowering the Q.

It will be shown in Chapter 11 that a lumped circuit model applies to a cavity mode in the vicinity of resonance. This circuit model is of the type studied in Chapter 1, and from it we can deduce that the Q, defined in terms of stored energy and power loss, is also useful in estimating bandwidth of the cavity just as for the lumped resonant circuit. If Δf is the distance between points on the response curve for which amplitude response is down to $1/\sqrt{2}$ of its maximum value,

$$\frac{\Delta f}{f_0} \approx \frac{1}{Q}. \tag{6}$$

Thus, for the foregoing, a Q of 10,000 in a cavity resonant at 10,000 megacycles per second will yield a bandwidth between "halfpower" points of 1 megacycle per second.

An equivalent series resistance for the cavity may be computed by utilizing the power loss and the total vertical current in the resonator walls or an equivalent shunt conductance may be found from the loss and the voltage between top and bottom at the center. Although these are of limited usefulness, the latter will be found. Utilizing (2),

$$G = \frac{2W_L}{(E_0 b)^2} = \frac{R_s}{\eta^2}\left[\frac{2b(a^3 + d^3) + ad(a^2 + d^2)}{2b^2(a^2 + d^2)}\right]. \tag{7}$$

Problems

10.6a Show that for resonance the same expression (1) for energy stored is obtained by calculating it from the magnetic fields when they are at their maximum.

10.06b For the mode of this article, plot the Q versus b/a for a square prism with $d = a$. Take air dielectric and copper conductor at 10,000 Mc/sec. Why does Q decrease as b decreases?

10.06c Plot the equivalent conductance defined by (7) as a function of b/a under the same conditions as in Prob. b.

10.06d Show that, for any mode in any shape of resonator, the Q due to an imperfect dielectric filling the resonator is

$$Q_d = \frac{\omega\epsilon}{\sigma} = \frac{\epsilon'}{\epsilon''}.$$

Note the value of this for a very good glass with $\epsilon' = 4$, $\epsilon'' = 0.004$.

10.06e Suppose that a perfect dielectric were available with $\epsilon' = 5$. How would the Q of a dielectric-filled cube compare with that of an air-filled one for the simple mode studied? Why are they different?

10.07 Other Modes in the Rectangular Resonator

As has been noted, the particular mode studied for the rectangular box is only one of infinite number of possible modes. If we adopt the point of view that a resonant mode is the standing wave pattern for incident and reflected waveguide modes, any one of the infinite number of possible waveguide waves might be used, with any integral number of half waves between shorting ends. We recognize that this description of a particular field pattern is not unique, for it depends on the axis chosen to be the "direction of propagation" for the waveguide modes. Thus (see Prob. 10.05a) the simple mode studied in past articles would be a TE_{101} mode if the z axis or x axis were considered the direction of propagation, but it would be a TM_{110} mode if the vertical (y) axis were taken as the propagation direction. In the following, a coordinate system will be chosen as in Fig. 10.05a, and field patterns will be obtained by superposing incident and reflected waves for various waveguide modes propagating in the z direction.

The TE_{mnp} Mode. If we select the TE_{mn} mode of a rectangular waveguide (see Art. 8.02), addition of positively and negatively traveling waves for H_z gives

$$H_z = (Ae^{-j\beta z} + Be^{j\beta z}) \cos \frac{m\pi x}{a} \cos \frac{n\pi y}{b} .$$

Since the normal component of magnetic field, H_z, must be zero at $z = 0$ and $z = d$, $B = -A$ and $\beta d = p\pi$ with p an integer. Let $C = -2jA$.

$$H_z = A(e^{-j\beta z} - e^{j\beta z}) \cos \frac{m\pi x}{a} \cos \frac{n\pi y}{b}$$

$$= C \cos \frac{m\pi x}{a} \cos \frac{n\pi y}{b} \sin \frac{p\pi z}{d} . \tag{1}$$

Then, substituting in Eqs. 7.02(7) to (10), remembering that for the negatively traveling waves all terms multiplied by γ change sign,

$$H_x = -\frac{j\beta}{k_c^2} (Ae^{-j\beta z} - Be^{j\beta z})\left(-\frac{m\pi}{a}\right) \sin \frac{m\pi x}{a} \cos \frac{n\pi y}{b}$$

$$= -\frac{C}{k_c^2}\left(\frac{p\pi}{d}\right)\left(\frac{m\pi}{a}\right) \sin \frac{m\pi x}{a} \cos \frac{n\pi y}{b} \cos \frac{p\pi z}{d} . \tag{2}$$

Similarly combining terms for the other components, we have

$$H_y = -\frac{C}{k_c^2}\left(\frac{p\pi}{d}\right)\left(\frac{n\pi}{b}\right)\cos\frac{m\pi x}{a}\sin\frac{n\pi y}{b}\cos\frac{p\pi z}{d} \tag{3}$$

$$E_x = \frac{j\omega\mu C}{k_c^2}\left(\frac{n\pi}{b}\right)\cos\frac{m\pi x}{a}\sin\frac{n\pi y}{b}\sin\frac{p\pi z}{d} \tag{4}$$

$$E_y = -\frac{j\omega\mu C}{k_c^2}\left(\frac{m\pi}{a}\right)\sin\frac{m\pi x}{a}\cos\frac{n\pi y}{b}\sin\frac{p\pi z}{d} \tag{5}$$

where

$$k_c^2 = \left(\frac{m\pi}{a}\right)^2 + \left(\frac{n\pi}{b}\right)^2 \tag{6}$$

$$\beta = \left[\left(\frac{2\pi}{\lambda}\right)^2 - k_c^2\right]^{\frac{1}{2}} = \frac{p\pi}{d}$$

so

$$k = \frac{2\pi}{\lambda} = \left[\left(\frac{m\pi}{a}\right)^2 + \left(\frac{n\pi}{b}\right)^2 + \left(\frac{p\pi}{d}\right)^2\right]^{\frac{1}{2}}. \tag{7}$$

The TE_{mnp} Mode. In a similar manner, positively and negatively traveling TM_{mn} modes in a rectangular waveguide may be combined to yield

$$E_z = D\sin\frac{m\pi x}{a}\sin\frac{n\pi y}{b}\cos\frac{p\pi z}{d} \tag{8}$$

$$E_x = -\frac{D}{k_c^2}\left(\frac{p\pi}{d}\right)\left(\frac{m\pi}{a}\right)\cos\frac{m\pi x}{a}\sin\frac{n\pi y}{b}\sin\frac{p\pi z}{d} \tag{9}$$

$$E_y = -\frac{D}{k_c^2}\left(\frac{p\pi}{d}\right)\left(\frac{n\pi}{b}\right)\sin\frac{m\pi x}{a}\cos\frac{n\pi y}{b}\sin\frac{p\pi z}{d} \tag{10}$$

$$H_x = \frac{j\omega\epsilon D}{k_c^2}\left(\frac{n\pi}{b}\right)\sin\frac{m\pi x}{a}\cos\frac{n\pi y}{b}\cos\frac{p\pi z}{d} \tag{11}$$

$$H_y = -\frac{j\omega\epsilon D}{k_c^2}\left(\frac{m\pi}{a}\right)\cos\frac{m\pi x}{a}\sin\frac{n\pi y}{b}\cos\frac{p\pi z}{d}. \tag{12}$$

The quantity k_c^2 and resonant wavelength λ are as in (6) and (7).

General Comments. We note first that TM and TE modes of the same order m, n, p have identical frequencies. Such modes with different field patterns but the same resonant frequency are known as *degenerate* modes. Other cases of degeneracy may exist as in a cube, $a = b = d$, where orders 112, 121, and 211 of both TM and TE types have the same resonant frequency.

It is also apparent from (7) that, as the order of a mode becomes higher, the wavelength decreases or resonant frequency increases. Put differently, it means that to be resonant at a given frequency, the box must be made bigger as the order increases. This is to be expected, since more half-sine waves are to fit in each dimension. Although we will not derive the general expression for Q, it turns out that Q increases at a given frequency as one goes to higher mode orders. This too is logical, since the larger box has a greater volume-to-surface ratio, and energy is stored in the volume, whereas it is lost on the imperfectly conducting surface. The high-order modes are consequently useful in "echo boxes" where a high Q is desired so that the energy will decay at a very slow rate after being excited by a pulse. Because modes become very close together in frequency as the order increases, it may be difficult to excite one mode only in such applications.

Problems

10.07a   Derive the expression for Q of a TE_{mmm} mode in a cube, $a = b = d$, and show that it increases as m increases, for a given dielectric and resonant frequency. Explain the result.

10.07b   Repeat Prob. a for a TM_{mmm} mode.

10.07c   Sketch the form of fields for a TM_{111} mode, utilizing significant cross sections to show the variations.

10.08   Circular Cylindrical Resonator

For a circular cylindrical resonator, Fig. 10.08, there is a simple mode analogous to that first studied for the rectangular box (Art. 10.05). The vertical electric field has a maximum at the center and dies off to zero at

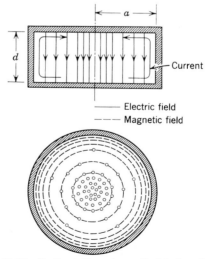

Fig. 10.08   Sections through a cylindrical cavity.

the conducting side walls. A circumferential magnetic field surrounds the displacement current represented by the time-varying electric field. Neither component varies in the axial or circumferential direction. Equal and opposite charges exist on the two end plates, and a vertical current flows in the side walls between them. The mode may be considered a TM_{01} mode in a circular waveguide operating at cutoff (to give the constancy with respect to z), or it may be thought of as the standing wave pattern produced by inward and outward radially propagating waves of the radial transmission line type, Art. 8.12. From either point of view we obtain the field components

$$E_z = E_0 J_0(kr) \qquad (1)$$

$$H_\phi = \frac{jE_0}{\eta} J_1(kr) \qquad (2)$$

$$k = \frac{p_{01}}{a} = \frac{2.405}{a}. \qquad (3)$$

Then the resonant wavelength is

$$\lambda = \frac{2\pi}{k} = 2.61a. \qquad (4)$$

The energy stored in the cavity at resonance may be found from the energy in the electric fields at the instant these have their maximum value. Take a and d, respectively, as radius and length of the cavity. Thus we have

$$U = d \int_0^a \frac{\epsilon |E_z|^2}{2} 2\pi r \, dr = \pi\epsilon \, dE_0^2 \int_0^a r J_0^2(kr) \, dr.$$

This may be integrated by Eq. 3.27(22).

$$U = \pi\epsilon \, dE_0^2 \frac{a^2}{2} J_1^2(ka). \qquad (5)$$

If the walls are of imperfect conductors, the power loss may be calculated approximately:

$$W_L = 2\pi a d \frac{R_s}{2} |J_z|^2 + 2 \int_0^a \frac{R_s}{2} |J_r|^2 2\pi r \, dr.$$

The first term represents losses on the side wall, the second on top and bottom. The current per unit width J_r on top and bottom is $\pm H_\phi$, and J_z on the side wall is the value of H_ϕ at $r = a$. Substituting from (2), we see that

$$W_L = \pi R_s \left[ad \frac{E_0^2}{\eta^2} J_1^2(ka) + 2 \int_0^a \frac{E_0^2}{\eta^2} r J_1^2(kr) \, dr \right].$$

This may also be integrated by Eq. 3.27(22), recalling that $J_0(ka) = 0$ is the condition for resonance.

$$W_L = \frac{\pi a R_s E_0^{\,2}}{\eta^2} J_1^{\,2}(ka)[d + a]. \tag{6}$$

The Q of the mode may then be obtained as usual from power losses and energy stored. An equivalent conductance may also be defined in terms of power losses and voltage at the center, or an equivalent resistance may be defined in terms of losses and the total current in the side walls.

$$Q = \frac{\omega U}{W_L} = \frac{\eta}{R_s} \frac{p_{01}}{2(a/d + 1)} \tag{7}$$

$$G = \frac{2W_L}{(E_0 d)^2} = \frac{R_s}{\eta^2} \frac{2\pi a}{d} \left(1 + \frac{a}{d}\right) J_1^{\,2}(p_{01}) \tag{8}$$

$$R = \frac{2W_L}{|2\pi a H_\phi(a)|^2} = R_s \frac{d}{2\pi a} \left(1 + \frac{a}{d}\right) \tag{9}$$

where

$$p_{01} \approx 2.405.$$

An infinite number of additional modes may be obtained for the cylindrical resonator by considering others of the possible waveguide modes for circular cylindrical guides as propagating in the axial direction with an integral number of half guide wavelengths between end plates. In this manner the standing wave pattern formed by the superposition of incident and reflected waves fulfills the boundary conditions of the conducting ends. Table 10.08 shows a TE_{11} mode, a TM_{01} mode, and a TE_{01} mode, each with one half guide wavelength between ends. The resonant wavelengths shown are obtained by solving the equation

$$d = \frac{p\lambda_g}{2} = \frac{p\lambda}{2}\left[1 - \left(\frac{\lambda}{\lambda_c}\right)^2\right]^{-\frac{1}{2}}. \tag{10}$$

The integer p is unity for (10), and cutoff wavelength λ_c is obtained from Art. 8.04. Note that in the designations TE_{111}, TM_{011}, TE_{011}, the order of subscripts is not in the cyclic order of coordinates, r, ϕ, z, since it is common in circular waveguides to designate the ϕ variation by the first subscript.

Of the foregoing modes, the TE_{011} is perhaps the most interesting since it has only circumferential currents in both the cylindrical wall and the end plates. Thus, if a resonator for such a wave is tuned by moving the end plate, one does not need a good contact between the ends and the cylindrical wall since no current flows between them. For both of the other modes shown (and in fact all except those of type TE_{0mp}) a finite current does flow between the cylinder and its ends so that any sliding contact must be good to prevent serious loss.

TABLE 10.08

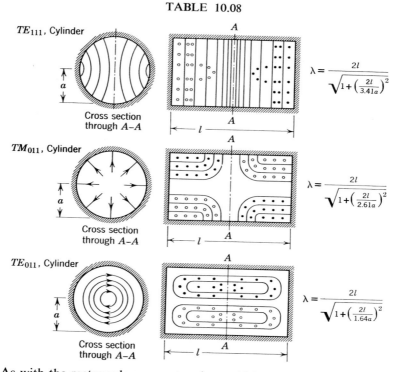

TE_{111}, Cylinder

Cross section
through A–A

$$\lambda = \frac{2l}{\sqrt{1 + \left(\frac{2l}{3.41a}\right)^2}}$$

TM_{011}, Cylinder

Cross section
through A–A

$$\lambda = \frac{2l}{\sqrt{1 + \left(\frac{2l}{2.61a}\right)^2}}$$

TE_{011}, Cylinder

Cross section
through A–A

$$\lambda = \frac{2l}{\sqrt{1 + \left(\frac{2l}{1.64a}\right)^2}}$$

As with the rectangular resonator, it would be found that higher wave orders (those having more variations with any or all coordinates r, ϕ, z) would require larger resonators to be resonant at a given wavelength. The Q would become higher because of the increased volume-to-surface ratio, but the modes would become close together in frequency so that it might be difficult to excite one mode only.

Problems

10.08a Give the field components and obtain expressions for energy storage, power loss, and Q for the TM_{011} mode.

10.08b Repeat Prob. a for the TE_{011} mode.

10.08c An air-filled circular waveguide of radius 1 cm is to be made into a resonator for the TM_{021} mode at 30,000 Mc/sec by placing end plates in the guide. Find the distance between end plates.

10.08d A circular cylindrical cavity of radius a and length d has a dielectric post of radius b and permittivity ϵ_2 extending from top to bottom. Obtain the solution for field components and the equation determining resonance, taking the simple mode analogous to that of Fig. 10.08.

10.08e A circular resonator has height h and radius a. Give the lowest frequency for which a degeneracy between two modes occurs and the designations of these modes. Make rough sketches of the field patterns. How might a small perturbation be added to change the frequency of one mode but not of the other?

10.08f Plot curves of d/λ vs a/d for all the significant modes in a circular cylindrical cavity over the range $0 < d/\lambda < 2$, $0 < a/d < 5$. Note especially ranges of operation where there is only one mode over a considerable region of operation.

10.08g Consider a TM_{010} mode in a circular cylinder cavity containing a plasma. Magnetic field is in the z direction. Find the field distribution in the cavity and the dependences of resonant frequency and Q on magnetic field and number density ($N_{max} = 10^{18}$ per cubic meter).

10.09 Wave Solutions in Spherical Coordinates

Before considering the specific problem of a spherical cavity resonator, we shall look at the solutions of Maxwell's equations in spherical coordinates. We shall sketch here only those solutions with axial symmetry, $\partial/\partial\phi = 0$. The solutions with general ϕ variations are more involved, but have been given completely by Schelkunoff[2] and Stratton[3]. It is found that with axial symmetry the solutions separate into waves with components, E_r, E_θ, H_ϕ and those with components H_r, H_θ, E_ϕ. These are called TM and TE types, respectively, the spherical surface r constant serving here as the transverse surface.

Consider then TM spherical modes with axial symmetry by setting $\partial/\partial\phi = 0$ in Maxwell's equations in spherical coordinates. The three curl equations containing E_r, E_θ, H_ϕ are

$$\frac{\partial}{\partial r}(rE_\theta) - \frac{\partial E_r}{\partial\theta} = -j\omega\mu(rH_\phi) \tag{1}$$

$$\frac{1}{r\sin\theta}\frac{\partial}{\partial\theta}(H_\phi\sin\theta) = j\omega\epsilon E_r \tag{2}$$

$$-\frac{\partial}{\partial r}(rH_\phi) = j\omega\epsilon(rE_\theta). \tag{3}$$

Equations (2) and (3) may be differentiated and substituted in (1), leading to an equation in H_ϕ alone.

$$\frac{\partial^2}{\partial r^2}(rH_\phi) + \frac{1}{r^2}\frac{\partial}{\partial\theta}\left[\frac{1}{\sin\theta}\frac{\partial}{\partial\theta}(rH_\phi\sin\theta)\right] + k^2(rH_\phi) = 0. \tag{4}$$

[2] S. A. Schelkunoff, "Transmission Theory of Spherical Waves," *Trans. A.I.E.E.*, **57**, 744–750 (1938).
[3] J. A. Stratton, *Electromagnetic Theory*, McGraw-Hill, New York, 1941, Chapter VII.

To solve this partial differential equation, we follow the product solution technique. Assume

$$(rH_\phi) = R\Theta, \tag{5}$$

where R is a function of r alone, Θ is a function of θ alone. If this is substituted in (4), the functions of r may be separated from the functions of θ, and these must then be separately equal to a constant if they are to equal each other for all values of r and θ. For a definitely ulterior motive, we label this constant $n(n+1)$.

$$\frac{r^2 R''}{R} + k^2 r^2 = -\frac{1}{\Theta}\frac{d}{d\theta}\left[\frac{1}{\sin\theta}\frac{d}{d\theta}(\Theta\sin\theta)\right] = n(n+1). \tag{6}$$

Thus there are two ordinary differential equations, one in r only, one in θ only. Let us consider that in θ first, making the substitutions

$$u = \cos\theta \qquad \sqrt{1-u^2} = \sin\theta \qquad \frac{d}{d\theta} = -\sin\theta\frac{d}{du}.$$

Then

$$(1-u^2)\frac{d^2\Theta}{du^2} - 2u\frac{d\Theta}{du} + \left[n(n+1) - \frac{1}{1-u^2}\right]\Theta = 0. \tag{7}$$

The differential equation (7) is reminiscent of Legendre's equation (Art. 3.30) and is in fact a standard form. This form is

$$(1-x^2)\frac{d^2 y}{dx^2} - 2x\frac{dy}{dx} + \left[n(n+1) - \frac{m^2}{1-x^2}\right]y = 0. \tag{8}$$

One of the solutions is written

$$y = P_n{}^m(x),$$

and the function defined by this solution is called an associated Legendre function of the first kind, order n, degree m. These are actually related to the ordinary Legendre functions by the equation

$$P_n{}^m(x) = (1-x^2)^{m/2}\frac{d^m P_n(x)}{dx^m}. \tag{9}$$

As a matter of fact, (8) could be derived from the ordinary Legendre equation by this substitution. A solution to (7) may then be written

$$\Theta = P_n{}^1(u) = P_n{}^1(\cos\theta). \tag{10}$$

And, from (9),

$$P_n{}^1(\cos\theta) = -\frac{d}{d\theta}P_n(\cos\theta). \tag{11}$$

Thus for integral values of n these associated Legendre functions are also polynomials consisting of a finite number of terms. By differentiations according to (9) in Eq. 3.30(8), the polynomials of the first few orders are found to be

$$P_0^1(\cos \theta) = 0$$
$$P_1^1(\cos \theta) = \sin \theta$$
$$P_2^1(\cos \theta) = 3 \sin \theta \cos \theta \tag{12}$$
$$P_3^1(\cos \theta) = \tfrac{3}{2} \sin \theta (5 \cos^2 \theta - 1)$$
$$P_4^1(\cos \theta) = \tfrac{5}{2} \sin \theta (7 \cos^3 \theta - 3 \cos \theta).$$

Other properties of these functions that will be useful to us, and which may be found from a study of the above, are as follows:

1. All $P_n^1(\cos \theta)$ are zero at $\theta = 0$ and $\theta = \pi$.
2. $P_n^1(\cos \theta)$ are zero at $\theta = \pi/2$ if n is even.
3. $P_n^1(\cos \theta)$ are a maximum at $\theta = \pi/2$ if n is odd, and the value of this maximum is given by

$$P_n^1(0) = \frac{(-1)^{-(n-1)/2} n!}{2^{n-1}\left[\left(\dfrac{n-1}{2}\right)!\right]^2} \qquad n \text{ odd.} \tag{13}$$

4. The associated Legendre functions have orthogonality properties similar to those of the Legendre polynomials studied previously.

$$\int_0^\pi P_l^1(\cos \theta) P_n^1(\cos \theta) \sin \theta \, d\theta = 0, \qquad l \neq n \tag{14}$$

$$\int_0^\pi [P_n^1(\cos \theta)]^2 \sin \theta \, d\theta = \frac{2n(n+1)}{2n+1}. \tag{15}$$

5. The differentiation formula is

$$\frac{d}{d\theta}[P_n^1(\cos \theta)] = \frac{1}{\sin \theta}[n P_{n+1}^1(\cos \theta) - (n+1) \cos \theta \, P_n^1(\cos \theta)]. \tag{16}$$

Note that only one solution for this second-order differential equation (7) has been considered. The other solution becomes infinite on the axis, and so will not be required in problems such as those to be considered in this text, where the region of the axis is included in the solution.

To go back to the r differential equation obtainable from (6), substitute the variable $R_1 = R/\sqrt{r}$:

$$\frac{d^2 R_1}{dr^2} + \frac{1}{r}\frac{dR_1}{dr} + \left[k^2 - \frac{(n+\frac{1}{2})^2}{r^2}\right]R_1 = 0.$$

By comparing with Eq. 3.26(3) it is seen that this is Bessel's differential equation of order $(n + \frac{1}{2})$. A complete solution may then be written

$$R_1 = A_n J_{n+\frac{1}{2}}(kr) + B_n N_{n+\frac{1}{2}}(kr) \tag{17}$$

and

$$R = \sqrt{r}\, R_1.$$

If n is an integer, these half-integral order Bessel functions reduce simply to algebraic combinations of sinusoids.[4] For example, the first few orders are

$$J_{\frac{1}{2}}(x) = \sqrt{2/\pi x}\, \sin x \qquad\qquad N_{\frac{1}{2}}(x) = -\sqrt{2/\pi x}\, \cos x$$

$$J_{\frac{3}{2}}(x) = \sqrt{2/\pi x}\left[\frac{\sin x}{x} - \cos x\right] \qquad N_{\frac{3}{2}}(x) = -\sqrt{2/\pi x}\left[\sin x + \frac{\cos x}{x}\right]$$

$$J_{\frac{5}{2}}(x) = \sqrt{2/\pi x}\left[\left(\frac{3}{x^2} - 1\right)\sin x \qquad N_{\frac{5}{2}}(x) = -\sqrt{2/\pi x}\left[\frac{3}{x}\sin x\right.$$

$$\left. - \frac{3}{x}\cos x\right] \qquad\qquad\qquad \left. + \left(\frac{3}{x^2} - 1\right)\cos x\right].$$

$$\tag{18}$$

The linear combination of the J and N functions into Hankel functions (Art. 3.26) represent waves traveling radially inward or outward, and boundary conditions will be as found previously for other Bessel functions:

1. If the region of interest includes the origin, $N_{n+\frac{1}{2}}$ cannot be present since it is infinite at $r = 0$.

2. If the region of interest extends to infinity, the linear combination of J and N into the second Hankel function, $H^{(2)}_{n+\frac{1}{2}} = J_{n+\frac{1}{2}} - jN_{n+\frac{1}{2}}$, must be used to represent a radially outward traveling wave.

The particular combination of $J_{n+\frac{1}{2}}(kr)$ an $N_{n+\frac{1}{2}}(kr)$ required for any problem may be denoted as $Z_{n+\frac{1}{2}}(kr)$, and now by combining correctly (17), (10), and (5), H_ϕ is determined. E_r and E_θ follow from (2) and (3) respectively.

$$H_\phi = \frac{A_n}{\sqrt{r}} P_n^{\ 1}(\cos\theta) Z_{n+\frac{1}{2}}(kr)$$

$$E_\theta = \frac{A_n P_n^{\ 1}(\cos\theta)}{j\omega\epsilon r^{\frac{3}{2}}}\left[nZ_{n+\frac{1}{2}}(kr) - krZ_{n-\frac{1}{2}}(kr)\right] \tag{19}$$

$$E_r = -\frac{A_n n Z_{n+\frac{1}{2}}(kr)}{j\omega\epsilon r^{\frac{3}{2}}\sin\theta}\left[\cos\theta P_n^{\ 1}(\cos\theta) - P_{n+1}^1(\cos\theta)\right].$$

[4] Special notations for the spherical or half-integral order Bessel functions have been introduced and are useful if one has much to do with these functions. Thus Stratton, following Morse (*Vibration and Sound*, McGraw-Hill, New York, 1936, p. 246) uses $j_n(x)$ to denote $(\pi/2x)^{\frac{1}{2}}J_{n+\frac{1}{2}}(x)$, and similar small letters denote other spherical Bessel and Hankel functions. Schelkunoff follows the definitions of spherical Bessel functions given by Bateman (*Partial Differential Equations*, Dover, 1944, p. 386), although in a different notation, using $\hat{J}_n(x)$ to denote $(\pi x/2)^{\frac{1}{2}}J_{n+\frac{1}{2}}(x)$, and similarly for other Bessel and Hankel functions. Because of our limited need for spherical coordinates, we shall retain the original Bessel function forms so that standard recurrence formulas may be used.

The spherically symmetric TE modes may be obtained by the above and the principle of duality, Art. 8.14. We then replace E_r and E_θ by H_r and H_θ respectively, and H_ϕ by $-E_\phi$.

$$E_\phi = \frac{B_n}{\sqrt{r}} P_n^{\ 1}(\cos\theta) Z_{n+\frac{1}{2}}(kr)$$

$$H_\theta = -\frac{B_n P_n^{\ 1}(\cos\theta)}{j\omega\mu r^{\frac{3}{2}}} [nZ_{n+\frac{1}{2}}(kr) - krZ_{n-\frac{1}{2}}(kr)] \qquad (20)$$

$$H_r = \frac{B_n n Z_{n+\frac{1}{2}}(kr)}{j\omega\mu r^{\frac{3}{2}} \sin\theta} [\cos\theta P_n^{\ 1}(\cos\theta) - P_{n+1}^1(\cos\theta)].$$

10.10 Spherical Resonators

The general discussion of spherical waves from the preceding section will now be applied to the study of some simple modes in a hollow conducting spherical resonator. Since the origin is included within the region of the solution, the Bessel functions can only be those of first kind, $J_{n+\frac{1}{2}}$. For the lowest-order TM mode, let $n = 1$ in Eq. 10.09(19) and utilize the definitions of Eqs. 10.09(12) and 10.09(18). Letting $C = A(\pi/2k)^{\frac{1}{2}}$, we then have

$$H_\phi = \frac{C\sin\theta}{kr}\left(\frac{\sin kr}{kr} - \cos kr\right) \qquad (1)$$

$$E_r = -\frac{2j\eta C\cos\theta}{k^2 r^2}\left(\frac{\sin kr}{kr} - \cos kr\right) \qquad (2)$$

$$E_\theta = \frac{j\eta C\sin\theta}{k^2 r^2}\left[\frac{(kr)^2 - 1}{kr}\sin kr + \cos kr\right] \qquad (3)$$

The mode may be designated TM_{101}, the subscripts here giving variations in the order r, ϕ, and θ. Electric and magnetic field lines are sketched in Fig. 10.10a.

To obtain the resonance condition, we know that E_θ must be zero at the radius of the perfectly conducting shell, $r = a$. From (3), this requires

$$\tan ka = \frac{ka}{1 - (ka)^2}. \qquad (4)$$

Roots of this transcendental equation may be determined graphically, and the first is found at $ka \approx 2.74$, giving a resonant wavelength of

$$\lambda \approx 2.29a. \qquad (5)$$

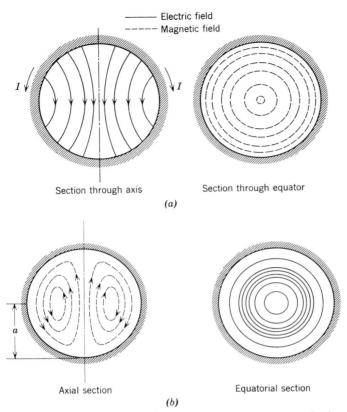

Section through axis   Section through equator

(a)

Axial section   Equatorial section

(b)

Fig. 10.10 (a) Field patterns for simple TM_{101} mode in spherical resonator. (b) Field patterns for TE_{101} mode in spherical resonator.

The energy stored at resonance may be found from the peak energy in magnetic fields.

$$U = \int_0^a \int_0^\pi \frac{\mu}{2} |H_\phi|^2 2\pi r^2 \sin \theta \, d\theta \, dr.$$

The value of H_ϕ is given by (1), and the result of the integration may be simplified by the resonance requirement (4):

$$U = \frac{2\pi\mu C^2}{3k^3} \left[ka - \frac{1 + (ka)^2}{ka} \sin^2 ka \right]. \tag{6}$$

The approximate dissipation in conductors of finite conductivity is

$$W_L = \int_0^\pi \frac{R_s |H_\phi|^2}{2} 2\pi a^2 \sin \theta \, d\theta = \frac{4\pi R_s}{3} a^2 C^2 \sin^2 ka. \tag{7}$$

So the Q of this mode is

$$Q = \frac{\eta}{2R_s(ka)^2}\left[\frac{ka}{\sin^2 ka} - \frac{1 + (ka)^2}{ka}\right] \approx \frac{\eta}{R_s}. \tag{8}$$

The "dual" of the above mode is the TE_{101} mode, and its field components may be obtained by substituting in (1) to (3) E_ϕ for H_ϕ, $-H_r$ for E_r, and $-H_\theta$ for E_θ. The fields are sketched in Fig. 10.10b. Note that the resonance condition for this mode, obtained by setting $E_\phi = 0$ at $r = a$, requires

$$\tan ka = ka.$$

Numerical solution of this yields $ka \approx 4.50$, or

$$\lambda \approx 1.395a. \tag{9}$$

Problems

10.10a Determine an equivalent conductance for the TM_{101} mode in terms of the conductor losses and a voltage between poles taken along the axis.

10.10b By utilizing solutions and definitions of Art. 10.09, write expressions for the components in a TE mode with $n = 2$.

10.10c Determine the Q of the TE_{101} mode in the spherical resonator.

SMALL-GAP CAVITIES AND COUPLING

10.11 Small-Gap Cavities

Because of their shielded nature and high Q possibilities, resonant cavities are ideal for use in many high-frequency tubes such as klystrons, magnetrons, and microwave triodes. When they are used with an electron stream, it is essential for efficient energy transfer that the electron transit time across the active field region be as small as possible. If resonators such as those studied in preceding articles were used, very thin cylinders or prisms would be required, so that impedance and Q would be low. Certain special shapes are consequently employed which have a small gap in the region that is to interact with the electron stream. Several examples of useful small-gap cavities will follow.

Foreshortened Coaxial Lines. A resonator of the general form of Fig. 10.11a may be considered a coaxial line A terminated in the gap capacitance B (leading to the equivalent circuit of Fig. 10.11b) provided

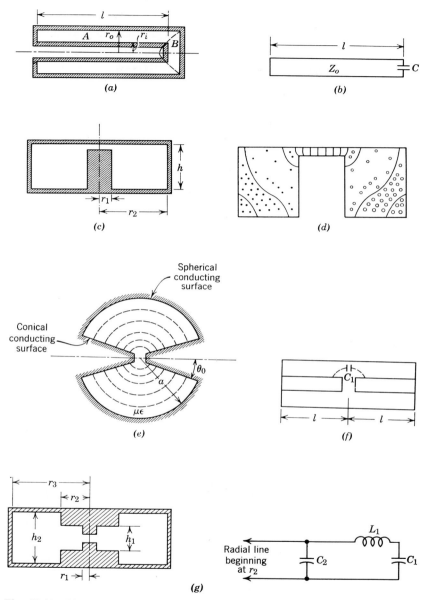

Fig. 10.11 (a) Foreshortened coaxial line resonator. (b) Approximate equivalent circuit for (a). (c) Foreshortened radial line resonator. (d) Resonator intermediate between foreshortened coaxial line and foreshortened radial line. (e) Conical line resonator. (f) Figure for Problem e. (g) Figure for Problem h.

that the region B is small compared with wavelength. The method is particularly useful when the region B is not uniform, but contains dielectrics or discontinuities, so long as a reasonable estimate of capacitance may be made.

For resonance, the impedance at any plane should be equal and opposite, looking in opposite directions. Selecting the plane of the capacitance for this purpose,

$$jZ_0 \tan \beta l = -\left(\frac{1}{j\omega_0 C}\right)$$

or

$$\beta l = \tan^{-1}\left(\frac{1}{Z_0\omega C}\right). \tag{1}$$

If C is small ($Z_0\omega C \ll 1$), the line is practically a quarter-wave in length. For larger values of C, the line is foreshortened from the quarter-wave value and would approach zero length if $Z_0\omega C$ approached infinity.

Foreshortened Radial Lines. If the proportions of the resonator are more as shown in Fig. 10.11c, it is preferable to look at the problem as one of a resonant radial transmission line (Art. 8.12) loaded or foreshortened by the capacitance of the post or gap. Then, for resonance, the inductive reactance of the shorted radial line looking outward from radius r_1 should be equal in magnitude to the capacitive reactance of the central post. Using the results and notation of Art. 8.12 we see that

$$\frac{1}{\omega C} = -\frac{h}{2\pi r_1} Z_{01} \frac{\sin (\theta_1 - \theta_2)}{\cos (\psi_1 - \theta_2)}$$

or

$$\theta_2 = \tan^{-1}\left[\frac{\sin \theta_1 + (2\pi r_1/\omega C Z_{01}h) \cos \psi_1}{\cos \theta_1 - (2\pi r_1/\omega C Z_{01}h) \sin \psi_1}\right]. \tag{2}$$

Once θ_2 is found, kr_2 is read from Fig. 8.12c.

Resonators of Intermediate Shape. In the coaxial line resonator of Fig. 10.11a the electric field lines would be substantially radial in the region far from the gap. In the radial line resonator of Fig. 10.11c the electric field lines would be substantially axial in the region far from the gap. For a resonator of the same general type, but with intermediate proportions, the field lines may be transitional between these extremes as indicated in Fig. 10.11d, and neither of these approximations may yield good results. An exact approach will be outlined in the following chapter. Some useful design curves have been given in the literature.[5] Of course, if the capacitive loading at the center is great enough, the entire resonator

[5] T. Moreno, *Microwave Transmission Design Data*, McGraw-Hill, New York, 1948.

will be relatively small compared with wavelength, and the outer portion may be considered a lumped inductance of value

$$L = \frac{\mu l}{2\pi} \ln \left(\frac{r_2}{r_1} \right). \tag{3}$$

Resonance is computed from this inductance and the known capacitance.

Conical Line Resonator. A somewhat different form of small-gap resonator, formed by placing a spherical short at radius a on a conical line as studied in Art. 8.15, is shown in Fig. 10.11e. Since this is a uniform line, formula (1) applies to this case as well. For the conical line, $\beta = k$ and

$$Z_0 = \frac{\eta}{\pi} \ln \cot \frac{\theta_0}{2}. \tag{4}$$

In the limit of zero capacitance (the two conical tips separated by an infinitesimal gap), the radius a becomes exactly a quarter-wavelength. The field components in this case, obtained by forming a standing wave from Eqs. 8.15(5) and (6), are

$$E_\theta = \frac{C}{\sin \theta} \frac{\cos kr}{r} \tag{5}$$

$$H_\phi = \frac{C}{j\eta \sin \theta} \frac{\sin kr}{r}. \tag{6}$$

The Q of the resonator in this limiting case may be shown to be

$$Q \approx \frac{\eta \pi}{4R_s} \frac{\ln \cot (\theta_0/2)}{\ln \cot (\theta_0/2) + 0.825 \csc \theta_0}. \tag{7}$$

Problems

10.11a A coaxial line of radii 0.5 and 1.5 cm is loaded by a gap capacitance of 1 pf. Find the length l for resonance at 3000 Mc/sec.

10.11b A radial line of spacing $h = 1$ cm has a central post of radius 0.5 cm and capacitance 1 pf. Find the radius r_2 for resonance at 3000 Mc/sec.

10.11c Obtain expressions for the Q and the impedance referred to the gap for the resonator of Fig. 10.11a, neglecting losses in region B. Calculate values for a copper conductor and the data of Prob. a.

10.11d Find Q and impedance if in addition to copper losses there are losses in region B representable by a shunt resistance R_0. Repeat the numerical calculation of c, taking $R_0 = 10,000$ ohms.

10.11e By extension of the concepts of this article, show that the expression for resonant frequency for the resonator of Fig. 10.11f, having total gap capacitance C_1, is

$$\beta l = \tan^{-1}\left(\frac{1}{2Z_0\omega C_1}\right).$$

10.11f For a cone angle θ_0 of 15° in Fig. 10.11e, find radius a for resonance at 3000 Mc/sec if center capacitance is 1 pf.

10.11g For the conical resonator with no loading capacitance, show that there is a value of θ_0 which gives maximum Q. Calculate the value of Q for a copper resonator designed for $\lambda = 15$ cm with this optimum angle.

10.11h A radial cavity is loaded at the center by a section as shown in Fig. 10.11g. If r_2 is relatively small compared with wavelength, it is possible to represent approximately the region inside r_2 by a lumped-circuit equivalent, as shown. Here C_1 is the center post capacitance, L_1 is an inductance calculated from d-c formulas for the coaxial region of height h_1 between radii r_1 and r_2, and C_2 is approximately the capacitance calculated on the basis of parallel disks spaced h_1, and of radii r_1 and r_2. If $C_1 = 1$ pf, $h_1 = 0.5$ cm, $h_2 = 1.0$ cm, $r_1 = 0.50$ cm, $r_2 = 1.0$ cm, find the approximate value of r_3 for resonance at $\lambda = 15$ cm.

10.12 Coupling to Cavities

The types of electromagnetic waves that may exist inside closed conducting cavities have been discussed without specifically analyzing ways of exciting these oscillations. Obviously they cannot be excited if the resonator is completely enclosed by conductors. Some means of coupling electromagnetic energy into and out of the resonator must be introduced from the outside. Some of these coupling methods have been implied in past articles. All are similar to those discussed in Art. 8.06 for exciting waves in wave guides. The most straightforward methods are:

1. Introduction of a conducting probe or antenna in the direction of the electric field lines, driven by an external transmission line.

2. Introduction of a conducting loop with plane normal to the magnetic field lines.

3. Introduction of a pulsating electron beam passing through a small gap in the resonator, in the direction of electric field lines.

4. Introduction of a hole or iris between the cavity and a driving wave guide, the hole being located so that some field component in the cavity mode has a common direction to one in the wave mode.

For example, in a velocity modulation device of the klystron type, as in Fig. 10.12a, the input cavity may be excited by a probe, the oscillations in this cavity producing a voltage across gap g_1 and causing a velocity modulation of the electron beam. The velocity modulation is converted to convection current modulation by a drifting action so that the electron beam may then excite electromagnetic oscillations in the second resonator by passing through the gap g_2. Power may be coupled out of this resonator by a coupling loop and a coaxial transmission line. Iris coupling between a TM_{010} mode in a cylindrical cavity and the TE_{10} mode in a rectangular

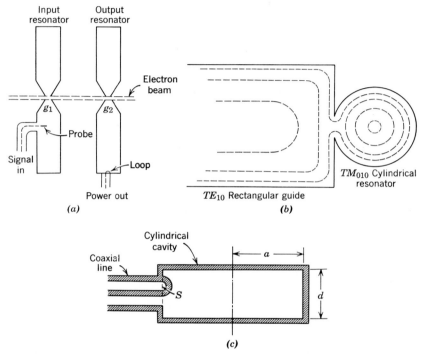

Fig. 10.12 (a) Couplings to the cavities of a velocity modulation tube amplifier. (b) Section showing approximate form of magnetic field lines in iris coupling between a guide and cavity. (c) Magnetic coupling to a cylindrical cavity.

waveguide is illustrated in Fig. 10.12b. Here the H_ϕ of the cavity and the H_x of the guide are in the same direction over the hole.

The rigorous approach to a quantitative analysis of cavity coupling is given in the following chapter. Some comments and an approximate approach are, however, in order here. Let us concentrate on the loop coupling to a TM_{010} cylindrical mode as sketched in Fig. 10.12c. If a current is made to flow in the loop, all wave types will be excited which have a magnetic field threading the loop. The simple TM_{010} mode is one of these, and, if it is near resonance, certainly it will be excited most.

However, this wave is known to fit the boundary conditions imposed by the perfectly conducting box alone. Other waves will have to be superposed to make the electric field zero along the perfectly conducting loop, but these will in general be far from resonance and so will contribute only a reactive effect. In fact, they may be thought of as producing the self-inductive reactance of the loop, taking into account the presence of the cavity as a shield.

The total induced voltage in the loop may be written

$$V_0 = j\omega\mu HS + j\omega L I_L,$$ (1)

where H is an averaged magnetic field from the TM_{010} mode over the loop, S the area of the loop, I_L the loop current, and L the self-inductance of the loop in the presence of the cavity. If the simple mode is at resonance for the unperturbed condition, no reactive energy need be supplied to it, but only a power to account for the real losses in the cavity. The first term of (1) then represents a voltage in phase with current, and the real power input is

$$W_L = \tfrac{1}{2}I_L(j\omega\mu HS).$$ (2)

If we equate this to the expression for conductor losses, Eq. 10.08(6), with H obtained from Eq. 10.08(2) by taking H_ϕ at $r = a$, we have

$$\tfrac{1}{2}I_L j\omega\mu HS = \frac{\pi a R_s E_0^{\ 2}}{\eta^2}(d + a)J_1^{\ 2}(ka) = -\pi a R_s H^2(d + a)$$

or

$$H = \frac{-j\omega\mu S}{2\pi a(d + a)R_s} I_L.$$ (3)

This equation enables us to find the level of excitation of the mode for a given loop current. Also, by substituting in (1), we may find the input impedance:

$$Z = \frac{V_0}{I_L} = \frac{(\omega\mu S)^2}{2\pi a(d + a)R_s} + j\omega L.$$ (4)

Problems

10.12a For the simple mode in a rectangular resonator perform an approximate analysis like the foregoing leading to an expression for input impedance of a loop introduced at the center of a side wall.

10.12b For the TM_{010} cylindrical mode, suppose that the coupling to the line is by means of a small probe of length d extending axially from the bottom center. Taking voltage induced in the probe as the probe length multiplied by electric field of the mode, find an expression for input admittance at resonance of the unperturbed mode, utilizing a procedure similar to the above. The probe capacitance is C.

10.12c Discuss the extension of the preceding approximate approach to other frequencies near resonance of the unperturbed mode by utilizing the Q in its relation to bandwidth. How would this enable one to find a new resonance defined as the frequency at which input impedance Z is real?

10.12d For a circular cylindrical cavity of radius 10 cm, height 10 cm, resonant in the TM_{010} mode, find the approximate resistance coupled into a transmission line by a loop of area 1 cm² introduced at the position of maximum magnetic field. Repeat for a probe of length 1 cm introduced at the position of maximum electric field.

10.13 Cavity Q and Other Figures of Merit

The Q of a cavity has been defined in terms of power loss and energy storage and has been calculated for a number of ideal configurations. It has also been noted that the Q is useful in describing bandwidth of a cavity mode, just as for a lumped-element resonant system such as those studied in Chapter 1. The reason for this is that in the vicinity of resonance for a single mode, a lumped element equivalent circuit is a good representation, as illustrated in Fig. 10.13a. The elements G, L, and C represent the mode near resonance, and jX the reactive effect of modes far from resonance. Such an equivalent circuit might be suspected to give correct qualitative results, but as will be shown in the next chapter, it actually gives correct quantitative results near resonance. The equivalent circuit also permits one to devise ways of measuring Q when it is difficult or impossible to calculate.

Many methods of Q measurement are possible,[6] but we will describe only one simple technique by way of example. It is assumed that the cavity mode is coupled to a waveguide by a means which we will illustrate here by the ideal transformer of turns ratio $m:1$, Fig. 10.13b. The guide is assumed to have unity characteristic impedance for simplicity, so that terminating impedances are automatically normalized. The input impedance at reference a is then

$$Z_a = m^2 \left[jX + \frac{1}{G + j(\omega C - 1/\omega L)} \right].$$ (1)

By defining $Q_0 = \omega_0 C/G$, $\omega_0{}^2 = 1/LC$, and $R_0 = 1/G$, this is

$$Z_a = m^2 \left[jX + \frac{R_0}{1 + j(\omega/\omega_0 - \omega_0/\omega)} \right].$$ (2)

[6] See for example E. L. Ginzton, *Microwave Measurements*, McGraw-Hill, New York, 1957, Chapter 9.

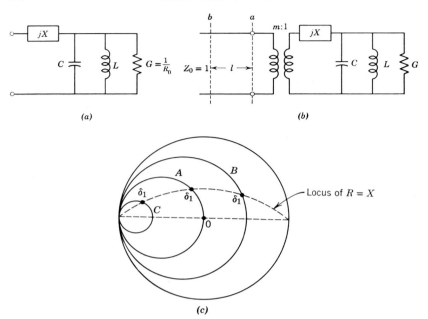

Fig. 10.13 (a) Cavity equivalent circuit. (b) Equivalent circuit for cavity with coupling to a waveguide. (c) Locus of impedance on Smith chart for Q measurement.

In the vicinity of resonance, $\omega = \omega_0(1 + \delta')$ where δ' is small,

$$Z_a \approx jm^2X + \frac{m^2R_0}{1 + 2jQ_0\delta'}. \tag{3}$$

The series reactance may be removed either by defining a new resonant frequency, or by referring input to a shifted point on the waveguide. The latter is common, and the new reference may be taken as the position of the "detuned short." That is, the cavity is detuned enough to make $Q_0\delta' \gg 1$, either by detuning the cavity itself (changing ω_0) or by changing frequency ω. By (3) the termination is then essentially jm^2X and the "detuned short" will be at position l from the end where

$$\tan \beta l = -m^2X. \tag{4}$$

The impedance at this position is then

$$Z_b = \frac{Z_a + j\tan \beta l}{1 + jZ_a\tan \beta l} = \frac{m^2R_{0b}}{1 + 2jQ_0\delta} \tag{5}$$

where

$$R_{0b} = R_0(1 + m^4X^2)^{-1}$$

$$\delta = \frac{\delta' - (m^4XR_0)}{2Q_0(1 + m^4X^2)}.$$

The locus of impedance may now be measured as δ is varied (again either by detuning the cavity or by changing frequency). As impedance is of the linear fraction form, it will produce a circular locus when plotted on the Smith chart as illustrated in Fig. 10.13c. Circle A, for which $m^2 R_{0b} = 1$, passes through the origin and is called the condition of *critical coupling* since it provides a perfect match to the guide at resonance; circle B with $m^2 R_{0b} < 1$ is said to be *undercoupled*, and circle C with $m^2 R_{0b} > 1$ is *overcoupled*. To match the last two, the coupling ratio m^2 would have to be changed. As with the lumped resonant system, the value of Q_0 can now be found from the specific value of δ which reduces impedance magnitude at reference b by $1/\sqrt{2}$ its resonant value. On the Smith chart, this is the point $R = X$ and the corresponding δ may be denoted δ_1. Then

$$Q_0 = \frac{1}{2\delta_1}. \tag{6}$$

The value of Q_0 determined in (6) is the "unloaded Q" since it does not account for loading by the guide. A loaded Q which accounts for this is also used, and may be found from Fig. 10.13b as

$$\frac{1}{Q_L} = \frac{G + m^2}{\omega_0 C} = \frac{1}{Q_0} + \frac{1}{Q_{ext}}, \tag{7}$$

where "external Q," Q_{ext}, results from

$$Q_{ext} = \frac{\omega_0 C}{m^2}. \tag{8}$$

It is assumed here that the generator is matched so that the impedance looking toward the guide is its characteristic impedance, taken here as unity.

In problems such as the klystron cavity described in Art. 10.12, the gain may be proportional to shunt resistance R_0, and bandwidth proportional to $1/Q$ by Eq. 10.06(6), so that R_0/Q may be a useful figure of merit in describing the effect of the cavity on *gain-bandwidth product*. This ratio is recognized as equivalent to the ratio $(L/C)^{\frac{1}{2}}$ introduced in lumped element circuits, Chapter 1. The quantity may be calculated for ideal cavities of simple shape of the type studied earlier in the chapter, although electron-beam loading might modify R_0 by adding losses in addition to those from the conductor. If R_0 of the cavity is defined in terms of a voltage across the gap, and electric field is approximately uniform,

$$W_L = \frac{V^2}{2R_0} = \frac{(E_0 d)^2}{2R_0}, \tag{9}$$

and this figure of merit is

$$\frac{R_0}{Q} = \frac{(E_0 d)^2}{2W_L} \cdot \frac{W_L}{\omega_0 U} = \frac{(E_0 d)^2}{2\omega_0 U}. \tag{10}$$

For the measurement of R_0/Q, we see by (10) that we need to measure the field E_0 along the axis and relate it to U, the energy stored. The field may be probed in a variety of ways, but the perturbation technique, to be described in the following article, is one of the most accurate.

Problems

10.13a For a cavity with $m^2 R_0 = 2$ and $Q_0 = 5000$, plot the locus of impedance on the Smith chart as δ is varied, showing selected values of δ on the locus. Modify m^2 to yield critical coupling and repeat.

10.13b Plot standing wave ratio in the guide versus δ for both parts of Probs. 10.13a. Describe how one might use the plot of SWR versus δ to determine Q as an alternate to the impedance function.

10.13c Find Q_L and Q_{ext} for Prob. b.

10.13d Find R_0/Q for a pillbox resonator of the type studied in Art. 10.08, operating in its lowest mode. Frequency is 10Gc/sec and $d = 0.5$ cm.

10.13e Derive the expression for R_0/Q for the small-gap coaxial line resonator pictured in Fig. 10.11a.

10.13f Repeat Prob. d if the cavity is of copper and there is an added shunt loading of 10^5 ohms at the axis arising from an electron stream.

10.14 Cavity Perturbations

Given a cavity at resonance, we know that average stored magnetic and electric energies are equal. If a small perturbation is made in one of the cavity walls, this will in general change one type of energy more than the other, and resonant frequency would then shift by an amount necessary to again equalize the energies. Slater[7] has given an important development for the amount of frequency shift when a small volume ΔV is removed from the cavity by pushing in the boundaries. This may be written

$$\frac{\Delta\omega}{\omega} = \frac{\int_{\Delta V}(\mu H^2 - \epsilon E^2)\, dV}{\int_V(\mu H^2 + \epsilon E^2)\, dV} = \frac{\int_{\Delta V}(\mu H^2 - \epsilon E^2)\, dV}{4U}. \tag{1}$$

To illustrate, imagine a small volume ΔV taken out of the pillbox resonator of Fig. 10.14, along the axis where electric field is maximum and magnetic field negligible. The change in energy stored is then

$$\frac{1}{4}\int_{\Delta V}(\mu H^2 - \epsilon E^2)\, dV \approx -\frac{\epsilon E_0^2}{4}\Delta V. \tag{2}$$

---

[7] J. C. Slater, *Microwave Electronics*, Van Nostrand, Princeton, N.J., 1950, p. 81 *et seq.*

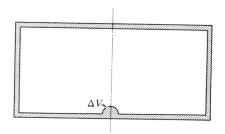

Fig. 10.14 Small perturbation in bottom
of cylindrical cavity.

The total energy of the resonator is given by Eq. 10.08(5). Frequency
shift from (1) for the lowest mode with $ka = 2.405$ is then

$$\frac{\Delta\omega}{\omega} = -\frac{\epsilon E_0^2 \Delta V}{2\pi\epsilon \, dE_0^2 a^2 J_1^2(ka)} = -1.85\frac{\Delta V}{V_0}.\qquad(3)$$

Note that this may also be written, from (1) and (2), as

$$\frac{\Delta\omega}{\omega} = \frac{-\epsilon E_0^2 \Delta V}{4U}.\qquad(4)$$

Thus the shift in resonant frequency determines the ratio E_0^2/U needed in
Eq. 10.13(10) for determination of R_0/Q. Frequency shifts can be measured
accurately, and the perturbation can be made in the form of a small
conducting bead moved by an insulating thread along the axis. Field can
be measured at all points on the axis, and thus its integral found even
when field cannot be assumed to be uniform across the gap.

Problems

10.14a Obtain the approximate expression for frequency shift if the small
volume ΔV is taken from the side wall of the TM_{010} mode where magnetic field
is large and electric field small.

10.14b Discuss qualitatively the effect of a dielectric bead introduced along the
axis; also a thin dielectric sheet along the bottom of the cavity; also a thin
cylinder along the axis. (Note that the last two problems can be solved exactly.)

10.14c Consider a periodic circuit as in Art. 8.19 with parallel perfectly conducting planes introduced a number of periods apart. Discuss resonance for
such a system. Will there be a resonance corresponding to each of the space
harmonics defined in Art. 8.19?

10.14d For Prob. c, show how measurement of the number of nodes (voltage
minima) between planes as frequency is changed permits plotting of the ω-β
diagram.

RESONATORS FOR OPTICAL SYSTEMS

10.15   Optical Resonators with Plane and Spherical Mirrors

In principle, all cavity resonator types studied might be used for any electromagnetic wave, no matter how short the wavelength. For lasers (optical masers),[8] with operation in the visible range, the infrared, or the ultraviolet, we are interested in wavelengths of the order of microns. (One micron is 10^{-6} meter.) Thus any closed cavity of reasonable dimensions

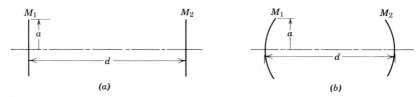

Fig. 10.15   Open resonant systems utilizing plane mirrors (a) and curved mirrors (b).

for machining (say millimeters) would have to operate on a very high order mode (e.g., Art. 10.07), and the resonances of the modes would be close together in frequency. In many cases they would be so closely grouped that the natural bandwidths of the oscillating modes could not be separated, and the use as a resonant system for such masers would be impractical.

Schawlow and Townes[9] suggested that the removal of sides from a closed cavity would eliminate a large number of modes which would be rapidly damped by the radiation from the open sides. It is not entirely obvious that any low-loss modes would remain, but the important work of Fox and Li[10] determined that there are low-loss mode patterns for open resonators. Fox and Li considered the simple system shown in Fig. 10.15a, consisting of the space between parallel-plane reflectors of finite size. By computer solutions to be described, they found stable mode patterns with relatively small radiation losses, and some of the first lasers utilized such systems. The system of parallel-plane reflectors has long been used in the

[8] A. Yariv and J. P. Gordon, "The laser," *Proc. I.E.E.E.*, **51**, 4–29 (Jan. 1963).
[9] A. L. Schawlow and C. H. Townes, "Infrared and optical masers," *Phys. Rev.*, **112**, 1940–49 (Dec. 1958).
[10] A. G. Fox and T. Li, "Resonant modes in a maser interferometer," *Bell Syst. Tech. Jour.*, **40**, 453–458 (March 1961).

classical Fabry-Perot interferometer,[11] so this simple system is frequently referred to as a Fabry-Perot resonator or *etalon*. As will be seen, adjustments are simpler if the reflectors are given some curvature, as illustrated in Fig. 10.15*b*.

Fox and Li, in solving the problem, assumed an initial field distribution over one of the mirrors and then calculated the pattern at the second

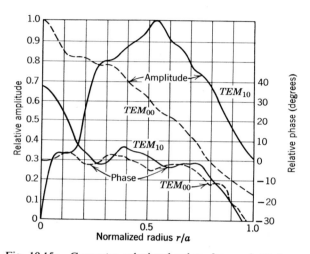

Fig. 10.15*c* Computer calculated values from ref. 10 for amplitude and phase distribution over circular planar mirrors, as in (*a*) for $a^2/d\lambda = 5$.

mirror by summing over the elemental *Huygen's sources* of the first field. This concept of field elements as sources is explained more fully in Chapter 12. With the resulting distribution over mirror 2, the calculation was reversed, yielding a new distribution for mirror 1. The process was repeated by high-speed computer for hundreds of transits, with final convergence to a stable field pattern. Figure 10.15*c* shows relative amplitude and phase as a function of radius for two modes obtained by Fox and Li for $a^2/d\lambda = 5$. One mode has a maximum field along the axis and the other has zero field. Both modes were symmetrical about a plane midway between the mirrors, thus yielding identical patterns on the two mirrors. Continuation of computer calculations, after the form of the field distribution converged, yielded the values of loss and phase shift per transit. Diffraction

[11] F. A. Jenkins and H. E. White, *Fundamentals of Optics*, 3rd ed., McGraw-Hill, New York, 1957.

losses (i.e., radiation into the open space) for these modes were found to be small enough for practical use as laser resonators. Although the modes are substantially *TEM* modes, they may have transverse variations, described by the subscripts, as will be discussed more in Art. 10.17.

Once it is known that stable, low-loss modes exist in the open structure, it is logical to look for approximate solutions of Maxwell's equations to represent these. One can then fit mirrors to the wave fronts of such solutions. Boyd and Gordon[12] obtained a most useful analytical expression by solving the integral equation describing the iterative process carried out by Fox and Li. Goubau and Schwering[13] obtained a related solution for a sequence of periodic lenses, which is equivalent to the two-mirror problem (Art. 10.16). Pierce[14] also studied the periodic lens problem and obtained like results as approximate solutions of Maxwell's equations. The general modal forms will be written in a following article, but the simplest form, known as the fundamental mode, is of Gaussian form in the transverse direction:

$$E = \frac{A w_0}{w(z)} e^{-r^2/w^2(z)}. \tag{1}$$

In this form E is magnitude of electric field parallel to the phase fronts, A is a constant, and w is a function of z of the form

$$w(z) = w_0 \left[1 + \left(\frac{z}{z_0} \right)^2 \right]^{\frac{1}{2}} \tag{2}$$

where
$$z_0 = \frac{\pi w_0^2}{\lambda}, \tag{3}$$

λ is wavelength, and w_0 is the minimum value of w at $z = 0$. Although fields actually extend to infinity, they are e^{-1} of their axial value at $r = w$ and die off very rapidly beyond, so that w is frequently referred to as "beam radius" or "spot size."

If in the foregoing solution one follows the curves of w versus z for a given w_0, hyperbolic forms are found as indicated in Fig. 10.15d. So long as one uses envelopes with small slopes, the phase fronts normal to the families of hyperbolas are essentially spherical, and one may place spherical

[12] G. D. Boyd and J. P. Gordon, "Confocal multimode resonator for millimeter through optical masers," *Bell Syst. Tech. Jour.*, **40**, 489–508 (March 1961).

[13] G. Goubau and F. Schwering, "On the guided propagation of electromagnetic wave beams," *IRE Trans. PGAP*, **AP-9**, 248–255 (May 1961).

[14] J. R. Pierce, "Modes in sequences of lenses," *Proc. Nat. Acad. Sci.*, **47**, 1808–31 (1961).

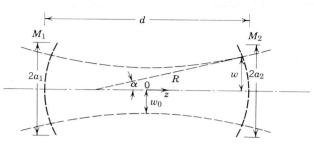

Fig. 10.15d Plots of diffraction expansion of beam by Eq. (2), showing nearly spherical wave fronts.

mirrors M_1 and M_2 as shown to form a resonator. Referring to Fig. 10.15d, the radius of curvature of the wave fronts is approximately

$$R(z) \approx \frac{w(z)}{\alpha} \approx w \frac{dz}{dw}. \tag{4}$$

By differentiating (2) and setting $R(z) = R$ at $z = d/2$, we have

$$R = \frac{d}{2}\left[1 + \left(\frac{2z_0}{d}\right)^2\right]. \tag{5}$$

One important configuration is the *confocal* one in which mirror radius is equal to the spacing, $R = d$. From (5) we then see that $2z_0$ is just the spacing for this confocal configuration,

$$2z_0 = d_{\text{conf}}, \tag{6}$$

and from (3) the minimum spot size is

$$w_0 = \left(\frac{d_{\text{conf}}\lambda}{2\pi}\right)^{1/2}. \tag{7}$$

From (2) the spot size at the mirrors is

$$w\left(\frac{d}{2}\right) = \sqrt{2}\,w_0. \tag{8}$$

Problems

10.15a For a field distribution of the form (1), estimate the fraction of energy outside the radius corresponding to $r = w$.

10.15b For a wavelength of 1 micron, separation between mirrors of 1 meter, and radius of curvature of the two like mirrors of 0.70 meter, find the minimum spot size w_0, and the spot size at the mirrors. Compare with the confocal configuration in which each mirror radius is 1 meter.

10.16 Classification of Optical Resonators; Stability

The example of the preceding article used mirrors of like radii of curvature. This is not necessary, for one may still utilize the solution of Eq. 10.15(1) and place mirrors asymmetrically with respect to the minimum spot size, as illustrated in Fig. 10.16a. An equation of the form 10.15(5) may then be written for each mirror

$$R_1 = \frac{d_1}{2}\left[1 + \left(\frac{2z_0}{d_1}\right)^2\right]$$ (1)

$$R_2 = \frac{d_2}{2}\left[1 + \left(\frac{2z_0}{d_2}\right)^2\right].$$ (2)

The equations may be solved for d_1 and d_2 respectively, and these added to obtain total spacing d:

$$d_1 = R_1 \pm \sqrt{R_1{}^2 - 4z_0{}^2}$$ (3)

$$d_2 = R_2 \pm \sqrt{R_2{}^2 - 4z_0{}^2}$$ (4)

$$d = d_1 + d_2.$$ (5)

As d, R_1, and R_2 are usually the specified quantities, (3) to (5) may be solved for z_0 in terms of these, giving

$$z_0{}^2 = \frac{d(R_1 - d)(R_2 - d)(R_1 + R_2 - d)}{(R_1 + R_2 - 2d)^2}.$$ (6)

With z_0 known, minimum spot size is determined by Eq. 10.15(3), its

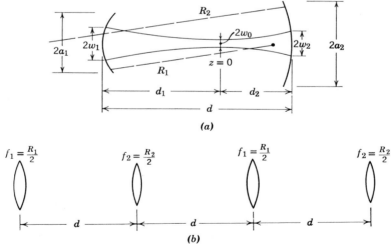

Fig. 10.16 (a) Asymmetric mirror arrangement.
(b) Biperiodic system of lenses.

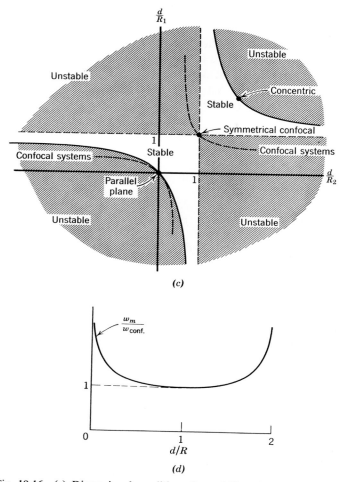

(c)

(d)

Fig. 10.16 (c) Dimensional conditions for stability of optical resonators.
(d) Spot size in symmetrical-mirror resonator.

position by (3) or (4) above, and spot size at the mirrors by the results of (3) and (4) substituted in Eq. 10.15(2). As an example, if $d = 1$ meter, $R_1 = 2$, and $R_2 = 4$, $z_0{}^2 = 0.938$ from (6). Then $d_1 = 1.5$ and $d_2 = 0.5$ from (3) and (4). If $\lambda = 10^{-6}$ meter, minimum spot size w_0 is 0.554 millimeter from Eq. 10.15(3), and $w_1 = 0.70$ millimeter, $w_2 = 0.57$ millimeter from Eq. 10.15(2). Other convenient relations among radii of curvature, spot size, etc. are given in Boyd and Kogelnik.[15]

[15] G. D. Boyd and H. Kogelnik, *Bell Syst. Tech. Jour.*, **41**, 1347–1369 (July 1962).

Not all combinations of R_1, R_2, and d give stable modes. For certain mirror spacings in comparison with radii of curvature, the bounding rays may leave the mirror system after a relatively few passes, yielding a high-loss or unstable situation. This is best seen by comparing with the equivalent system of periodic lenses, sketched in Fig. 10.16b. This is recognized as the system analyzed in Art. 8.20, for which we had the difference equation 8.20(5), with its coefficient b given by Eq. 8.20(13),

$$r_{n+2} - 2\left(1 - \frac{2d}{R_1} - \frac{2d}{R_2} + \frac{4d^2}{R_1 R_2}\right)r_{n+1} + r_n = 0. \tag{7}$$

This equation has stable solutions in terms of sines and cosines if

$$-1 \leqslant 1 - \frac{2d}{R_2} + \frac{4d^2}{R_1 R_2} \leqslant 1,$$

or by adding unity to all terms and factoring,

$$0 \leqslant \left(1 - \frac{d}{R_1}\right)\left(1 - \frac{d}{R_2}\right) \leqslant 1. \tag{8}$$

It is useful to present this stability condition as a diagram, as in Boyd and Kogelnik.[15] The bounds defined by (8) are thus shown in Fig. 10.16c with the shaded areas unstable, and the clear areas stable. We can use this diagram to relate a number of the special configurations for optical resonators.

Confocal Resonator. The symmetrical confocal resonator with $d = R_1 = R_2$ has been defined earlier, and in many ways seems to be an ideal configuration. We see from Fig. 10.16c, however, that this resonator is represented by a singular point between stable and unstable regions, so that slight irregularities could make it fall into the unstable region. Configurations which are clearly in the stable region may then be better. Note the locus for asymmetrical confocal resonators in Fig. 10.16c. These exist when the focus of either mirror occurs at the position of the other.

Parallel-Plane Resonator. If $R_1 = R_2 = \infty$, we have the parallel-plane resonator first discussed in the preceding article. It also lies at the edge of the unstable region and so is also less desirable than other configurations. Parallel-plane resonators are also very sensitive to adjustment.

Concentric Resonator. If $R_1 = R_2 = d/2$, the centers of the two spherical mirrors coincide, and the configuration is thus called concentric. It lies at the edge of an unstable region just as does the planar configuration.

Stable Spherical Mirror Configurations. Although the special cases listed earlier lie on the edges of unstable regions, there are many designs lying well within the stable regions, and one of these will usually be selected. Fig. 10.16d shows a plot of normalized spot size at the mirrors $(R_1 = R_2 = R)$ vs. d/R. The symmetry about the confocal condition $d/R = 1$ is especially interesting, with the spot sizes approaching infinity in the limit of both parallel-plane and concentric resonators. Designs with d/R around 0.6 or 1.4 have spot sizes only a little more than the confocal design, but lie well within the stable region of Fig. 10.16c.

Problems

10.16a For $\lambda = 1$ micron, $d = 2$ meters, $R_1 = 1.33$ meters, and $R_2 = 1$ meter, show location in the stability diagram. Find minimum spot size, its position, and the spot size at the two mirrors.

10.16b Discuss the significance of the multiple solutions of (3) and (4).

16.16c Yariv and Gordon[16] state the simple rule that for a configuration to be stable "either the center of curvature of one mirror or that mirror itself, but not both, must cut the axis between the other mirror and its center of curvature." Show that this is consistent with the condition in the form (8).

10.16d Show that there are stable configurations in which the mirror curvatures are in the same direction. (That is, the mode exists between a concave and convex surface.) Also show that the "half confocal" resonator with $R_1 = \infty$, $R_2 = 2d$ is stable by finding its representation on the stability diagram. Since this is, in effect, just a reflection in a plane at $z = 0$ to obtain the equivalent one one side of a confocal system, why should it be different in stability? Discuss similarly the "half concentric" resonator with $R_1 = \infty$, $R_2 = d$.

10.16e Explain the two branches of the Fig. 10.16c representing asymmetrical confocal configurations.

10.17 Modes, Phase Constants, and Losses of Optical Resonators

The open reflecting systems described in the preceding two articles may have an infinite number of transverse modes in addition to the dominant mode of Gaussian form so far described. Boyd and Gordon[17] have obtained solutions for rectangular coordinates with these approximations: relatively small slopes of the "ray" directions and large spacings in comparison with wavelength. A field component parallel to a wave front is then

$$E = E_0 H_n \left(\frac{\sqrt{2}\, x}{w} \right) H_m \left(\frac{\sqrt{2}\, y}{w} \right) e^{-(x^2 + y^2)/w^2} \tag{1}$$

[16] A. Yariv and J. P. Gordon, footnote ref. 8.
[17] G. D. Boyd and J. P. Gordon, "Confocal multimode resonator for millimeter through optical masers," *Bell Syst. Tech. Jour.*, **40**, 489–508 (March 1961).

where H_m and H_n, Hermite polynomials[18] of order m and n respectively, are defined in the literature. Goubau and Schwering[19] gave the corresponding forms for polar coordinates in the transverse plane,

$$E = E_0\left(\frac{\sqrt{2}\,r}{w}\right)^l L_p{}^l\left(\frac{2r^2}{w^2}\right)e^{-r^2/w^2}\cos l\phi, \tag{2}$$

where $L_p{}^l$ are the associated Laguerre polynomials.[18] Some photographs of modal patterns, taken by Kogelnik and Rigrod,[20] are shown in Fig. 10.17.

The phase variation along the z axis was also found for these modes. For the forms of (1), it is found that

$$\beta z = kz - (m + n + 1)\tan^{-1}\frac{z}{z_0}. \tag{3}$$

The corresponding expression for the cylindrical coordinate forms (2) is the same with $(2p + l)$ replacing $(m + n)$ in (3). Since kz is usually large at the mirrors, the second term will introduce only a small correction, at least for the lower transverse mode orders. And since the resonant condition will require a multiple of 2π phase for a round trip, we have

$$\beta d = q\pi \approx kd, \qquad q = 1, 2, 3 \ldots. \tag{4}$$

The frequency separation between longitudinal modes is then

$$\Delta f = \frac{c}{2d} \tag{5}$$

where c is the velocity of light in the resonator medium. For $d = 1$ meter, and $c = 3 \times 10^8$, this would yield a frequency separation of 150 megacycles per second, so that several longitudinal modes might be found within the line width of a particular laser transition.

Losses in the resonators under discussion occur both as reflection losses at the mirrors and as diffraction. Reflection losses are straightforward in principle, and with carefully ground and coated mirrors they may be made of the order of 0.1 per cent. Diffraction losses are small if the spot size calculated in the preceding articles is much smaller than mirror diameters. As the spot size approaches the mirror diameter, diffraction is likely to be the limiting loss. The Fresnel number,

$$N = \frac{a_1 a_2}{\lambda d}, \tag{6}$$

[18] L. I. Schiff, *Quantum Mechanics*, 2nd ed., McGraw-Hill, New York, 1955; or A. Erdelyi (ed.), *Higher Transcendental Functions*, Vol. III, McGraw-Hill, New York, 1955.
[19] G. Goubau and F. Schwering, "On the guided propagation of electromagnetic wave beams," *IRE Trans. PGAP*, **AP-9**, 248–255 (May 1961).
[20] H. Kogelnik and W. W. Rigrod, "Visual display of isolated optical modes," *Proc. IRE*, **50**, 220 (1962).

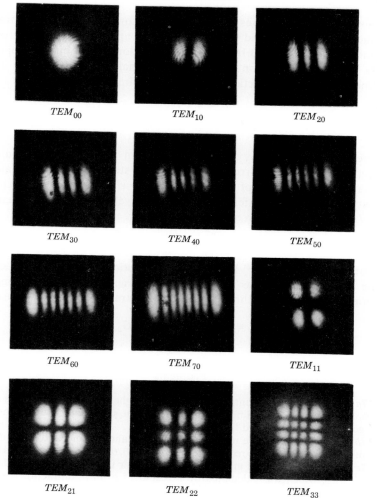

Fig. 10.17 Modal patterns in optical resonators (after Kogelnik and Rigrod, ref. 17).

determines whether or not diffraction is of importance, where a_1 and a_2 are radii of the mirrors. For values of N much larger than unity, diffraction is negligible. It is important in the range of N around unity, and becomes dominant as N decreases below unity. Actual values of the loss have been obtained by the computer calculations described in Art. 10.15. These calculations showed that nearly confocal mirrors have much smaller diffraction losses than plane or concentric systems with the same Fresnel numbers. The calculations also showed that for a given Fresnel number, diffraction losses increased very rapidly as one approached and entered an unstable region of Fig. 10.16c. Boyd and Gordon[17] also obtained approximate values of diffraction loss from their analytic solution. For large Fresnel numbers, the fractional loss is approximately

$$\alpha \approx \pi^2 2^4 N e^{-4\pi N}, \tag{7}$$

whereas for small N it approaches

$$\alpha \approx 1 - \pi^2 N^2. \tag{8}$$

The Q of a mode may now be obtained in terms of diffraction plus reflection losses at the mirrors, and the energy stored in the usual manner. The approximate value of energy stored is $\pi w^2 d U_v$, where U_v is energy density. The power transfer is given by group velocity and energy density, $\pi w^2 c U_v$. Thus, if fraction α is lost at a mirror,

$$Q = \frac{\omega_0 U}{W_L} = \frac{\omega_0 d}{\alpha c} = \frac{2\pi d}{\alpha \lambda}. \tag{9}$$

Gordon and Kogelnik[21] have shown that optical resonators scale in the sense that mode patterns are similar and fractional losses per mirror identical if the following three dimensionless parameters are held constant:

$$N = \frac{a_1 a_2}{\lambda d}, \qquad G_1 = \frac{a_1}{a_2}\left(1 - \frac{d}{R_1}\right), \qquad G_2 = \frac{a_2}{a_1}\left(1 - \frac{d}{R_2}\right). \tag{10}$$

Problems

10.17a Note the fundamental degeneracy of higher modes, that is, the same resonant conditions for different m and n with the same sum. How might such degeneracies be separated?

10.17b Find the difference in phase between βd and kd for confocal and concentric resonators for the rectangular modes $(0, 0), (0, 1), (1, 1), (1, 2),$ and $(2, 1)$.

10.17c Calculate the Q of an optical resonator for the fundamental mode with $a^2/d\lambda = 1$, which was calculated by Fox and Li to have diffraction losses of about 10^{-4} per reflection. Reflection loss at a mirror may be taken as 5×10^{-3}. Take $d = 1$ meter and $\lambda = 1$ micron. What bandwidth in megacycles would this yield? Compare with longitudinal mode spacing.

10.17d Using the scaling relations of (8) find an asymmetrical system, $a_1/a_2 = 2$, having the same losses as in Prob. c.

10.17e The optical *resolving power* of a Fabry-Perot etalon used in spectroscopy is the ratio of wavelength to the difference in wavelength between points of half-maximum intensity. The *finesse* of the device is defined as the ratio of linewidth (between half intensity points) to the spacing of modes. Relate these quantities to the defined Q, mirror spacing and wavelength. Substitute the relation (9) for Q and note the significant parameters.

[21] J. P. Gordon and H. Kogelnik, "Equivalence relations among spherical mirror optical resonators," *Bell Syst. Tech. Jour.*, **43**, 2873–2886 (Nov. 1964).

11 MICROWAVE NETWORKS

11.01 Introduction

In the last several chapters we have considered wave-propagating systems such as transmission lines and waveguides, and cavity resonant wave systems. These are important elements in microwave systems, as has been implied in previous discussions, but now we want to be more specific about the manner in which they must be treated if they are combined into systems. A typical system of this type may use a cavity as the resonant element in coupling power from an electron stream. A coupling system may, in turn, excite the dominant mode of a waveguide which is to carry the power to an antenna. On the way it may pass through other cavities with associated coupling systems designed to act as filters, and will also have to encounter unavoidable bends and discontinuities as well as other discontinuities purposely added for matching, power monitoring, or impedance measurement.

One approach to the analysis of such a system would be to solve the wave equation for each element of the system (for example, a section of waveguide with a step in height) with proper boundary or continuity conditions applied in passing from each element to the next. This would be a hopelessly complex procedure if it had to be repeated for each system, and would be useless for synthesis of new systems. Moreover, it would reveal the distribution of fields everywhere in the system, which is more information than is wanted. One usually desires only the characteristics of each part of the system as a transducer or power transfer element over the frequency range of interest. The aim of this chapter is to find a minimum number of parameters which may be used to represent the essential characteristics of a component. Specifically, we can define voltages and currents to represent the electric and magnetic fields in the dominant modes entering and leaving the component. Voltage and current are defined in such a way that their product is a measure of the power flow and their ratio is an impedance. In this way the parameters of the simplified representation take on the same functions as the network parameters of ordinary low-frequency circuits.

In addition to minimizing the number of parameters required to describe an element of the system, this representation also makes it convenient to tabulate parameters for a particular type of component having a variety of dimensions by making a single set of calculations. We shall also see ways of measuring the network parameters for a particular component or combination of components. Furthermore, the impedance representation gives additional insight in that the familiar concepts of inductance, capacitance, and resistance aid in indicating how components should be interconnected to achieve a desired system function. The parameters satisfy certain theorems analogous to classical network theorems so that some general things can be said about the behavior of all such systems which may be of help even when the specific problem cannot be solved.

Moreover, the parameters of the overall system may be found by suitable combination of the networks of its component elements, much as a lumped-element network is formed from individual elements. The overall system may also be considered to be a network. Consequently the definitions, general theorems, and some examples for microwave networks are given in this chapter with some comments on determining the parameters of the system by measurement or by analysis. Although voltage and current concepts are useful, it is also possible to formulate the interactions among elements in terms of incident and reflected waves. Such a formulation is convenient for many waveguide systems, and is especially natural for optical systems. Thus scattering and transmission parameters interrelating the wave quantities will be introduced, with some of their important properties.

DEFINITIONS AND NETWORK THEOREMS

11.02 Definition of a Microwave Network

Consistent with the preceding discussion, we shall mean by a microwave network a dielectric region of arbitrary shape having certain waveguide or transmission line inlets and outlets. The waveguides are assumed to support a finite number of noncutoff modes. Examples are the cavity resonator coupled to a single transmission line (Fig. 11.02a), the rectangular waveguide with change of height (Fig. 11.02b), the E-plane T in rectangular waveguide (Fig 11.02c), and the magic T or bridge (Fig. 11.02d). These may be said to be microwave networks with, respectively, one, two, three, and four waveguide terminal ports. (This assumes only one noncutoff mode per guide.) In considering the defined arrangements as microwave networks, it will also be assumed that we are interested only in the behaviors of the dominant modes in certain of the guides when various load conditions are placed on the remaining guides, and not in the detailed solution

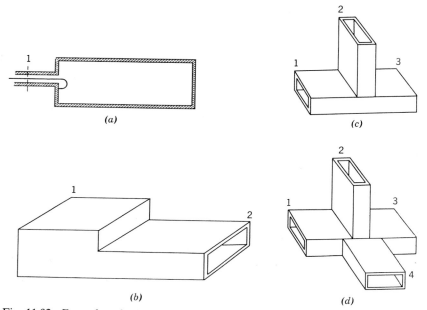

Fig. 11.02   Examples of microwave networks. (a) Coupling from a line to a cavity (one-port). (b) Discontinuity in rectangular guide (two-port). (c) E-plane T (three-port). (d) Magic T or microwave bridge (four-port).

of the electromagnetic field in the vicinity of the discontinuities. Dielectric waveguides may also serve as the terminals, and although the region is usually enclosed by good conductors, it may be open if fields die off properly at infinity.

Although we may excite only the dominant mode in any of the waveguide terminals, it is true that higher-order modes will be excited in the vicinity of the junctions, and, although these modes may be cut off, they will have reactive energy which will affect the transmission between the propagating dominant modes of the various guides. But, if we are interested only in the manner in which such transmission is affected, it can be expressed in terms of certain coefficients or equivalent circuits, and the details of the higher mode fields need not be described. Thus the microwave two-port of Fig. 11.02b may be represented by a T or π network just like a lumped-element two-port. It is interesting to note that Carson[1] recognized the validity of this representation as early as 1924, although the thorough development for distributed systems occurred much later.[2]

Finally, a combination of elements such as those in the foregoing example is also a microwave network, fitting the definition of the first paragraph. An important part of the study will be concerned with the finding of network parameters for an overall system when they are known for the individual components. The propagating media of this chapter will be considered to be linear and isotropic, but not necessarily homogeneous.

11.03 Voltage, Current, and Impedance in Waveguides

In discussing the microwave structure as a network, it is convenient to employ the usual terms, voltage, current, and impedance, in order to make easy use of the large body of applicable network theory. We have already seen in Art. 8.07 that certain simple problems may be solved by using only the field impedance (ratio of transverse E to transverse H), but in these there is a uniform discontinuity over an entire cross-sectional plane. For a problem such as that of Fig. 11.02b, where there is a change in height of a rectangular guide propagating the TE_{10} mode, a more general approach is required. One might feel intuitively that a good definition of voltage for this case would be obtained by taking the integral of electric field from top to bottom at the center of the guide, with a current defined as the total longitudinal current in the top (returning in the bottom). Then we might say that for a first approximation these defined voltages and currents should be continuous at the change of section. An exact treatment (to be discussed later) would show that, although the approximation of the last sentence is not too good, an equivalent circuit representing the exact transformation between input or output can be obtained with the stated definitions, but also other exact equivalent circuits could be obtained to fit an infinite number of possible definitions of voltage and current. Thus the attempt to arrive at a proper definition of voltage and current by physical reasoning does not lead to anything wrong, but it is not particularly purposeful because of the lack of uniqueness of the definitions. Incidentally, it is clear that in a mode such as the TE_{01} in a circular guide, it would

[1] J. R. Carson, *A.I.E.E.*, **43**, 908–913 (Oct. 1924).

[2] C. G. Montgomery, R. H. Dicke, E. M. Purcell, *Principles of Microwave Circuits*, MIT Radiation Laboratory Series, Vol. 8, McGraw-Hill, New York, 1948. See also R. N. Ghose, *Microwave Circuit Theory and Design*, McGraw-Hill, New York, 1963; and A. F. Harvey, *Microwave Engineering*, Academic Press, New York, 1963.

be difficult to apply the physical reasoning to decide on sensible definitions anyway, since electric field lines form closed circles and there is no longitudinal current.

In spite of the lack of uniqueness, it is useful to make certain definitions and to employ the terms, as will be demonstrated in following articles. The following points may be made.

1. Voltage and current of a particular waveguide mode are *always* defined so that voltage is proportional to the strength of transverse electric field of the mode, with current proportional to the strength of transverse magnetic field.

2. Voltage and current are *usually* defined so that their product gives the power flow of the mode.

3. Voltage and current are *often* defined so that the ratio of voltage and current of a single traveling wave agrees with some preselected characteristic impedance Z_0. Thus Schelkunoff in his discussion[3] makes this impedance equal to the wave impedance, and others have defined Z_0 to be unity, so that all impedances are automatically normalized.

It is recognized that points 2 and 3 resolve the lack of uniqueness inherent in 1, but other selections (such as the physical feelings mentioned in connection with the TE_{10} mode) might be substituted for either 2 or 3 or both. For reasons of convenience, we shall adopt all these points in following discussions. From point 1, we then write transverse fields:

$$\bar{E}_t(x, y, z) = V(z)\bar{f}(x, y) \tag{1}$$

$$\bar{H}_t(x, y, z) = I(z)\bar{g}(x, y). \tag{2}$$

For a single traveling wave, for example,

$$\bar{E}_t(x, y, z) = V_0 e^{-j\beta z}\bar{f}(x, y) \tag{3}$$

$$\bar{H}_t(x, y, z) = I_0 e^{-j\beta z}\bar{g}(x, y). \tag{4}$$

The arbitrariness is shown here by the manner in which any multiplicative constant is divided between the voltage V and the function $\bar{f}$ in the first expression, and similarly between I and $\bar{g}$ in the second. The arbitrariness is resolved by writing relations for points 2 and 3.

$$V_0 I_0 = 2W_T \tag{5}$$

$$\frac{V_0}{I_0} = Z_0. \tag{6}$$

[3] S. A. Schelkunoff, "Impedance Concept in Wave Guides," *Quart. Appl. Math.*, **2**, 1–15 (April 1944).

As an example, take the TE_{10} mode in rectangular guide:

$$E_y = E_0 \sin \frac{\pi x}{a} = V_0 f(x) \tag{7}$$

$$H_x = -\frac{E_0}{Z_z} \sin \frac{\pi x}{a} = I_0 g(x). \tag{8}$$

Utilizing (5), we have

$$V_0 I_0 = 2b \int_0^a \frac{E_0^2}{2Z_z} \sin^2 \frac{\pi x}{a} \, dx = \frac{ab E_0^2}{2Z_z}.$$

This result, combined with (6), gives current and voltage:

$$V_0 = E_0 \left(\frac{ab Z_0}{2Z_z}\right)^{1/2} \qquad I_0 = \left(\frac{E_0}{Z_z}\right)\left(\frac{ba Z_z}{2Z_0}\right)^{1/2}, \tag{9}$$

and, by comparsion with (7) and (8), the remaining functions are

$$f(x) = \left(\frac{2Z_z}{ab Z_0}\right)^{1/2} \sin \frac{\pi x}{a} \qquad g(x) = -\left(\frac{2Z_0}{ba Z_z}\right)^{1/2} \sin \frac{\pi x}{a}. \tag{10}$$

As noted in point 3, Z_0 can be made unity in order to normalize automatically all subsequent impedances.

Problems

11.03a   Apply the above points to determine unique definitions of voltage and current of a single TE_{01} mode in circular cylindrical guide.

11.03b   Apply the suggested physical definitions discussed in the first part of this article for determining voltage and current of the TE_{10} rectangular mode, and compare with (9). How is the product VI related to power flow in this case?

11.03c   From the relations of Arts. 7.13 and 7.14, show that the functions $\bar{f}$ and $\bar{g}$ are always related as follows:

$$\bar{g}(x, y) = \left(\frac{Z_0}{Z_z}\right) \bar{a}_z \times \bar{f}(x, y).$$

Show that the results for the rectangular guide satisfy this vector relation.

11.03d   Repeat Prob. a for the TE_{11} mode in circular guide; for the TM_{11} mode in rectangular guide.

11.04   The Network Formulation

Consider as an example a general microwave network with three wave guide terminals as defined in Art. 11.02 and pictured in Fig. 11.04. Each waveguide is assumed to support one propagating mode only, and reference planes are at first chosen far enough from junctions so that all higher-order (cutoff) modes have died out.[4] The forms of the propagating or dominant modes are assumed to be known, so that field is completely specified at each reference plane by giving two amplitudes, such as the voltage and current defined in the preceding article. It is clear that it is not possible to specify independently all voltages and currents of the network. The network formulation will tell us how many of these may

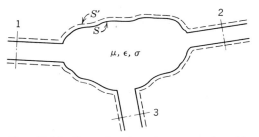

Fig. 11.04 General microwave network with three waveguide terminals.

be specified to determine the problem, and how the remaining ones are related to those specified. The following three points are cited in casting the problem in network form.

Uniqueness. It has been shown[5] that there is one and only one steady state solution of Maxwell's equations within a region if tangential electric field is specified over the closed boundary surrounding that region, or if tangential magnetic field is specified over the closed boundary, or if tangential electric field is specified over some of the boundary and tangential magnetic field over the remainder. The required specification of fields throughout the region at some initial time, mentioned in Art. 4.15, is not usually of concern to the steady-state problem. Coupling is ordinarily to a finite set of modes at any port. For a real, lossy network, all modes not coupled to the energy source will decay and take no part in the steady-state solution. In an ideal loss-free system, the uncoupled modes could oscillate forever if once excited, but would still not disturb the modes which take part in the energy transfer.

---

[4] The reference planes can actually be chosen by convenience at any place, but transmission line measurements to determine the network should not be made in the region where local waves are of importance, nor will the calculations from the network give *total* fields in that region.

[5] J. A. Stratton, *Electromagnetic Theory*, McGraw-Hill, New York 1941, pp. 486–488.

588 FIELDS AND WAVES

Linearity. Maxwell's equations are linear for linear media (μ, ϵ, and σ not functions of field strength) so that relations between various field quantities will be linear ones.

Reciprocity. An important reciprocity theorem is given in some detail in the following article. This too is usually of importance to the network formulation, as noted later.

In Fig. 11.04, consider the closed region bounded by the conducting surface S and reference planes 1, 2, 3. If the conductor is first taken as perfectly conducting, the tangential electric field is known to be zero over the surface S. Then, if voltages are given for each of the reference terminals, tangential electric fields are known there, and, by the statement of uniqueness just given, one and only one solution of Maxwell's equations is determined. $\bar{E}$ and $\bar{H}$ are then determinable for any point inside the region, so $\bar{H}$ may be computed at the reference planes so that the currents (amplitudes of the tangential magnetic field distributions) may be found there. By the linearity argument, the relations must be linear ones and may therefore be written

$$\begin{aligned} I_1 &= Y_{11}V_1 + Y_{12}V_2 + Y_{13}V_3 \\ I_2 &= Y_{21}V_1 + Y_{22}V_2 + Y_{23}V_3 \\ I_3 &= Y_{31}V_1 + Y_{32}V_2 + Y_{33}V_3. \end{aligned} \tag{1}$$

Similarly, if currents are given for all reference planes, tangential magnetic fields are known there, and, with the known zero tangential electric field over S, the uniqueness argument again applies so that tangential electric fields and hence voltages could be found at the reference planes. Relations will again be linear.

$$\begin{aligned} V_1 &= Z_{11}I_1 + Z_{12}I_2 + Z_{13}I_3 \\ V_2 &= Z_{21}I_1 + Z_{22}I_2 + Z_{23}I_3 \\ V_3 &= Z_{31}I_1 + Z_{32}I_2 + Z_{33}I_3. \end{aligned} \tag{2}$$

Forms (1) and (2) are identical with the forms that would be found relating voltages and currents at the terminals of a three-port lumped-element network. Here also the coefficients Y_{ij} and Z_{ij} are functions of frequency and are known as the admittance parameters and impedance parameters, respectively. As will be shown in the next article, application of the reciprocity theorem to a region without sources, and with proper definitions of voltages and currents, will require

$$Y_{ij} = Y_{ji} \qquad Z_{ij} = Z_{ji}. \tag{3}$$

Although the argument has been given for a perfectly conducting surface S, the foregoing forms also apply to an imperfectly conducting boundary. A reasonably convincing way of seeing this comes from moving the bounding surface several depths of penetration within the conductor to S', Fig. 11.04. The electric field here is substantially zero, so that an imagined perfect conductor could be introduced along S' without changing the behavior of the system, and the argument would proceed as above. The conducting portion between S and S' will contribute to the parameters Y_{ij} or Z_{ij} since it is now part of the interior, and those coefficients will be complex because of the losses.

Problems

11.04a Supply the proof of the uniqueness theorm cited in Art. 11.04. To do this, assume that there are two possible solutions, $(\bar{E}_1, \bar{H}_1)$ and $(\bar{E}_2, \bar{H}_2)$, and apply the Poynting theorem to the difference field $(\bar{E}_1 - \bar{E}_2, \bar{H}_1 - \bar{H}_2)$. Note Art. 3.03 for a typical uniqueness argument.

11.04b Suppose that an N-port has a load impedance Z_L connected to the terminals 1, and voltage generators connected to the other $N - 1$ terminals. Show that the following Thévenin equivalent circuits are valid *so far as calculations of effects in the load are concerned: A.* A voltage generator V_0 connected to Z_L through a series impedance Z_g. V_0 is the voltage produced at terminals 1 with these terminals open-circuited, and Z_g is the impedance seen looking into 1 with all voltage generators short-circuited (and any current generators open-circuited). *B.* A current generator I_0 connected across Z_L with internal admittance Y_g in parallel. I_0 is the current that would flow at terminals 1 if these terminals were shorted, and $Y_g = 1/Z_g$.

11.05 Reciprocity

A general form of the electromagnetic reciprocity theorem due to Lorentz states that fields $\bar{E}_a$, $\bar{H}_a$ and $\bar{E}_b$, $\bar{H}_b$ from two different sinusoidal sources a and b of the same frequency satisfy the condition

$$\nabla \cdot (\bar{E}_a \times \bar{H}_b - \bar{E}_b \times \bar{H}_a) = 0. \tag{1}$$

The medium should be isotropic but need not be homogeneous. Equation (1) is readily verified by expanding the indicated vector operations and substituting from Maxwell's equations in complex form. A volume integral of (1), with application of the divergence theorem, gives

$$\oint_S (\bar{E}_a \times \bar{H}_b - \bar{E}_b \times \bar{H}_a) \cdot \overline{dS} = 0. \tag{2}$$

The general reciprocity theorem may be applied to show the result 11.04(3) for a microwave network. Let us consider Fig. 11.04 with all reference planes but 1 and 2 closed by perfect conductors (shorted). Fields at 1 and 2 may be written [Eqs. 11.03(1) to (2)]

$$\bar{E}_{t1} = V_1 \bar{f}_1(x_1, y_1) \qquad \bar{H}_{t1} = I_1 \bar{g}_1(x_1, y_1) \tag{3}$$

$$\bar{E}_{t2} = V_2 \bar{f}_2(x_2, y_2) \qquad \bar{H}_{t2} = I_2 \bar{g}_2(x_2, y_2). \tag{4}$$

We assume also that *voltage and current are defined to have the same relation to power flow in both guides*, which requires that

$$\int_{S_1} (\bar{f}_1 \times \bar{g}_1) \cdot \overline{dS} = \int_{S_2} (\bar{f}_2 \times \bar{g}_2) \cdot \overline{dS}. \tag{5}$$

Note that this is certainly satisfied if the second point of Art. 11.03 is adopted. The surface integral of (2) is zero along the conducting surfaces S of Fig. 11.04 (or S', if imperfectly conducting), and along the shorted planes. For planes 1 and 2, substitution of (3) and (4) gives

$$(V_{1a}I_{1b} - V_{1b}I_{1a})\int_{S_1} (\bar{f}_1 \times \bar{g}_1) \cdot \overline{dS}$$

$$+ (V_{2a}I_{2b} - V_{2b}I_{2a})\int_{S_2} (\bar{f}_2 \times \bar{g}_2) \cdot \overline{dS} = 0.$$

If (5) is satisfied, this reduces to

$$V_{1a}I_{1b} - V_{1b}I_{1a} + V_{2a}I_{2b} - V_{2b}I_{2a} = 0.$$

Relations between current and voltage are introduced from Eq. 11.04(1):

$$V_{1a}(Y_{11}V_{1b} + Y_{12}V_{2b}) - V_{1b}(Y_{11}V_{1a} + Y_{12}V_{2a})$$

$$+ V_{2a}(Y_{21}V_{1b} + Y_{22}V_{2b}) - V_{2b}(Y_{21}V_{1a} + Y_{22}V_{2a}) = 0$$

$$(V_{1a}V_{2b} - V_{1b}V_{2a})(Y_{12} - Y_{21}) = 0. \tag{6}$$

In this argument the sources a and b are arbitrary so that the first factor need not be zero. Hence the second is zero.

$$Y_{21} = Y_{12}. \tag{7}$$

The argument for the impedance coefficients may be supplied by placing "open circuits" at all but two of the terminals. This done in the wave guides by placing a perfect short a quarter-wave in front of the reference planes. Moreover, since the numbering system is arbitrary, 1 and 2 may represent any two of the guides and the general relation 11.04(3) is valid.

In lumped-element networks the reciprocity theorem is frequently stated: "The positions of an impedanceless generator and an impedanceless ammeter may be interchanged without affecting the ammeter reading." This also requires relations like 11.04(3) for the lumped-element network. The same wording may then be used if desired for the microwave network if one makes use of the extended definitions of voltage, current, and impedance.

Problems

11.05a Verify (1) for the conditions stated.

11.05b Complete the proof to show that $Z_{21} = Z_{12}$.

11.05c For a lumped-element network, show that the statement of the reciprocity theorem in the last paragraph requires $Z_{21} = Z_{12}$. What similar word statement corresponds to $Y_{21} = Y_{12}$?

WAVEGUIDE JUNCTIONS AND CAVITY COUPLING

11.06 Equivalent Circuits for a Two-Port

The microwave network with two waveguide terminals, as pictured in Fig. 11.02b, is of greatest importance since it includes the cases of discontinuities in a single guide or the coupling between two guides. Most filters, matching sections, phase-correction units, and many other components are of this type. There is a large body of literature on the lumped-element equivalents, frequently known as fourpoles, four-terminal networks, or two-terminal pairs. The name "two-port" is very natural to microwave networks with waveguide terminals, but because of its simplicity, it is now widely used for networks for any frequency. Thus a port denotes a single waveguide mode at a specific reference plane for a microwave network, and a terminal-pair for a lumped-element network.

From Art. 11.04, the equations for a two-port may be written in terms of either impedance or admittance coefficients.

$$V_1 = Z_{11}I_1 + Z_{12}I_2 \tag{1}$$
$$V_2 = Z_{21}I_1 + Z_{22}I_2$$
$$I_1 = Y_{11}V_1 + Y_{12}V_2 \tag{2}$$
$$I_2 = Y_{21}V_1 + Y_{22}V_2.$$

Another convenient form expresses output quantities in terms of input quantities.

$$V_1 = \mathcal{A}V_2 - \mathcal{B}I_2 \tag{3}$$
$$I_1 = \mathcal{C}V_2 - \mathcal{D}I_2.$$

The reciprocity relations (Art. 11.05) are expressed

$$Z_{21} = Z_{12} \qquad Y_{21} = Y_{12} \qquad \mathcal{A}\mathcal{D} - \mathcal{B}\mathcal{C} = 1. \tag{4}$$

FIELDS AND WAVES

592

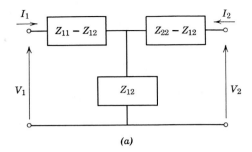

(a)

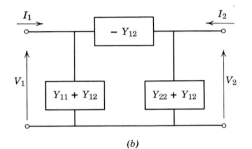

(b)

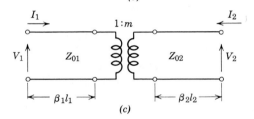

(c)

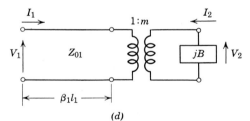

(d)

Fig. 11.06 (a) T equivalent circuit and (b) π equivalent circuit for a general two-port. (c) Equivalent circuit for a general two-port in terms of sections of transmission line and an ideal transformer. (d) Similar equivalent circuit in terms of section of transmission line, transformer, and shunt element.

A little algebra shows that the relations between the above forms for a network with reciprocity may be written

$$Y_{11} = \frac{Z_{22}}{\Delta(Z)} = \frac{\mathcal{D}}{\mathcal{B}}$$

$$Y_{12} = -\frac{Z_{12}}{\Delta(Z)} = -\frac{1}{\mathcal{B}}$$

$$Y_{22} = \frac{Z_{11}}{\Delta(Z)} = \frac{\mathcal{A}}{\mathcal{B}}$$

(5)

$$\Delta(Z) = Z_{11}Z_{22} - Z_{12}^2.$$

An infinite number of equivalent circuits may be derived which yield any of the forms (1) to (4). Two important ones are the well-known T and π forms shown in Figs. 11.06a and b. They may be shown to be equivalent to (1) and (2), respectively, by setting down the circuit equations. Other interesting ones utilize ideal transformers and sections of transmission lines, two of which are pictured in Figs. 11.06c and d. These are of greatest importance for lossless microwave networks since the arbitrary reference planes in the input or output guides can be shifted in such a way that only an ideal transformer is left in the representation of Fig. 11.06c or an ideal transformer and shunt element in Fig. 11.06d. This will be explained in more detail when the measurement problem is discussed in the next article. The quantities of Fig. 11.06c are related to the impedance parameters as follows:

$$\tan \beta_1 l_1 = \left[\frac{1 + c^2 - a^2 - b^2}{2(bc - a)}\right] \pm \sqrt{\left[\frac{1 + c^2 - a^2 - b^2}{2(bc - a)}\right]^2 + 1}$$

$$\tan \beta_2 l_2 = \frac{1 + a \tan \beta_1 l_1}{b \tan \beta_1 l_1 - c}$$

(6)

$$\frac{m^2 Z_{01}}{Z_{02}} = \frac{1 + a \tan \beta_1 l_1}{b + c \tan \beta_1 l_1},$$

where

$$a = -\frac{jZ_{11}}{Z_{01}}$$

$$b = \frac{Z_{11}Z_{22} - Z_{12}^2}{Z_{01}Z_{02}}$$

(7)

$$c = -j\frac{Z_{22}}{Z_{02}}.$$

Problems

11.06a Set up the relation between currents and voltages for Fig. 11.06d, and from these determine the impedance parameters in terms of Z_{01}, $\beta_1 l_1$, m and B.

11.06b For $Z_{11} - Z_{12} = j2$, $Z_{22} - Z_{12} = j5, Z_{12} = j$, find the admittance coefficients, the π circuit, and the $\mathcal{A}$, $\mathcal{B}$, $\mathcal{C}$, $\mathcal{D}$ constants.

11.06c For the numerical values of Prob. b, obtain the values for the equivalent circuit of Fig. 11.06c.

11.06d For a terminating impedance of 1 ohm, find input impedance, using all the forms of Probs. b and c.

11.07 Determination of Junction Parameters by Measurement

In certain cases where the geometrical configuration is relatively simple, techniques are available for the calculation of the parameters representing a microwave junction, and some of these will be discussed in later articles. For many configurations actually used, the boundaries are not simple enough for such a calculation, and it is desirable to find the pertinent parameters by measurement. The situation is not different from that encountered at low frequencies where one finds values of inductance, capacitance, and mutuals perhaps more often by measurement than by calculation from the known dimensions of the elements. We wish to describe here some of the approaches to measurement for microwave elements. There is an infinite number of possible ways, as there is an infinite number of possible equivalent circuits. The few approaches that can be discussed here are useful in themselves, and will suggest others. The examples given will be for a two-port, as in the junction represented in Fig. 11.07a.

Most often the parameters of a junction are desired for determination of the impedance transfer through it, although the information may be expressed alternatively in terms of reflection coefficient or standing-wave data. If so, it is logical to determine the unknown parameters by impedance transformation measurements also. Since there are three parameters in a two-port which satisfies reciprocity, it is necessary to make three measurements of input impedance corresponding to known load impedances for each frequency of interest. The load and input impedances might be measured, for example, by means of standing-wave data on output and input guides, respectively (Chapter 1). A particularly simple way is to place a good short at different positions along the output guide to produce the known load impedances. These are then reactive (neglecting guide losses), and may be computed from a knowledge of the short positions with respect to the reference plane so that standing-wave equipment on the output side is not needed.

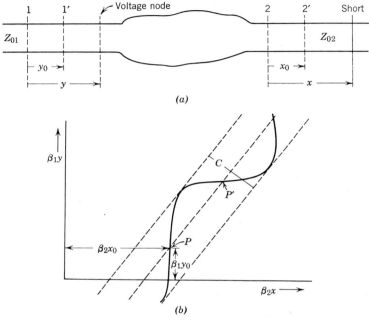

(a)

(b)

Fig. 11.07   (a) General two-port. (b) Typical S curve obtained by measurement on (a).

From Eq. 11.06(1), load impedance $Z_L = -V_2/I_2$ produces input impedance $Z_i = V_1/I_1$ as follows:

$$Z_i = Z_{11} - \frac{Z_{12}^2}{Z_{22} + Z_L}. \tag{1}$$

Algebraic elimination from three equations of the form of (1) shows that, if Z_{L1} produces Z_{i1}, Z_{L2} produces Z_{i2}, and Z_{L3} produces Z_{i3}, the impedance parameters are

$$Z_{11} = \frac{(Z_{i1} - Z_{i3})(Z_{i1}Z_{L1} - Z_{i2}Z_{L2}) - (Z_{i1} - Z_{i2})(Z_{i1}Z_{L1} - Z_{i3}Z_{L3})}{(Z_{i1} - Z_{i3})(Z_{L1} - Z_{L2}) - (Z_{i1} - Z_{i2})(Z_{L1} - Z_{L3})} \tag{2}$$

$$Z_{22} = \frac{(Z_{i1}Z_{L1} - Z_{i2}Z_{L2}) - Z_{11}(Z_{L1} - Z_{L2})}{(Z_{i2} - Z_{i1})} \tag{3}$$

$$Z_{12}^2 = (Z_{11} - Z_{ip})(Z_{22} + Z_{Lp}), \qquad p = 1, 2, 3. \tag{4}$$

If the network is lossless and if purely reactive terminations are used, input impedances will also be pure reactances, and Z's may be replaced by X's everywhere in these equations. The form of (2) to (4) may also be shown to be valid for determination of admittance parameters Y_{11}, Y_{12}, and Y_{22} when pairs of input-output admittances $Y_{L1} Y_{i1}$, $Y_{L2} Y_{i2}$, $Y_{L3} Y_{i3}$ are measured. The Z's are then replaced by Y's in (2) to (4). It is always a good idea to check for numerical errors by computing Z_{12} from all three pairs of data [$p = 1, 2, 3$, in (4)], although this checks nothing about the correctness of measurements. Note also that the sign of Z_{12} cannot be determined from impedance transformation measurements alone, since it does not enter into (1). For the same reason, it is of no interest if results are to be used only for impedance transformations by the network. For some purposes it may be necessary to know this sign, and, if so, an arrangement for measuring relative phase between input and output must be added. For simple configurations, the sign may sometimes be deduced by physical reasoning.

For regions that may be considered lossless, the representation of Fig. 11.06c is especially useful. This follows because a shift of the input reference plane from 1 to 1' (Fig. 11.07a) by a distance $\beta_1 y_0 = \pi - \beta_1 l_1$ and a shift of output reference plane from 2 to 2' by $\beta_2 x_0 = \pi - \beta_2 l_2$ gives as the equivalent circuit an ideal transformer with half-wave lines at input and output. But the latter give unity impedance transformation and so may be ignored, leaving only the ideal transformer representing the region between 2' and 1'. A load impedance referred to 2' is multiplied simply by $(1/m)^2$ to give the input impedance referred to 1'.

A little thought shows that the parameters of this representation may be determined as follows. The output guide is perfectly terminated ($Z_L = Z_{02}$); the position of the minimum impedance point on the input guide corresponds to 1', and the value of this minimum impedance gives m^2,

$$m^2 = \frac{Z_{02}}{Z_{min}} .$$ (5)

Similarly, if the network is reversed, the input guide terminated, and like measurements made on the output guide, the reference plane 2' is obtained as well as a check on m^2.

An alternative procedure to the above has advantages in some cases. Weissfloch[6] has shown that for a lossless junction a plot of position of voltage minimum on the input guide as a function of position of a short on the output guide has the "S curve" form shown in Fig. 11.07b, where $\beta_1 y$ is the electrical distance of the minimum from the originally selected reference 1, and $\beta_2 x$ is the electrical distance of the short from 2. The form

[6] A. Weissfloch, *Hochfrequenztechnik u. Electroakustik*, **60**, 67–73 (Sept. 1942).

of the equation is

$$\tan \beta_1(y - y_0) = \frac{Z_{02}}{m^2 Z_{01}} \tan \beta_2(x - x_0). \tag{6}$$

The new reference planes $1'$ and $2'$ are given by the positions x_0, y_0 of the maximum slope of the S curve, point P of Fig. 11.07b. The value of this maximum slope is $Z_{02}/m^2 Z_{01}$. The turns ratio may also be determined in terms of the distance C between the envelope tangents.

$$\frac{m^2 Z_{01}}{Z_{02}} = \tan^2 \left(\frac{\pi}{4} - \frac{\sqrt{2} \, C}{4} \right) \tag{7}$$

For the measurement, many points of input minimum are then measured as a short is moved along the output, and the curve determined. There is the advantage that the consistency of measurement and discrepancies caused by neglected losses may be told more easily than in the methods first described where only a few points are measured.

Problems

11.07a If one selects the point of minimum slope, P' of Fig. 11.07b to determine x_0, y_0 and equates this slope to $Z_{02}/m^2 Z_{01}$, a second correct representation results. Show that transformations calculated by the latter are equivalent to those from the representation described.

11.07b For the numerical values of Prob. 11.06b, plot an "S" curve as in Fig. 11.07b. Show that the values of m^2, x_0, and y_0 agree with those calculated in Prob. 11.06c.

11.08 Junction Parameters by Analysis

It has been noted that we do not require the complete field solution for a network formulation. Nevertheless, solution of the boundary value problem for fields has been useful in obtaining the network representations for certain junctions. The results are largely tabulated in handbooks.[7,8] A brief discussion of the approach to such problems may be helpful in the proper use of the tabulated results.

For junctions small in comparison with wavelength, it may be possible to set down a reasonably good equivalent circuit from quasistatic reasoning. The basis for this follows from the wave equation,

$$\frac{\partial^2 E}{\partial x^2} + \frac{\partial^2 E}{\partial y^2} + \frac{\partial^2 E}{\partial z^2} + \left(\frac{2\pi}{\lambda} \right)^2 E = 0. \tag{1}$$

[7] T. Moreno, *Microwave Transmission Design Data*, McGraw-Hill, New York, 1948.
[8] N. Marcuvitz, *Waveguide Handbook*, M.I.T. Rad. Lab. Series, Vol. 10, McGraw-Hill, New York, 1951.

Thus if variations arise from changes in dimensions x, y, or z, small in comparison with wavelength, the first terms dominate over the last and the equation reduces to Laplace's equation giving static forms for the field solutions. As an example, consider the step in the parallel-plane line of Fig. 11.08a. The electrostatic solution of this problem is known (Art. 3.19), and a "fringing" or "excess" capacitance may be found as the excess of total capacitance between electrodes over that which would exist if field lines were straight across. Letting $\alpha = a/b$, one has

$$C_d = \frac{\epsilon}{\pi}\left[\left(\frac{\alpha^2+1}{\alpha}\right)\ln\left(\frac{1+\alpha}{1-\alpha}\right) - 2\ln\left(\frac{4\alpha}{1-\alpha^2}\right)\right] \text{farads/meter width.} \quad (2)$$

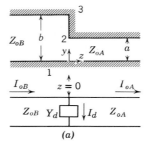

(a)

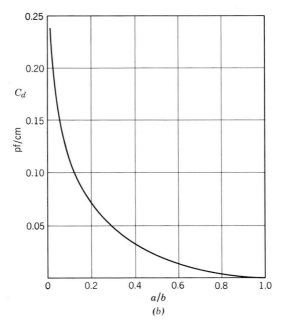

(b)

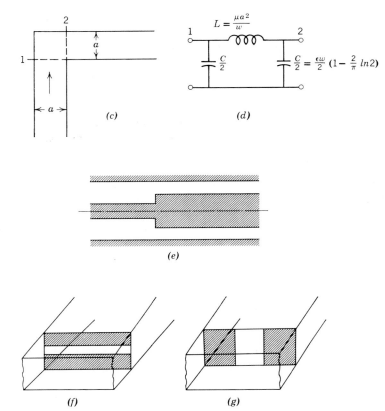

Fig. 11.08 (*a*) Step discontinuity in parallel-plane transmission line and exact equivalent circuit. (*b*) Curve of discontinuity capacitance per unit width for (*a*). (*c*, *d*) Right-angle bend in parallel-plane transmission line and equivalent circuit. (*e*) Typical discontinuity in coaxial line. (*f*) Capacitive diaphragm in rectangular guide. (*g*) Inductive diaphragm in rectangular guide.

The curve for this is plotted in Fig. 11.08*b* in picofarads per centimeter width of the line. This capacitance is placed in shunt with the two transmission lines at the junction. As we shall see later, the shunt representation is exact. The use of

$$Y_d \approx j\omega C_d \tag{3}$$

is a good approximation if the transverse dimension *b* is less than about 0.2λ.

A second case in which quasistatic approximations are useful is the right-angle bend in a parallel-plane line illustrated in Fig. 11.08*c*. Physical reasoning leads us to include an inductance to account for the Faraday's law difference in voltage between planes 1 and 2, and this may be estimated by assuming magnetic field uniform in the corner. There is also an excess capacitance as in the preceding example, and this may be divided equally because of the symmetry. There results the π equivalent circuit as shown in Fig. 11.08d with the element values there indicated.

Let us return to Fig. 11.08a and argue more carefully the case for the shunt admittance as an exact representation of the junction effect. In an approximate transmission line treatment, it is common to consider this as two lines of different characteristic impedance joined at $z = 0$. Such a treatment, however, considers only the TEM or principal transmission-line waves which have E_y and H_x with no variations in y. The perfect conductor portion from (2) to (3) requires that $E_y = 0$ here. If there were only principal waves, E_y would then have to be zero everywhere at $z = 0$ because of the lack of variations with y in the principal wave. There could then be no energy passing into the second line A regardless of its termination since the Poynting vector would then also be zero across the entire plane, $z = 0$. Physical reasoning shows that the above situation does not occur generally but only in such special cases as when line A is shorted a half wave from the discontinuity. The difficulty is met by the higher-order waves which are excited at the discontinuity, so that E_y in the principal wave is not zero at $z = 0$, but total E_y (sum of principal and higher-order components) is zero from (2) to (3) but not from (1) to (2). For the example of Fig. 11.08a the higher-order waves excited are TM waves, since E_y, E_z, and H_x alone are required in the fringing fields. For spacings between planes not comparable to wavelength, these waves are far below cutoff, so that their fields are localized in the region of the discontinuity. They may consequently be called local waves.

To show that the effect of the local waves on the transmission of the principal waves may be expressed as a lumped admittance placed at $z = 0$ in the transmission line equivalent circuit, as in Fig. 11.08a, consider that current at any value of z may be expressed as one part $I_0(z)$ from the principal wave and a contribution $I'(z)$ from all local waves.

$$I(z) = I_0(z) + I'(z). \tag{1}$$

Now total current must be continuous at the discontinuity $z = 0$, but current in the principal wave need not be, since the difference in principal wave currents may be made up by the local wave currents.

$$I_{0A}(0) + I'_A(0) = I_{0B}(0) + I'_B(0)$$
$$I_{0B}(0) - I_{0A}(0) = I'_A(0) - I'_B(0). \tag{2}$$

Total voltage in the line as defined from $-\int \bar{E} \cdot \overline{dl}$ between planes, however, is only that in the principal wave, since a study of the local waves shows that their contribution is zero.

$$V(z) = V_0(z).$$

Continuity of total voltage across the discontinuity $z = 0$ then requires continuity of voltage in the principal wave.

$$V_{0A}(0) = V_{0B}(0) = V_0(0).$$

Now, if an equivalent circuit is drawn *for the principal wave only*, its continuity of voltage but discontinuity of current may be accounted for by a lumped *discontinuity admittance* at $z = 0$, the current through this admittance being

$$I_{0B}(0) - I_{0A}(0) = I_d = Y_d V_0(0).$$

Or, from (2),

$$Y_d = \frac{I'_A(0) - I'_B(0)}{V_0(0)}. \tag{3}$$

The complete analysis[9] reveals that, when local wave values are substituted in (4), numerical values of Y_d may be calculated which are independent of terminations so long as these are far enough removed from the discontinuity not to couple to the local wave fields. For Fig. 11.08a the shunt admittance acts as a pure capacitance if transverse dimensions are negligible compared with wavelength, and the value is accurately given by Fig. 11.08b. The reference[9] gives corrections when transverse dimension is comparable with a wavelength.

Results are available[10] for several forms of coaxial discontinuity, carried out by an important series method as formulated by Hahn.[11] To a fair approximation, discontinuity capacitance for Fig. 11.08a may be found by multiplying values from Fig. 11.08b by outer circumference. If the step is in the outer conductor, values from Fig. 11.08b are multiplied by inner circumference.

Schwinger[12] and colleagues applied many of the powerful methods for boundary value problems to waveguide discontinuities including integral

[9] J. R. Whinnery and H. W. Jamieson, "Equivalent Circuits for Discontinuities in Transmission Lines," *Proc. I.R.E.*, **32**, 98–114 (Feb. 1944).

[10] J. R. Whinnery, H. W. Jamieson, and T. E. Robbins, "Coaxial Line Discontinuities," *Proc. I.R.E.*, **32**, 695–709 (Nov. 1944).

[11] W. C. Hahn, "A New Method for the Calculation of Cavity Resonators," *J. Appl. Phys.*, **12**, 62–68 (Jan. 1941).

[12] N. Marcuvitz and J. Schwinger, *J. Appl. Phys.*, **22**, 806–819 (1951), and in unpublished work.

equation formulations and variational methods—probably the most powerful approximate methods for attacking wave problems of many types. The
variational methods are described in several modern texts.[13,14] Approximate solution of the integral equations leads to approximate but useful
forms for the two waveguide discontinuities shown in Figs. 11.08f and g.
For the diaphragm extending from top and bottom of a rectangular guide
propagating the TE_{10} mode (Fig. 11.08f), the energy of the higher-order
modes is predominately capacitive. The susceptance for a symmetrical
diaphragm of gap d in a guide of width a, height b, is approximately

$$\frac{B}{Y_0} = \frac{4b}{\lambda_g} \ln \csc \frac{\pi d}{2b}. \tag{4}$$

For the diaphragm extending from the side walls as in Fig. 11.08g, higher-
order modes give a net stored magnetic energy and the corresponding
inductive susceptance, with d the gap width in this case also, is

$$\frac{B}{Y_0} = -\frac{\lambda_g}{a} \cot^2 \frac{\pi d}{2a}. \tag{5}$$

Problems

11.08a Determine the form of the proper local waves in the example of Fig.
11.08a. Show that voltage between planes, $-\int \bar{E} \cdot \overline{dl}$, is zero for each of these.

11.08b Imagine a parallel-plane transmission line with two steps such as the
one in Fig. 11.08a. The first is from spacing b to spacing a; the second is
removed from the first by a half-wavelength and is from spacing a back to b.
The line to the right of b is perfectly terminated by its characteristic impedance,
Z_{0B}. If it were not for the discontinuity capacitances, the line to the left of the
first discontinuity would also be perfectly terminated. Calculate reflection
coefficient in this line, taking into account the discontinuity capacitances
from Fig. 11.08b. Take $a = 1$ cm, $b = 2$ cm, $\lambda = 12$ cm.

11.08c Using Fig. 11.08b, calculate an approximate discontinuity capacitance
for the coaxial line of Fig. 11.08e. Take $r_1 = 0.5$ cm, $r_2 = 1$ cm, $r_3 = 1.2$ cm.

11.08d A rectangular waveguide of dimensions 0.900 by 0.400 inch propagating
the TE_{10} mode at 9000 Mc/sec feeds a horn. Standing wave ratio in the guide is
measured as 2.5 with a voltage minimum 0.55 cm in front of the horn entrance.
Find the dimensions and placing of a capacitive diaphragm in order to produce
a match for waves approaching from the left.

11.08e Repeat Prob. d, using an inductive diaphragm.

11.08f Reason physically as to the field components required in higher-order
modes for the two waveguide discontinuities of Figs. 11.08f and g, and the
type of energy storage predominate in each.

[13] R. E. Collin, *Field Theory of Guided Waves*, McGraw-Hill, New York, 1960.
[14] R. F. Harrington, *Time-Harmonic Electromagnetic Fields*, McGraw-Hill, New York, 1961.

11.09 Scattering and Transmission Coefficients

The preceding discussions have been given in terms of the voltages, currents, and impedances defined for microwave networks. It was noted that those definitions are not unique. Moreover, the impedances are usually obtained by interpreting measured values of standing-wave ratios or reflection coefficients. It is then evident that for some problems it will be more convenient and direct to formulate the transformation properties

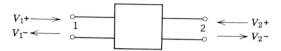

Fig. 11.09 Incident and reflected waves at ports of microwave network.

of the two-port directly in terms of waves. The two independent quantities required for each waveguide terminal are an incident and a reflected wave replacing the voltage and current. This article introduces two of the most useful forms based on wave quantities.

Suppose that incident and reflected voltage waves on the input guide are given in magnitude and phase at the chosen reference plane by V_{1+} and V_{1-} (Fig. 11.09). Similarly, incident and reflected waves looking toward the junction from reference plane 2 are V_{2+} and V_{2-}. It is common to normalize incident and reflected waves as follows,

$$a_n = \frac{V_{n+}}{\sqrt{Z_{0n}}}, \qquad b_n = \frac{V_{n-}}{\sqrt{Z_{0n}}}. \tag{1}$$

Thus voltage and current at reference plane n are related to these wave quantities as follows,

$$V_n = V_{n+} + V_{n-} = \sqrt{Z_{0n}}\,(a_n + b_n)$$
$$I_n = \frac{1}{Z_{0n}}(V_{n+} - V_{n-}) = \frac{1}{\sqrt{Z_{0n}}}(a_n - b_n). \tag{2}$$

The average power flowing into terminal n is

$$(W_n)_{\text{av}} = \tfrac{1}{2}\,\text{Re}\,(V_n I_n^*) = \tfrac{1}{2}\,\text{Re}\,[(a_n a_n^* - b_n b_n^*) + (b_n a_n^* - b_n^* a_n)].$$

The first parenthesis is a purely real quantity, and the second purely imaginary (since a quantity minus its conjugate is imaginary). Thus

$$2\,(W_n)_{\text{av}} = a_n a_n^* - b_n b_n^*. \tag{3}$$

That is, it is the power carried into terminal n by the incident wave, less that reflected away.

By arguments similar to those given previously, we know that linear relations must relate the wave quantities. In the first form to be used, we shall relate the two reflected waves to the two incident waves:

$$b_1 = S_{11}a_1 + S_{12}a_2$$
$$b_2 = S_{21}a_1 + S_{22}a_2. \tag{4}$$

The coefficients S_{11}, etc. are known as *scattering* coefficients. The above equations are frequently written in the matrix form,

$$\begin{bmatrix} b_1 \\ b_2 \end{bmatrix} = \begin{bmatrix} S_{11} & S_{12} \\ S_{21} & S_{22} \end{bmatrix} \begin{bmatrix} a_1 \\ a_2 \end{bmatrix} \tag{5}$$

or
$$[b] = [S][a] \tag{6}$$

with the $[S]$ array known as the *scattering matrix*. For a physical interpretation, note that if the output guide is matched so that $a_2 = 0$, then

$$b_1 = S_{11}a_1, \qquad b_2 = S_{21}a_1. \tag{7}$$

Thus S_{11} is just the input reflection coefficient (in magnitude and phase) when the output is matched, and S_{21} is the ratio of waves to the right at output and input under this condition. The energy equation (3) for this matched condition becomes for the two terminals,

$$2\,(W_1)_{\text{av}} = (1 - S_{11}S_{11}^*)a_1a_1{}^*$$
$$2\,(W_2)_{\text{av}} = -S_{21}S_{21}^*a_1a_1{}^*.$$

For a passive network with source at 1 as in this example, output power cannot be greater than that supplied at the input. Thus $(-W_2)_{\text{av}} \leqslant (W_1)_{\text{av}}$ or

$$S_{21}S_{21}^* \leqslant 1 - S_{11}S_{11}^*. \tag{8}$$

The equality holds only when the network is loss free.

By substituting the definitions (2) into Eq. 11.06(1), and utilizing (4), we can relate the scattering coefficients to the impedance coefficients.[15] The results are

$$DS_{11} = (Z_{11} - Z_{01})(Z_{22} + Z_{02}) - Z_{12}Z_{21}$$
$$DS_{12} = 2\sqrt{Z_{01}Z_{02}}\, Z_{12}$$
$$DS_{21} = 2\sqrt{Z_{02}Z_{01}}\, Z_{21} \tag{9}$$
$$DS_{22} = (Z_{22} - Z_{02})(Z_{11} + Z_{01}) - Z_{21}Z_{12},$$

where
$$D = (Z_{11} + Z_{01})(Z_{22} + Z_{02}) - Z_{12}Z_{21}. \tag{10}$$

[15] C. G. Montgomery, R. H. Dicke, and E. M. Purcell, *Principles of Microwave Circuits*, McGraw-Hill, New York, 1948, pp. 146–148.

From this we see that $S_{21} = S_{12}$ for a network satisfying reciprocity since then $Z_{21} = Z_{12}$. Through the relations of Eq. 11.06(5) the scattering coefficients may also be related to admittance coefficients or the transfer coefficients if necessary. They have been introduced primarily to remain in a wave formulation, however, and can be obtained directly from reflection measurements, as is shown in a following article.

A second important linear transformation of (4) gives output wave quantities in terms of input quantities,

$$b_2 = T_{11}a_1 + T_{12}b_1$$
$$a_2 = T_{21}a_1 + T_{22}b_1. \tag{11}$$

The coefficients T_{11}, etc. are known as the *transmission* coefficients, and are related to the scattering coefficients as follows,

$$T_{11} = S_{21} - \frac{S_{11}S_{22}}{S_{12}}, \qquad T_{12} = \frac{S_{22}}{S_{12}}$$

$$T_{21} = -\frac{S_{11}}{S_{12}}, \qquad T_{22} = \frac{1}{S_{12}}. \tag{12}$$

This form is especially useful for cascaded networks, as will be illustrated in Art. 11.11.

Problems

11.09a Relate the scattering coefficients to the admittance coefficients to obtain equations similar to (9).

11.09b Imagine that the source of energy is introduced at reference 2, with guide 1 perfectly terminated so that $a_1 = 0$. Derive the condition corresponding to (8). (Note that although these conditions are derived for special terminations of the network, they relate the basic parameters and must hold quite apart from the termination and driving conditions.)

11.09c Show that the condition for reciprocity in terms of the transmission coefficients is $T_{11}T_{22} - T_{12}T_{21} = 0$.

11.09d The matrix equivalents of (9) and Prob. a are

$$[S] = ([Z] - Z_{0n}[U])([Z] + Z_{0n}[U])^{-1} = \left(\frac{1}{Z_{0n}}[U] - [Y]\right)\left(\frac{1}{Z_{0n}}[U] + [Y]\right)^{-1}$$

where $[U]$ is the unit matrix and $[A]^{-1}$ denotes the inverse of $[A]$ so that $[A][A]^{-1} = [U]$. Derive these, starting from the matrix statements of the several formulations.

11.09e Find scattering and transmission coefficients for the network with numerical values given in Prob. 11.06b. Utilize the results to find input reflection coefficient if the output is matched.

11.10 Scattering Coefficients by Measurement

From Eqs. 11.09(2), the reflection coefficient at the input terminal may be found in terms of the reflection coefficient at the output. We will define reflection coefficient for both guides looking toward the right,

$$\rho_i = \frac{b_1}{a_1}, \qquad \rho_L = \frac{a_2}{b_2}. \tag{1}$$

Then
$$\rho_i = S_{11} - \frac{S_{12}^2}{S_{22} - 1/\rho_L}. \tag{2}$$

As this is of the same form as Eq. 11.07(1), the equations 11.07(2) to (4) may be adapted to give S_{11}, S_{22} and S_{12}^2 if we measure three values of input ρ_i corresponding to three independent known values of output ρ_L (assuming satisfaction of reciprocity).

We may simplify this procedure by selecting special values of load terminations when practical. In particular, as shown in Art. 11.09, if the output guide is matched so that $\rho_L = 0$, measurement of ρ_i gives S_{11} directly. If it is practical to place the source on guide 2 and match line 1, measurement of reflection coefficient looking into reference 2 similarly gives S_{22}. Then S_{12}^2 may be obtained by any other special termination, as a short on plane 2 giving $\rho_L = -1$ for (2). If the sign of S_{12} is required, a phase comparison measurement between input and output will be required. Note, however, that it will not be needed if the results are used only for impedance or reflection coefficient transfer through the network since only S_{12}^2 enters into (2).

Deschamps[16] has given a graphical method for determining the scattering coefficients utilizing plotted values of reflection coefficient directly on the Smith chart (Art. 1.20). This method has the advantage that extra measurements can readily be utilized to improve accuracy. Only a brief idea of the method will be given, and one planning to use it should consult the more detailed references.[16,17,18]

In its simplest form, the Deschamps method utilizes measured values of complex reflection coefficient at plane 1 when the output guide is terminated in a movable short. The short is set at discrete positions obtained

[16] G. A. Deschamps, "Determination of Reflection Coefficients and Insertion Loss of a Waveguide Junction," *J. Appl. Phys.*, **24**, 1046–1050 (Aug. 1953).

[17] J. E. Storer, L. S. Sheingold, and S. Stein, "A Simple Graphical Analysis of a Two-port Waveguide Junction," *Proc. IRE*, **41**, 1004–1013 (Aug. 1953).

[18] E. L. Ginzton, *Microwave Measurements*, McGraw-Hill, New York, 1957, pp. 336–345.

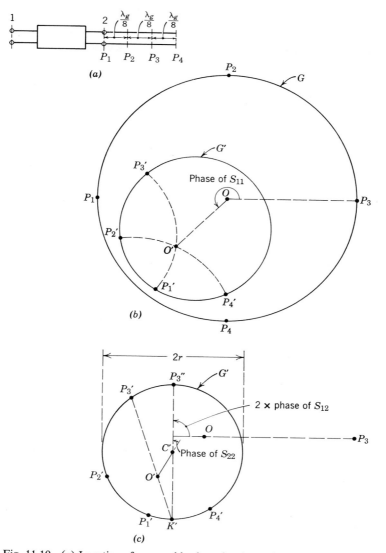

(a)

(b)

(c)

Fig. 11.10 (a) Locations for movable short for determination of scattering coefficients. (b) Smith chart construction for determination of S_{11}. (c) Construction using inner circle of (b) for determination of S_{22} and S_{12}.

by dividing a half-wavelength into an even number of equal parts. Thus Fig. 11.10a illustrates the short placed at points $P_1 \ldots P_4$ an eighth-wavelength apart. When losses in guide 2 are negligible, points on the unit circle of the Smith chart are evenly distributed, representing the different terminations defined with respect to plane 2 (Fig. 11.10b). The network (which may have losses) transforms these values to points $P'_1 \ldots P'_4$, which are the points found from the measured reflection coefficients at plane 1. These points determine a circle G', since the transformation (2) between ρ_i and ρ_L can be put in the form of a linear-fraction transformation, which transforms circles to circles (Prob. 3.18c). Because of this property, the diameters P_1P_3 and P_2P_4 transform to circular arcs $P'_1P'_3$ and $P'_2P'_4$ which may be constructed by simple geometrical procedures. The intersection of these arcs, O', is the transformed value of O; it is therefore the input standing-wave ratio corresponding to a matched load at 2, which by this argument is just S_{11}. Thus one of the three scattering coefficients is determined. Extra measurements (as every sixteenth-wavelength) would give four circular arcs, which should intersect at the point O', but if not, the error should give some idea of experimental accuracy.

Determination of S_{22} and S_{12} is slightly more complicated and will be described without proof. In the construction for S_{22}, the point P'_3 corresponding to an open circuit at reference 2 is utilized. Line P'_3O' is drawn and extended to intersect circle G' at K'; line $K'C'$ is then drawn and extended to intersect G' at P''_3, as shown in Fig. 11.10c. The phases of S_{22} and S_{12} are then the angles shown in the figure and their magnitudes are

$$|S_{22}| = \frac{\overline{O'C'}}{r} \tag{3}$$

$$|S_{12}| = \sqrt{r(1 - |S_{22}|^2)}, \tag{4}$$

where r is the radius of circle G' (normalized to the radius of the Smith chart) and C' is its center. For alternative constructions, extensions, and the proof for these, one should consult the references cited. The brief description given here should serve to illustrate the direct use of the Smith chart and the scattering coefficients when reflection measurements are made.

Problems

11.10a For a given network with a short placed at four positions $\lambda_g/8$ apart on the output guide, use the Deschamps constructions described to determine scattering coefficients if input impedances give the following values on the Smith chart:

$$P_1' = 0.93 - j1.2 \quad P_2' = 0.21 - j0.10 \quad P_3' = 0.83 + j0.30 \quad P_4' = 0.10 + j1.03$$

11.10b If the output guide is now terminated in a load with reflection coefficient $\rho_L = 0.8 e^{j\pi/4}$ at reference 2, find ρ_i for the network of Prob. *a*.

11.11 Cascaded Two-Ports

The $\mathcal{ABCD}$ transfer forms of Art. 11.06 and the transmission coefficients of Art. 11.09 are primarily useful when two-ports are cascaded

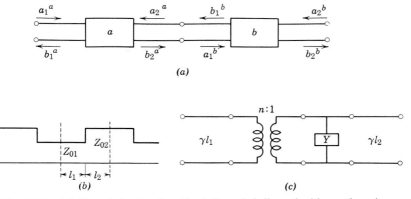

(a)

(b)   (c)

Fig. 11.11 (*a*) Cascaded networks. (*b*, *c*) Cascaded discontinuities and equivalent circuit of one section, where $n^2 = Z_{02}/Z_{01}$

because the output quantities (given either in terms of voltage and current or incident and reflected waves) of the first network become the input quantities of the second. Thus, referring to Fig. 11.11*a*, we may successively apply the form of Eq. 11.09(11) to networks *a* and *b*. In matrix form,[19]

$$\begin{bmatrix} b_2{}^a \\ a_2{}^a \end{bmatrix} = \begin{bmatrix} T_{11}^a & T_{12}^a \\ T_{21}^a & T_{22}^a \end{bmatrix} \begin{bmatrix} a_1{}^a \\ b_1{}^a \end{bmatrix}, \qquad \begin{bmatrix} b_2{}^b \\ a_2{}^b \end{bmatrix} = \begin{bmatrix} T_{11}^b & T_{12}^b \\ T_{21}^b & T_{22}^b \end{bmatrix} \begin{bmatrix} a_1{}^b \\ b_1{}^b \end{bmatrix} \tag{1}$$

but $b_2{}^a = a_1{}^b$ and $a_2{}^a = b_1{}^b$, so we may combine the two to give

$$\begin{bmatrix} b_2{}^b \\ a_2{}^b \end{bmatrix} = \begin{bmatrix} T_{11}^b & T_{12}^b \\ T_{21}^b & T_{22}^b \end{bmatrix} \begin{bmatrix} T_{11}^a & T_{12}^a \\ T_{21}^a & T_{22}^a \end{bmatrix} \begin{bmatrix} a_1{}^a \\ b_1{}^a \end{bmatrix}. \tag{2}$$

[19] R. N. Ghose, *Microwave Circuit Theory and Analysis*, McGraw-Hill, New York, 1963, Sec. 9.8.

Thus the T matrix for the two networks cascaded is

$$\begin{bmatrix} T_{11} & T_{12} \\ T_{21} & T_{22} \end{bmatrix} = \begin{bmatrix} T_{11}^b & T_{12}^b \\ T_{21}^b & T_{22}^b \end{bmatrix} \begin{bmatrix} T_{11}^a & T_{12}^a \\ T_{21}^a & T_{22}^a \end{bmatrix}. \tag{3}$$

The rules of matrix multiplication, Eq. 9.03(3), give for the individual coefficients

$$T_{11} = T_{11}^b T_{11}^a + T_{12}^b T_{21}^a$$
$$T_{12} = T_{11}^b T_{12}^a + T_{12}^b T_{22}^a$$
$$T_{21} = T_{21}^b T_{11}^a + T_{22}^b T_{21}^a \tag{4}$$
$$T_{22} = T_{21}^b T_{12}^a + T_{22}^b T_{22}^a.$$

This procedure may be repeated in an obvious fashion for more than two cascaded two-ports.

TABLE 11.11
Transmission Parameters for Simple Networks

	Transmission line	Ideal transformer	Series element	Shunt element
T_{11}	$e^{-\gamma l}$	$\frac{1}{2}(1/n + n)$	$1 - Z/2$	$1 - Y/2$
T_{12}	0	$\frac{1}{2}(1/n - n)$	$Z/2$	$-Y/2$
T_{21}	0	$\frac{1}{2}(1/n - n)$	$-Z/2$	$Y/2$
T_{22}	$e^{\gamma l}$	$\frac{1}{2}(1/n + n)$	$1 + Z/2$	$1 + Y/2$

Table 11.11 gives the T coefficients for some simple elements. To illustrate their use for cascaded units, Fig. 11.11c gives the circuit model for a section of the waveguide discontinuity problem of Fig. 11.11b. The ideal transformer in this case is introduced to take care of the change in characteristic impedances so that normalized impedances may be used in both lines (i.e., $Z_0 = 1$ for both). The overall T matrix is

$$\begin{bmatrix} T_{11} & T_{12} \\ T_{21} & T_{22} \end{bmatrix}$$

$$= \frac{1}{2} \begin{bmatrix} e^{-\gamma l_2} & 0 \\ 0 & e^{\gamma l_2} \end{bmatrix} \begin{bmatrix} 1 - \dfrac{Y}{2} & -\dfrac{Y}{2} \\ \dfrac{Y}{2} & 1 + \dfrac{Y}{2} \end{bmatrix} \begin{bmatrix} \dfrac{1}{n} + n & \dfrac{1}{n} - n \\ \dfrac{1}{n} - n & \dfrac{1}{n} + n \end{bmatrix} \begin{bmatrix} e^{-\gamma l_1} & 0 \\ 0 & e^{\gamma l_1} \end{bmatrix}. \tag{5}$$

The carrying out of the multiplications by successive use of (4) gives

$$T_{11} = \left[\left(1 - \frac{Y}{2} \right) \left(\frac{1}{n} + n \right) - \frac{Y}{2} \left(\frac{1}{n} - n \right) \right] e^{-\gamma(l_1 + l_2)}$$

$$T_{12} = \left[\left(1 - \frac{Y}{2} \right) \left(\frac{1}{n} - n \right) - \frac{Y}{2} \left(\frac{1}{n} + n \right) \right] e^{\gamma(l_1 - l_2)}$$

$$T_{21} = \left[\frac{Y}{2} \left(\frac{1}{n} + n \right) + \left(1 + \frac{Y}{2} \right) \left(\frac{1}{n} - n \right) \right] e^{\gamma(l_2 - l_1)}$$

$$T_{22} = \left[\frac{Y}{2} \left(\frac{1}{n} - n \right) + \left(1 + \frac{Y}{2} \right) \left(\frac{1}{n} + n \right) \right] e^{\gamma(l_1 + l_2)}.$$

(6)

A case of special interest is one where m like networks are cascaded. The overall transmission matrix then becomes just the mth power of that for a single network. The form for this is known,[20] and gives

$$T_{11} = \frac{T_{11}^0 \sinh m\Gamma - \sinh (m - 1)\Gamma}{\sinh \Gamma}$$

$$T_{12} = T_{12}^0 \frac{\sinh m\Gamma}{\sinh \Gamma}$$

$$T_{21} = T_{21}^0 \frac{\sinh m\Gamma}{\sinh \Gamma}$$

(7)

$$T_{22} = \frac{T_{22}^0 \sinh m\Gamma - \sinh (m - 1)\Gamma}{\sinh \Gamma}$$

where

$$\Gamma = \cosh^{-1} \frac{T_{11}^0 + T_{22}^0}{2}$$

(8)

and T_{11}^0, etc. denote the coefficients for a single network. Note that the expression for Γ in (8) is equivalent to Eq. 8.19(11) or (12) given for periodic wave guiding structures. It is also very similar to the periodic lens problem of Art. 8.20, and could in fact be solved by the difference equation approach used in that article.[21] Note also the filter properties demonstrated clearly by (8), for if Γ is real, signals will attenuate through the combination, whereas if it is imaginary, they propagate with changes in phase only.

[20] G. Birkhoff and S. Maclane, *A Survey of Modern Algebra*, Macmillan, New York, 1953.
[21] E. I. Gordon in "Optical Maser Oscillators and Noise," *Bell Syst. Tech. J.*, **43**, 507–539 (Jan. 1964) shows conversely interesting applications of cascaded network theory to optical maser systems.

Problems

11.11a Show that the $\mathcal{ABCD}$ constants of cascaded networks are found from those of the individual networks by formulas exactly similar to those for the transmission parameters.

11.11b Consider a disk-loaded waveguide in which disks which are equivalent to a normalized shunt susceptance B are placed an electrical distance βl apart in the guide. Write the transmission parameters for one section formed by a guide $\beta l/2$, the shunt element, and another length of guide $\beta l/2$. Write the parameters for N such sections.

11.11c For a lossless two-port considered as a filter, show that the pass-band occurs when

$$(T_{11} + T_{22})^2 > 4.$$

Apply this inequality to find the filter characteristics in Prob. *b*.

11.11d A dielectric window is formed by two adjacent dielectric slabs, ϵ_1 of length l_1, and ϵ_2 of length l_2, placed with air (ϵ_0) on each side. Find the transmission parameters for the overall unit. (Note that it is convenient to define all lines with unity Z_0, representing impedance changes by ideal transformers.) If there is only an outward propagating wave on the right, determine the conditions for no reflections to the left.

11.11e Solve the problem of a repeated cascading of like networks by the difference equation approach used in Art. 8.20 for periodic lenses, and derive the form (8) for propagation constant where solutions are assumed to be of the form $e^{-n\Gamma}$.

Characteristics of One-Ports

11.12 Simple Properties of a One-Port Impedance

Let us consider a closed region with one waveguide terminal or one-port, as in the cavity sketched in Fig. 11.02a. A reference plane 1 is selected far enough from the junction so that only the dominant mode in the guide is of importance, and we apply a form of the complex Poynting theorem,

$$\oint_S (\bar{E} \times \bar{H}^*) \cdot \overline{dS} = (j\omega\epsilon - \sigma)\int_V \bar{E} \cdot \bar{E}^* \, dV - j\omega\mu \int_V \bar{H} \cdot \bar{H}^* dV. \quad (1)$$

The surface integral on the left has a contribution only over S_1, for if the conductor is perfect, tangential $\bar{E}$ is zero over S, and if not, a surface S' is selected within the conductor where all fields are substantially zero, as in Art. 11.04. We select definitions of voltage and current so that the product gives power flow. Then

$$-VI^* = (j\omega - \sigma)\int_V \bar{E} \cdot \bar{E}^* \, dV - j\omega\mu \int_V \bar{H} \cdot \bar{H}^* \, dV.$$

The minus sign enters because we are concerned with power flow into the network, and the integral of (1) utilizes an outward normal. Defining voltage as the product of current and an input impedance Z,

$$-ZII^* = -2W_L + 4j\omega U_E - 4j\omega U_H$$

or
$$Z = R + jX = \frac{2W_L + 4j\omega(U_H - U_E)}{II^*}, \qquad (2)$$

where W_L is the average power loss in the region, U_E and U_H are *average* stored energies in electric and magnetic fields, respectively. Similarly for input admittance Y,

$$Y = G + jB = \frac{2W_L + 4j\omega(U_E - U_H)}{VV^*}. \qquad (3)$$

Certain properties of these impedance and admittance functions will be discussed. Note that the comments apply to the function $Z_{ii}(\omega)$ of a general microwave network (Art. 11.04), since this would be the input impedance of a two-port formed by shorting all but the ith terminal. Similarly, the theorems apply to Y_{ii} and to some other combinations of the impedance or admittance functions.

A study of (2) shows several simple results expected from physical reasoning. Impedance is purely imaginary (reactive) if power loss is zero. When power loss is finite, it must be positive, so the real (resistance) part of Z is always positive. If stored electric and magnetic average energies are equal, reactance is zero and the network is said to be resonant. If average magnetic energy is greater than electric, the reactance is positive (inductive), and if electric energy is the greater, reactance is negative (capacitive). Similar results can be deduced for the admittance function.

Problems

11.12a Making use of Maxwell's equations in complex form, derive the form (1) of the complex Poynting theorem.

11.12b State properties as in the last paragraph of Art. 11.12 specifically for the admitance of a one port.

11.12c To what does scattering matrix reduce for a one port? Give the properties of this that follow from (2) or (3) similar to those discussed earlier.

11.13 Frequency Characteristics and Equivalent Circuits of One-Ports

Little has been said up to this point concerning the frequency characteristics of the coefficients representing networks. Let us begin to consider these by looking at a one-port in which losses may be neglected. The input impedance for such a network is purely reactive, and Eqs. 11.12(2) and (3) become

$$X = \frac{4\omega(U_H - U_E)}{II^*} \qquad B = \frac{4\omega(U_E - U_H)}{VV^*}. \qquad (1)$$

The most important first theorem is Foster's reactance theorem which shows that the slope $dX/d\omega$ is always positive. As sketched in Probs. 11.13a, b, a variational form of the Poynting theorem can be derived and applied to give the rate of change of reactance with angular frequency in terms of stored energy in the system. The result is

$$\frac{dX}{d\omega} = \frac{4(U_E + U_H)}{II^*}. \qquad (2)$$

It is evident that the average stored energy $(U_E + U_H)$ is positive, and II^* is positive, so the rate of change of reactance with frequency for the lossless one port will be positive. The reactance must then go through a succession of zeros and poles as sketched in Fig. 11.13a. Similarly, the susceptance of the lossless one port has a positive slope given by

$$\frac{dB}{d\omega} = \frac{4(U_E + U_H)}{VV^*}, \qquad (3)$$

and its curve must also be of the general form of Fig. 11.13a.

Foster[22] first derived these results for loss-free lumped-element networks, and went on to show certain "canonical" equivalent circuits defined in terms of the zeros and poles of X or B. To show that these may be extended to a distributed system, consider again (1). If average stored

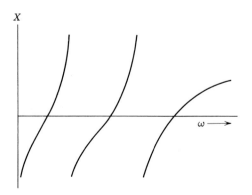

Fig. 11.13 (a) Typical form of reactance versus frequency for a lossless one-port.

[22] R. M. Foster, Bell Syst. Tech. J., 3, 259–267 (April 1924).

energies in electric and magnetic fields are equal, X is zero (resonance) provided that current is finite at the input terminals, and is infinite (anti-resonance) provided that voltage is finite at the input terminals. Because of the proof that the slope $dX/d\omega$ is positive, it follows that all zeros and poles must be simple (first order), resulting in the form of curve shown in Fig. 11.13a. It is also important to note that the function $X(\omega)$, if extended mathematically to negative frequencies by the definition (1), must be an odd function of frequency. An important consequence coming from the theory of functions of a complex variable states that the function $X(\omega)$ can be expanded in a series of "partial fractions" about the poles, provided that the following summation is convergent.

$$X(\omega) = \sum_{n=1}^{\infty} \left(\frac{a_n}{\omega - \omega_n} + \frac{a_{-n}}{\omega - \omega_{-n}} \right) + \frac{a_0}{\omega} + f(\omega), \qquad (4)$$

where a_0/ω represents the pole at zero frequency, if any is present, and $f(\omega)$ is an arbitrary entire function (one with no singularities in the finite plane). Since the function is odd, $\omega_{-n} = -\omega_n$ and $a_n = a_{-n}$. Moreover, $f(\omega)$ can have only odd powers of ω, and, since it must behave at most like a simple pole at infinity, it is known to be proportional to the first power of ω. With these specializations, (4) becomes

$$X(\omega) = \sum_{n=1}^{\infty} \frac{2\omega a_n}{\omega^2 - \omega_n^2} + \frac{a_0}{\omega} + \omega L_\infty. \qquad (5)$$

In (5), a_n is known as the residue of the pole ω_n. It may be obtained in terms of the slope of the *susceptance* curve, which can in turn be related to energy storage through (3). For in the vicinity of ω_n, the nth term of (5) predominates and

$$B(\omega) = -\frac{1}{X(\omega)} \approx -\frac{\omega^2 - \omega_n^2}{2\omega a_n}.$$

Differentiation shows that

$$\left. \frac{dB}{d\omega} \right|_{\omega=\omega_n} = -\frac{1}{a_n}.$$

Then, utilizing (3),

$$a_n = -\frac{1}{(dB/d\omega)_{\omega=\omega_n}} = -\left[\frac{VV^*}{4(U_E + U_H)} \right]_{\omega=\omega_n}. \qquad (6)$$

The form of (5) suggests an equivalent circuit consisting of anti-resonant LC circuits added in series as shown in Fig. 11.13b, for the nth component of this circuit yields a reactance

$$X_n = -\frac{1}{\omega C_n - 1/\omega L_n} = -\frac{\omega/C_n}{\omega^2 - 1/L_n C_n}$$

Comparison with the foregoing equation yields

$$a_n = -\frac{1}{2C_n} \quad \omega_n{}^2 = \frac{1}{L_nC_n} \quad a_0 = -\frac{1}{C_0} \tag{7}$$

or
$$C_n = -\frac{1}{2a_n} \quad L_n = -\frac{2a_n}{\omega_n{}^2} \quad C_0 = -\frac{1}{a_0}. \tag{8}$$

This representation, known as the first canonical form of Foster,[23] is then applicable to any lossless one-port for which the series in (5) is convergent. To find the circuit, we need to know the antiresonances, with energy storage quantities at those frequencies, both of which quantities were studied for cavity resonators in Chapter 10. The difficult part comes from the fact that the energy must be referred to the voltage in the input guide, see Eq. (6), and this requires some specific knowledge of the coupling network. The general representation may be useful for interpretation of measurements and for forming general conclusions even when this coupling problem cannot be solved.

Effect of Losses. The study of losses for practical cavity resonators in the last chapter was concerned with the calculation of a quality factor Q which expressed for a given mode the ratio of energy stored to energy lost per radian. For low-loss cavities, it might be expected that the equivalent circuit of Fig. 11.13b would be modified by adding a shunt conductance to each antiresonant element, as shown in Fig. 11.13c. The value of a given conductance G_n would be adjusted so that the Q calculated from the nth antiresonant circuit would agree with the known Q_n of the mode which it represents. That is,

$$G_n = \frac{\omega_nC_n}{Q_n}. \tag{9}$$

Justification for this procedure can be supplied by the theory of functions by making approximations appropriate to poles which are at a complex frequency near, but not exactly on, the real frequency axis.

If one accepts this modification of the lumped-circuit equivalent to account for losses, it is clear that the Q of a cavity, determined from energy calculations, is also useful for interpreting the frequency characteristics in the same manner as for a lumped circuit. This fact was stated without justification in Art. 10.06.

Second Foster Form. An expansion of the susceptance function about its poles yields a form similar to (5):

$$B(\omega) = \sum_{m=1}^{\infty} \frac{2\omega b_m}{\omega^2 - \omega_m{}^2} + \frac{b_0}{\omega} + \omega C_\infty, \tag{10}$$

[23] R. M. Foster, *Bell Sys. Tech. J.*, 3, 259–267 (April 1924).

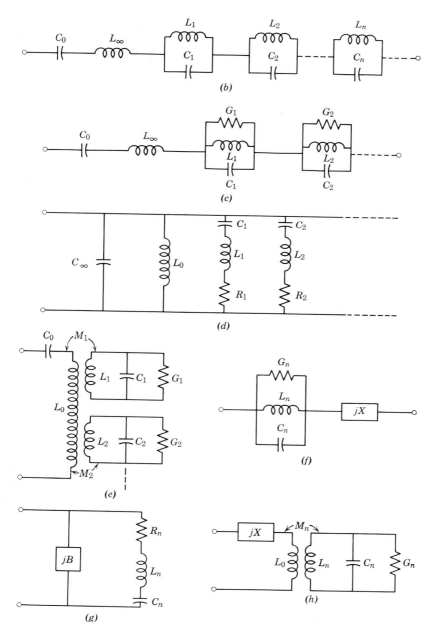

Fig. 11.13   (b–h) Various equivalent circuits for one-ports.

where the residues b_m are given by

$$b_m = -\frac{1}{[dX/d\omega]_{\omega=\omega_m}} = -\left[\frac{II^*}{4(U_E + U_H)}\right]_{\omega=\omega_m}. \qquad (11)$$

When the series is convergent, this equation has the equivalent circuit of Fig. 11.13d (known as the second Foster canonical form) with

$$L_m = -\frac{1}{2b_m} \quad C_m = -\frac{2b_m}{\omega_m^2} \quad L_0 = -\frac{1}{b_0}. \qquad (12)$$

Figure 11.13d also shows series resistance added to each resonant circuit to account for small losses, and, as in the foregoing discussion, these are selected to give the known Q for each mode.

$$R_m = \frac{\omega_m L_m}{Q_m}. \qquad (13)$$

Other Equivalent Circuits. Schelkunoff[24] has shown that other equivalent circuits may be derived by adding convergence factors to the series (5) or (10). These factors are necessary if the original series do not converge, the Mittag-Leffler theorem from the theory of functions telling how they may be formed to insure convergence. They may also be desirable in other case where the original series converge, but do so slowly. For example, Schelkunoff has shown that the form with one term of the convergence factor is

$$X(\omega) = \sum_{n=1}^{\infty} 2\omega a_n \left(\frac{1}{\omega^2 - \omega_n^2} + \frac{1}{\omega_n^2}\right) + \frac{a_0}{\omega} + \omega L_0. \qquad (14)$$

Note that, in addition to the convergence factor added in the series, the series inductance term has been modified, and inspection of (14) shows that L_0 is the entire series inductance of the circuit in the limit of zero frequency. The physical explanation of this procedure is then that this low-frequency inductance has been taken out as a separate term rather than being summed from its contributions from the various modes. It is reasonable to expect that this would often help convergence. A specific example for loop coupling to a cavity will be given in a later article.

The equivalent circuit of Fig. 11.13e gives the form of reactance function (14) (loss elements G_n being neglected at first), provided that

$$\frac{M_n^2}{L_n} = -\frac{2a_n}{\omega_n^2}, \qquad \frac{1}{L_n C_n} = \omega_n^2. \qquad (15)$$

Here one imagines the input guide coupled to the various natural modes of the resonator through transformers which gives a very natural way of

[24] S. A. Schelkunoff, *Proc. I.R.E.*, **32**, 83–90 (Feb. 1944).

looking at a problem of loop coupling to a cavity. Note, however, that one cannot determine the elements of the circuit uniquely since there are three elements, L_n, C_n, M_n, to be determined from the two basic quantities a_n and ω_n for each mode. One of the three may be chosen arbitrarily—perhaps by reference to physical feeling, but any choice will give a circuit which properly duplicates the behavior with respect to impedance at input terminals. Small losses are again accounted for by adding conductances G_n, calculated from form (9), to the circuits as shown in Fig. 11.13e.

Approximations in the Vicinity of a Single Mode. Finally, we note that when we are interested in operation in the vicinity of the natural frequency for one mode, other resonances being well separated, the dominant factor will be the one representing that mode. Other terms will vary only slowly with frequency over this range and may be lumped together as a constant impedance or admittance (predominantly reactive). The equivalent circuits of Figs. 11.13c, d, e then reduce to the simplified representations of Figs. 11.13f, g, h respectively. This is an important practical case, enabling one to use simplified lumped-element circuit analysis for the study of cavity resonator coupling problems.

Problems

11.13a Suppose that a small variation $\delta\omega$ in frequency produces variations $\delta\bar{E}$ and $\delta\bar{H}$ in fields. Starting from Maxwell's equations, show that

$$\oint_S (\bar{E} \times \delta\bar{H} - \delta\bar{E} \times \bar{H}) \cdot d\bar{S} = j\delta\omega \int_V (\mu H^2 - \epsilon E^2) \, dV.$$

11.13b Apply the result of Prob. a to derive (2) for a lossless network with one waveguide input.

11.13c Figure 11.13a shows reactance as starting from $-\infty$ at $\omega = 0$. It may also start with a zero value there. Show examples of circuits for each of these behaviors. Repeat for susceptance.

11.13d Illustrate by example that $dX/d\omega$ is not always positive for lossy networks.

11.13e Modify the form for $B(\omega)$, Eq. (10), to correspond to the form (14) with a convergence factor added, and find an equivalent circuit representation. *Hint:* Change the form of Fig. 11.13d by using T networks to replace the transformers, and look for the dual of this circuit.

11.14 Examples of Cavity Equivalent Circuits

Two examples will be given to clarify the calculation of element values in the equivalent circuits of Art. 11.13. It should be stressed again that the difficult part comes in solving enough of the coupling problem to refer the energy quantities within the resonator to defined voltage or current in the guide. In the first example, a uniform line is considered so that energy can be expressed directly in terms of the input current. In the second example, a reasonable approximation to the coupling problem can be made.

Open-Circuited Transmission Line. Let us consider a lossless open-circuited line of length l, inductance L per unit length, and capacitance C per unit length (Fig. 11.14a). We shall derive the second Foster form,

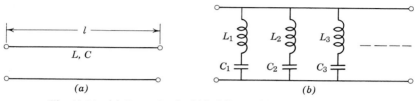

Fig. 11.14   (a) Open-circuited ideal line and (b) equivalent circuit.

Fig. 11.13d, starting from Eq. 11.13(10). For this calculation we need the natural modes having infinite susceptance at the input. Current is then a maximum at the input, zero at $z = l$, and length must be an odd multiple of a quarter-wavelength.

$$I_m(z) = I_{0m} \cos \omega_m z \sqrt{LC} \tag{1}$$

$$\omega_m = \frac{2\pi}{\lambda_m \sqrt{LC}} = \frac{2\pi m}{4l\sqrt{LC}} \quad \text{(m odd)} \tag{2}$$

The sum of *average* U_E and U_H is equal to the total energy stored at resonance, which may be computed as maximum energy in magnetic fields.

$$U_E + U_H = (U_H)_{\max} = \int_0^l \frac{LI_{0m}^2}{2} \cos^2 \omega_m z \sqrt{LC} \, dz = \frac{lLI_{0m}^2}{4} \tag{3}$$

Substitution in Eq. 11.13(11) gives the residue for the mth mode.

$$b_m = -\frac{I_{0m}^2}{4(U_E + U_H)} = -\frac{1}{Ll} .$$

Inductance and capacitance for the mth circuit are found from Eq. 11.13 (12).

$$L_m = -\frac{1}{2b_m} = \frac{Ll}{2} \tag{4}$$

$$C_m = -\frac{2b_m}{\omega_m^2} = \frac{8Cl}{\pi^2 m^2} \tag{5}$$

This leads to the equivalent circuit of Fig. 11.14*b*, which is valid for all frequencies provided the equation for $B(\omega)$ obtained from Eq. 11.13(10) is convergent. The series is convergent in this case, and in fact can be shown to be equivalent to the following closed form:

$$B(\omega) = -\sum_{m \text{ odd}} \frac{2\omega}{Ll[\omega^2 - m^2\pi^2/4l^2LC]} = \sqrt{C/L}\tan \omega l\sqrt{LC}. \qquad (6)$$

The last expression can be recognized as the input susceptance for an open-circuited ideal line obtained from simple transmission line theory, as it should be.

Loop-Coupled Cavity. For a second example, we shall return to the loop-coupled cylindrical cavity discussed in Art. 10.12 from an energy point of view. In particular, we shall concern ourselves with behavior in the vicinity of resonance for the simple TM_{010} mode, all other resonances being well separated, so that one of the approximate forms of Fig. 11.13*f*, *g* or *h* is appropriate. The form of Fig. 11.13*h*, arising from Eq. 11.13(14), is particularly useful because the self-inductance of the loop is separated out, and the remaining series may be thought of as representing more nearly the behavior of the unperturbed cavity. From the physical point of view, it is a natural equivalent circuit, since we picture the input line as being coupled to the cavity mode through a mutual which represents the loop.

The voltage at the loop terminals (computed with no self-inductance drop, as is appropriate for the zero current of antiresonance) is found approximately by taking magnetic field of the unperturbed mode flowing through the small loop of area S, as in Art. 10.12.

$$V = j\omega\mu HS \qquad (7)$$

Energy stored in the mode from Eq. 10.08(5) may be written

$$(U_E + U_H) = (U_H)_{\max} = \tfrac{1}{2}\pi\mu dH^2a^2. \qquad (8)$$

Substitution in Eq. 11.13(6) gives the residue for the mode:

$$a_1 = -\frac{VV^*}{4(U_E + U_H)_{\omega=\omega_1}} = -\frac{\omega_1^2\mu^2S^2}{2\pi a^2d}. \qquad (9)$$

Resonant frequency and Q are known from the analysis of Art. 10.08.

$$\omega_1 = \frac{p_{01}}{a\sqrt{\mu\epsilon}} \qquad (10)$$

$$Q_1 = \frac{\eta p_{01}d}{2R_s(d + a)} \qquad (11)$$

Here we meet the indeterminacy of the form selected, for we have three quantities, a_1, ω_1, Q_1 to determine four quantities, M_1, L_1, C_1, and G_1. As pointed out before, one of the four may be selected arbitrarily and the same input impedance will result. One choice is to leave the conductance G_1 as computed earlier from power loss and voltage across the center. This makes sense, for example, when an electron beam is to be shot across the center, in which case a beam admittance, calculated on the same basis, can simply be placed in parallel with G_1 in the equivalent circuit. Taking the value of G from Eq. 10.08(8),

$$G_1 = \frac{R_s}{\eta^2} \frac{2\pi a(d+a)}{d^2} J_1^{\,2}(p_{01}).$$ (12)

Application of Eqs. 11.13(9) and (15) then yields

$$C_1 = \frac{Q_1 G_1}{\omega_1} = J_1^{\,2}(p_{01})\left(\frac{\pi a^2 \epsilon}{d}\right)$$ (13)

$$L_1 = \frac{1}{\omega_1^{\,2} C_1} = \frac{\mu d}{\pi p_{01}^2 J_1^{\,2}(p_{01})}$$ (14)

$$M_1 = \left(-\frac{2a_1 L_1}{\omega_1^{\,2}}\right)^{\!1/2} = \frac{\mu S}{\pi a p_{01} J_1(p_{01})}.$$ (15)

Input impedance, computed at resonance for the unperturbed mode $(\omega^2 L_1 C_1 = 1)$, can then be shown to yield the same result as was found in Eq. 10.12(4) by energy considerations.

$$Z = j\omega L_0 + \frac{\omega^2 M^2}{j\omega L_1 + 1/(G_1 + j\omega C_1)} \approx j\omega L_0 + \frac{(\omega \mu S)^2}{2\pi a R_s(d+a)}.$$ (16)

Problems

11.14a   Derive the equivalent circuit of Fig. 11.13a for a shorted length l of ideal line. Show that the series form for $X(\omega)$ converges to the usual expression for reactance of a shorted ideal line.

11.14b   Derive the first Foster form for the open line and the second Foster form for the shorted line. Show that the series forms converge to proper expressions for reactance and susceptance, given that

$$\cot x = \frac{1}{x} + \sum_{n=1}^{\infty} \frac{2x}{x^2 + n^2\pi^2}.$$

11.14c   Show that the capacitance C_1 derived for the loop-coupled cavity is that which would be obtained by referring energy stored in electric fields to voltage at the center of the cavity. Compare the mutual M_1 to that which would be derived by referring induced voltage in the loop to total vertical current in the cavity wall.

11.14d Derive an equivalent circuit similar to Fig. 11.13*e* for coupling to the TM_{010} cylindrical mode by a small probe of length *s* extending axially from the top at the center. Assume that induced voltage is probe length times electric field of the unperturbed mode.

11.15 Relations between Real and Imaginary Parts of Impedance Functions

Certain important relations are known relating the real and imaginary parts of impedance or admittance functions for lumped elements.[25] These are direct analogs of the Kronig-Kramers relations between real and imaginary parts of complex permittivity stated in Art. 6.04. The proof in all cases is much the same, utilizing the fact that these functions, for passive systems, must be analytic in one-half of a complex frequency plane. Thus real and imaginary parts must be related by the Cauchy-Riemann equations or their equivalents.

The complex "frequency" variable commonly utilized is $\alpha + j\omega$. Zeros or poles of Z (or Y) would mean that natural frequencies exist for such values, giving finite solutions without a driving source. For passive networks (those without internal sources of energy), such solutions can only decay from any transient initial state. Thus α must be negative for such natural frequencies of passive networks. In other words the impedance (or admittance) function can have no zeros or poles in the right half $(\alpha + j\omega)$ plane. This analytic property permits the relation of real and imaginary parts.

In potential-function terms, specification of potential everywhere along the $j\omega$ axis determines potential everywhere in the right half-plane, if there are no sources there and potential dies off properly at infinity. Determination of potential at all points permits the finding of electric field, and this in turn permits the construction of a flux function. Conversely, a statement of flux along the $j\omega$ axis defines charge distribution there, and from it the potential is determined everywhere in the source-free region.

If the real part of a function $u + jv$ is defined along the imaginary axis, the imaginary part in a source-free right half-plane[26] (see also Prob. 11.15*d*) is

$$v(\alpha, \omega) = \frac{1}{\pi} \int_{-\infty}^{\infty} \frac{(\omega' - \omega)u(\omega')\,d\omega'}{\alpha^2 + (\omega' - \omega)^2}.$$ (1)

[25] H. W. Bode, *Network Analysis and Feedback Amplifier Design*, Van Nostrand, Princeton, N.J., 1945.
[26] H. Jeffreys and B. S. Jeffreys, *Methods of Mathematical Physics*, Cambridge, University Press, 3rd ed. 1956.

Thus if $R(\omega)$ is given, this may be used directly to find $X(\omega)$. Several specializations may be used in applying to the network function. Since we wish X for real frequency, α is set equal to zero in (1). $R(\omega')$ is an even function of ω' (Prob. 11.15b). Finally we may add the reactance function of any lossless two port in series if we allow idealized elements in the circuit, since such a function is known to have no R. Use of these three points leads to

$$X(\omega) = \frac{1}{\pi} \int_0^\infty R(\omega') \left(\frac{1}{\omega' - \omega} + \frac{1}{-\omega' - \omega} \right) d\omega' + X_0(\omega)$$

$$X(\omega) = \frac{2\omega}{\pi} \int_0^\infty \frac{R(\omega')}{\omega'^2 - \omega^2} d\omega' + X_0(\omega), \tag{2}$$

where $X_0(\omega)$ denotes the reactance function for the lossless part.

Since jZ is also analytic in the complex plane, (1) may also be used with u denoting $-X$ and v denoting R. In this application we again set $\alpha = 0$, and utilize the fact that X is an odd function of ω. We can also add in series a constant resistance without changing X, so the result is

$$R(\omega) = \frac{1}{\pi} \int_0^\infty -X(\omega') \left(\frac{1}{\omega' - \omega} - \frac{1}{-\omega' - \omega} \right) d\omega' + R_0$$

$$R(\omega) = -\frac{2}{\pi} \int_0^\infty \frac{\omega' X(\omega')}{\omega'^2 - \omega^2} d\omega' + R_0. \tag{3}$$

Similar relations apply to admittance functions, and to relations between magnitude and phase (Probs. 11.15c and d). The analogy to potential and flux functions has allowed the interesting use of electrolytic tanks and resistance paper for the study of network functions.[27] For practical use, one should be able to consider resonances unimportant beyond some upper frequency (i.e., all sources in the potential analog should remain in the finite part of the plane).

Problems

11.15a Conisder a simple shunt circuit of R and C. Find resistance as a function of frequency, $R(\omega)$, and by substituting in (2) derive $X(\omega)$ and compare with the known reactance function of this simple circuit.

11.15b Utilizing Eqs. 11.12(2) and (3), supply the argument for even $R(\omega)$ and odd $X(\omega)$.

11.15c Write relations similar to (2) and (3) between G and B of the admittance function for a passive one port.

11.15d If Z is analytic in the right half-plane, $\ln Z$ is also. Utilize this fact and the form (1) to relate magnitude and phase of impedance for a passive network, obtaining two equations analogous to (2) and (3).

[27] W. W. Hansen and O. C. Lundstrom, *Proc. I.R.E.*, **33**, 528–534 (August 1945).

11.15e The proof of (1) is most commonly given by Fourier transforms, but that most natural to this text is from potential theory. Let $u(\omega)$ correspond to a flux function given along the ω axis. By the Cauchy-Riemann equations, $du/d\omega$ determines $dv/d\alpha$ for $\alpha = 0$, which is the normal electric field entering that plane. This may be interpreted to arise from a surface charge distribution $\rho_s = -2\,dv/d\alpha$ along the plane $\alpha = 0$. (*Question*: Why the factor of 2 when it is absent if the plane is a conductor?) An element of charge $\rho_s\,d\omega'$ at ω' may be thought of as a line charge perpendicular to the plane, for which the potential at point α, ω can be found. Write an expression for the potential and integrate by parts to obtain the form (1). What conditions did you have to assume at infinity for the result to be valid?

N-PORT WAVEGUIDE JUNCTIONS

11.16   Extension of Formulation to N-Ports

The basic formulation at the beginning of this chapter was given for an arbitrary number of waveguide terminals. Most specific consideration to this point, however, has been on the one-port or two-port examples. These are undoubtedly most common, but there are some important junctions with more than two ports. Thus we wish to return to the general formulation in this article, and then in the following two articles consider two of the most important examples—the four-port directional couplers and hybrid networks.

If we wish to determine the characteristics of an N-port by measurement, the simplest procedure is usually that of terminating all but two of the ports in known impedances, leaving a two-port for which four of the parameters may be obtained by the methods of Art. 11.07. Repetition of this procedure for different pairs of ports will eventually give all the coefficients.

As an example of this, consider the admittance formulation of Eq. 11.04 (1) for the three-port of Fig. 11.04. If terminal 3 is terminated by a perfect short so that V_3 is zero, a generator may be applied to line 1 and known loads to line 2, leading to values of Y_{11}, Y_{12}, Y_{21}, and Y_{22} through any of the applicable methods of Art. 11.07. Then if terminal 1 is shorted and the terminals 2 and 3 used as input and output, we may obtain Y_{23}, Y_{32}, Y_{33}, and a check on Y_{22}. Shorting of terminal 2 and utilization of terminals 1 and 3 give the remaining Y_{13}, Y_{31} plus checks on Y_{11} and Y_{33}. The extension to more than three ports is obvious in principle, although tedious to carry out. Similarly, open circuits on the terminals in turn (by placing shorts a quarter-wave away) will give direct determination of all the impedance coefficients in the formulation of Eq. 11.04(2). Or if the scattering coefficients of Art. 11.09 are desired, matching of all the terminals except the ith and jth permits determinations of S_{ii}, S_{ij}, S_{ji}, and S_{jj} by the methods described in Art. 11.10, and by repetition of the procedure, all scattering coefficients for an N-port network.

In considering frequency characteristics of the type discussed in Art. 11.13 for a one-port, one notes that any coefficient Z_{ii} must satisfy the

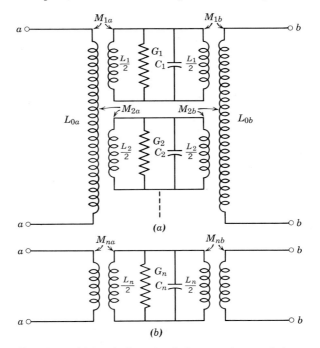

Fig. 11.16   (a) Equivalent circuit for a cavity coupled to two waveguide terminals, and (b) approximation in the vicinity of one resonant mode.

conditions for a one-port, since this represents the input impedance for a one-port formed by shorting all but the ith terminal. Similarly any Y_{ii} must satisfy conditions for the admittance function for a one-port. The transfer coefficients, however, need not satisfy such conditions (Prob. 11.16a).

When the N-port is a cavity resonator with more than one waveguide coupled to it, representation of frequency characteristics by an equivalent circuit may be desirable, generalizing Art. 11.13. Thus an extension of the form Fig. 11.13d would naturally lead to each waveguide terminal coupled to each of the normal modes by a mutual inductance as illustrated in Fig. 11.16a for a cavity with two-ports. Justification for this procedure has been supplied by Schelkunoff[28] from complex function theory, and by Slater[29] by normal mode theory. In the vicinity of a resonance, the circuit simplifies to that of Fig. 11.16b.

Relations between real and imaginary parts of transfer impedance (or admittance functions), extending the discussion of Art. 11.15, are also available in the literature.[30]

Problems

11.16a To show that transfer coefficients do not have all the properties of input coefficients, show that Z_{12} for a length l of loss-free transmission line does not satisfy Foster's reactance theorem.

11.16b Suppose that two well-separated loops, each of area 0.5 cm², are coupled to the TM_{010} cylindrical mode as for one loop in Art. 11.14. Draw the equivalent circuit, and calculate element values (except L_0) for an air-filled cavity resonant at 4000 Mc/sec with $h = 1$ cm, $R_s = 0.02$.

11.16c The Q of a cavity mode is sometimes measured by finding the curve of transmission vs. frequency between two guides coupled to the cavity. Using the values of Prob. a, calculate from the equivalent circuit the transmission at resonance and at a frequency $f_0(1 + 1/Q)$, $Q \gg 1$, and compare with the ratio $\sqrt{2}:1$. Take both lines of 50 ohms impedance and assume self-inductances of loops tuned out.

11.17 Directional Couplers

One of the most important four-ports is the directional coupler, designed to couple in a separable fashion to the positively and negatively traveling waves in a guide. Figure 11.17a gives the simplest conception of this device. Imagine a main waveguide with two small holes placed a quarter-wave apart coupling to an auxiliary guide terminated at each end by a matching resistance and meter as shown. If wave A progresses toward the right, coupled waves from the two holes at terminal 4 follow paths B and C of equal lengths, and the contributions add in that load, its meter recording the strength of A. The couplings through the two holes cancel at terminal 3, however, since the paths E and D differ in length by a half wavelength, and the couplings through the two holes are substantially the same in amount if the holes are small. By symmetry, a wave flowing to the left will register at terminal 3 but yield coupled waves which cancel at 4. Thus meter 4 reads the strength of the wave to the right, and meter 3 that to the left.

[28] S. A. Schelkunoff, *Proc. I.R.E.*, **32**, 83–90 (Feb. 1944).
[29] J. C. Slater, *Microwave Electronics*, Van Nostrand, Princeton, N.J., 1950.
[30] E. A. Guillemin, *Synthesis of Passive Networks*, John Wiley and Sons, New York, 1957, pp. 313–315.

This simple coupler is frequency sensitive since it depends on the quarter-wave spacing of holes. A like effect with greater bandwidth may be obtained by supplying several holes with properly graded couplings, as illustrated in Fig. 11.17b. Still other practical embodiments are described

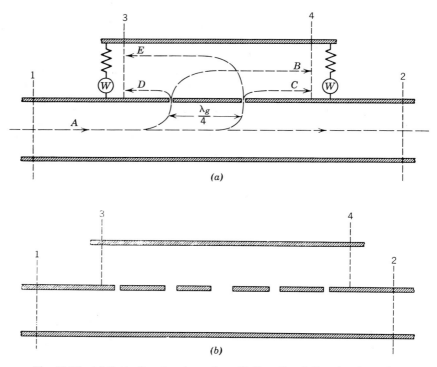

Fig. 11.17 (a) Basic directional coupler. (b) Broadband directional coupler.

in the references. All these couplers may be considered as four-ports with the four references as shown in Fig. 11.17a or Fig. 11.17b. Losses may normally be neglected. Several important general properties follow.

To study the properties of the coupler, it is most convenient to use the scattering matrix form defined in Art. 11.09. It is necessary not to couple between 1 and 3 with 2 and 4 matched, so $S_{13} = S_{31} = 0$. It is also necessary to have no coupling between 2 and 4 with 1 and 3 matched, so $S_{24} = S_{42} = 0$. Moreover, the ideal directional coupler should be matched so that all the power entering at one terminal divides between the other two for which there is coupling, leaving no reflections at the input. Thus S_{11}, S_{22}, etc. are zero. The network is also assumed to satisfy reciprocity so that $S_{12} = S_{21}$, $S_{14} = S_{41}$, etc. Thus the scattering matrix for a directional coupler has been specialized to

$$[S] = \begin{bmatrix} 0 & S_{12} & 0 & S_{14} \\ S_{12} & 0 & S_{23} & 0 \\ 0 & S_{23} & 0 & S_{34} \\ S_{14} & 0 & S_{34} & 0 \end{bmatrix}. \tag{1}$$

For negligible losses within the network, power conservation allows us to specialize still further. The net average power entering the network may be found by adding incident power and subtracting the reflected power for all the terminals. That is, Eq. 11.09(3) may be summed over all terminals, and should be zero for a loss-free network.

$$W_{\mathrm{av}} = \sum_n (a_n a_n{}^* - b_n b_n{}^*) = 0. \tag{2}$$

This relation must hold for the special case of incident power at only one of the terminals, say 1—the other terminals being matched. For the directional coupler of Fig. 11.17a or b, there is no coupling to terminal 3, so (2) then specializes to

$$a_1 a_1{}^* - b_2 b_2{}^* - b_4 b_4{}^* = a_1 a_1{}^*(1 - S_{12}S_{12}^* - S_{14}S_{14}^*) = 0$$

or

$$S_{12}S_{12}^* + S_{14}S_{14}^* = 1. \tag{3}$$

A similar relation holds if power is introduced at terminal 3 with the others matched, so

$$S_{12}S_{12}^* + S_{23}S_{23}^* = 1. \tag{4}$$

Comparison of (3) and (4) gives the first interesting specialization,

$$|S_{14}| = |S_{23}|, \tag{5}$$

and continuation of the process through terminals 3 and 4 give, in a like fashion,

$$|S_{12}| = |S_{34}|. \tag{6}$$

Next let us introduce incident waves into both terminals 1 and 3 with the remaining ports matched. Eq. (2) then becomes

$$a_1 a_1{}^* + a_3 a_3{}^* - (S_{12}a_1 + S_{32}a_3)(S_{12}^* a_1{}^* + S_{32}^* a_3{}^*) -$$

$$(S_{14}a_1 + S_{34}a_3)(S_{14}^* a_1{}^* + S_{34}^* a_3{}^*) = 0.$$

But application of (3) and the similar equation derived for incident power at 3 leaves

$$S_{12}S_{23}^* + S_{14}S_{34}^* = 0. \tag{7}$$

Similar procedure with incident power introduced at 2 and 4 gives

$$S_{21}S_{41}^* + S_{32}S_{34}^* = 0. \tag{8}$$

Thus (5), (6), (7), and (8) give four additional relationships among the remaining scattering coefficients. These may be better visualized if reference plane 2 is selected with respect to 1 so that S_{12} is real and positive, and similarly 4 with respect to 3 so that S_{34} is real and positive. Then the relation (6) yields

$$S_{12} = S_{34} = \alpha. \tag{9}$$

Use of this in (7) gives

$$\alpha(S_{23}^* + S_{14}) = 0. \tag{10}$$

And, if reference plane 4 is selected with respect to 1 so that S_{14} is real, S_{23} is also, and (10) gives

$$S_{23} = -S_{14} = \beta. \tag{11}$$

Thus we have reduced the scattering matrix to the very simple form

$$[S] = \begin{bmatrix} 0 & \alpha & 0 & -\beta \\ \alpha & 0 & \beta & 0 \\ 0 & \beta & 0 & \alpha \\ -\beta & 0 & \alpha & 0 \end{bmatrix}. \tag{12}$$

Note that β gives the coupling from the main guide to the auxiliary guide and is known as the coupling factor (often expressed in db). The coefficient α may be called the transmission factor and the two are related by the energy relation (3)

$$\alpha^2 + \beta^2 = 1. \tag{13}$$

Although α and β are the only two parameters of an ideal directional coupler, real units give some coupling to the terminal for which zero coupling is desired. That is, S_{13} and S_{24} will not be exactly zero for a real coupler. The coupling to the desired terminal in the auxiliary guide, as compared with the undesired terminal, is defined as the "front-to-back ratio," usually expressed in db.

Several important theorems may be proved for loss-free reciprocal four ports.

I. A four-port with two pairs of noncoupling elements is completely matched. That is, the setting of S_{11}, S_{22}, etc. equal to zero was not a separate condition but followed from $S_{13} = 0$ and $S_{24} = 0$ because of power relations (3), (4), (7), (8), and their counterparts for other terminals.

II. Any completely matched junction of four waveguides is a directional coupler. (Note that this does not mean that an arbitrary four port may be made into a directional coupler by externally introducing matching transformers, since the adjustment of one of these in such a case disturbs matching for the other ports; it must be an internal property giving $S_{11} = S_{22} = S_{33} = S_{44} = 0$.)

III. A four-port with two noncoupling terminals matched is a directional coupler. That is, if $S_{13} = 0$, $S_{11} = 0$, and $S_{33} = 0$, the other properties defined earlier follow.

Problems

11.17a For a loss-free four-port with all scattering coefficients present, write the generalized form of (3) by applying incident energy to the ith terminal and matching all others; similarly derive the generalized form of (7) or (8) by applying incident power to the ith and jth terminals and matching the other two.

11.17b The properties found in Prob. a may also be derived from the fact that $[S]$ for a loss-free reciprocal network is a *unitary matrix*. That is, the inverse of $[S]$ is equal to its transposed conjugate, $[S]^{-1} = [\tilde{S}]^*$. The elements of a transposed matrix are given by $\tilde{S}_{ij} = S_{ji}$. Prove the unitary property and derive results of Prob. a from this fact.

11.17c Prove theorem I from the results of Probs. a and b.

11.17d Prove theorem II.

11.17e Prove theorem III.

11.18 The Magic T and Other Hybrid Networks

The special case of a directional coupler with $\alpha^2 = \beta^2 = \frac{1}{2}$ is of particular interest in that it may be used as a bridge or "hybrid" network. (The latter name is taken from the properties of the classical hybrid coil.[31]) One of the most common configurations used for this purpose in rectangular guides for the TE_{10} mode is the Magic T pictured in Fig. 11.02d. A wave introduced into the "E" arm, 2, will, from considerations of symmetry, divide equally between arms 1 and 3 but not couple to the "H" arm, 4. Conversely a wave introduced into 4 divides between arms 1 and 3 with no coupling to 2. Thus the scattering coefficient S_{24} is zero. By theorem III, Art. 11.17, this becomes a directional coupler if the unit is internally matched so that S_{22} and S_{44} are zero. This matching is normally accomplished by introducing pins or diaphragms or both within the guides near the junction. It then follows from the theorem that S_{11}, S_{33}, and S_{13} are also zero. By symmetry, the transmission and coupling coefficients are equal so that

$$\alpha^2 = \beta^2 = \frac{1}{2}. \tag{1}$$

[31] C. G. Montgomery, R. H. Dicke, and E. M. Purcell, *Principles of Microwave Circuits*, McGraw-Hill, New York, 1948, p. 307.

Fig. 11.18a   Coaxial "rat race" hybrid network.

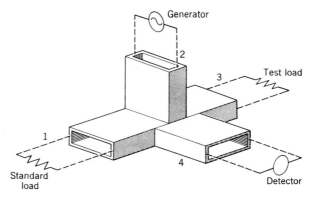

Fig. 11.18b   Magic T network as a bridge.

Other configurations accomplishing the same goal are known. One general type utilizes cancellation of waves around a "rat race" structure, as pictured for coaxial lines in Fig. 11.18a. The division of power and phase changes by the two paths to each outlet produce the cancellations or additions desired.

A typical use of one of these units as a bridge is pictured in Fig. 11.18b. With the generator at 2 and detector at 4, no output is observed if the loads on 1 and 3 are equal. Thus a standard load may be placed on 1 and test loads on 3 which are nominally the same. Any deviation from the standard will produce a reading in the detector at 4.

Problem

11.18 Reason through the wave reflections to support the statement that Fig. 11.18a is a hybrid network of the type defined.

12 RADIATION

12.01 The Problems of Radiation Engineering

Radiation of electromagnetic energy, to an engineer, is important in at least two cases. (1) It may be a desired end result if energy is to be transferred from a high-frequency transmitter to electromagnetic waves in space by means of some antenna system. (2) It may be a leakage phenomenon, adding undesired losses to an imperfectly shielded circuit or transmission line or to a cavity resonator with holes.

To perform an intelligent job of engineering in either of these radiation problems, it is first desirable to have a good physical picture of radiation. In this picture radiation is not a mysterious and unknown link between transmitter and receiver, but a phenomenon following naturally from the excellent pictures of wave propagation, reflection, and excitation built up from familiarity with transmission lines and waveguides. It is desirable that this physical picture be concrete enough to give qualitative answers to specific questions that may arise in either of the above roles of radiation. It is, of course, also necessary to have methods available for obtaining quantitative design information about the amount of radiation and the effects on the radiating system. If radiation is the desired product, several or all of the following problems may arise in design of the radiating system:

1. The field strength at a known distance and in a known direction from the radiator excited by a given voltage may be desired. Often the relative field strength vs. direction, that is, the directivity pattern, is a sufficient answer for this problem.

2. The total power radiated from the antenna structure when excited by a known voltage or current may be desired. (The answer may often be expressed in terms of a radiation resistance.)

3. The input impedance of the radiator to the exciting voltage or current may be desired.

4. The resonant frequency and bandwidth of the radiator may be required. Bandwidth questions are often answered if impedance vs. frequency is known; however, it may be necessary sometimes to know the change in the radiation pattern with frequency.

5. The power dissipated in ohmic losses in the radiator, as compared to the power radiated, may be desired. The result may be expressed as a radiation efficiency.

6. The value of maximum gradient along the antenna may be required if corona difficulties are important.

If radiation is the leakage product, the problems are not essentially different, although a knowledge of power lost by radiation is usually sufficient. To assure ourselves that it is only in magnitude of importance that this differs from radiation as a desired product, it may be recalled that it is in the role of a leakage phenomenon that radiation was met previously in Art. 5.12. The radiation becomes more important as the circuit is made large compared with wavelength, suggesting the obvious conclusion that a well-designed antenna system is simply a circuit made purposely large compared with wavelength to increase the importance of radiation. Also, in the study of transmission lines, it was pointed out that the waves excited in space by the end effects of a transmission line, required for matching to these end effects, may take energy from the guided wave of the line. This too is radiation, and to obtain it as a major effect it is necessary only to accentuate these end effects or to match more closely to the waves in space. This latter point of view is excellent, and one that will be developed further.

An exact solution of the problem from Maxwell's equations would at once yield the answer to all the foregoing problems. The approach to such an exact solution is straightforward, since it requires a solution of Maxwell's equations subject to the boundary conditions of the antenna system, which was the approach applied successfully to waveguiding systems and cavity resonators in previous chapters. For the antenna, the exciting source and the region at infinity must be included in the boundary conditions, and sometimes the effect of ground or couplings to adjacent antennas cannot be ignored. Because of these complications, but mostly because of the geometrical forms of practical antennas, the details of the exact solution cannot be carried through except in a few simple cases, such as for spherical, spheriodal, and conical antennas. Some of these solutions, which are of greatest usefulness in shedding light on the problems of input impedance and antenna gradients, are discussed in a later part of the chapter. But approximate approaches to others of the problems are needed as well.

Fortunately, successful approximations to the problems of directivity and power radiated, which are two of the most important, have been available for many years. This comes about because fields at a great distance from the antenna are relatively insensitive to small changes in current distribution over the radiation system (at least for most practical antennas), so with a little experience some good approximations to current distribution can be made. Fields at any point can then be calculated in terms of these currents, and the Poynting theorem enables one to find the power radiated. This technique is one of the first to be demonstrated in this chapter.

Fields across an aperture may also be considered as sources of radiation as in the classical Huygen's principle of optics. The concept is useful not only for optical apertures, which may usually be treated by scalar diffraction theory, but also for the openings of horn antennas, parabolic reflectors, and lens directors at microwave frequencies. For these a vector formulation of the principle may be needed. It will be seen that this formulation can be set down in a form very close to that for radiation from current elements.

12.02 Some Types of Practical Radiating Systems

To give point to comments and analyses which follow, let us look for a moment at some of the typical systems that have been used as radiators. No attempt will be made to provide complete discussions of operation here, since the remainder of the chapter will be devoted to more thorough analyses of some of these systems. Nor does the list cover all types of radiators. The ones given are chosen as examples to make clearer the discussions of principles in sections to follow.

"Dipole" Antennas. Among the most common radiators is the dipole, which consists of a straight conductor (often a thin wire or circular cylinder of larger diameter) broken at some point where it is excited by a voltage derived from a transmission line, waveguide, or directly from a generator (Fig. 12.02a). In most cases, the exciting source is at the center, yielding a symmetrical dipole, although asymmetrical dipoles are also used. If the arms are very short compared with wavelength, it is known as an infinitesimal dipole, or *Hertzian dipole*. Resonant dipoles, and especially the half-wave dipole with $2l$ approximately equal to a half-wavelength, are more common.

Loop Antennas. Radiation from a loop of wire excited by a generator has been discussed in Chapter 5, and such loop antennas are useful radiators, although often they have many turns (Fig. 12.02*b*). The field from a small loop is much like that from the small dipole, with electric and magnetic fields interchanged. Such a small loop is sometimes known for this reason as a *magnetic dipole*.

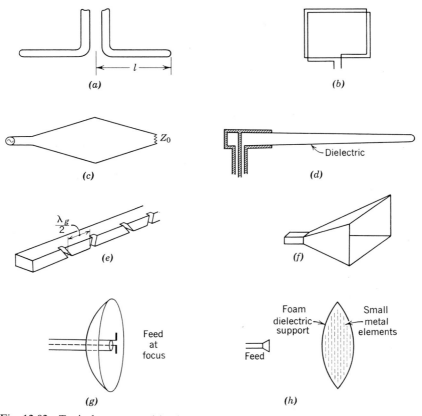

Fig. 12.02   Typical antennas: (*a*) Dipole. (*b*) Loop. (*c*) Rhombic. (*d*) Dielectric rod. (*e*) Slot array. (*f*) Pyramidal horn. (*g*) Parabolic reflector. (*h*) Artificial dielectric. (*i*) Metal lens.

Traveling-Wave Antennas. If the radiator is made to have a traveling wave in one direction with a phase velocity about equal to the velocity of light, waves in space may be excited strongly in this direction as compared with other directions, thus yielding desired directivity. Figure 12.02*c* shows the important rhombic antenna, which utilizes waves along wires and is analyzed in more detail later. Figure 12.02*d* shows a version in which the traveling wave is guided by the dielectric as in Art. 8.11. Near cutoff, phase velocity is approximately the velocity of light and the fields which always extend outside a dielectric guide may excite appreciable radiation in space.

Slot and Aperture Antennas. As noted in Art. 12.01, fields across an aperture may excite radiation in space. If the apertures are small, they must generally be resonant to excite appreciable amounts of power (although nonresonant holes in cavities may produce enough leakage to damage the *Q* of low-loss cavities). A narrow resonant half-wave slot has many similarities to the half-wave wire dipole, although electric and magnetic fields are interchanged, as will be seen. Figure 12.02*e* illustrates a series of half-wave slots in a rectangular guide to form a "leaky wave-guide" array. When apertures are large, they need not be resonant to produce significant radiation. Electromagnetic horns are examples of radiators designed to match waves from a guiding system to a large radiating aperture by properly shaping the transition, much as in the acoustic horns used for sound waves. Figure 12.02*f* gives one example. Since the horns are not resonant, they, like the traveling-wave antennas, are especially useful for broadband signals.

Reflectors and Lenses. A parabolic reflector, as illustrated in Fig. 12.02*g*, is a most important device for microwave radiation. This may be considered as a mirror, serving to reflect the rays from the primary radiator at the focus. Geometrical optics would then predict an exactly parallel beam emerging from such a reflector if the primary radiator is infinitesimal. Alternatively, it may be considered that the primary source serves to illuminate the aperture, and radiation from this aperture produces the far field. From this point of view (which is also called "physical optics" or "diffraction theory"), there is always spreading of the beam. The spreading decreases as aperture size increases—an aperture 140 wavelengths in diameter producing a beam width of about 1 degree. Lenses serve a similar purpose in directing the rays from a primary radiator. These may be of solid dielectric, of artificial dielectrics as illustrated in Fig. 12.02*h*, of or metal waveguide paths to supply proper phase shifts to direct the beam. Lenses can also be considered as aperture radiators.

Any of these radiators may be combined with like or different elements to form *arrays* which have particular directions in which phases add and radiation is concentrated. A most important use of arrays is in "electrical scanning" of the direction of concentration by control of phase shift from element to element.

12.03 Physical Pictures of Radiation

The examples of radiators given in Art. 12.02 suggest several pictures of radiation. In the wire antennas, the current elements and their attendant charges are the natural sources of fields in space. For a complete system, continuity considerations tell us that there must be an equal number of positive and negative sources, and when these are close together in comparison with a wavelength, the effects at large distances will essentially cancel. (For example, the *static* field from a small dipole decreases as the inverse cube of distance.) When the distance between positive and negative sources is comparable with a wavelength, the phase shift or retardation in going from different parts of the circuit to a point in space prevent cancellation, and in fact may produce reinforcement of effects in certain directions. From this picture we would expect that practical radiators would be comparable in size with wavelength.

This picture is also consistent with the circuit picture found in Chapter 5. There it was found that a circuit large compared with wavelength has the possibility of losing energy because induced fields from sinusoidally varying currents and charges of the circuit may shift in phase as a result of retardation over the circuit, and may have components in phase with current. Such components represent an energy flow from the circuit into the fields in space. The picture is quantitatively useful for certain antennas, such as the loop antenna of Fig. 12.02b, and will be treated briefly as the "induced emf method."

Fields or wave fronts over the aperture of an antenna system can also be considered the sources of radiation, as in the Huygen's principle. Effects may add in selected directions where contributions are in phase, as in the picture which considered current sources. This is a natural picture for horns and other aperture antennas as discussed in Art. 12.02. It can also be made to serve usefully for the treatment of antennas such as the dipole radiator of finite length, which may appear most naturally approached through current sources. To demonstrate this interrelation among the points of view, let us consider in somewhat more detail the physical picture of a problem to be treated quantitatively later—the biconical dipole antenna of Fig. 12.03a. A voltage source is applied between apices A and B of the two coaxial cones ending ar $r = \ell$. If the cone angle ψ is large, this might be considered as a horn antenna (called a biconical horn), and if ψ is small, it will look much like the dipole antenna of Fig. 12.02a. The discussion of both cases together does show the unity of viewpoints.

If we were to attempt an exact solution of Fig. 12.03*a*, we would look for a solution of Maxwell's equations satisfying the boundary conditions of the conducting cones, the source at the center, and the conditions at

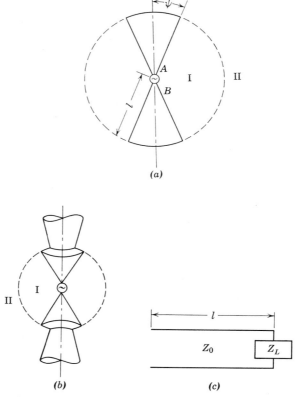

Fig. 12.03 (*a*) Axial section through biconical antenna. (*b*) Discontinuity in conical line. (*c*) Equivalent circuit of biconical antenna.

infinity. It would be natural to divide the problem into two regions, $r < l$ and $r > l$, looking for individual solutions of the type we have called waves appropriate to the two regions. Those appropriate to the former region would satisfy the boundary conditions at the cones, and would allow for the source at the center. Those appropriate to the latter region would satisfy the condition at infinity. Proper amounts of each would then be added to produce continuity of tangential field components over the common boundary, $r = l$, $\psi < \theta < \pi - \psi$, as well as zero tangential field E_θ over the perfectly conducting cap $r = l$, $0 < \theta < \psi$.

We have studied the *TEM* or principal wave of the biconical system in Art. 8.15 and found it to be like a transmission line mode along a uniform system. This mode will certainly be excited by the source at the center because it is one with a finite voltage between cones, and, if the cones continued to infinity, it would be the only wave excited. However, if there were a discontinuity such as the abrupt change in cone angle pictured in Fig. 12.03*b*, other higher-order modes would be excited just as in the changes in section of transmission lines discussed in Art. 11.08. From one point of view, the ending of the cones at $r = l$ in Fig. 12.03*a* is just a more grandiose discontinuity, and higher-order modes will be excited on the conical system, as well as some waves in the space outside. This all seems very natural, but the interesting point, as shown by Schelkunoff[1] in an exact analysis of this problem, is that the effect of the higher-order modes inside and outside may be represented in the principal wave's equivalent circuit as a lumped impedance at the end exactly as in the simple transmission line discontinuities discussed in Art. 11.08. This is pictured in Fig. 12.03*c*, with the impedance Z_L complex, since it includes the effect of energy carried away as radiation. Radiation in this picture is then regarded as an end effect, with the antenna as a guiding system from the exciting system to this end effect.

If the antenna is a thin-wire dipole (cone angle ψ small), we feel intuitively that there will not be a good match between the waves on the antenna and those in space, but instead most of the principal wave will be reflected at the end, forming a nearly perfect standing wave pattern on the antenna. In terms of the equivalent circuit Fig. 12.03*c*, the impedance Z_L will be very large compared with the characteristic impedance Z_0. This is true, and in fact, to obtain a good approximation to current distribution on a thin antenna, it may be sufficient to neglect the termination, in which case the open-circuited transmission line gives the perfectly sinusoidal standing wave pattern represented by complete reflection of the principal wave. Careful measurements on thin-wire antennas have, in fact, revealed current distributions very close to this perfect sinusoid. It cannot be strictly true, however, for this would mean that there were no waves in the space outside and no waves on the antenna except the *TEM* wave, perfectly reflected at the antenna end, giving a maximum of electric field and a zero of magnetic field there. But, with no waves outside, there would be a discontinuity at $r = l$ between the large tangential electric field of the principal wave inside

[1] S. A. Schelkunoff, "Antennas of Arbitrary Size and Shape," *Proc. I.R.E.*, **29**, 493–521 (September 1941); S. A. Schelkunoff and C. B. Feldman, *Proc. I.R.E.*, **20**, 512–516 (November 1942).

and the zero field outside, so we know there must be fields outside, and of course we expect them from other pictures of radiation. When we study the spherical waves appropriate to the outer region, we find that they must have radial electric field components; therefore continuity requires that there be higher-order modes inside the antenna region to match these, since the *TEM* mode has no radial field.

An interesting point is raised here, as one of the first methods for calculation of radiation from a long thin dipole that we shall meet is the classical one of assuming a sinusoidal current distribution on the antenna and computing the fields outside by means of the retarded potentials. Here we consider the current distribution appropriate to the principal wave only; consequently, are we neglecting all higher-order modes which by the foregoing discussion means the neglect of all radiation? The answer, of course, is no, since radiation fields in this approach are computed from the current distribution as the source, and the total current is well approximated by the principal wave's current. Non-zero fields are computed in the external region, and these may be thought of as equal to the totality of all the external waves. The approximation can actually be considered the first step in a converging step-by-step method of which we shall later go to the second step. These steps are:

1. Assume only principal waves in region I.
2. Calculate corresponding higher-order waves in region II.
3. Calculate higher-order waves in region I to match radial field components of the region II higher-order waves obtained in step 2.
4. Correct back and forth through as many succeeding steps as required.

Before returning to a quantitative discussion of this approach, we shall consider some of the useful approximate methods using assumptions concerning current or field distributions on the radiator.

FIELD AND POWER CALCULATIONS WITH CURRENTS ASSUMED ON THE ANTENNA

12.04 The Small Current Element or Dipole Antenna

In computing radiated power and the field distributions around an antenna when current distribution is assumed over the surface of the antenna's conductors, the simplest example is that of a linear element so short that current may be considered uniform over its length. Certain more complex antennas can be considered to be made up of a large number of such differential antennas with the proper magnitudes and phases of their currents. We shall consider only the case in which the current varies sinusoidally with time. Accordingly let the current be expressed by $I_0 e^{j\omega t}$ or, better yet, by its peak value I_0 along with the factor $e^{j\omega t}$ understood.

The direction of the current element will be the z direction, and its location the origin of a set of spherical coordinates (Fig. 12.04). Its length

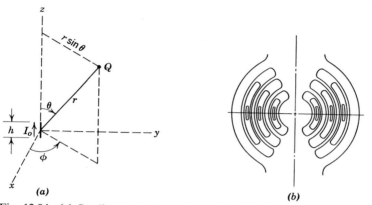

Fig. 12.04 (a) Small current element at origin of spherical coordinates. (b) Axial section showing electric field lines in first-order symmetrical *TM* waves.

is h, and it is understood that h is very small compared with wavelength. By continuity, equal and opposite time-varying charges must exist on the two ends $\pm h/2$, so the element is frequently called a small dipole or *Hertzian dipole*.

One way of finding fields once current is given is through the retarded potentials studied in Chapter 4. Article 4.18 gives a form of $\bar{A}$ suitable for present purposes. Since current vector points in the z direction, the vector potential can be only in the z direction. For any point Q at radius r, $\bar{A}$ of Art. 4.18 becomes simply

$$A_z = \mu \frac{hI_0}{4\pi r} e^{-j(\omega r/v)}. \tag{1}$$

Or, in the system of spherical coordinates,

$$A_r = A_z \cos \theta = \mu \frac{hI_0}{4\pi r} e^{-jkr} \cos \theta$$

$$A_\theta = -A_z \sin \theta = -\mu \frac{hI_0}{4\pi r} e^{-jkr} \sin \theta, \tag{2}$$

where $k = \omega/v = \omega\sqrt{\mu\epsilon} = 2\pi/\lambda$. There is no ϕ component of $\bar{A}$, and there are no variations with ϕ in any expressions because of the symmetry of the structure about the axis. The electric and magnetic field components may be found directly from the components of $\bar{A}$ by use of the other equations listed in Art. 4.18. Thus,

$$H_\phi = \frac{I_0 h}{4\pi} e^{-jkr} \left(\frac{jk}{r} + \frac{1}{r^2} \right) \sin \theta$$

$$E_r = \frac{I_0 h}{4\pi} e^{-jkr} \left(\frac{2\eta}{r^2} + \frac{2}{j\omega\epsilon r^3} \right) \cos \theta \qquad (3)$$

$$E_\theta = \frac{I_0 h}{4\pi} e^{-jkr} \left(\frac{j\omega\mu}{r} + \frac{1}{j\omega\epsilon r^3} + \frac{\eta}{r^2} \right) \sin \theta.$$

For the region very near the element (r small) the most important term in H_ϕ is that varying as $1/r^2$. The important terms in E_r and E_θ are those varying as $1/r^3$. Thus, in this region near the element, magnetic field is very nearly in phase with current, and H_ϕ may be identified as the usual induction field obtained from Ampère's law. Electric field in this region may be identified with that calculated for an electrostatic dipole. (By continuity, $I_0/j\omega$ represents the charge on one end of the dipole.) As the important components of electric and magnetic field in this region are 90° out of time phase, so these components represent no time average energy flow according to the Poynting theorem.

At very great distances from the source, the only terms important in the expressions for E and H are those varying as $1/r$.

$$H_\phi = \frac{jkI_0 h}{4\pi r} \sin \theta \, e^{-jkr}$$

$$E_\theta = \frac{j\omega\mu I_0 h}{4\pi r} \sin \theta \, e^{-jkr} = \eta H_\phi \qquad (4)$$

$$\eta = \sqrt{\mu/\epsilon} \approx 120\pi \quad \text{ohms for space.}$$

At great distances from the source, any portion of a spherical wave surface is essentially a plane wave, so the foregoing characteristics typical of uniform plane waves might be expected. E_θ and H_ϕ are in time phase, related by η, and at right angles to each other and the direction of propagation. The Poynting vector is then completely in the radial direction. The time-average flow of energy is of interest. The time average of the products of any two sinusoids of equal frequency and of the same phase is one-half the product of their magnitudes. So time-average P_r,

$$P_r = \frac{\eta k^2 I_0^2 h^2}{32\pi^2 r^2} \sin^2 \theta \quad \text{watts/meter}^2.$$

The total energy flow out must be the total surface integral of the Poynting vector over any surrounding surface. For simplicity this surface may be taken as a sphere of radius r. From Fig. 12.04a,

$$W_{av} = \oint_S \bar{P} \cdot \overline{dS} = \int_0^\pi P_r 2\pi r^2 \sin\theta \, d\theta$$

$$= \frac{\eta k^2 I_0^2 h^2}{16\pi} \int_0^\pi \sin^3\theta \, d\theta$$

$$W_{av} = \frac{\eta \pi I_0^2}{3} \left(\frac{h}{\lambda}\right)^2 = 40\pi^2 I_0^2 \left(\frac{h}{\lambda}\right)^2 \quad \text{watts.} \tag{5}$$

A radiation resistance may be defined as the resistance which would dissipate the same amount of power with this same constant current flowing.

$$R_r = \frac{2 W_{av}}{I_0^2} = 80\pi^2 \left(\frac{h}{\lambda}\right)^2 \quad \text{ohms.} \tag{6}$$

It is interesting and important to note that the field of the small dipole has the same form as the first-order TM spherical wave studied in Art. 10.09. From Eqs. 10.09(19) with $n = 1$ and the Bessel function taken as the second Hankel form which is appropriate to a region extending to infinity,

$$H_\phi = A_1 r^{-\frac{1}{2}} P_1^{\ 1}(\cos\theta) H_{\frac{3}{2}}^{(2)}(kr)$$

$$E_\theta = \frac{A_1}{j\omega\epsilon r^{\frac{3}{2}}} [H_{\frac{3}{2}}^{(2)}(kr) - kr H_{\frac{1}{2}}^{(2)}(kr)] P_1^{\ 1}(\cos\theta) \tag{7}$$

$$E_r = -\frac{A_1 H_{\frac{3}{2}}^{(2)}(kr)}{j\omega\epsilon r^{\frac{3}{2}} \sin\theta} [\cos\theta P_1^{\ 1}(\cos\theta) - P_2^{\ 1}(\cos\theta)].$$

But, from the relations of Art. 10.09 it may be shown that

$$H_{\frac{3}{2}}^{(2)}(kr) = \sqrt{\frac{2}{\pi kr}} e^{-jkr}\left(\frac{j}{kr} - 1\right)$$

$$P_1^{\ 1}(\cos\theta) = \sin\theta.$$

With these substitutions and the identification of A_1 with

$$\frac{I_0 h k^{\frac{3}{2}}}{4j\sqrt{2\pi}},$$

(7) and (3) are identical. The electric field lines for this mode are sketched in Fig. 12.04b.

Problems

12.04a   An inspection of (3) shows that there are other in-phase parts than those considered in forming the power flow above. Taking into account all terms, show that the result (5) is correct. *Suggestion:* Use the form

$$W = \tfrac{1}{2} \operatorname{Re} \oint (\bar{E} \times \bar{H}^*) \cdot \overline{dS}.$$

12.04b   Study the $n = 2$ *TM* wave and show that it corresponds to a quadrupole field, that is, field from two small current elements at right angles.

12.05   The Long Straight Antenna

If the antenna length is appreciable compared with wavelength, which is true of practical antennas, current may not be considered constant over the length. The antenna can, however, be broken into a large number of the differential elements of the type analyzed in Art. 12.04 and the fields from all of these superposed. Although fields or potentials, which are proportional to current, may be superposed, power, which varies as square of current, may not. Thus, to use the integration method employed in Art. 12.04, which we shall call the Poynting method, will require that the total $\bar{E}$ and $\bar{H}$ be first evaluated at each point of the large enclosing sphere.

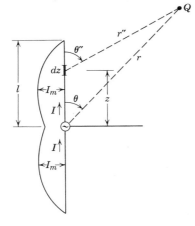

Fig. 12.05   Long straight dipole antenna.

The long dipole of Fig. 12.05 with voltage applied at its midpoint is shown with an assumed sinusoidal distribution of current. The standing wave has zero current at the ends, and is selected with distance between zero and a maximum equal to a quarter free-space wavelength. A qualitative discussion of this assumption has been given in Art. 12.03.

$$I = \begin{cases} I_m \sin\,[k(l - z)], & z > 0 \\ I_m \sin\,[k(l + z)], & z < 0. \end{cases} \tag{1}$$

From Eq. 12.04(4) the contributions to H_ϕ and E_θ at a great distance r'' from a differential element dz are

$$dE_\theta = \eta \, dH_\phi = \frac{j\eta kI \, dz}{4\pi r''} e^{-jkr''} \sin \theta''$$

where r'' is the distance from any element to Q, whereas r is the distance from the origin to Q. These may be taken so large that the difference between r and r'' is important only as it affects phase, and is completely insignificant in its effect on magnitude. Similarly, the difference between θ and θ'' will be negligibly small. In the phase difference,

$$r'' = \sqrt{r^2 + z^2 - 2rz \cos \theta} \cong r - z \cos \theta.$$

Otherwise,

$$\frac{1}{r''} \cong \frac{1}{r}, \quad \theta'' \cong \theta$$

$$E_\theta = \eta H_\phi = \int_{-l}^{+l} dE_\theta$$

$$= \frac{j\eta kI_m}{4\pi r} \sin \theta e^{-jkr} \left\{ \int_{-l}^{0} e^{jkz \cos \theta} \sin [k(l + z)] \, dz \right.$$

$$\left. + \int_{0}^{l} e^{jkz \cos \theta} \sin [k(l - z)] \, dz \right\}.$$

The integral

$$\int e^{ax} \sin (bx + c) \, dx = \frac{e^{ax}}{a^2 + b^2} [a \sin (bx + c) - b \cos (bx + c)]$$

so $\quad E_\theta = \eta H_\phi = \dfrac{j\eta kI_m}{4\pi r} \sin \theta e^{-jkr} \left\{ \dfrac{2}{k \sin^2 \theta} [\cos (kl \cos \theta) - \cos kl] \right\}$

$$= \frac{j\eta I_m}{2\pi r} e^{-jkr} \left[\frac{\cos (kl \cos \theta) - \cos kl}{\sin \theta} \right]. \tag{2}$$

Total $\bar{E}$ and $\bar{H}$ at long distances from the antenna are also at right angles to each other and the direction of propagation, in time phase, and related by η. So, as with the differential antenna of Art. 12.04, the time average Poynting vector is half the product of field magnitudes.

$$P_r = \frac{1}{2} |E_\theta| \, |H_\phi| = \frac{\eta I_m^2}{8\pi^2 r^2} \left[\frac{\cos (kl \cos \theta) - \cos kl}{\sin \theta} \right]^2. \tag{3}$$

Total power radiated from the long dipole in free space,

$$W = \oint_S \bar{P} \cdot \overline{dS} = \int_0^\pi P_r 2\pi r^2 \sin \theta \, d\theta$$

$$= \frac{\eta I_m^2}{4\pi} \int_0^\pi \frac{[\cos (kl \cos \theta) - \cos kl]^2}{\sin \theta} \, d\theta \quad \text{watts}. \tag{4}$$

Since current varies along the antenna, the value of radiation resistance depends upon the current used to define it. Suppose for this case that radiation resistance is defined in terms of maximum current, wherever it may occur.

$$R_r = \frac{2W}{I_m^{\,2}} = \frac{\eta}{2\pi} \int_0^\pi \frac{[\cos(kl\cos\theta) - \cos kl]^2 \, d\theta}{\sin\theta}. \tag{5}$$

By taking $\eta = 120\pi$, this integral may be shown to have the following result:

$$R_r = 60\{C + \ln 2kl - Ci(2kl) + \tfrac{1}{2}\sin 2kl[Si(4kl) - 2Si(2kl)]$$
$$+ \tfrac{1}{2}\cos 2kl[C + \ln(kl) + Ci(4kl) - 2Ci(2kl)]\} \text{ ohms}, \tag{6}$$

where $C = 0.5772\ldots$ and the following functions (sine and cosine integrals) are tabulated.

$$Si(x) = \int_0^x \frac{\sin x}{x} \, dx \quad Ci(x) = -\int_x^\infty \frac{\cos x}{x} \, dx. \tag{7}$$

Problem

12.05 Perform the integration (5) leading to (6). (*Hint:* Substitute $u = \cos\theta$, separate denominator by partial fractions, and note $\lim_{x\to 0} Ci(x) = C + \ln x$.)

12.06 The Half-Wave Dipole; Antenna Gain

The most important special case of the long center-fed antenna is that of the *half-wave dipole* in which $l = \lambda/4$. Field intensity, power density, and radiation resistance then become, from Eqs. 12.05(2), (3), and (6), respectively,

$$|E_\theta| = \frac{60I_m}{r} \left| \frac{\cos[(\pi/2)\cos\theta]}{\sin\theta} \right| \text{ volts/meter} \tag{1}$$

$$P_r = \frac{15I_m^{\,2}}{\pi r^2} \left\{ \frac{\cos[(\pi/2)\cos\theta]}{\sin\theta} \right\}^2 \text{ watts/meter}^2 \tag{2}$$

$$R_r = 73.09 \text{ ohms.} \tag{3}$$

Polar plots of the bracketed parts of the field and power density expressions are shown in Fig. 12.06. The field pattern for the infinitesimal dipole of Art. 12.04 is also shown for comparison. The radiation resistance given in (3) is also a good approximation to the input impedance of practical half-wave dipoles, since these are nearly resonant, and the maximum of current, to which radiation resistance is referred, appears at the central input terminals.

From the polar plots in Fig. 12.06, it is evident that radiated fields are a maximum in the plane perpendicular to the antenna and are zero along the axis of the antenna. We say then that this antenna has a certain *directivity* as compared with an imagined isotropic radiator which radiates equally in all directions. This is, of course, an advantage if we desire to have the signal radiated in the plane of the maximum, since there is less power required to produce a given field in the desired direction than there would

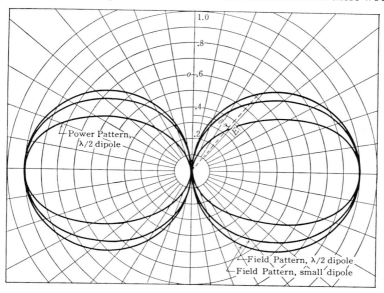

Fig. 12.06   Polar plots of field and power density for a half-wave dipole, and of field for an infinitesimal dipole in plane of dipole.

be for the isotropic radiator. The amount of the saving is frequently expressed as the *gain* of the antenna, defined as the ratio of power required from the isotropic radiator to produce the given intensity in the desired direction to that required from the actual antenna.

$$g = \frac{4\pi r^2 P_r}{W}. \tag{4}$$

As defined, gain may be given for any direction from the antenna, but it is most often given as its maximum value. For the half-wave dipole, this maximum direction is for $\theta = \pi/2$.

$$g_{max} = 4\pi r^2 \times \frac{15 I_m{}^2}{\pi r^2} \times \frac{2}{I_m{}^2 \times 73.09} \approx 1.64. \tag{5}$$

For the infinitesimal dipole of Art. 12.04, the gain is

$$g_{max} = 4\pi r^2 \times \frac{\eta I_0^2 h^2}{8 r^2 \lambda^2} \times \frac{3\lambda^2}{\eta \pi I_0^2 h^2} = \frac{3}{2}. \tag{6}$$

It is interesting to note that directivity pattern and gain are not very different for the half-wave and infinitesimal dipoles, but of course radiation resistances are very different.

Problems

12.06a Considering gain as defined by (4) a function of direction, plot curves of gain versus θ for the half-wave and infinitesimal dipoles.

12.06b Compare the currents that would be required in a half-wave dipole and a small dipole of height 0.05λ to produce 100 watts of radiated power from each.

12.07 Antennas above Perfect Earth

If the earth near an antenna must be taken into account, two very difficult problems can result: (1) effect of earth conductivity, (2) effect of earth curvature. It is common to assume that the earth is plane and perfectly conducting, not alone because it avoids these two difficulties, but also because it gives answers which agree well with actual results in many practical cases. If earth is so assumed, it is then possible to account for it by imaging the antenna in the earth. For example, given a single cone with axis vertical above earth (Fig. 12.07a), the boundary condition of zero electric field tangential to the earth may be satisfied by removing the earth and utilizing a second cone as an image of the first. The problem then reduces to that of the biconical antenna studied previously. Note that current is in the *same vertical* direction at any instant in the two cones. Given a single wire above earth and parallel to it, as in Fig. 12.07b, our knowledge of symmetry in the transmission line problem tells us that the condition of electric field lines normal to the earth is met by removing the earth and placing the image with current in the *opposite horizontal* direction. Generalizing from these two cases, we guess that current direction in the image will be selected so that vertical components are in the same direction, horizontal components in opposite directions at any instant. An example is shown in Fig. 12.07c.

The technique of replacing the earth by the antenna image, of course, gives only the proper value of field above the earth plane. The proper value below the perfectly conducting earth plane should be zero. For example, given a long straight vertical antenna above earth, excited at the base, the image reduces the problem to that solved in Art. 12.05. Field strength for maximum current I_m in the antenna is given exactly by Eq. 12.05(2) for all points above the earth $(0 < \theta < \pi/2)$, but is zero for all points below $(\pi/2 < \theta < \pi)$. Thus, for power integration, the integral of Eq. 12.05(4) extends only from 0 to $\pi/2$, and radiation resistance is just half

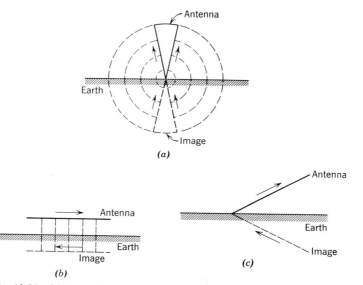

(a)

(b)

(c)

Fig. 12.07   (a) Cone above plane conducting earth and image cone. (b) Horizontal wire above plane conducting earth and image wire. (c) Inclined wire above plane conducting earth and image wire.

that for the corresponding complete dipole.

$$W = \frac{\eta I_m{}^2}{4\pi} \int_0^{\pi/2} \frac{[\cos (kl \cos \theta) - \cos kl]^2}{\sin \theta} \, d\theta \quad \text{watts.} \tag{1}$$

Thus, for a quarter-wave vertical antenna above earth, the radiation resistance is just half that of the half-wave dipole of Eq. 12.06(3).

$$R_r = 36.54 \text{ ohms.} \tag{2}$$

Problems

12.07a   Prove by a study of the resulting vector potential the *same vertical direction, opposite horizontal direction* rule for image currents given in Art. 12.07.

12.07b   Simpson's rule is useful for evaluation of the radiation integrals. If the area to be evaluated is divided into $2m$ even-numbered portions by

$(2m + 1)$ lines spaced an equal distance Δ apart, and values of the function at these lines are $f_0, f_1, \ldots, f_{2m+1}$, the area under the curve is approximately

$$I = \frac{\Delta}{3} [(f_0 + f_{2m}) + 4(f_1 + f_3 + \cdots + f_{2m-1}) + 2(f_2 + f_4 + \cdots + f_{2m-2})].$$

Evaluate the integral of Eq. 12.07(1) for a vertical quarter-wave antenna above earth, $kl = \pi/2$, using $m = 3$ in Simpson's rule. Calculate the radiation resistance and compare with (2).

12.08 Systemization of Poynting Calculations

In using the Poynting integration for calculation of radiated power from antennas, many of the same mathematical approximations are introduced each time the method is employed. Short cuts are soon discovered and are extremely time saving. It will be desirable therefore to place these on a systematic basis. Schelkunoff has given this systemization in the literature.[2]

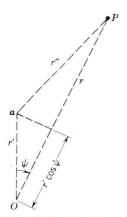

In the Poynting method, field is usually calculated at a great distance from the radiator. The following assumptions are then justified.

1. Differences in radius vector to different points of the radiator are absolutely unimportant in their effect on *magnitudes*.

2. Differences in direction of the radius vector to different points on the radiator are negligible.

3. All field components decreasing with distance faster than $1/r$ are completely negligible compared with those decreasing as $1/r$.

Fig. 12.08 Coordinates of general current element at a and distant point P with respect to origin O.

4. Differences in radius vector to different points on the radiator for purposes of finding phase differences are taken as $r' \cos \psi$ of Fig. 12.08, where r' is the radius to the radiating element from the origin, ψ the angle between r' and r, and r is the radius from the origin to the distant point at which field is to be calculated.

Consider the vector potential at point P, distance r from the origin of a radiating system made up of current elements arranged in any manner whatsoever, the element a shown at radius r' from the origin being one of these.

$$\bar{A} = \mu \int_{V'} \frac{\bar{i}_a e^{j\omega[t-(r''/v)]}}{4\pi r''} dV'.$$

[2] S. A. Schelkunoff, "A General Radiation Formula," *Proc. I.R.E.*, **27**, 660–666 (Oct. 1939).

From these assumptions, and $e^{j\omega t}$ understood, we see that

$$\bar{A} = \mu \frac{e^{-jkr}}{4\pi r} \int_{V'} \bar{i}_a e^{jkr' \cos \psi} \, dV'. \tag{1}$$

The function of r is now completely outside the integral; the integral itself is only a function of the antenna configuration, current distribution assumption, and direction in which field is to be calculated. Define this integral as the radiation vector $\bar{N}$.

$$\bar{N} = \int_{V'} \bar{i}_a e^{jkr' \cos \psi} \, dV'. \tag{2}$$

Then

$$\bar{A} = \mu \frac{e^{-jkr}}{4\pi r} \bar{N}. \tag{3}$$

In the most general case, $\bar{A}$, and hence $\bar{N}$, may have components in any direction. In spherical coordinates, employing the unit vectors,

$$\bar{A} = \mu \frac{e^{-jkr}}{4\pi r} (\bar{a}_r N_r + \bar{a}_\theta N_\theta + \bar{a}_\phi N_\phi).$$

A study of the equation $\bar{B} = \nabla \times \bar{A}$ in spherical coordinates (see inside back cover) shows that the only components which do not decrease faster than $1/r$ are

$$H_\theta = -\frac{1}{\mu r} \frac{\partial}{\partial r} (rA_\phi) = \frac{jk}{4\pi r} e^{-jkr} N_\phi \tag{4}$$

$$H_\phi = \frac{1}{\mu r} \frac{\partial}{\partial r} (rA_\theta) = -\frac{jk}{4\pi r} e^{-jkr} N_\theta.$$

An examination of

$$\bar{E} = -\frac{j\omega}{k^2} \nabla(\nabla \cdot \bar{A}) - j\omega \bar{A}$$

shows that the only components of $\bar{E}$ which do not decrease faster than $1/r$ are

$$E_\theta = -\frac{j\omega\mu}{4\pi r} e^{-jkr} N_\theta, \qquad E_\phi = -\frac{j\omega\mu}{4\pi r} e^{-jkr} N_\phi. \tag{5}$$

The Poynting vector $\bar{E} \times \bar{H}$ has a time average value

$$P_r = \frac{1}{2} \times \frac{\eta}{2\lambda r} \times \frac{1}{2\lambda r} [|N_\theta|^2 + |N_\phi|^2]. \tag{6}$$

Total time average power radiated is

$$W = \int_0^\pi \int_0^{2\pi} P_r r^2 \sin\theta \, d\theta \, d\phi$$

$$= \frac{\eta}{8\lambda^2} \int_0^\pi \int_0^{2\pi} [|N_\theta|^2 + |N_\phi|^2] \sin\theta \, d\theta \, d\phi. \qquad (7)$$

The expression is independent of r, as it should be.

The Poynting vector $\bar{P}$ gives the actual power density at any point. To obtain a quantity which does not depend on distance from the radiator, define K, radiation intensity, as the power radiated in a given direction per unit solid angle. This is the time-average P on a sphere of unit radius.

$$K = \frac{\eta}{8\lambda^2} [|N_\theta|^2 + |N_\phi|^2] \qquad (8)$$

and $$W = \int_0^\pi \int_0^{2\pi} K \sin\theta \, d\theta \, d\phi. \qquad (9)$$

A plot of K against direction may then define the radiation pattern. It should be recognized that this is a power radiation pattern and not a field strength radiation pattern.

Currents All in One Direction. If current in a radiating system flows all in one direction, this may be taken as the direction of the axis of a set of spherical coordinates. Vector $\bar{A}$ (hence $\bar{N}$) can have a z component only. Then

$$N_\phi = 0 \qquad N_\theta = -N_z \sin\theta \qquad (10)$$

$$K = \frac{\eta}{8\lambda^2} |N_z|^2 \sin^2\theta.$$

Circularly Symmetric Currents. If all current in some radiating system is circularly symmetric about an axis, this axis may be taken as the axis of a set of spherical coordinates. Vector $\bar{A}$ (hence $\bar{N}$) can have a ϕ component only. Then

$$K = \frac{\eta}{8\lambda^2} |N_\phi|^2$$

and $$W = 2\pi \int_0^\pi K \sin\theta \, d\theta. \qquad (11)$$

Useful Relations for Spherical Coordinates. It sometimes may be desirable to calculate N_θ and N_ϕ from the cartesian components N_x, N_y, N_z,

$$N_\theta = (N_x \cos\phi + N_y \sin\phi) \cos\theta - N_z \sin\theta \qquad (12)$$
$$N_\phi = -N_x \sin\phi + N_y \cos\phi.$$

The angle ψ appearing in the equation for radiation vector (2) may be found as follows, if θ, ϕ are the angular coordinates of the distant point P, and θ', ϕ' are angular coordinates of the variable point a on the element (Fig. 12.08).

$$\cos \psi = \cos \theta \cos \theta' + \sin \theta \sin \theta' \cos (\phi - \phi'). \tag{13}$$

12.09 Progressive Wave on a Straight Wire

As an example of the application of the general relations derived in Art. 12.08, let us consider a straight wire extending from $z = 0$ to $z = l$, excited by a single traveling wave of current, assumed to be unattenuated and with phase velocity equal to $1/\sqrt{\mu\epsilon}$ (Fig. 12.09). Since all current is in the z direction, the radiation vector of Eq. 12.08(2) will have only a z component. The special forms of Eqs. 12.08(10) then apply.

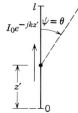

Fig. 12.09 Thin wire of length l supporting a progressive wave.

$$N_z = I_0 \int_0^l e^{-jkz'} e^{jkz' \cos \theta} \, dz'$$

$$= \frac{I_0[1 - e^{-jkl(1-\cos \theta)}]}{jk(1 - \cos \theta)}$$

$$|N_z| = \frac{2I_0 \sin [(kl/2)(1 - \cos \theta)]}{k(1 - \cos \theta)} \tag{1}$$

$$K = \frac{\eta |N_z|^2}{8\lambda^2} \sin^2 \theta = \frac{I_0^2 \eta}{2\lambda^2} \frac{\sin^2 [(kl/2)(1 - \cos \theta)]}{k^2(1 - \cos \theta)^2} \sin^2 \theta. \tag{2}$$

In addition, since there is symmetry about the axis,

$$W = 2\pi \int_0^\pi K \sin \theta \, d\theta = 2\pi \int_0^\pi \frac{I_0^2 \eta}{2\lambda^2} \frac{\sin^2 [(kl/2)(1 - \cos \theta)]}{k^2(1 - \cos \theta)^2} \sin^3 \theta \, d\theta$$

$$W = 30I_0^2 \int_0^\pi \frac{\sin^3 \theta \sin^2 [(kl/2)(1 - \cos \theta)]}{(1 - \cos \theta)^2} \, d\theta.$$

If the foregoing integral is evaluated,[3]

$$W = 30I_0^2 \left[1.415 + \ln \frac{kl}{\pi} - Ci(2kl) + \frac{\sin 2kl}{2kl} \right]. \tag{3}$$

From the general discussion of wave antennas in Art. 12.02, this single traveling wave might be expected to produce a maximum of radiation

[3] J. A. Stratton, *Electromagnetic Theory*, McGraw-Hill, New York, 1941; p. 445.

in the direction of wave propagation. Actually, radiation is zero at $\theta = 0$ as seen from (2), but only because radiation from each element of current is zero in that direction. A study of the form of (2) would reveal that lobes near $\theta = 0$ will be the largest, and those near $\theta = \pi$ will be small.

Problems

12.09a Plot the form of radiation intensity as a function of θ for $kl = \pi, 2\pi, 4\pi$. Find the direction and value of maximum gain for $kl = \pi$.

12.09b Apply the generalized method of Art. 12.08 to the long antenna with sinusoidal current, showing that the same results as in Art. 12.05 are obtained for power radiated. Show in particular that the radiation intensity of a half-wave dipole is

$$K = \frac{15}{\pi} I_m{}^2 \frac{\cos^2 [(\pi/2) \cos \theta]}{\sin^2 \theta}.$$

12.10 Small Circular Loop Antenna

We wish now to apply the generalized forms to a circular loop antenna, assumed small in circumference compared with a wavelength, and with constant current about the circumference. Because of the symmetry about the axis (Fig. 12.10), we may use the special forms of Eq. 12.08(11), and N_ϕ may be computed at $\phi = 0$ since it is independent of angle. The coordinates of the element of the antenna are ϕ' and $\theta' = \pi/2$. Loop radius is a. Then, from Eq. 12.08(13),

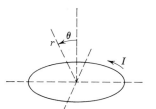

Fig. 12.10 Circular loop carrying current.

$$\cos \psi = \sin \theta \cos \phi'$$

$$N_\phi = I \int_0^{2\pi} e^{jka \sin \theta \cos \phi'} \cos \phi' \, a \, d\phi'$$

$$\approx I \int_0^{2\pi} [1 + jka \sin \theta \cos \phi'] \cos \phi' \, a \, d\phi'$$

$$= jk\pi I a^2 \sin \theta. \tag{1}$$

The radiation intensity,

$$K = \frac{\eta}{8\lambda^2} k^2 \pi^2 I^2 a^4 \sin^2 \theta = \frac{\eta}{32} (ka)^4 I^2 \sin^2 \theta. \tag{2}$$

The power radiated,

$$W = 2\pi \int_0^\pi K \sin \theta \, d\theta = \frac{\pi \eta}{12} (ka)^4 I^2. \tag{3}$$

The radiation resistance,

$$R_r = \frac{2W}{I^2} = \frac{\pi\eta}{6}(ka)^4 = 20\pi^2(ka)^4 \quad \text{ohms.} \tag{4}$$

Problems

12.10a What current is required to radiate 100 watts from a loop of circumference equal to 0.1 wavelength?

12.10b Compare the form of the radiation intensity from the small loop with that from the small dipole. Compare the variation of electric and magnetic fields with angle in the radiation field. (Note that these may be derived simply from the radiation vector.) On the basis of this comparison, explain why the small loop is frequently called a magnetic dipole.

12.10c Find the maximum gain of the small loop antenna.

12.11 The Induced EMF Method

We have seen that a Poynting integration of distant fields gave the power radiated from a small loop antenna with assumed current about the loop. This value of power might also be calculated from the real value of induced fields as explained in Art. 5.12. Such a method is called *the induced emf method*.

First, it is important to note that, for a given assumption of current, one should expect the same result by the Poynting and induced emf methods. Certainly the fields are fixed and are determined by the same equations in the two cases. Moreover, in the induced emf method, radiated power is computed by integrating over the conductor surface the product of surface current density and in-phase component of induced electric field, which actually amounts to finding the average Poynting flow through a surface taken along the conductor, since surface current density is equal to tangential magnetic field. The average Poynting flow should be the same through this surface as through the large exterior sphere utilized in the other method, since there are no sources between.

There are many practical difficulties in the use of this method. It is seldom easier to perform the integrations for this method than for the Poynting method of previous articles, and yet this method tells nothing about the form of the distant field. Because the induced emf method is concerned with conditions near the antenna, it would seem that it might tell us more about antenna impedance, yet this is difficult to carry out for other than filamentary currents, and we have found earlier that reactive calculations for such filamentary paths yield infinite results. It has, how-ever, been applied as a step in more powerful methods of finding antenna impedance, and has been extended to give mutual effects between radiators. It is also of importance in adding to one's concepts of radiation. Let us consider as an example a form useful for straight-wire antennas such as the dipole pictured in Fig. 12.11 with variations in current magnitude con-sidered. If current on the antenna has a distribution $I = I_0 f(z)$, where $f(z)$

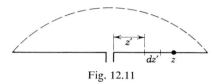

Fig. 12.11

is assumed real, vector potential at any point z is given as

$$A_z = \mu I_0 \int_{-l}^{l} \frac{f(z')e^{-jk|z-z'|}}{4\pi |z - z'|} \, dz'. \tag{1}$$

Radiated power is obtained by integrating the component of electric field tangential to the antenna and in phase with current. We are interested then in the real part of E_z, which is the negative of applied field E_0.

$$W = \tfrac{1}{2} \int_{-l}^{l} |I| \, |E_0| \, dz = -\tfrac{1}{2} \int_{-l}^{l} |I| \, \mathrm{Re}\,(E_z) \, dz. \tag{2}$$

Referring to Eq. 4.18(7), we see that

$$\mathrm{Re}\,(E_z) = -j\omega \left[\mathrm{Im}\,(A_z) + \frac{1}{k^2} \, \mathrm{Im} \left(\frac{\partial^2 A_z}{\partial z^2} \right) \right]. \tag{3}$$

And, from (1),

$$\mathrm{Im}\,(A_z) = -\frac{j\mu I_0}{4\pi} \int_{-l}^{l} \frac{f(z') \sin k\,|z - z'|}{|z - z'|} \, dz'. \tag{4}$$

This integral can be evaluated for certain forms of $f(z)$. It is sometimes easier, however, to proceed by series methods. If the sine term of (4) is expressed as a power series, it can be shown that

$\mathrm{Im}\,(A_z)$

$$= -\frac{2\mu j k I_0}{4\pi} \left[\alpha_0 - \frac{k^2}{3!} (z^2 \alpha_0 + \alpha_2) + \frac{k^4}{5!} (z^4 \alpha_0 + 6z^2 \alpha_2 + \alpha_4) + \cdots \right] \tag{5}$$

$$\alpha_n = \int_0^{l} (z')^n f(z') \, dz'. \tag{6}$$

Substitution in (2) and (3) yields

$$W = \frac{\eta k^2 I_0^2}{3\pi}\left[\alpha_0^2 - \frac{k^2}{5}\alpha_0\alpha_2 + \frac{k^4}{140}(\alpha_0\alpha_4 + 3\alpha_2^2) + \cdots\right]. \tag{7}$$

We may define a radiation resistance in terms of I_0:

$$R_r = \frac{2W}{I_0^2} = 80k^2\left[\alpha_0^2 - \frac{k^2}{5}\alpha_0\alpha_2 + \frac{k^4}{140}(\alpha_0\alpha_4 + 3\alpha_2^2) + \cdots\right]. \tag{8}$$

For a half-wave dipole $l = \lambda/4$, and $f(z)$ is taken as $\cos kz$. From (6),

$$\alpha_0 = \int_0^{\lambda/4} \cos kz'\, dz' = \frac{1}{k}$$

$$\alpha_2 = \int_0^{\lambda/4} (z')^2 \cos kz'\, dz' = \frac{[(\pi/2)^2 - 2]}{k^3} \cong \frac{0.467}{k^3}$$

$$\alpha_4 = \int_0^{\lambda/4} (z')^4 \cos kz'\, dz' = \frac{[(\pi/2)^4 - 12(\pi/2)^2 + 24]}{k^5} \cong \frac{0.479}{k^5}.$$

Substitution in (8) then gives a radiation resistance of about 73.2 ohms, which checks the previously derived result.

RADIATION FROM FIELDS OVER AN APERTURE

12.12 Fields as Sources of Radiation

For wire antennas, it is fairly natural to assume a current distribution over the antenna, and to consider the current elements as the sources of radiation. For other antennas, such as the electromagnetic horn, the slot antennas, the parabolic reflectors, the lens directors, and all optical systems, it is more natural to think in terms of the fields as sources. Huygen's principle states that any wave front can be considered the source of secondary waves that add to produce distant wave fronts. Thus the knowledge (or assumption) of field distribution over an aperture should yield the distant field. The methods to be described show how to proceed quantitatively.

The classical quantitative formulation of Huygen's principle is that for scalar fields. It is useful for electromagnetic fields when the aperture is large compared with wavelength, and the vector nature of the fields are not of concern. It is thus especially useful in optical problems where apertures are large compared with wavelength, and a single component of field ma be sufficient to describe the problem. Kirchhoff's formula for these conditions (derived earlier by Helmholtz for acoustic waves) is[4,5]

$$U(P) = \frac{1}{4\pi} \int_S \left[\frac{e^{-jkr}}{r} \frac{\partial U}{\partial n} + U \frac{\partial}{\partial n}\left(\frac{e^{-jkr}}{r} \right) \right] dS, \qquad (1)$$

where $U(P)$ is the scalar quantity to be found for the point P in terms of the values of U on the surface S. The radius r is distance from the source point

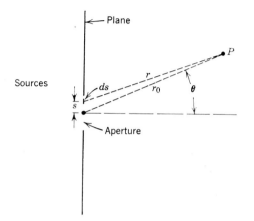

Fig. 12.12　Radiation through an aperture.

dS to field point P, and n is the direction of the normal to dS, counted positive toward the space containing P.

As a typical problem for which Kirchhoff's formula may be applied, consider the slit in the plane pictured in Fig. 12.12, with sources on the left. To calculate the field at point P on the right, we need to know the exact values of U and $\partial U/\partial n$ both in the aperture and on the right side of the plane. In practical use of the method, it is common to assume that the plane shields the source so that values of U and $\partial U/\partial n$ may be neglected on the right surface on the plane; moreover, a value for distribution of these quantities over the aperture itself is assumed. For example, if the aperture is large in comparison with wavelength, and the sources are distant, it is typical to assume the aperture field that of a single traveling plane wave.

If the field point P of Fig. 12.12 is distant so that r is large in comparison with aperture size and with wavelength, approximations like those for the

[4] S. Silver, *Microwave Antenna Theory and Design*, McGraw-Hill, New York, 1948; p. 158 *et seq.*
[5] M. Born and E. Wolf, *Principles of Optics*, Pergamon Press–Macmillan, New York, 2nd ed., 1964, pp. 375–386.

far-zone field from currents (Art. 12.08) are appropriate. That is, variations in r over the aperture are important only with respect to phase, and for this, r is approximated by

$$r \approx r_0 - s \sin \theta. \tag{2}$$

In optics this far-zone field is called the region of *Fraunhofer diffraction*. For the near zone, or region of *Fresnel diffraction*, better approximations to r are necessary.[4,5] The optical modes studied in Arts. 10.15 to 10.17 are useful to give the form of spreading in the near zone. We will proceed, however, to the general vector formulation and the approximations appropriate to far-zone or radiation fields.

12.13 Vector Formulation for Radiation from Electromagnetic Fields

Stratton and Chu[6] derived the vector equivalent of the Kirchhoff formula by direct integration of Maxwell's equations. Thus one form for fields $\bar{E}'$ and $\bar{H}'$ at a point inside a region enclosed by surface S is

$$\bar{E}' = -\frac{1}{4\pi} \oint_S \{-j\omega\mu(\bar{n} \times \bar{H})\psi + (\bar{n} \times \bar{E}) \times \nabla\psi + (\bar{n} \cdot \bar{E})\nabla\psi\} \, dS \tag{1}$$

$$\bar{H}' = \frac{1}{4\pi} \oint_S \{-j\omega\epsilon(\bar{n} \times \bar{E})\psi - (\bar{n} \times \bar{H}) \times \nabla\psi - (\bar{n} \cdot \bar{H})\nabla\psi\} \, dS, \tag{2}$$

where $\bar{E}$ and $\bar{H}$ are the values of fields on the surface, r is the distance from the differential element dS to the point at which $\bar{E}'$ and $\bar{H}'$ are to be evaluated, and $\psi = e^{-jkr}/r$. In practical use, fields are usually assumed finite only over the aperture, and zero over the remainder of the closed surface. There is thus a discontinuity at the contour of the aperture which Stratton and Chu take into account by adding contributions $\bar{E}''$ and $\bar{H}''$ resulting from the charges of the discontinuity,

$$\bar{E}'' = \frac{1}{4\pi j\omega\epsilon} \oint (\nabla\psi)\bar{H} \cdot d\bar{l} \tag{3}$$

$$\bar{H}'' = -\frac{1}{4\pi j\omega\mu} \oint (\nabla\psi)\bar{E} \cdot d\bar{l}. \tag{4}$$

The line integrals are about the contour of the aperture.

Schelkunoff has given a different formulation equivalent to (1) through (4) which is convenient in that it breaks the procedure into steps similar to

[6] J. A. Stratton and L. J. Chu, *Phys. Rev.*, **56**, 99–107 (1939).

those used for current sources, and in fact can be thought of in terms of equivalent current sheets over the aperture. Because of its similarity to our earlier approach, and the opportunity for clear physical pictures, we will largely use this method. To illustrate, consider Fig. 12.13a and suppose that field to the right of the conducting plane is desired. If the exact current and charge sources in region A to the left of the plane, the sources which actually produce the electromagnetic energy, were known, we could in

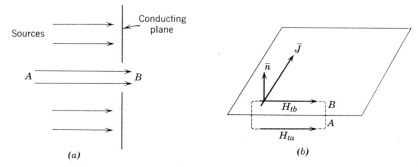

Fig. 12.13   (a) Conducting plane with aperture. (b) Relation of surface currents and fields.

principle solve for the desired field, subject to the boundary conditions of the leaky plane. If the field at the surface of the opening arising from those sources were known exactly, however, it would do just as well, as far as region B is concerned, to replace the actual currents and charges of region A by fictitious currents and charges lying in the surface of the opening, provided these could be made to produce the same fields at the opening. For, with the conditions over the opening unchanged, and all other boundaries of region B unchanged, the proper solution to Maxwell's equations in region B would be unchanged.

   In general, the field that must be produced along the selected surface may have normal and tangential components of electric field, and normal and tangential components of magnetic field. However, at any boundary it is necessary only to know the tangential magnetic and electric fields, for then Maxwell's equations will provide the normal components (Art. 4.13). Let us consider then what fictitious currents must be placed over the opening in the absence of the actual sources to give the same fields in region B that the true sources in region A were causing. The problem is easy and old to us in the case of the tangential magnetic field. For, as indicated in Fig. 12.13b, a surface current density J on a given surface will result in a discontinuity of magnetic field components tangential to the surface and normal to $\bar{J}$. That is, the difference between tangential H on one side of the sheet and that on the other,

$$H_{tb} - H_{ta} = J.$$

Thus, if the current sheet over the opening in the plane is to replace completely the effect of the sources in A which are producing a given H_t tangent to the boundary, there must be a current density $\bar{J}$ on this sheet, given by $J = H_t$ in magnitude. The direction will be included if we write

$$\bar{J} = \bar{n} \times \bar{H}. \tag{5}$$

where $\bar{n}$ is the unit vector normal to the surface pointing into the region B, and $\bar{H}$ is the total magnetic field. Such a current sheet will wipe out the tangential magnetic field on the A side of the surface (just as though there were no sources in A) but will leave a tangential field as before of magnitude $J = H_t$ on the B side. Thus the current sheet is exactly as effective as the source, which is now assumed absent, in producing tangential magnetic field at the boundary.

Now, the replacing of the sources insofar as they produce tangential electric field would be done just as quickly if only there were such a thing as magnetic currents. Then we could write that the magnetic surface current density $\bar{M}$ is

$$\bar{M} = -\bar{n} \times \bar{E}. \tag{6}$$

Also, by analogy with the magnetic vector potential, which for surface currents is written

$$\bar{A} = \mu \int_S \frac{\bar{J}e^{-jkr}}{4\pi r} \, dS, \tag{7}$$

there could be defined an electric vector potential, say,

$$\bar{F} = \epsilon \int_S \frac{\bar{M}e^{-jkr}}{4\pi r} \, dS. \tag{8}$$

The free-space integrals (7) and (8) can be used only where $\bar{J}$ and $\bar{M}$ include all sources in region B. That is, the conductor is accounted for by including induced currents on its surface in the integrals, or by the use of images of $\bar{J}$ and $\bar{M}$ in the conductor. Maxwell's equations, if there were such things as magnetic current i_m and magnetic charge ρ_m, would be

$$\begin{aligned}
\nabla \cdot \bar{D} &= \rho_e \\
\nabla \cdot \bar{B} &= \rho_m \\
\nabla \times \bar{E} &= -\bar{i}_m - \frac{\partial \bar{B}}{\partial t} \\
\nabla \times \bar{H} &= \bar{i}_e + \frac{\partial \bar{D}}{\partial t}
\end{aligned} \tag{9}$$

and the fields at any distance from the source currents would be obtained from the two vector potentials $\bar{A}$ and $\bar{F}$.

$$\bar{E} = -j\omega\bar{A} - \frac{j\omega}{k^2}\nabla(\nabla \cdot \bar{A}) - \frac{1}{\epsilon}\nabla \times \bar{F} \tag{10}$$

$$\bar{H} = -j\omega\bar{F} - \frac{j\omega}{k^2}\nabla(\nabla \cdot \bar{F}) + \frac{1}{\mu}\nabla \times \bar{A}. \tag{11}$$

Although these forms of the augmented Maxwell's equations would be directly applicable if magnetic currents and charges were found in nature, that is not the point for the present discussion. We are using these names and symbols as equivalents, respectively, for tangential electric field and normal magnetic field at a surface. The intermediate quantities need not appear, since we could substitute $-(\bar{n} \times \bar{E})$ for $\bar{M}$ in (8) and $(\bar{n} \times \bar{H})$ for $\bar{J}$ in (7), so potentials would be given directly in terms of tangential field components. This is equivalent to the Stratton and Chu formulation of (1) to (4). The terms arising from the contour integrals (3) and (4) are implicit in the Schelkunoff formulation because it includes the continuity relations. In this sense it is like the formulation for radiation from wire antennas given in terms of currents only; the charge sources are included by virtue of continuity, Eq. 4.03(5).

If we are concerned only with the radiation field, the usual approximations appropriate to great distances can be employed, and the general formulation of Art. 12.08 extended. A magnetic radiation vector $\bar{L}$ may be related to vector potential $\bar{F}$ as $\bar{N}$ was to $\bar{A}$. Thus, consistent with the assumptions listed previously,

$$\bar{F} = \epsilon\frac{e^{-jkr}}{4\pi r}\bar{L} \tag{12}$$

where
$$\bar{L} = \int_{V'} \bar{i}_m e^{jkr'\cos\psi}\,dV'. \tag{13}$$

If electric and magnetic field components are now written in the usual way in terms of these two vector potentials, the only components not decreasing faster than $(1/r)$ are

$$E_\theta = -j\frac{e^{-jkr}}{2\lambda r}(\eta N_\theta + L_\phi) \qquad H_\phi = \frac{E_\theta}{\eta} \tag{14}$$

$$E_\phi = j\frac{e^{-jkr}}{2\lambda r}(-\eta N_\phi + L_\theta) \qquad H_\theta = -\frac{E_\phi}{\eta}. \tag{15}$$

So the radiation intensity,

$$K = \frac{\eta}{8\lambda^2}\left[\left|N_\theta + \frac{L_\phi}{\eta}\right|^2 + \left|N_\phi - \frac{L_\theta}{\eta}\right|^2\right]. \tag{16}$$

The reader should bear in mind that (16) has been obtained using (7) and (8) and therefore applies to sources located in free space.

12.14 Elemental Plane Wave Source

The radiation vector and radiation intensity may be calculated for a differential surface element on a uniform plane wave. Such an element

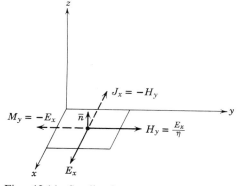

Fig. 12.14 Small plane wave source and equivalent current sheets.

might be considered the elemental radiating source in radiation calculations from field distributions, as was the differential current element for radiation calculations from current distributions.

The plane wave source, that is, one that produces $\bar{E}$ and $\bar{H}$ of constant direction, normal to each other, and in the ratio of magnitudes η over the area of interest may be replaced by equivalent electric and magnetic current sheets over that area, Fig. 12.14.

If

$$\bar{E} = \bar{a}_x E_x \quad \text{and} \quad \bar{H} = \bar{a}_y H_y = \bar{a}_y \frac{E_x}{\eta}, \tag{1}$$

the equivalent current sheets are

$$J_x = -H_y = -\frac{E_x}{\eta} \qquad M_y = -E_x. \tag{2}$$

If this is a source of infinitesimal area dS (actually it need only be small compared with wavelength for following results to hold), the radiation vectors $\bar{N}$ and L become simply

$$N_x = -\frac{E_x\,dS}{\eta} \qquad L_{\hat{y}} = -E_x\,dS.$$

The components in spherical coordinates:

$$N_\theta = -\frac{E_x\,dS}{\eta}\cos\phi\cos\theta \qquad N_\phi = \frac{E_x\,dS}{\eta}\sin\phi \tag{3}$$

$$L_\theta = -E_x\,dS\sin\phi\cos\theta \qquad L_\phi = -E_x\,dS\cos\phi.$$

According to Eq. 12.13(16) the radiation intensity in this case may be given by

$$K = \frac{E_x^{2}(dS)^2}{\eta 8\lambda^2}\left[(-\cos\phi\cos\theta - \cos\phi)^2 + (\sin\phi + \sin\phi\cos\theta)^2\right]$$

$$K = \frac{E_x^{2}(dS)^2}{2\eta\lambda^2}\cos^4\frac{\theta}{2}. \tag{4}$$

Problem

12.14 From (2) we see that the plane wave source is equivalent to crossed electric and magnetic infinitesimal dipoles. Find the fields for the latter, utilizing duality and the known results for the electric dipole in Art. 12.04. By superposition, find fields for the two crossed dipoles and show that the pattern is consistent with that found in Art. 12.14.

12.15 Circular Aperture or Parabolic Reflector

Consider next a circular aperture illuminated by a uniform plane wave polarized with electric and magnetic fields as shown in Fig. 12.15a. We assume that field sources outside this circular aperture are negligible, so the problem is best represented by transmission through a circular hole in an absorbing screen. However, the results also apply approximately to a paraboloid of revolution in which one attempts to obtain a uniform plane wave illumination in the plane of the aperture from an approximate point source placed at the focus, although in practice this exact uniformity is not obtained.

We may utilize the results of the last article for radiation intensity from any small element of the plane wave, adding up contributions from various

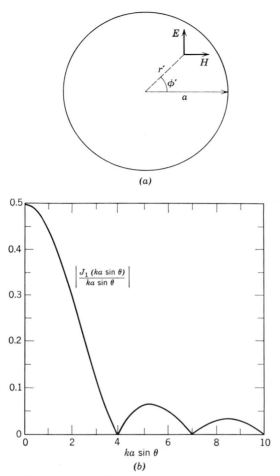

Fig. 12.15 (a) Circular aperture illuminated by uniform plane wave. (b) Approximate form of radiation pattern from a circular aperture for small θ.

elements as explained in Art. 12.13. For an element at r', ϕ', as shown in Fig. 12.15a, the angle ψ is given by

$$\cos \psi = \sin \theta \cos (\phi - \phi').$$

Then utilizing the result from Eq. 12.14(4),

$$K = \frac{E_0{}^2}{2\eta\lambda^2} \cos^4 \frac{\theta}{2} \left| \int_0^{2\pi} \int_0^a e^{jkr' \sin \theta \cos (\phi-\phi')} r' \, dr' \, d\phi' \right|^2$$

$$= \frac{E_0{}^2}{2\eta\lambda^2} \cos^4 \frac{\theta}{2} \left| 2\pi \int_0^a J_0(kr' \sin \theta) r' \, dr' \right|^2. \tag{1}$$

The ϕ' integration was effected by means of the integral

$$\int_0^{2\pi} e^{jq \cos \phi} \, d\phi = 2\pi J_0(q).$$

The remaining integration utilizes Eq. 3.27(20).

$$K = \frac{2E_0^2 \pi^2 a^4}{\eta \lambda^2} \cos^4 \frac{\theta}{2} \left| \frac{J_1(ka \sin \theta)}{(ka \sin \theta)} \right|^2. \tag{2}$$

For small θ the bracketed part of the expression governs the pattern and is plotted in Fig. 12.15b. Width of main beam between zeros is approximately

$$\Delta \approx 2\theta_0 = 2 \times \frac{3.83\lambda}{2\pi a} = \frac{1.22\lambda}{a}. \tag{3}$$

This corresponds to a gain of approximately

$$g \approx \left(\frac{2\pi a}{\lambda} \right)^2, \qquad ka \gg 1. \tag{4}$$

Note that this can be written in the form

$$g = \frac{4\pi}{\lambda^2} \times \text{area}, \tag{5}$$

which can be shown to be generally applicable to large apertures of any shape with uniform illumination. Equations (3) and (4) are useful for a number of problems in microwaves or optics where circular apertures are used. We have mentioned the ideal parabolic reflector as one example. In an actual parabolic mirror, the feed system placed at the focus to illuminate the paraboloid necessarily disturbs the radiation pattern somewhat. Also, the feed is not a point source; therefore it produces variations in phase and amplitude over the circular aperture not previously accounted for. Sometimes the illumination is purposely decreased near the edges to diminish the side lobes caused by diffraction at the edges. Most often illumination is not uniform in angle about the axis, so that the beam is wider in one plane than in another at right angles. Finally, radiation and diffraction effects from the supports may be of importance.

Problems

12.15a When a half-wave dipole is used as the feed for a parabolic antenna, the radiated pattern from the system is known to be broader in the E plane (parallel to the dipole) than in the H plane (perpendicular to the dipole). On the basis of what has been given, explain qualitatively why this is expected. What happens if the feed system itself is made too directive?

12.15b Suppose that all radiation was confined to a cone of angle Δ given by (3) and was of constant amplitude over this cone. Give the gain and compare with (4).

12.15c For $ka = 10$, give beam angle and gain, and plot K vs. θ.

12.15d Assuming that ka is large and that all significant radiation occurs in a region of small θ, derive the approximate formula for gain (4), starting from (2). Given the integral,

$$\int \frac{1}{x} J_1{}^2(\alpha x)\, dx = -\tfrac{1}{2}[J_0{}^2(\alpha x) + J_1{}^2(\alpha x)].$$

12.15e Find the expression for radiation intensity for a rectangular aperture of dimensions a and b with uniform illumination. By assumptions appropriate to large apertures, verify formula (5) for this shape.

12.15f If the distribution of fields over the aperture are taken as Gaussian in radius, $E = E_0 e^{-r^2/w^2}$, find the corresponding form for radiation intensity K. Define a width for this pattern and relate to w. (Assume $w \ll a$ so that the aperture can be considered essentially infinite in radius.)

12.15g Referring to the optical modes of Art. 10.15, note that the rays approach cones for large z/w_0. Compare the cone angles with the result (3) to show that the mode can be thought of as radiation or diffraction from the central spot of radius w_0.

12.15h Repeat Prob. g using the result of the Gaussian form (Prob. f) in place of (3) which resulted from the uniform distribution.

12.16 Resonant Slot Antenna

Another important class of radiators in which the emphasis is on the field in the aperture is that of the slot antenna mentioned qualitatively in Art. 12.02. Let us consider the resonant slot antenna (approximately a half-wave long) in an infinite plane conductor.[7] In Fig. 12.16, the electric field E_x across the gap is assumed to be the only significant aperture field, and this is assumed to be uniform in x and to have a half-sine distribution in z with its maximum at the center. By reference to Eq. 12.13(6), the magnetic current sheet equivalent to this would be found to lie in the z direction and to be equal to E_x.

$$M_z = E_x = E_m \cos kz. \tag{1}$$

Since E_x is zero behind M_z, the gap can be considered closed with an electric conductor. It is convenient to take account of the infinite conductor by replacing it with the image of M_z. As shown in Prob. 12.16a, M_z and its image are in the same direction so the value in (1) must be doubled in using free-space field expressions.

---

[7] N. Begovich, *Proc. I.R.E.*, **38**, 803–806 (July 1950).

If gap width g is taken as small, the equation for magnetic radiation vector, Eq. 12.13(13), becomes

$$L_z = \int_{-\lambda/4}^{\lambda/4} 2gE_m \cos kz' \, e^{jkz' \cos \theta} \, dz'. \tag{2}$$

The integral is evaluated as in Art. 12.05.

$$L_z = \frac{4gE_m \cos [(\pi/2) \cos \theta]}{k \sin^2 \theta}. \tag{3}$$

Then, utilizing Eq. 12.13(15), we see that the fields are

$$E_\phi = -\eta H_\theta = \frac{je^{-jkr}gE_m}{\pi r} \left\{ \frac{\cos [(\pi/2) \cos \theta]}{\sin \theta} \right\}. \tag{4}$$

We should note here that this is of the same form as the expression for fields about a half-wave dipole antenna (Art. 12.06) except for the interchange in electric and magnetic fields. Another difference is that expression (4) applies to only one side of the plane. If radiation is allowed in the backward direction, fields must be reversed there since normal electric field and tangential magnetic field are discontinuous at the conducting plane because of currents and charges there.

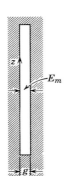

The power radiated corresponding to (4), counting both sides, is

$$W = \frac{2\pi(gE_m)^2}{2\pi^2\eta} \int_0^\pi \frac{\cos^2 [(\pi/2) \cos \theta]}{\sin \theta} \, d\theta. \tag{5}$$

This may be interpreted in terms of a radiation conductance defined in terms of the maximum gap voltage:

Fig. 12.16
Resonant
half-wave
slot.

$$(G_r)_{\text{slot}} = \frac{2W}{(gE_m)^2} = \frac{2}{\pi\eta} \int_0^\pi \frac{\cos^2 [(\pi/2) \cos \theta]}{\sin \theta} \, d\theta. \tag{6}$$

By comparing with the expression for radiation resistance of the half-wave dipole, Eq. 12.05(5), we find

$$(G_r)_{\text{slot}} = \frac{4(R_r)_{\text{dipole}}}{\eta^2} \approx 0.00205 \quad \text{mho}. \tag{7}$$

The reciprocity between results for the slot and dipole can also be shown to follow from *Babinet's principle*, which is an extension of the principle of duality discussed in Art. 8.14.

Problems

12.16a Prove that the image of a magnetic current in a perfectly conducting plane requires horizontal currents in the same direction for source and image. In what sense is the field for this problem the dual of the field for the half-wave dipole?

12.16b Find the approximate radiation conductance if the slot is fed from a waveguide entering from the back so that shielding prevents radiation in the backward direction.

12.16c For the open end of a coaxial line of radii a and b, set up the problem of determining power radiated, assuming the electric field of the *TEM* mode as the only important field in the aperture. Make approximations appropriate to a line small in radius compared with wavelength, and show that the equivalent radiation resistance of the open end is

$$ R = \frac{3\eta}{2\pi^3} \left[\frac{\lambda^2 \ln (b/a)}{\pi(b^2 - a^2)} \right]^2 . $$

Calculate the value for $a = 0.3$ cm, $b = 1$ cm, $\lambda = 30$ cm. What standing wave ratio would this produce in the line?

12.16d In Prob. *c*, assume the magnetic field of the *TEM* mode at the open end of sufficient magnitude to account for the energy calculated above. Show that a recalculation of power radiated including effects from this magnetic field leads to only a small correction to the first calculation. Take radii small compared with wavelength.

12.17 Electromagnetic Horns

The electromagnetic horns discussed qualitatively in Art. 12.02 are of interest both as directive radiators in themselves, and also as feed systems for reflectors or directive lens systems. In the horn, there is a gradual flare from the waveguide or transmission line to a larger aperture. This large aperture is desired to obtain directivity, and also to produce more efficient radiation by providing a better match to space. Usually, a fair approximation to aperture field may be made by studying the fields in the feeding system and the possible modes in the horn structure. This then makes possible approximate radiation calculations starting from these fields, by the methods discussed in preceding articles. The steps may be difficult because of difficulties in evaluating certain integrals, but as there are no new principles the details will not be covered here. Much is given in the literature.[8,9] In utilizing theoretical results for practical horns, it should

---

[8] L. J. Chu, *J. Appl. Phys.*, **11**, 603–610 (1940).
[9] W. L. Barrow and L. J. Chu, *Proc. I.R.E.*, **27**, 51–64 (1939); *Trans. A.I.E.E.*, **58**, 333–338 (1939).

be remembered that the side-lobe structure especially will be different because of higher-order modes, edge effects, and radiation from external surfaces and supports not accounted for in the assumptions for fields. Because of variations across the aperture, the gain will always be somewhat less than for the ideal large aperture with uniform illumination, Eq. 12.15(5).

$$g < \frac{4\pi}{\lambda^2} \times \text{area.} \tag{1}$$

For horns of rectangular apertures and moderate flare angles, the following results worked out by Chu[10] for radiation from the open end

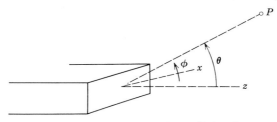

Fig. 12.17   Coordinate system for radiation from rectangular guide.

of a rectangular waveguide will be of help in estimating patterns. The coordinate system is as in Fig. 12.17.

TM_{mn} **Modes.** Field components in the radiation field are

$$E_\theta = \frac{mn\beta_{mn}\pi^3 ab}{4\lambda^2 r k_{cmn}^2} \sin\theta \left[1 + \frac{k}{\beta_{mn}}\cos\theta + \rho\left(1 - \frac{k}{\beta_{mn}}\cos\theta\right) \right] \Psi_{mn}(\theta, \phi), \tag{2}$$

where

$$\Psi_{mn}(\theta,\phi) = \left[\frac{\sin\left(\tfrac{1}{2}ka\sin\theta\cos\phi + \frac{m\pi}{2}\right)}{(\tfrac{1}{2}ka\sin\theta\cos\phi)^2 - \left(\frac{m\pi}{2}\right)^2} \right] \left[\frac{\sin\left(\tfrac{1}{2}kb\sin\theta\sin\phi + \frac{n\pi}{2}\right)}{(\tfrac{1}{2}kb\sin\theta\sin\phi)^2 - \left(\frac{n\pi}{2}\right)^2} \right] \tag{3}$$

and ρ is the complex reflection coefficient in the guide, referred to the end.

[10] Given in S. Silver, *Microwave Antenna Theory and Design*, McGraw-Hill, New York, 1949, Chapter 10.

TE_{mn} **Modes.** With the same definition as (3),

$$E_\theta = -\frac{\eta(\pi a b)^2 \sin\theta}{2\lambda^3 r k_{cmn}^2}\left[1 + \frac{\beta_{mn}}{k}\cos\theta + \rho\left(1 - \frac{\beta_{mn}}{k}\cos\theta\right)\right]$$

$$\times \left[\left(\frac{m\pi}{a}\sin\phi\right)^2 - \left(\frac{n\pi}{b}\cos\phi\right)^2\right]\Psi_{mn}(\theta,\phi) \quad (4)$$

$$E_\phi = -\frac{\eta(\pi a b)^2 \sin\theta\sin\phi\cos\phi}{2\lambda^3 r}$$

$$\times \left[\cos\theta + \frac{\beta_{mn}}{k} + \rho\left(\cos\theta - \frac{\beta_{mn}}{k}\right)\right]\Psi_{mn}(\theta,\phi). \quad (5)$$

The important special case of the TE_{10} mode is obtained by putting $m = 1$, $n = 0$ in (4) and (5).

12.18   Radiation from Slits and Diffraction Gratings

Slits and diffraction gratings have long been of importance at optical frequencies, and are becoming increasingly so with the coherent light now available from lasers. Radiation characteristics of these may be analyzed either from the Kirchhoff formula (Art. 12.12), or the vector formulation illustrated in preceding articles. For the latter method, we would analyze the far-zone (Fraunhofer) pattern for a single long slit (Fig. 12.18a) in a manner exactly analogous to that for the circular aperture of Art. 12.15 or the resonant slit of Art. 12.16. The result for the long slit is

$$K = K_0\left[\frac{\sin(kw\cos\theta)}{kw\cos\theta}\right]^2 \quad (1)$$

where K_0 is a constant related to the intensity of illumination. The bracketed factor gives the pattern with angle, and is plotted in Fig. 12.18b in terms of the ratio of slit width to wavelength.

If single frequency light from the same source passes through two slits (Fig. 12.18c), there are enhancements or cancellations depending on the phase differences between paths. For the far-zone field, using the usual approximation for radius difference,

$$r_2 \approx r_1 + d\sin\theta. \quad (2)$$

The pattern now depends not only on the basic pattern of one slit, but also on the spacing of the two slits in wavelengths. A typical result is shown in Fig. 12.18d, plotted for slit spacing three times the width of one slit.

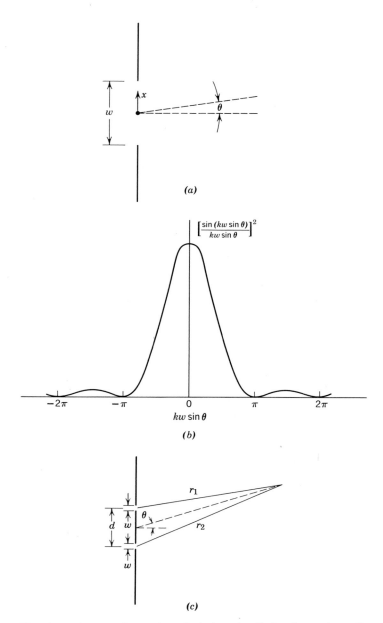

(a)

$$\left[\frac{\sin(kw\sin\theta)}{kw\sin\theta}\right]^2$$

-2π $-\pi$ 0 π 2π

$kw\sin\theta$

(b)

(c)

Fig. 12.18 *(a)* Coordinates for calculation of radiation from a long slit.
(b) Fraunhofer (far-zone) pattern for single slit of *(a)*. *(c)* Pair of long
slits. *(d)* Fraunhofer pattern for slits of *(c)*. *(e)* Diffraction grating with

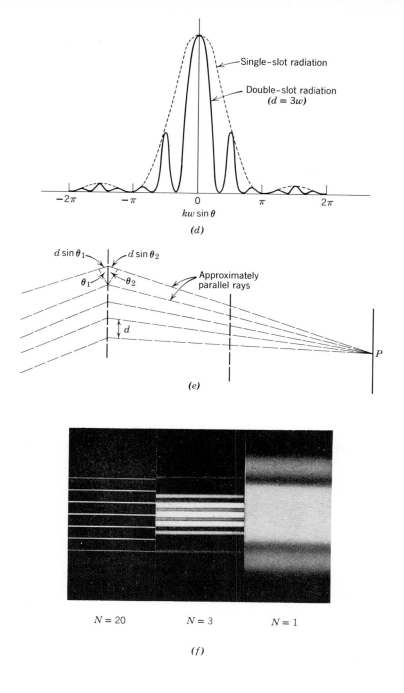

Single-slot radiation

Double-slot radiation
$(d = 3w)$

-2π $-\pi$ 0 π 2π

$kw \sin \theta$

(d)

$d \sin \theta_1$ $d \sin \theta_2$

θ_1 θ_2 Approximately
parallel rays

d

P

(e)

$N = 20$ $N = 3$ $N = 1$

(f)

large number of slits. *(f)* Diffraction patterns showing effect of changing
number of slits.

A most useful extension of the two-slit arrangement is the diffraction grating, Fig. 12.18e, which may have hundreds or even thousands of radiating sources for the light. (For practical reasons, these are often rulings on a solid reflector rather than open slits, but they act very similarly in terms of radiation pattern.) As with the example of two slits, the phase additions and cancellations from the several lines govern the pattern, and produce rapid variations as compared with the radiation from a single slit or ruling. Thus the lines in the radiation pattern are very much sharpened. Each major maximum (lobe in the antenna terminology) has subsidiary maxima (side lobes), as will be seen in the curve for $N = 10$ in Fig. 12.23b, but for very large N these will be very near the principal maxima as compared with the spacing between such maxima.

The photograph of Fig. 12.18f shows clearly the affect of increasing N. Note especially the sharp lines for the photo of $N = 20$. (The subsidiary maxima are not registered on this photograph.) This clear separation is of utmost importance in the use of diffraction gratings for spectroscopy, or other applications where it is desired to separate patterns of different frequency.

That the position of a principal maximum is a function of frequency if either source or receptor wavefront is at an angle with the normal is shown by the simple grating formula

$$kd(\sin \theta_1 + \sin \theta_2) = m(2\pi), \qquad m = 1, 2, 3, \ldots. \qquad (3)$$

This formula is simply interpreted by noting that it requires the phase differences of all paths in Fig. 12.18e to be multiples of 2π if the elementary contributions from the many slits are to add constructively. This is the same principle as that employed in the phase scanning of large arrays, Art. 12.23.

12.19 Lenses for Direction of Radiation

The lenses used in radiating systems, like the parabolic reflector, act to focus the radiation from primary sources into desired directions. Most lenses are conceived from the point of view of geometrical optics, and in this approximation would produce a plane parallel beam of radiation from an ideal point radiator at the focus. The actual lens behavior is disturbed from this ideal by the finite character of the primary radiator, and by diffraction arising from the finite aperture of the lens. The latter effect causes the beam to spread in a manner predicted by the aperture analysis of Art. 12.15. Thus we will leave this aspect of the matter and consider the various first-order designs suggested by geometrical optics.

The most direct conception is that of a primary source placed at the focus of a converging lens, of the type discussed in Art. 6.17, so that the beam emerges parallel. The technique is well developed at optical frequencies, including the coating of the surfaces to eliminate reflections (Art. 6.10). The solid lenses most often used are small enough for convenient handling. Direct extension of solid lenses to microwave frequencies

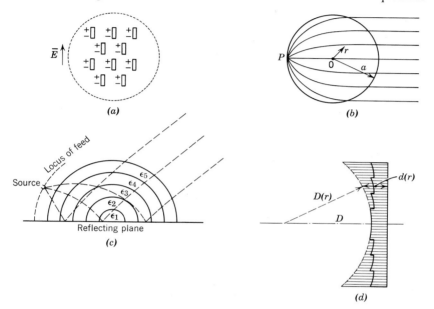

(a)

(b)

(c)

(d)

Fig. 12.19 (a) Artificial-dielectric lens. (b) Luneberg lens. (c) Practical form of Luneberg lens. (d) Metal lens antenna.

results in large and heavy structures if the aperture is made large enough in size to produce a reasonably narrow beam. Thus one of two variants to be described are commonly used.

A fairly direct extension of the solid lens concept to microwaves is possible with reasonable weights through the use of "artificial dielectrics." These lenses are made of metal spheres, disks, or rods imbedded in a light material such as polyfoam. If the metal particles are small in comparison with wavelength, they act very much as individual molecules in a solid dielectric. That is, the metal particles are "polarized" by the applied electric field (Fig. 12.19a), with the positive and negative charges displaced from each other. Each particle then acts as a small dipole, contributing to total displacement and thus to an effective dielectric constant. Effective dielectric constants in the hundreds have been obtained with usefully light structures.[11] The use of disks or cylinders leads to anisotropic properties, but the structure can be designed for use with the desired ray direction and direction of polarization. One illustration has been pictured in Fig. 12.02h. Inhomogeneous properties are also possible by varying spacing or size of particles; this technique may be used instead of shaping to produce focusing action.

One of the most important lenses which utilizes an inhomogeneous effective dielectric constant is the Luneberg lens.[12,13] This is made in the form of a sphere with effective dielectric constant varying with radius as

$$\epsilon(r) = \epsilon_r \sqrt{2 - (r/a)^2}. \tag{1}$$

A sketch of ray paths by the technique of Art. 8.21 shows that all rays originating from a point on the surface will emerge from the other side as a parallel beam with the direction of the diameter through the source point (Fig. 12.19b). The importance arises in that the beam direction may be changed by changing the position of the source. Since the source is at constant radius, angular motion of the source leads to a wide range of mechanical scanning of the beam. Practical variants of the Luneberg principle utilize a feed point outside the sphere, a reflection plane to eliminate the need for half the sphere, and step discontinuities in effective dielectric constant to approximate the continuous form (1). These points are all illustrated in Fig. 12.19c.

An interesting and different means of realizing lens-type focusing action is with the *metal lens antenna*[14] which utilizes sections of parallel-plane waveguides. As illustrated in Fig. 12.19d, polarization is such that the mode between the plates is a *TE* mode, normally with one half-sine variation in field distribution. The ratio of spacing to wavelength is such that phase velocity v_p is appreciably greater than that in free space. The concept used is that of Art. 6.17 where we want all paths from focus to the lens plane to yield the same phase:

$$\frac{D}{C} + \frac{d(0)}{v_p} = \frac{D(r)}{C} + \frac{d(r)}{v_p}. \tag{2}$$

Since the waveguide sections advance rather than delay phase, the outer parts of the lens are longer than the center parts for a converging lens, as noted in Fig. 12.19d. Whole wavelengths contribute nothing from the point of view of phase, so these may be cut out to save weight, resulting in the final stepped configuration shown by the solid lines of the figure.

[11] W. E. Kock, "Metallic Delay Lens," *Bell Syst. Tech. J.*, **27**, 58–82 (Jan. 1948).

[12] Born and Wolf, *op. cit.*, p. 146.

[13] R. F. Rinehart, *J. Appl. Phys.*, **19**, 860 (1948).

[14] W. E. Kock, "Metal Lens Antenna," *Proc. I.R.E.*, **34**, 828–836 (Nov. 1946).

Problems

12.19a A converging lens is to be made of an artificial dielectric of cylindrical form (radius a and thickness w). If dielectric constant at the center is $\epsilon_r(0)$, find the desired radial variation $\epsilon_r(r)$ to produce a lens of focal length f.

12.19b By utilizing the equation for ray paths in an inhomogeneous medium (Art. 8.21), illustrate that the spherically symmetric Luneberg lens with dielectric constant given by (1) yields the described focusing.

12.19c As in Prob. b, illustrate that a spherically symmetric dielectric constant of the form $\epsilon_r[1 + (r/a)^2]^{-2}$ focuses the rays from one point on the spherical surface to another point diametrically opposite. (This is Maxwell's Fish Eye.[15])

12.19d Zone plates in optics provide focusing by shielding a region from "out-of-phase" portions of the wave front. For a point source at $z = -0.5$ meter, $\lambda = 3$ centimeters, find in the plane $z = 0$ the radii of zones for which phase is $\pi(2n + \frac{1}{2}) < \phi < \pi(2n + \frac{3}{2})$ in comparison with that at $z = 0, r = 0$. Explain qualitatively why shielding of these zones should produce a focusing effect.

12.19e A metal lens antenna of the type described has plate spacing of 1.75 cm and is used at a frequency of 10 gigacycles/second. For a focal length of 1 meter and a maximum radius of 0.5 meter, sketch the outline of the lens, with and without full-wave sections removed.

ARRAYS OF ELEMENTS

12.20 Radiation Intensity with Superposition of Effects

If there are several complete radiators operating together, currents or fields might be assumed over the entire group, and a complete calculation made for potentials or fields at any point in the radiation field. If the radiation patterns of the individual elements are known, however, some labor may be saved by superposing these with proper attention to phase, direction, and magnitude of the fields. This is actually only an extension of the procedure we have already used to add up the effects of infinitesimal elements. We have also seen physically in the example of the diffraction grating the qualitative effect of the addition or cancellation of radiation in selected directions by the proper spacing of many radiating elements. As a practical matter, the synthesis of desired antenna patterns by the addition of individual radiators is a most important tool, so that efficient methods for the analysis of arrays become most important. A few of these, with examples, are set down in this and several following articles.

---

[15] Born and Wolf, *op. cit.*, p. 147.

The usual problem in array theory is that of identical radiators with similar current or field distributions (although magnitudes and phases of currents or fields in individual radiators may differ). The radiation vectors for one of these alone may be calculated as $\bar{N}_0$ and $\bar{L}_0$. ($\bar{N}_0$ alone is sufficient if we consider contributions only from electric current elements.) In adding contributions from the individual radiators for the far-zone field, the usual approximation is made in that differences in distances to

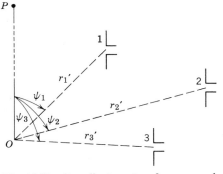

Fig. 12.20   Coordinate system for a general
array.

the individual radiators need be taken into account only with respect to phase; also, the approximate form for distance differences may be calculated by assuming the field point far removed. Thus the total radiation for a system of radiators as pictured in Fig. 12.20 is

$$\bar{N} = \bar{N}_0(C_1 e^{jkr_1' \cos \psi_1} + C_2 e^{jkr_2' \cos \psi_2} + \cdots) \tag{1}$$

$$\bar{L} = \bar{L}_0(C_1 e^{jkr_1' \cos \psi_1} + C_2 e^{jkr_2' \cos \psi_2} + \cdots). \tag{2}$$

The constants C_1, C_2, etc. are the complex numbers giving relative magnitudes and phases of currents in the several individual radiators; r_1', r_2', etc. are the radii from a common origin to the reference origin of the individual radiators; ψ_1, ψ_2, etc. are the angles between r_1', r_2', and the direction of the radius from the common origin to the distant field point P. It follows that the total radiation intensity may be written in terms of the radiation intensity K_0 for one radiator alone:

$$K = K_0 \, |C_1 e^{jkr_1' \cos \psi_1} + C_2 e^{jkr_2' \cos \psi_2} + \cdots|^2. \tag{3}$$

Examples will follow to make the use of these forms more specific. We should note one important point, however, that will not be touched on specifically in the examples. Mutual couplings between the elements, including effects from the near-zone fields, may affect the amount and phase of current that a given array element receives from the driving source, so that the excitation problem may become quite difficult. Carter[16] has calculated mutual effects of parallel linear radiators, but the adjustment for desired current distribution among elements for more complex elements must often be done by tedious experimental procedures.

Problems

12.20a A section of parallel-wire transmission line when properly terminated may be approximately considered as two wires along which waves are propagating, the currents being opposite in phase at any point along the line. Neglect the radiation from the termination and the mutual effect between the termination and the lines, and compute the radiated power from the line by the method described in Art. 12.20. Use results for a single wire with traveling wave from Art. 12.09.

12.20b Given a radiator with horizontal current elements only of radiation intensity K_0, show that, if this is placed at a height h above earth which may be assumed plane and perfectly conducting,

$$K = 4K_0 \sin^2 (kh \cos \theta).$$

The vertical direction is taken as the axis, $\theta = 0$.

12.20c How is the result of Prob. b revised if the $\theta = 0$ axis is taken horizontal and the vertical direction defines $\phi = 0$?

12.20d What conclusions similar to those of Prob. b can be derived for antennas with vertical current elements only, if placed with their reference origin a distance h above earth?

12.20e Write the more general forms of (1) and (2) if the individual radiators of Fig. 12.20 are not of the same type.

12.20f With the assumptions made above, explain why the constants C_1, C_2, etc. are the same in the expressions for $\bar{N}$ and $\bar{L}$, equations (1) and (2).

12.21 Example: Array of Two Half-Wave Dipoles

Consider two half-wave dipoles separated by a quarter-wavelength and fed by currents equal in magnitude and 90° out of time phase, as in Fig. 12.21a. For a single dipole (Prob. 12.09b),

$$K_0 = \frac{15}{\pi} I_m^2 \frac{\cos^2 [(\pi/2) \cos \theta]}{\sin^2 \theta}.$$

For the two dipoles with the origin as shown in Fig. 12.21a,

$$r_1' = 0 \quad r_2' = \frac{\lambda}{4} \quad \theta_2' = \frac{\pi}{2} \quad \phi_2' = 0$$

[16] P. S. Carter, *Proc. I.R.E.*, **20**, 1004–1041 (June 1932).

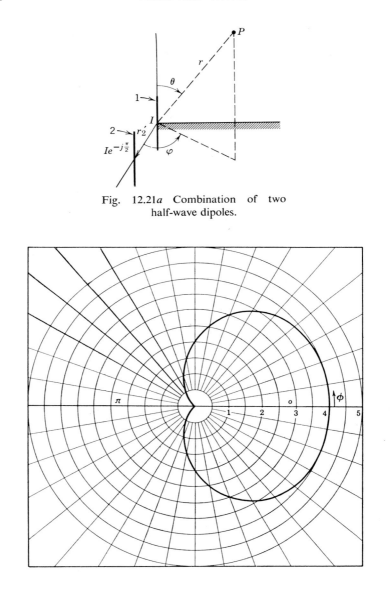

Fig. 12.21*a* Combination of two
half-wave dipoles.

Fig. 12.21*b*   Polar plot of relative power intensity radiation for array in
Fig. 12.21*a* in the plane $\theta = \pi/2$.

so
$$\cos \psi_2 = \sin \theta \cos \phi.$$

If
$$I_2 = I_1 e^{-j(\pi/2)},$$

then
$$K = K_0 \,|1 + e^{-j(\pi/2)} e^{j(\pi/2)(\sin \theta \cos \phi)}|^2$$

$$= 4K_0 \cos^2 \left[\frac{\pi}{4} (\sin \theta \cos \phi - 1)\right].$$

A horizontal radiation intensity pattern is plotted in Fig. 12.21b.

Problem

12.21 Plot radiation intensity patterns for the following half-wave dipole arrays in vertical and horizontal planes.
(a) Two parallel dipoles fed in phase with equal currents and placed $\lambda/2$ apart.
(b) Four parallel dipoles fed in phase with equal currents and spaced $\lambda/2$ apart.
(c) Two dipoles placed end to end, fed in phase with equal currents.
(d) Same as (c) but with four dipoles.
(e) Same as (d) but with a perfectly conducting reflecting plane parallel to the dipoles at distance $\lambda/4$.

12.22 The Rhombic Antenna

The rhombic antenna[17,18] has been an important antenna in long-distance communications, and is useful to illustrate the extension of the array procedures to elements not in the same direction in space. As the name implies, this antenna has four wire elements arranged in the form of a rhombus (Fig. 12.22).

The antenna is fed at O and terminated at A by the proper resistance; therefore energy travels along the wires only from O toward A, no reflected waves traveling back from A toward O. This may be analyzed as a system of combined elements, the elements having energy traveling along them in only one direction. Since the elements do not have the same orientation, addition must be by components.

The radiation vector for a single wire with energy traveling at the velocity of light in only one direction, Ie^{-jkl}, has only the direction of the wire (Art. 12.09). Neglect, for now, the presence of the earth.

$$N_s = \frac{I[1 - e^{-jkl(1-\cos \psi)}]}{jk(1 - \cos \psi)} = \frac{I}{jk} f(\psi). \tag{1}$$

[17] D. Foster, *Proc. I.R.E.*, **25**, 1327–1353 (Oct. 1937).
[18] E. Bruce, A. C. Beck, L. R. Lowry, *Proc. I.R.E.*, **23**, 24–46 (Jan. 1935).

The subscript s denotes the direction of the wire, and ψ is the angle between the wire and the radius vector to the distant point (r, θ, ϕ) at which field is desired. The angles ψ for the various elements, in terms of the coordinates shown in Fig. 12.22, are found to be

$$\cos \psi_{OC} = \cos \psi_{DA} = \sin \theta \cos (\phi + \alpha)$$
$$\cos \psi_{OD} = \cos \psi_{CA} = \sin \theta \cos (\phi - \alpha). \tag{2}$$

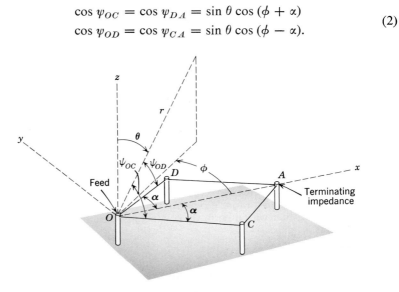

Fig. 12.22

The currents at O for OC and OD are 180° out of phase. They may be taken as I and $-I$. The currents at the beginning of CA and DA (at C and D respectively) are then Ie^{-jkl} and $-Ie^{-jkl}$. Components of radiation vector may now be added, taking into account the differences in phase with respect to the common origin O.

$$r'_{OC} = r'_{OD} = 0 \qquad r'_{CA} = r'_{DA} = l.$$

So
$$N_x = \cos \alpha[N_1 + N_2 + N_3 e^{jkl \cos \psi_{OC}} + N_4 e^{jkl \cos \psi_{OD}}]$$
$$N_y = \sin \alpha[-N_1 + N_2 + N_3 e^{jkl \cos \psi_{OC}} - N_4 e^{jkl \cos \psi_{OD}}]$$
$$N_z = 0$$

where
$$N_1 = \frac{I}{jk} f(\psi_{OC}) \qquad N_2 = -\frac{I}{jk} f(\psi_{OD})$$
$$N_3 = \frac{Ie^{-jkl}}{jk} f(\psi_{OD}) \qquad N_4 = -\frac{I}{jk} e^{-jkl} f(\psi_{OC})$$

and $f(\psi)$ is defined by (1).

Define also

$$S = S(\psi_{OC}\psi_{OD}) = \frac{[1 - e^{-jkl(1-\cos\,\psi_{OC})}][1 - e^{-jkl(1-\cos\,\psi_{OD})}]}{(1 - \cos\,\psi_{OC})(1 - \cos\,\psi_{OD})}. \quad (3)$$

Then

$$N_x = \frac{IS\cos\alpha}{jk}(\cos\,\psi_{OC} - \cos\,\psi_{OD})$$

$$= -\frac{2IS}{jk}\sin\theta\sin\phi\sin\alpha\cos\alpha. \quad (4)$$

Similarly,

$$N_y = -\frac{2IS}{jk}\sin\alpha(1 - \sin\theta\cos\phi\cos\alpha). \quad (5)$$

The components of radiation vector in spherical coordinates may be written in terms of the cartesian components N_x and N_y [Eq. 12.08(12)].

$$N_\theta = (N_x\cos\phi + N_y\sin\phi)\cos\theta = -\frac{2IS}{jk}\sin\alpha\sin\phi\cos\theta \quad (6)$$

$$N_\phi = (-N_x\sin\phi + N_y\cos\phi) = -\frac{2IS}{jk}\sin\alpha(\cos\phi - \sin\theta\cos\alpha). \quad (7)$$

The radiation intensity is [Eq. 12.08(8)],

$$K = \frac{\eta}{8\lambda^2}[|N_\theta|^2 + |N_\phi|^2]$$

$$= \frac{4I^2\eta}{8\lambda^2 k^2}|S|^2[\sin^2\phi\cos^2\theta + (\cos\phi - \sin\theta\cos\alpha)^2]\sin^2\alpha. \quad (8)$$

By trigonometric substitutions in the quantity in brackets,

$$K = \frac{4I^2\eta^2}{8\lambda^2 k^2}|S|^2\{[1 - \sin\theta\cos(\phi + \alpha)][1 - \sin\theta\cos(\phi - \alpha)]\}\sin^2\alpha$$

$$= \frac{4I^2\eta}{8\lambda^2 k^2}|S|^2(1 - \cos\,\psi_{OC})(1 - \cos\,\psi_{OD})\sin^2\alpha, \quad (9)$$

where S, defined by (3), has a magnitude,

$$|S| = \frac{4\sin\,[(kl/2)(1 - \cos\,\psi_{OC})]\sin\,[(kl/2)(1 - \cos\,\psi_{OD})]}{(1 - \cos\,\psi_{OC})(1 - \cos\,\psi_{OD})}.$$

For air,

$$\eta = 120\pi \quad \text{and} \quad k = \frac{2\pi}{\lambda}$$

so

$$K = \frac{240I^2}{\pi}\sin^2\alpha\,\frac{\sin^2\,[(kl/2)(1 - \cos\,\psi_{OC})]\sin^2\,[(kl/2)(1 - \cos\,\psi_{OD})]}{(1 - \cos\,\psi_{OC})(1 - \cos\,\psi_{OD})} \quad (10)$$

where ψ_{OC} and ψ_{OD} are defined by (2).

From this expression for radiation intensity, it is seen that, for large values of $kl/2$, K may become zero many times [each time $\cos \psi_{OC}$, $\cos \psi_{OD}$ are unity, or when $(kl/2)(1 - \cos \psi) = n\pi$]. The radiation pattern may then have many lobes. By properly proportioning the angle α and the length l, these lobes may be changed in relative magnitude and the directivity pattern altered greatly.

If a horizontal rhombic antenna is located at height h above a plane earth which may be considered perfectly conducting, the result of Prob. 12.20b may be applied directly to find total radiation intensity.

$$K = 4K_0 \sin^2 (kh \cos \theta), \tag{11}$$

where K_0 is the radiation intensity for a single rhombic by (10).

Problems

12.22a   For a rhombic with $l = 3.5\lambda$, $\alpha = 24°$, plot a vertical radiation intensity pattern (in plane $\phi = 0$) and a horizontal pattern (in plane $\theta = \pi/2$).

12.22b   How is the vertical pattern of Prob. a revised if the rhombus is placed 2λ above earth?

12.23   Linear Arrays

An especially important class of arrays is that in which the elements are arranged along a straight line, usually with equal spacing between them, as indicated in Fig. 12.23a. Let the line be the z axis, with the basic spacing d and coefficients $a_0, a_1, \ldots a_{N-1}$ representing the relative currents in elements at $z = 0, d, \ldots, (N - 1)d$. (Note that any of the elements can be missing, in which case the coefficient is zero, so the elements need only be of commensurate spacing instead of equal spacing.) If the elements have a radiation vector $\bar{N}_0$, Eq. 12.20(1) becomes for this case

$$\bar{N} = \bar{N}_0[a_0 + a_1 e^{jkd \cos \theta} + \cdots + a_{N-1}e^{j(N-1)kd \cos \theta}] = \bar{N}_0 S(\theta), \tag{1}$$

where $S(\theta)$ may be called the space factor of the array,

$$S(\theta) = \sum_{n=0}^{N-1} a_n e^{jnkd \cos \theta}. \tag{2}$$

The radiation intensity from Eq. 12.20(3) is then

$$K = K_0 |S|^2. \tag{3}$$

Broadside Array.   If all currents in the linear array are equal in magnitude and phase, it is evident from physical reasoning that the contributions to radiation will add in phase in the plane perpendicular to the axis of the array ($\theta = \pi/2$). For this reason, the array is called a *broadside array*. Moreover, it is evident that, if the total length l is long compared with wavelength, the phase of contributions from various elements will change rapidly as angle is changed slightly from the maximum, so that maximum

Fig. 12.23*a* Coordinate system for a linear
array.

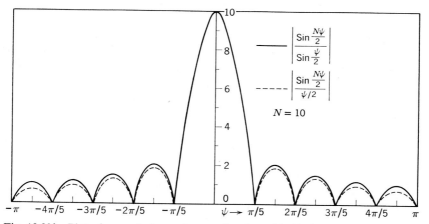

Fig. 12.23*b* Plot of space factor and approximation with 10 elements. ψ is $kd \cos \theta$ for a broadside array and $(1 - kd \cos \theta)$ for an end-fire array.

in this case would be expected to be sharp. To see this from (2), let all $a_n = a_0$:

$$S(\theta) = a_0 \sum_{n=0}^{N-1} e^{jnkd \cos \theta} = a_0 \frac{1 - e^{jNkd \cos \theta}}{1 - e^{jkd \cos \theta}}. \qquad (4)$$

Summation (4) is effected by the rule for a geometric progression. Then

$$|S|^2 = a_0^2 \frac{\sin^2 \frac{1}{2}(Nkd \cos \theta)}{\sin^2 \frac{1}{2}(kd \cos \theta)}. \qquad (5)$$

Relation (4) is plotted as a function of $(kd \cos \theta)$ in Fig. 12.23*b* for $N = 10$. Note that the peak of the main lobe occurs at $kd \cos \theta = 0$ (or $\theta = \pi/2$) as expected. The width of the main lobe may be described by giving the angles at which radiation goes to zero. If we set these angles as $\theta = \pi/2 \pm \Delta/2$,

$$Nkd \cos\left(\frac{\pi}{2} \pm \frac{\Delta}{2}\right) = \mp 2\pi$$

$$\Delta = 2\sin^{-1}\left(\frac{\lambda}{Nd}\right) \approx \frac{2\lambda}{l}. \tag{6}$$

The last approximation is for large N. So we see that the beam becomes narrow as l/λ becomes large, as predicted.

If N is large, the denominator of (5) remains small over several of the lobes near the main lobe. Over this region it is then a good approximation to set the sine equal to the angle in the denominator.

$$|S|^2 \approx N^2 a_0^2 \frac{\sin^2 \frac{1}{2}(Nkd \cos\theta)}{(\frac{1}{2}Nkd \cos\theta)^2}. \tag{7}$$

This approximation is compared as a dotted curve with the accurate curve for $N = 10$ in Fig. 12.23b, and is found to agree well over several maxima. Thus, for large N, this universal form applies near $\theta = \pi/2$ and the first secondary maximum is observed to be about 0.045 of the absolute maximum, or 13.5 db below.

The gain of an array is usually expressed as though the elements were isotropic radiators. The gain is of course modified if actual elements having some directivity are employed, but, for high-gain arrays, the modification is small. (Note that it is not correct to multiply gain of the array by gain of a single element.) For the array,

$$g = \frac{4\pi |S_{\max}|^2}{2\pi \int_0^\pi |S|^2 \sin\theta \, d\theta}. \tag{8}$$

The high-gain broadside array gives most of its contribution to the integral in the denominator near $\theta = \pi/2$, where the approximate expression (7) applies.

$$\int_0^\pi |S|^2 \sin\theta \, d\theta = \frac{2N^2 a_0^2}{Nkd} \int_0^{Nkd} \frac{\sin^2 \psi/2}{(\psi/2)^2} d\psi \to \frac{4N^2 a_0^2}{Nkd} \cdot \frac{\pi}{2}.$$

From (8),

$$g \approx \frac{N^2 a_0^2}{N^2 a_0^2 \pi} \times Nkd = \frac{2l}{\lambda} \quad \left(\text{large } \frac{l}{\lambda}\right). \tag{9}$$

End-Fire Arrays. If the elements of the array are progressively delayed in phase just enough to make up for the retardation of the waves, it would be expected that the radiation from all elements of the array could be made to add up in the direction of the array axis. Such an array is called an *end-fire array*. To accomplish this, let

$$a_n = a_0 e^{-jnkd}. \tag{10}$$

Then in (2),

$$S = a_0 \sum_{n=0}^{N-1} e^{-jnkd(1-\cos\theta)} = a_0 \frac{1 - e^{-jNkd(1-\cos\theta)}}{1 - e^{-jkd(1-\cos\theta)}} \tag{11}$$

$$|S|^2 = \frac{\sin^2 \frac{1}{2}[Nkd(1-\cos\theta)]}{\sin^2 \frac{1}{2}[kd(1-\cos\theta)]} a_0^2. \tag{12}$$

By comparison with (5), it is recognized that the plot of Fig. 12.23b made for a broadside array may be utilized for the end fire also if the abscissa is interpreted as $kd(1-\cos\theta)$. The pattern as a function of θ of course looks different, but the ratio of secondary to primary maxima is the same. It may also be shown to follow that the formula for gain (9) applies also to an end-fire array with large l/λ. To obtain the angular width of the main lobe, let $\Delta/2$ be the angle at which S goes to zero.

$$Nkd\left(1 - \cos\frac{\Delta}{2}\right) = 2\pi$$

$$\Delta \approx 2\sqrt{2\lambda/l}. \tag{13}$$

Phase Scanning of Arrays. By interpretation of the broadside and end-fire examples, it is clear that a phase delay between elements somewhere between the extremes for the two cases should give a maximum lobe between these extremes. Moreover, if this phase delay is controllable by any means, the direction of the lobe can be scanned without physical motion of the antenna. This may be most important in large installations that must continually scan a large range of directions in short times, as in airport surveillance radar.

Quantitatively, for the linear array, we see the scanning if we allow the phase delay to be $\Delta\varphi$ between elements. Then replacing (10) for the end fire,

$$a_n = a_0 e^{-jn\Delta\varphi}. \tag{14}$$

Following procedures as for (7) or (12), the space factor here is

$$|S|^2 = \frac{\sin^2 (N/2)(kd\cos\theta - \Delta\varphi)}{\sin^2 (kd\cos\theta - \Delta\varphi)} a_0^2. \tag{15}$$

The direction of the principal maximum is then given by

$$kd\cos\theta_m = \Delta\varphi \tag{16}$$

and so can be varied if $\Delta\varphi$ is varied.

This principle can of course be extended to two-dimensional as well as linear arrays, although the number of phases to control then increases. Simple methods for rapid control of phases are most important for practical use of such a system. One of the most direct and first methods used was achieved by designing fixed time delays from the source to the various elements. These delays were then translated to variable phases by a variation of frequency ω. Ferrite and other solid-state phase shifters have been developed, however, which give greater flexibility in the phase variations which can be obtained.

Unequally-Spaced Arrays. Although the formulation has been given only for arrays of equal element spacing, unequal spacing of elements provides an additional degree of freedom which may sometimes be used to advantage. Unequally spaced arrays have been used to give greater gain and lower side lobes than an equally spaced array with the same number of elements.[19] The amplitude of excitation of the elements may be retained more nearly constant in the array of unequal spacing. Thus this form of array will be useful for many purposes. Analysis is more difficult than for the array with equal spacings, but can at least be carried out by digital computation once element spacings and excitations are specified.

12.24 Polynomial Formulation of Arrays and Limitations on Directivity

Schelkunoff[20] has shown that linear arrays with equal element spacings may be formulated as polynomials, with useful results obtained by interpretation of the zeros of the polynomials in the complex plane.

$$\zeta = e^{j\psi} = e^{jkd \cos \theta}. \tag{1}$$

Equation 12.23(2) may then be written as a polynomial in ζ,

$$S = \sum_{n=0}^{N-1} a_n \zeta^n. \tag{2}$$

Concentration is now on the properties of S in the complex ζ plane.

Note first that real θ corresponds to values of ζ on the unit circle with phase angles between $-kd$ and kd. All, a part, or none of the $N-1$ zeros of S may occur in this part of the unit circle. When they do so occur, they

[19] D. D. King, R. F. Packard, and R. K. Thomas, *IRE Transactions*, **AP-8**, 380–384 (July 1960).

[20] S. A. Schelkunoff, "A Mathematical Theory of Linear Arrays," *Bell Syst. Tech. J.*, **22**, 80–107 (Jan. 1943).

correspond to true zeros of the pattern, or "cones of silence." The broad-side array, Eq. 12.23(5), has its zeros spread out uniformly over the entire unit circle except for the missing one at $\psi = 0$ (Fig. 12.24a), where the very large main lobe builds up. One approach to the synthesis of arrays is then that of positioning zeros on this picture so that they are close together where the pattern is to be of small amplitude, and farther apart where it is to build up to a relatively large value. Potential analogues to

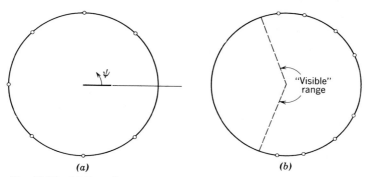

Fig. 12.24 (a) Location of zeros of polynomial representing a uniform broadside array. (b) Positioning of zeros of polynomial to produce a super-gain array.

the complex function are useful in this synthesis procedure.[21] This formulation is also especially useful in interpretation of the so-called "super-gain" antennas.

If we limit ourselves to linear arrays with currents in phase, it can be shown that the uniform array (one with all currents of equal amplitude) gives more gain than arrays with nonuniform excitations. Still greater gains are possible in principle, however, if one goes to excitations of other phases. Arrays having more gain than the uniform array are known as *super-gain arrays*.

In terms of the picture in the ζ plane, we see that for an element spacing less than a half-wavelength ($kd = \pi$) the range of real θ covers only a part of the unit circle. The uniform array, however, has its zeros spread over all the unit circle, so some are "invisible." Schelkunoff has shown that arbitrarily high gain for a given antenna size is possible in principle by moving the zeros into the range of real θ, properly distributed to give the desired directivity (Fig. 12.24b). The trouble here is that a monstrous lobe builds up in the "invisible" range from which the zeros have been eliminated, which might seem to be of no concern, but it turns out to represent

[21] T. T. Taylor and J. R. Whinnery, *J. Appl. Phys.*, **22**, 19–29 (1951).

reactive energy and so is of importance. It is surprising to find the rapidity with which this limitation takes over. For high-gain broadside arrays, no significant increase in gain is possible over that of the uniform array before the reactive energy becomes impossibly large.[22] For end-fire arrays, a modest increase is possible, and has been utilized in practice.[23] Another way of stating this limitation is that currents of the elements become huge for a given power radiated and fluctuate in phase from one element to the next so that it would be impossible to feed such an array.

A physical picture is provided by looking at the problem from a wave point of view. Imagine that we are attempting to produce a high-gain broadside array with a thin pancake pattern near the equator. We may imagine the distant fields (H_ϕ and E_θ) of this pattern expanded in a series of the spherically symmetrical TM modes of the type studied in Art. 10.09. If the pattern is to be sharp, it is clear that we shall require waves of very high order to represent this pattern (order of $2\pi/\Delta$ for a narrow beam of angle Δ). A study of the Hankel functions shows that these functions change character at a radius such that n is of the order kr, becoming rapidly reactive for radii less than this value. Hence, the antenna boundary must extend approximately to this radius if excessive reactive power is to be avoided. That is,

$$\frac{2r}{\lambda} \approx \frac{n}{\pi} \approx \frac{2}{\Delta}, \tag{3}$$

which gives a relation between angle and length equivalent to that for a uniform broadside array, Eq. 12.23(6). The phenomenon is a cutoff of the type found in sectoral horns, Art. 9.11, where it was found that reactive effects caused an effective cutoff when the cross section became too small to support the required number of half-wave variations in the pattern. The rapidity with which the limitation takes over must again be stressed. For an array 50 wavelengths long, a halving in size from that of the uniform array would require reactive power 10^{59} times the radiated power.

It should not be inferred from the foregoing discussion that uniform arrays are always best. Often the side-lobe level (13.5 db) is higher than can be tolerated. These can be reduced at a sacrifice in gain. Dolph[24] has given the procedure for finding the array of a given number of elements which gives the lowest side lobes for a prescribed antenna gain, or highest gain for a prescribed side-lobe level. The polynomial $S(\zeta)$ in (2) has in this case the form of a Tchebycheff polynomial.

[22] L. J. Chu, *J. Appl. Phys.*, **19**, 1163–1175 (Dec. 1948).
[23] W. W. Hansen and J. R. Woodyard, *Proc. I.R.E.*, **26**, 333–345 (March 1938).
[24] C. L. Dolph, *Proc. I.R.E.*, **34**, 335–348 (June 1946).

Problems

12.24a Show the location of the zeros of S in the ζ plane for the end-fire array.

12.24b By studying the properties of the spherical-wave functions, verify the statements made above that wave orders up to at least $2\pi/\Delta$ will be required to represent thin patterns of angle Δ and that energy is predominantly reactive for radii less than $n\lambda/2\pi$. Demonstrate that at this transition radius, the number of sinusoidal variations in the pattern just fits the number of wavelengths about the spherical surface.

12.24c Consider the following polynomials representing five element arrays with spacing $kd = \pi/2$.

$$S_1(\zeta) = (\zeta - e^{j2\pi/5})(\zeta - e^{-j2\pi/5})(\zeta - e^{j4\pi/5})(\zeta - e^{-j4\pi/5})$$
$$S_2(\zeta) = (\zeta - e^{j\pi/5})(\zeta - e^{-j\pi/5})(\zeta - e^{j2\pi/5})(\zeta - e^{-j2\pi/5}).$$

The first is a uniform array and the second a "super-gain" array, since it has all zeros in the visible range. Multiply out to display the relative element currents and comment on the comparison. Plot $|S(\theta)|$ versus θ for both arrays and compare.

12.25   Frequency-Independent Antennas

The frequency band over which a system can operate is limited by the component of the system with the narrowest bandwidth and for this reason it is of interest to have antennas with characteristics that are independent of frequency over a wide band. Since an antenna has the function of radiating energy in prescribed directions and providing a match between the feed system and space, its pattern and input impedance should be as constant as possible over the desired frequency range. Various kinds of broadband antennas have been developed. The rhombic configuration of Art. 12.22 has an input impedance constant to a useful degree over a wide range. Although the pattern changes, its variation is satisfactory for some purposes, as for ionospherically reflected waves in the "short-wave" range. The wave antenna of Art. 12.09 is another example of an antenna with constant input impedance over a broadband. There are other examples including the biconical shape shown in Fig. 12.02 and helices and spirals. However, although these are broadband radiators, their finite dimensions impose important bandwidth restrictions. In this article we will introduce one antenna with characteristics inherently independent of frequency and then a second antenna, derived from the first, with substantially constant characteristics. The finite dimensions of these structures impose much weaker restrictions on the bandwidth than do those of other antennas.

In the radiation expressions for various antennas, as Eq. 12.05(3) for the straight antennas or Eq. 12.22(10) for the rhombic array, kl or equivalently, the ratio of antenna length to wavelength l/λ determines the radiation pattern. The same ratio is also a characteristic parameter for input impedance for any given form of structure. We can therefore say that geometrically similar structures have the same radiation characteristics if the ratios of antenna dimensions to wavelength are the same. Rumsey[25] suggested that it might be possible to make an antenna with a pattern and input impedance independent of frequency by using a form for which

Fig. 12.25a   Equiangular spiral antenna.

geometrically similar forms are obtained by rotation. Then a change of wavelength leads only to a rotation of the pattern. The form he suggested for the conductors is the equiangular or logarithmic spirals given by

$$r = Ce^{a(\phi-\delta)}, \tag{1}$$

where r and ϕ are coordinates in a spherical system and C, a and δ are constants. It is clear that these characteristics depend on having the spirals start at $r = 0$ and extend to infinity. For practical antennas, such as the simple equiangular spiral structure shown in Fig. 12.25a, it is necessary to leave a gap to connect the input transmission line in the center and to limit the outer radius. These conditions limit the low-frequency radiation at a free-space wavelength comparable with the average antenna diameter and the high-frequency radiation where the spacing of the input terminals at the center is of the order of a wavelength.

A physical picture of the radiation considers the space between the spiral arms as a slot radiator of increasing width, with the electric field vectors directed between the spiral arms. A wave traveling out from the center radiates little until it reaches the point where the width of the slot is about a half wavelength. At this point a resonance occurs as in the resonant slot antenna, Art. 12.16, and the radiation is strong. The wave is radiated in this region, and currents and fields at increasing radii are small. Since the energy has been almost completely radiated when the wave reaches the outer boundary, the fact that the antenna does not extend to infinity is of little importance. This conclusion is modified when the radiation region moves close to the outer edge. Each of the curves forming the structure of Fig. 12.25a is described by (1). The parameters a and C are the same for all curves but the rotation parameter δ differs. If we take δ to be zero for one curve and δ_i for the curve on the opposite edge of the free-space region, the radial separation between them is

$$\Delta r = Ce^{a\phi}(1 - e^{-a\delta_i}) = r(1 - e^{-a\delta_i}). \tag{2}$$

The equiangular spiral derives its name from the property that it makes the same angle with a radius vector at all points. Therefore the separation between conductors is just a constant times (2) and so is proportional to radius. Since the radiating region occurs where the separation is a half wavelength, the ratio of wavelength to the distance between center and radiation region is constant. Considering the radiating regions as elements of an array, we see from Eq. 12.20(3) that the invariance of this ratio ensures invariance of the radiation intensity pattern.

A field analysis of this structure has been made on the basis of a model similar to the idealization of the helix used in Art. 8.17.[26] That is, the conducting arms are replaced by a sheet having infinite conductivity along the spiral directions and zero conductivity in the orthogonal directions. It is as though spiral slits are cut into a conducting sheet of infinitesimal thickness. Then it is assumed that the arms are fed by generators at the center in such a way as to have $2n\pi$ radians of phase shift in the currents fed to the arms as ϕ goes through 2π radians. For example, the model for the two-arm structure of Fig. 12.25a would use $n = 1$. The analysis shows that the radiation field is circularly polarized, with E_ϕ given by

$$E_\phi \approx A(\theta)e^{-j[\psi(\theta) - n\phi - \pi/2]}\frac{e^{-jkr}}{r}, \tag{3}$$

where
$$A(\theta) = \frac{\cos\theta(\tan\theta/2)^n e^{[(n/a)\tan^{-1}(a\cos\theta)]}}{\sin\theta\sqrt{1 + a^2\cos^2\theta}} \tag{4}$$

and
$$\psi(\theta) = \frac{n}{2a}\ln|1 + a^2\cos^2\theta| + \tan^{-1}(a\cos\theta). \tag{5}$$

[26] B. R-S. Cheo, V. H. Rumsey, and W. J. Welch, *IRE Trans. on Antennas and Propagation*, AP-9, 527–534 (November 1961).

The parameter a describes the rate of rotation of the spiral conductors. Radiation patterns in terms of the field magnitude are shown in Fig. 12.25b for one, two, three, and four circumferential cycles in the feed system. It is of particular interest to note that no radiation occurs along the plane of the sheet. This is a general criterion for the successful operation of

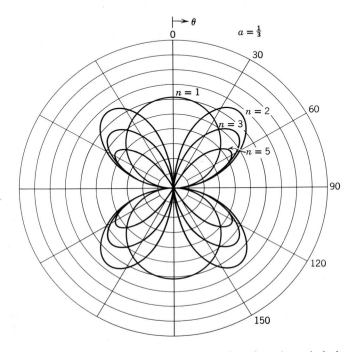

Fig. 12.25b Theoretical radiation pattern of equiangular spiral sheet antenna. Sheet is in plane $\theta = 90°$.

frequency-independent antennas, since radiation in this direction would be reflected from the necessarily finite boundaries of the structure.

Ordinarily, radiation from only one side of an antenna is desired, and this can be achieved without losing the freedom from dimensional restrictions if a nonplanar equiangular spiral is used. In general, if the arms have shapes described by

$$r = Ce^{a(\phi - \delta)}F(\theta), \qquad (6)$$

where $F(\theta)$ is an arbitrary function of the polar angle, a wavelength change then corresponds to a rotation in azimuth only. The arguments for frequency independence of the planar spiral $F(\theta) = 1$ also apply in this case. The choice of $F(\theta)$ to represent a cone gives an antenna having a pattern with a single lobe along the $\theta = 0$ axis on the apex side of the cone.

A second kind of antenna may be derived from equiangular spiral forms. In this case the characteristics repeat periodically as a function of the logarithm of frequency and may not vary too much between points of repetition, depending on the particular design. An example of an antenna

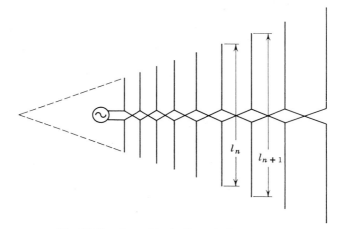

Fig. 12.25c   Logarithmically periodic antenna.

with these characteristics is shown in Fig. 12.25c. This array of dipoles can be derived from the conical equiangular spiral mentioned earlier. That is, if the spiral arms on the cone are narrow (Δr small) and they have a thickness determined by another cone of smaller angle with the same axis and apex, a plane containing the axis of the cones will intersect the arms in a pattern as shown in Fig. 12.25c. The lengths of the dipoles increase in fixed ratio

$$l_{n+1} = \tau l_n. \tag{7}$$

Also, the distances to successive dipoles from the apex increase with the same ratio. If the wavelength is multiplied by τ, or the logarithm of wavelength increased by adding a factor $\log \tau$, dipole $n + 1$ is related to wavelength in the same way as was dipole n before the increase; this effect occurs for all dipoles on an ideal structure. Thus, the geometrically similar structure, scaled by τ, is identical to the unscaled structure.

As was discussed earlier in connection with the equiangular spiral, the point of maximum radiation for Fig. 12.25c moves radially outward from the apex in proportion to the wavelength. In view of these considerations, we see that the characteristics repeat as periodic functions of the logarithm of frequency. The energy supplied at the center terminals is largely radiated at the radius where the dipoles are of the order of a half wavelength; the currents reaching the end dipoles are negligible. Thus the existence of finite boundaries is significant only for frequencies where the largest dipole is of the order of a half wavelength. The high-frequency end of the pass band occurs where the smallest dipole is of the order of a half wavelength. The construction just described, in which a plane is passed through a conical spiral, leads to the switching of the feed to the successive dipoles seen in Fig. 12.25c. This is an essential factor in the frequency independence of the operation since the radiation is thereby directed away from the array (toward apex). As noted earlier, if the radiation were not so directed, the existence of the finite boundary would cause reflections and obviate frequency independent operation.

A variety of logarithmically periodic structures have been tried and although all have characteristics which are periodic with the logarithm of frequency, not all are usefully frequency independent between the periods. The concept nevertheless permits considerable flexibility compared with the equiangular spiral. Logarithmically periodic arrays of dipoles have been successfully made having bandwidths as high as 20:1.[27]

ANTENNA SOLUTIONS AS BOUNDARY-VALUE PROBLEMS

12.26 The Spherical Antenna

As was stated in Art. 12.01, exact solution of the boundary-value problem would answer most of the important questions of radiation engineering described there. As also stressed there, however, the method has been useful for only a few simple geometrical configurations, and, even for these, approximations are necessary. Enough important results have been obtained to warrant some description of the method, so the next few articles will be devoted to the subject. We shall start with one of the simplest shapes—that of the spherical antenna driven by a symmetrical voltage applied across a small gap at the equator (Fig. 12.26a). This is not in itself a terribly important antenna configuration, but going through the problem in some detail will illustrate the direct field solution method, and the difficulties of extending it to very complicated shapes.

[27] E. C. Jordan, G. A. Deschamps, J. D. Dyson, R. E. Mayes, *IEEE Spectrum*, **1**, 58–71 (April 1964).

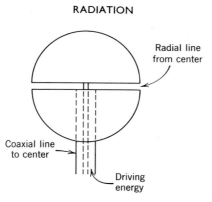

Fig. 12.26a Spherical antenna and possible driving system.

Superposition of TM Waves to Match Boundary Conditions. A study of the fields of Fig. 12.26a suggests solutions in spherical coordinates, uniform in azimuthal angle ϕ, and with field components E_r, E_θ, and H_ϕ. Such solutions have been given as the spherical *TM* waves of Eq. 10.09(19). No single one of these will satisfy the boundary conditions of the spherical antenna, as the lowest order mode has been identified with the small dipole solution (Art. 12.04), and higher order modes correspond to higher order multipoles. So, as in similar static problems, we attempt a solution formed by a series of the modes with coefficients chosen to satisfy the appropriate boundary conditions.

The boundary conditions to be satisfied on the surface of the spherical antenna (assuming perfect conductivity for the sphere in the first approximation) are:

1. $E_\theta = 0$ at $r = a$, except across gap.
2. $E_\theta =$ applied field across gap, $\theta = (\pi/2) - \alpha$ to $(\pi/2) + \alpha$.

The distribution of E_θ across the gap is not known, but its integral across the gap (which is the same as the integral from 0 to π since E_θ is elsewhere zero) must be equal to the applied voltage.

$$V_0 = \int_{(\pi/2)-\alpha}^{(\pi/2)+\alpha} E_\theta a \, d\theta = \int_0^\pi E_\theta a \, d\theta. \tag{1}$$

Now, if the exact distribution of E_θ across the gap were known, the function E_θ at $r = a$ could be expanded in a series. This series would be written in associated Legendre polynomials so that it might be compared directly with previous *TM* wave solutions. Known functions may be expanded in terms of these functions in a manner similar to that used to expand functions in a Fourier series, a series of Bessel functions, Art. 3.29, or a series of ordinary Legendre polynomials, Art. 3.30. The formula for the coefficients follows from the orthogonality properties of Eqs. 10.09(14) and (15).

$$f(\theta) = \sum_{n=1}^{\infty} b_n P_n^{1}(\cos \theta), \tag{2}$$

where
$$b_n = \frac{2n + 1}{2n(n + 1)} \int_0^{\pi} f(\theta) P_n^{1}(\cos \theta) \sin \theta \, d\theta. \tag{3}$$

The exact form of the $f(\theta)$ to be expanded, that is, E_θ, is not known except that it is zero everywhere but at the gap. If the gap is truly small, we may approximate the answer to the integral (3) by assuming that $P_n^{1}(\cos \theta)$ and $\sin \theta$ do not vary appreciably across the gap. That is, assume that $P_n^{1}(\cos \theta)$ is approximately constant at its maximum value given by Eq. 10.09(13) and that $\sin \theta$ is constant at its maximum value of unity over the gap. Then

$$b_n = \frac{2n + 1}{2n(n + 1)} P_n^{1}(0) \int_{(\pi/2)-\alpha}^{(\pi/2)+\alpha} E_\theta \, d\theta.$$

The latter integral may be found directly from (1):

$$b_n = \frac{(2n + 1)P_n^{1}(0)V_0}{2n(n + 1)a}$$

$$\tag{4}$$

and
$$E_\theta|_{r=a} = \sum_{n=1}^{\infty} b_n P_n^{1}(\cos \theta).$$

The foregoing is exactly correct for an infinitesimal gap, but for any gap of finite size it will not give correct coefficients for the highest harmonics that vary appreciably over the region of the gap.

For the wave solution in the space surrounding the antenna, we are to add an infinite number of the TM waves found in Eq. 10.09(19). Following previous reasoning, the Bessel function solution should be the Hankel function of the second kind since the region surrounding the antenna extends to infinity. Then E_θ at $r = a$ from Eq. 10.09(19) may be written

$$E_\theta|_{r=a} = \frac{j}{\omega \epsilon a^{3/2}} \sum_{n=1}^{\infty} A_n P_n^{1}(\cos \theta)[ka H_{n-1/2}^{(2)}(ka) - n H_{n+1/2}^{(2)}(ka)]. \tag{5}$$

By comparing (5) with (4), we may evaluate A_n:

$$A_n = \frac{\omega \epsilon a^{3/2} b_n}{j[ka H_{n-1/2}^{(2)}(ka) - n H_{n+1/2}^{(2)}(ka)]}. \tag{6}$$

In (4) b_n is defined, so A_n, the arbitrary coefficients of the solution, are completely determined in terms of applied voltage and the antenna dimensions. Field at any point is now expressed in a series of TM waves with determined coefficients. Thus, if desired, the field distribution at any radius could be mapped and thus the radiation pattern obtained. However, we shall go directly to the calculation of antenna impedance. It is at least evident, though, that E_θ and H_ϕ in the radiation field at large distances are zero along the axis and a maximum at $\theta = \pi/2$, since all odd $P_n{}^1(\cos \theta)$ (the only ones excited) are zero at $\theta = 0$, maximum at $\theta = \pi/2$.

Input Admittance of Antenna. The magnetic field H_ϕ is now determined since the coefficients A_n are known by (6) and (4).

$$H_\phi = \sum_{n=1}^{\infty} \frac{A_n}{r^{\frac{1}{2}}} P_n{}^1(\cos \theta) H_{n+\frac{1}{2}}^{(2)}(kr). \tag{7}$$

Surface current density is given in terms of the magnetic field at the conductor surface:

$$\bar{J} = \bar{n} \times \bar{H}$$

or

$$J_\theta = -H_\phi\big|_{r=a}.$$

Thus total current flow on the antenna at any angle θ is

$$I_\theta = 2\pi a \sin \theta J_\theta = -2\pi a \sin \theta \, H_\phi\big|_{r=a}. \tag{8}$$

The total current flow away from the gap, at $\theta = \pi/2$, from (7) and (8) is

$$I = -I_\theta\big|_{\theta=\pi/2}$$

$$= 2\pi a \sum_{n=1}^{\infty} \frac{P_n{}^1(0)A_n}{a^{\frac{1}{2}}} H_{n+\frac{1}{2}}^{(2)}(ka). \tag{9}$$

The constant A_n as defined by (4) and (6) is proportional to V_0, so the ratio of I to V_0 may be written as an admittance:

$$Y = \frac{I}{V_0} = \sum_{n=1}^{\infty} Y_n \tag{10}$$

where

$$Y_n = \frac{j\pi(2n+1)[P_n{}^1(0)]^2}{n(n+1)\eta}\left[\frac{1}{\dfrac{n}{ka} - \dfrac{H_{n-\frac{1}{2}}^{(2)}(ka)}{H_{n+\frac{1}{2}}^{(2)}(ka)}}\right].$$

As usual, $\eta = \sqrt{\mu/\epsilon}$.

The form of (10) is particularly interesting, because it represents total admittance as the sum of a number of admittances, one for each harmonic solution corresponding to a given n. This is of the form for the admittance of a group of circuits in parallel. Each circuit then corresponds to a given harmonic solution and has admittance characteristics determined by (10). $P_n{}^1(0)$ is defined by Eq. 10.09(13), and the $H_{n+\frac{1}{2}}^{(2)}$ functions by Eq. 10.09(18) and the usual definition for Hankel functions, $H_n^{(2)}(x) = J_n(x) - jN_n(x)$. Thus this admittance characteristic may be calculated. Its conductance and susceptance parts are plotted against ka for air dielectric ($\eta = 120\pi$) in Figs. 12.26b and c. Note that there are no even harmonics since

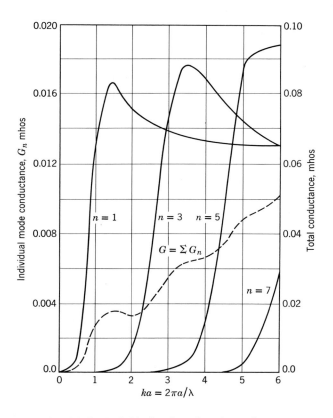

Fig. 12.26b Individual and total mode conductances
for spherical antenna.

$P_n^1(0) = 0$ for n even. This is as would be expected because $P_n^1(\cos\theta)$ for n even are all odd functions with respect to the equator and should not be stimulated by a configuration symmetrical with respect to the equator.

The higher harmonics may be readily approximated.

$$Y_n \cong \frac{j\pi(2n+1)[P_n^1(0)]^2}{\eta n^2(n+1)} ka \qquad \text{if} \quad ka \ll n.$$

A study of this equation will show that, if an infinite number of n's are present, the total Y does not converge since finite contributions to susceptance are added by the higher n's forever. This is only true, however, for an infinitesimal gap, for which an infinite susceptance term might be

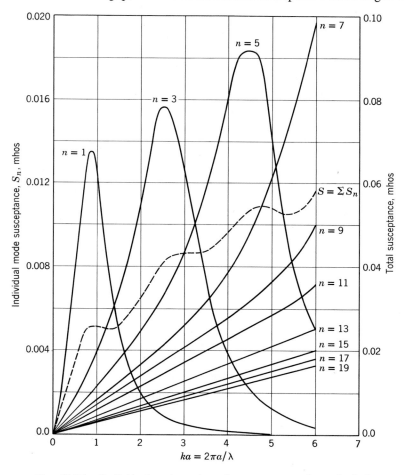

Fig. 12.26c Individual and total mode susceptances for spherical antenna.

expected. When the gap is finite a point will be reached at which the coefficients b_n (and hence Y_n) will begin to decrease, approaching zero as n approaches infinity. This occurs for harmonic solutions which vary appreciably in the $P_n^1(\cos \theta)$ function over the region of the gap. Consequently, the actual total admittance cannot be obtained until the width of the gap is known. However, the form of the curve and the order of magnitude of admittance will be changed little by missing the point by a few n's above which contributions to Y from Y_n should cease. Thus sums of the individual mode conductances and susceptances are shown in Figs. 12.26b and c using up to $n = 19$. The conductance or real part does converge and so the curve for conductance should be quite accurate.

These conclusions from the curves are of importance.

1. Admittance of any mode, Y_n, is zero at zero frequency.

2. For low frequencies ($ka \ll n$) admittance is mainly a susceptance proportional to frequency, thus representing a pure capacitance: the capacitance between the hemispheres.

3. Input admittance is capacitive at any frequency; there are no resonant points as there are in thin antennas.

4. Admittance curves have several fairly flat regions, indicating that the antenna has broadband possibilities.

Although stress in the interpretation has been placed on the impedance problem, other items of interest in antenna engineering may in principle be calculated, as will be illustrated by some of the problems.

Problems

12.26a Show that admittances in a given mode in air approach these values at low and high frequencies.

$$Y_n \to jkaK_n, \qquad ka \ll n$$
$$Y_n \to K_n, \qquad ka \gg n$$

where
$$K_n = \frac{(2n + 1)[P_n{}^1(0)]^2}{120n(n + 1)} \text{ mhos.}$$

12.26b Calculate voltage required to radiate 100 watts at the first flat point on the susceptance-frequency curve, Fig. 12.26c.

12.26c Find the point of maximum gradient E_r in the antenna, and calculate approximately its value in terms of applied voltage. Take ka in the vicinity of unity. (*Suggestion:* Calculate only that in the predominant wave mode.)

12.26d Write the complete series for field H_ϕ at any radius r. Make approximations appropriate to the far-zone field by using asymptotic forms for the Hankel functions of kr, and investigate the problem of plotting the antenna pattern from the series.

12.26e Calculate, by taking only a few terms of the series at $ka = 1$, the approximate power lost on the antenna if the conductor has a finite surface resistivity R_s. Compare with the power radiated and note the high efficiency of the device in this respect.

12.26f Demonstrate that the solutions satisfy the radiation conditions at infinity (Art. 4.15).

12.27 Spheroidal Antennas

Stratton and Chu[28] have given solutions not only for spherical antennas but also for prolate spheroidal antennas. Such a solution includes all spheroidal shapes between the sphere just studied and a thin wire (Fig. 12.27a).

The assumptions of Stratton and Chu are those used in the spherical antenna of the previous articles. Axial symmetry is assumed, and voltage is applied across a very small gap at the center. Results are quite similar in nature but different in magnitude from the results for the sphere. Input admittance may again be expressed as the sum of a large number of input admittances, one for each harmonic mode of oscillation of the antenna. However, for large eccentricities (large ratios of length to diameter) the resonances of each of these modes are very sharp, as contrasted to the broad resonances of the sphere. At a given order of resonance ($n = 1, 3,$ 5, etc.) the other modes are correspondingly less important than in the sphere, so the resonant mode practically determines the antenna characteristics in the neighborhood of resonance.

In the limit of an infinitesimally thin wire, the nth mode becomes resonant slightly below $L = n\lambda/2$. These are true resonances in that the susceptance component of Y_n actually goes through zero and becomes inductive for frequencies above resonance, whereas for the sphere it is always positive (capacitive). At frequencies much higher than resonance, susceptance in the nth mode approaches zero and conductance approaches a small but constant value. This constant value is zero in the limiting case of an infinitesimally small wire, the value found in Prob. 12.26a in the limiting case of a sphere, and something between for medium eccentricities.

These characteristics are shown in the curves for input impedance in the vicinity of the first resonance, as plotted by Stratton and Chu, Figs. 12.27b and c. Again it must be realized that the harmonics cannot be combined exactly until the exact distribution of applied field across the gap is known, yet the forms of the curves are accurate and magnitudes are nearly correct unless the gap is infinitesimal (in which case an infinite input capacitance must result). The $L/D = 1$ curve is of course the case of the sphere calculated earlier.

A study of the curves shows many features associated with past antenna knowledge. The radiation resistance for $L/\lambda = 0.5$ (a half-wave dipole) is found to be about 72 ohms, near the value calculated previously. This varies little for any eccentricity. The condition for zero reactance occurs

[28] J. A. Stratton and L. J. Chu, *J. Appl. Phys.*, **12**, 230–248 (March 1941).

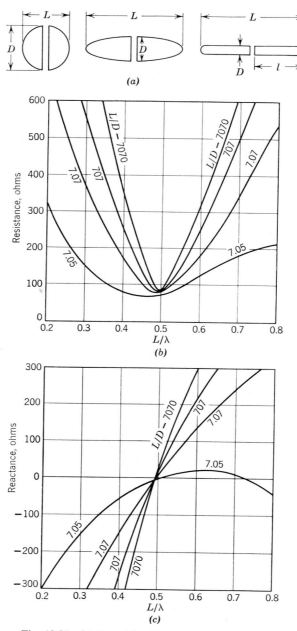

Fig. 12.27 (*a*) Transition from sphere to thin spheroidal wire dipole. (*b*) Resistance and (*c*) reactance of spheroidal antennas fed at the center. From Stratton and Chu.[28]

at something less than a half-wavelength for long thin wires (about 0.49λ or 98 per cent of the antenna length). For fatter wires this condition of zero reactance actually may occur for L greater than a half-wavelength (or at a higher frequency than before). In the limit of the sphere there is no place at which input reactance is zero; there is always a capacitive component.

The increase in broadness of the impedance curve is evident for the fatter antennas, thus making available reasonably wide bandwidths, although not comparable with those discussed in Art. 12.25.

Finally, Stratton and Chu have plotted the actual current distribution along the antenna for a thin spheroid (large L/D) and found it to vary little from the sinusoidal distribution usually assumed in the conventional methods of calculating antennas.

We will be able to compare some of these results with those obtained by Schelkunoff in the later articles.

12.28 The Biconical Antenna

Another antenna simple enough to make possible an approximate wave solution is the biconical antenna (Fig. 12.03a) used as an example for the qualitative discussion of Art. 12.03. This has been one of the most important in yielding useful results for the antenna impedance problem. The wave solutions required are similar to those utilized for the spherical antenna (Art. 12.26) except that a *TEM* wave is required in the region of the antenna, $r < l$, and the forms of the *TM* waves are modified there, as will be noted later. A series of *TM* modes for the external region is then written, and a series of *TM* modes appropriate to the inner region plus the spherical *TEM* mode is written for $r < l$. The unknown amplitudes of the series are to be evaluated by making tangential fields continuous across the common boundary at $r = l$. The procedure has been carried through approximately for cones of any angle by Tai[29] and Smith.[30] We shall concentrate, however, on the approximate solution appropriate to small angles given by Schelkunoff,[1] since this is particularly rich in physical pictures.

Form of Solutions. The form of solutions for the outer region (Fig. 12.03a) is exactly that for the spherical wave types developed in Art. 10.09. That is, axial symmetry ($\partial/\partial\phi = 0$) will be assumed and only the *TM* wave components H_ϕ, E_r, and E_θ will be excited; the axis ($\theta = 0, \pi$) is included in this region, so only the $P_n^1(\cos\theta)$ functions are required, and n must be an integer; the region extends outward to infinity, so the second

[29] C. T. Tai, *J. Appl. Phys.*, **20**, 1076–1084 (Nov. 1949).
[30] P. D. P. Smith, *J. Appl. Phys.*, **19**, 11–23 (Jan. 1948).

Hankel function will be used for the Bessel function solution. Equation 10.09(19) may then be used directly for the region $r > l$ with $Z_{n+\frac{1}{2}}$ read as $H^{(2)}_{n+\frac{1}{2}}$.

For the region between the cones, $r < l$, there is the principal wave, and to this must be added higher-order TM waves similar to those in the space outside the antenna. The TM waves for this region will, however, be somewhat different in form. The Bessel function solution in this region can contain only a $J_{n+\frac{1}{2}}$ term since $N_{n+\frac{1}{2}}$ becomes infinite at $r = 0$. For future purposes note that all field components in these higher-order waves then disappear at $r = 0$ since $J_{n+\frac{1}{2}}(0) = 0$. Moreover, a second Legendre function solution is required for this region to account for the two boundary conditions of the cones at $\theta = \psi$ and $\pi - \psi$. This second solution is usually denoted $Q_n{}^1(\cos \theta)$. Its value of infinity on the axis does not trouble us because the axis is excluded from the dielectric region over which the wave solution is to apply by the conducting cones. Thus with the Bessel function read as $J_{n+\frac{1}{2}}$ and an extra associated Legendre function, the TM waves applicable to the region $r < l$ will be similar to Eq. 10.09(19). The order n (probably better written ν) is in general not an integer because of the presence of the cones.[31] This is in fact determined by the boundary conditions $E_r = 0$ at $\theta = \psi, \pi - \psi$.

Exact Equivalent Circuit. Schelkunoff showed that an exact equivalent circuit could be set down for the principal wave, with the higher-order TM waves affecting this wave as a terminal impedance, exactly as in the waveguide discontinuity problem discussed in Art. 11.08. This is not surprising since current flow in the cones is proportional to H_ϕ and has contributions from both the principal and complementary waves,

$$I(r) = 2\pi r \sin \psi H_\phi(r, \psi) = I_0(r) + I'(r). \tag{1}$$

Current flow at the origin, however, is just that of the principal wave,

$$I(0) = I_0(0). \tag{2}$$

Also a total voltage between the two conical conductors, defined as the integral of E_θ over a surface of $r = $ constant, is only that of the principal wave, as the contribution from the complementary waves integrates to zero.

$$V(r) = -r \int_\psi^{\pi-\psi} E_\theta \, d\theta = V_0(r). \tag{3}$$

[31] It is then possible to use $P_\nu{}^m (-\cos \theta)$ as a second independent solution in place of $Q_\nu{}^m (\cos \theta)$, as is done by Schelkunoff; he also gives equations in terms of the ordinary Legendre functions rather than the associated, since the two are related by the simple derivative.

Thus input impedance at $r = 0$ is given only by the principal wave values, and can be obtained from the principal wave equivalent transmission-line circuit of Fig. 12.03c. The terminal impedance Z_L shown there is given by

$$Z_L = \frac{V_0(l)}{I_0(l)} = \frac{V_0(l)}{-I'(l)}. \tag{4}$$

The current of the denominator is written as the contribution from complementary waves in the second form since total current is assumed zero at $z = l$ which requires cancellation of I_0 and I' there.

Impedance Calculations for the Biconical Antenna. To make the equivalent transmission line useful for calculation, it is necessary to transform (4) into a more specific form. Schelkunoff did this in two ways. In the first method, the complex Poynting flow of power from an infinitesimal biconical antenna is computed, and the result compared with that obtained from the equivalent circuit when $Z_0 \gg Z_L$. Then Z_L is found to have the form

$$Z_L = Z_0^2[G(kl) + jF(kl)]^{-1}, \tag{5}$$

where Z_0 as found in Art. 8.15 is

$$Z_0 = \frac{\eta}{\pi} \ln \cot \frac{\psi}{2}, \tag{6}$$

and $G(kl)$ and $F(kl)$ are functions of the electrical length and are defined below.

In the second method, Schelkunoff also goes to the limit of a thin antenna but stresses more directly the fact that Z_L arises from the higher-order waves. He assumes that the field at large distances is of the same form as that for a thin dipole antenna (Art. 12.05), and expands this in a series of TM waves by the rules of Art. 12.26. Also, for the thin antenna, coefficients of TM waves for $r < l$ will be the same as for those for $r > l$. Use of these results in (4) again leads to an expression of the form (5) with

$$G(kl) = \sum_{m=0}^{\infty} b_m J_{2m+\frac{3}{2}}^2(kl)$$

$$F(kl) = -\sum_{m=0}^{\infty} b_m J_{2m+\frac{3}{2}}(kl) N_{2m+\frac{3}{2}}(kl) \tag{7}$$

where

$$b_m = \frac{30\pi kl(4m + 3)}{(m + 1)(2m + 1)}.$$

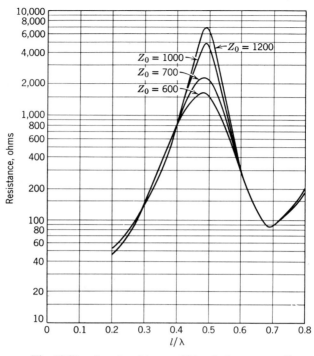

Fig. 12.28a   Input resistance of biconical antennas. From
Schelkunoff.[1]

Final curves calculated by the foregoing method for input resistance and
reactance are shown in Figs. 12.28a and 12.28b respectively. Some of the
important conclusions from these curves, and other parts of Schelkunoff's
work, are:

1. Input resistance in the neighborhood of the first resonance is close
to the value 73 ohms for a half-wave dipole (Art. 12.06) regardless of the
size of the antenna.

2. Resonance occurs for the antenna somewhat shorter than the corresponding integral number of half-waves, this shortening being greater for
the lower characteristic impedances.

3. Resonance is sharper for high characteristic impedances, again
demonstrating the broadband input impedance properties of the fatter
antennas.

4. In the neighborhood of the second resonance (high driving-point-
impedance antennas) input resistance is a definite function of Z_0 as shown
by Fig. 12.28a.

5. The current distribution was computed by this method in order to compare with the usual sinusoidal approximation. For $Z_0 = \infty$, the contribution from higher-order modes is zero and the sinusoidal form is exact. For lower values of Z_0, the deviation from a sinusoid becomes greater, especially in the imaginary part but for values of Z_0 as low as 1000 ohms the deviation in the real part is scarcely noticeable.

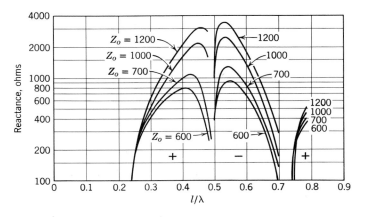

Fig. 12.28*b*   Input reactance of biconical antennas. From Schelkunoff.[1]

Problems

12.28a   Consider a biconical antenna with $l = \lambda/4$. From the approximate value of power radiated from a half-wave dipole in Art. 12.06, find the expression for the appropriate value of resistance to use for Z_L to account for this radiated power, if the reactive part of this is neglected. For a thin antenna $\psi = 0.1°$, and a thick antenna $\psi = 5°$, find the values of this resistance. Assuming that the resistance does not vary appreciably with frequency over a small range, plot input impedance of the antenna over a small range about the resonant length $l = \lambda/4$ for the two antennas. What conclusion do you draw on impedance bandwidth of thick antennas versus slender ones?

12.28b   For the first antiresonant point, $l/\lambda \approx 0.5$, calculate the power radiated in terms of maximum current on the antenna by Eq. 12.05(6). From the equivalent circuit for the antenna, considering that this maximum current is that of the principal wave, find the voltage at the end in terms of the current and Z_0. From this, find the terminating impedance in terms of Z_0 for this case, assuming Z_L real. Note that, since the line is a half-wave long, this is also the input resistance, and compare with the antiresonant peaks given in Fig. 12.28a.

12.28c   Expand the field of a dipole antenna calculated approximately in Art. 12.05 in a series of spherical transverse magnetic waves.

12.28d If current in the higher-order waves approaches zero as $Z_0 \to \infty$, the terminating impedance Z_L in the equivalent circuit approaches infinity. It seems that the possibility of accounting for radiation in the equivalent circuit is then excluded. Demonstrate that such reasoning is faulty.

12.29 Thin Dipole Antennas of General Shape

Schelkunoff[1] has extended results of the analysis based on the biconical antenna to antennas of other shape. The method is approximate, but, if antennas are not of too great diameter to length ratio, these approximations are easy to accept on a physical basis. It is assumed that the same equivalent circuit applies (Fig. 12.03c), but the shape of the antenna is taken into

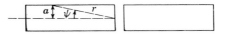

Fig. 12.29a Cylindrical dipole interpreted as a nonuniform transmission line.

account by considering the antenna as a nonuniform transmission line. For example, if the antenna is cylindrical (Fig. 12.29a), the capacity and inductance per unit length may be obtained approximately at any radius by considering the values for a cone that would just pass through this radius. For small ratios of a/r (a = antenna radius, r = distance along antenna from center),

$$L \simeq \frac{\mu}{\pi} \ln \frac{2}{\psi} = \frac{\mu}{\pi} \ln \frac{2r}{a} \qquad C \simeq \frac{\pi\epsilon}{\ln(2r/a)}. \qquad (1)$$

Thus L and C, and hence Z_0, are functions of r.

As a first approximation, all previous curves plotted for the biconical antennas may be used, with characteristic impedance taken as an average value over the length defined by

$$Z_{0a} = \frac{1}{l} \int_0^l Z_0(r)\, dr. \qquad (2)$$

Formulas for the average characteristic impedance for cylindrical, spheroidal, and diamond-shaped longitudinal-section wires were tabulated by Schelkunoff.

A better approximation may be had by utilizing nonuniform transmission line theory to transfer the load impedance, obtained from the biconical analysis, to the input. Schelkunoff has supplied particularly useful equations for this purpose appropriate to lines with only slight nonuniformities. Curves of input resistance and reactance for the cylindrical antenna, calculated in this manner, are shown in Figs. 12.29b and c.

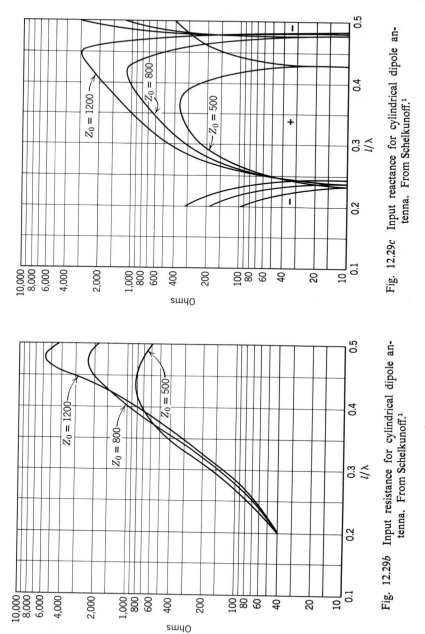

Fig. 12.29c Input reactance for cylindrical dipole antenna. From Schelkunoff.[1]

Fig. 12.29b Input resistance for cylindrical dipole antenna. From Schelkunoff.[1]

Nonuniform transmission line theory shows also that there is a correction to resonant length owing to the antenna shape which may be either in the same direction or the opposite direction to the correction from the terminating reactance. Approximate formulas for these corrections are also given by Schelkunoff.

Problem

12.29 Plot on a Smith transmission line chart the locus of impedance for a cylindrical dipole of 800 ohms characteristic impedance, a biconical antenna of 700 ohms characteristic impedance, and of the spherical antenna of Art. 12.26, all referred to a 70-ohm line. Comment on the comparison.

RECEIVING ANTENNAS AND RECIPROCITY

12.30 A Transmitting-Receiving System

The discussion in previous articles has generally implied that the radiating system was to be used as a transmitting antenna, exciting waves in space from some source of high-frequency energy. The same devices useful for transmission are also useful for reception, and it will be seen that the quantities already calculated (such as the pattern, antenna gain, and input impedance for transmission) are the useful parameters in the design of a receiving system also. This might at first seem surprising, since the two problems have some noticeable differences. In the transmitting antenna, a generator is generally applied at localized terminals, and waves are set up which go out in space approximately as spherical wave fronts. In the receiving antenna, a wave coming in from a distant transmitter approximates a portion of a uniform plane wave, and so sets up an applied electric field on the antenna system quite different from that associated with the localized sources in the transmitting case. As a consequence, the induced fields must be different so that total field meets the boundary conditions of the antenna, and the current distribution in general is different for the same antenna on transmission or reception. The currents set up on the receiving antenna system by the plane wave will convey useful power to the load (probably through a transmission line or guide), but will also produce re-radiation or scattering of some of the energy back into space. The mechanism of this scattering is exactly the same as that discussed in preceding sections for radiation from a transmitting antenna, but the form may be different for a given antenna because of the different current distribution.

Thus, we seem to have somewhat different pictures of the mechanism of transmitting and receiving electromagnetic radiation. Reciprocity theorems related to those already discussed (Art. 11.05) provide ties between the two phenomena such as the following:

1. The antenna pattern for reception is identical with that for transmission.

2. The input impedance of the antenna on transmission is the internal impedance of the equivalent generator representing a receiving system.

3. An effective area for the receiving antenna can be defined and by reciprocity is related to the gain defined in Art. 12.06. These points will be discussed in this and following articles. An excellent treatment in more detail has been given by Silver.[32]

Fig. 12.30a   A system of transmitting and receiving antennas.

We wish to begin the discussion by considering the transmitting and receiving antennas with intermediate space (Fig. 12.30a) as a system in which energy is to be transferred from the first to the second. We select terminals in the feeding guide where voltage and current may be defined in the manner explained in Art. 11.03, and similarly select a reference in the guide from the receiving antenna. The region between, including both antennas, the space, and any intermediate conductors and dielectric (assumed linear) may be represented as a two-terminal pair or transducer as indicated in Fig. 12.30b. That is,

$$V_1 = Z_{11}I_1 + Z_{12}I_2 \tag{1}$$

$$V_2 = Z_{21}I_1 + Z_{22}I_2. \tag{2}$$

The systems discussed in Chapter 11, for which proofs of (1) and (2) were given, were assumed to be closed by conducting boundaries, whereas the present system extends to infinity. The theorems given there, however, can be extended to regions extending to infinity[33] because of the manner in which fields die off there (Art. 4.15).

[32] S. Silver, *Microwave Antenna Theory and Design*, M.I.T. Radiation Laboratory Series, Vol. 12, McGraw-Hill, 1949, Chapter 2.
[33] W. K. Saunders, *Proc. Nat. Acad. Sci.*, **38**, 342–348 (April 1952).

The present system is specialized in another respect in that the coupling impedance Z_{12} in (1) is very small for a large separation between transmitter and receiver. It may then be neglected in (1), and the impedance coefficient Z_{11} is just the input impedance of the transmitting antenna calculated by itself.

$$V_1 \approx Z_{11}I_1 \approx Z_AI_1. \qquad (3)$$

The coupling term in (2) cannot be neglected, since this coupling is the effect being studied. Equation (2), however, can be represented by the usual equivalent circuit of Thévenin's theorem (Prob. 11.04b) in which

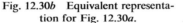
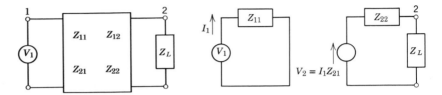

Fig. 12.30b Equivalent representation for Fig. 12.30a.

Fig. 12.30c Approximate equivalent circuit neglecting reaction of receiver back on transmitting system.

an equivalent voltage generator I_1Z_{21} is connected to the load impedance Z_L through an antenna impedance Z_{22} (which is essentially the input impedance of antenna 2 if driven as a transmitter). Thus, because of the small coupling, the reaction of the receiving antenna on the transmitting antenna can be neglected and the equivalent circuit separated as in Fig. 12.30c.

The equivalent circuit will be discussed again later. For the moment, we shall discuss transmission over the system from another point of view. For this purpose, an *effective area* of the receiving antenna is defined so that the useful power removed by the receiving antenna is given by this area multiplied by the average Poynting vector (power density) in the oncoming wave.

$$W_r = A_{er}P_{\text{av}}. \qquad (4)$$

Like antenna gain defined previously, this is in general a function of direction about the antenna, and of the condition of match in the guide. When not otherwise specified, it will be assumed to be the value for a matched load and for the maximum direction. The power density at the receiver is the power density of an isotropic radiator ($W_t/4\pi r^2$) multiplied by gain of the transmitting antenna in the given direction.

$$W_r = W_t\frac{A_{er}g_t}{4\pi r^2}, \qquad (5)$$

where W_t is the power transmitted, r is the distance between transmitter and receiver, g_t is gain of the transmitting antenna, and A_{er} is the effective area of the receiving antenna. As will be noted in Art. 12.31, the gain of a given antenna is proportional to the above-defined effective area for that antenna,

$$g = \frac{4\pi}{\lambda^2} A_e. \tag{6}$$

Therefore (5) may be written in either of the following forms given by Friis.[34] Subscripts r and t refer to receiving and transmitting antennas, respectively.

$$\frac{W_r}{W_t} = \frac{g_r g_t \lambda^2}{(4\pi r)^2} = \frac{A_{er} A_{et}}{\lambda^2 r^2}. \tag{7}$$

Problem

12.30 Calculate power received corresponding to a transmitted power of 100 watts and a distance between transmitter and receiver of 10^3 meters under the following conditions:
  a. Gain of transmitting antenna = 1.5; effective area of receiver = 0.40 meter^2.
  b. Gain of both antennas = 2; wavelength = 0.10 meter.
  c. Effective area of both antennas = 1 meter^2; wavelength = 0.03 meter.

12.31 Reciprocity Relations

From the equivalent circuit of Fig. 12.30c, we can obtain a different form for the power delivered to the receiving antenna. For this purpose, let us assume that there is a conjugate match

$$Z_L = Z_{22}^* = R_{r2} - jX_{r2}, \tag{1}$$

which is known to be the condition for maximum power transfer from the equivalent generator to the load. The power delivered to the load under this condition is

$$W_r = \frac{|I_1 Z_{21}|^2}{8R_{r2}}. \tag{2}$$

If the transmitting antenna has input resistance R_{r1}, transmitted power is

$$W_t = \tfrac{1}{2} |I_1|^2 R_{r1} \tag{3}$$

so

$$\frac{W_r}{W_t} = \frac{|Z_{21}|^2}{4R_{r1}R_{r2}}. \tag{4}$$

[34] H. T. Friis, *Proc. I.R.E.*, **34**, 254–256 (May 1946).

By comparing (4) with Eq. 12.30(5), we see that

$$|Z_{21}|^2 = \frac{R_{r1}R_{r2}g_1A_{e2}}{\pi r^2}. \tag{5}$$

If we now reverse the roles of transmitting and receiving antennas, we find for the transfer impedance in the reverse direction

$$|Z_{12}|^2 = \frac{R_{r2}R_{r1}g_2A_{e1}}{\pi r^2}. \tag{6}$$

By the reciprocity argument of Art. 11.05 (modified so that it applies to a region extending to infinity), Z_{12} and Z_{21} are equal, so we conclude

$$\frac{g_1}{g_2} = \frac{A_{e1}}{A_{e2}}. \tag{7}$$

The antennas in the foregoing argument were arbitrary, so it follows from (7) that the defined effective area of any antenna is proportional to the gain of that antenna. The constant of proportionality can be found by solving the problem for one of the simple shapes, such as the small dipole[35] or the small loop antenna. The result is as given in Eq. 12.30(6). Note that this is the same relation between gain and *actual* area of large apertures with uniform plane wave illumination found in Eq. 12.15(5) (and Prob. 12.15e). Thus, for large apertures with uniform illumination, the effective area is equal to the actual aperture area, as might be expected. For small antennas, this relation does not hold. In fact, for an infinitesimal dipole, we found the gain to be 1.5, so the effective area is

$$(A_e)_{\text{dipole}} = \frac{\lambda^2}{4\pi} g = \frac{3}{8\pi} \lambda^2, \tag{8}$$

which is finite and sizable even though antenna size is infinitesimal.

Another relation following from reciprocity, which is probably more important in practice, is that the pattern of a given antenna is the same for transmission or reception. This is useful because the pattern may then be calculated or measured in the easiest way and then be used for both transmission or reception designs. To show this, imagine, as in Fig. 12.31a, that antenna 2 is moved about the arc of a circle to measure the pattern of antenna 1. Let $\theta = 0$ be the angle of maximum response (position a) and angle θ (position b) be a general position. Also, for simplicity we assume that 1 watt is radiated in all the measurements to be described. Then, if 1 is transmitting and 2 receiving, the power received in position b, as compared with position a, by (4) is

$$\frac{W_{2b}}{W_{2a}} = \frac{|Z_{21}|_b^2}{|Z_{21}|_a^2}. \tag{9}$$

[35] D. O. North, *RCA Review*, **6**, 332–343 (Jan. 1942).

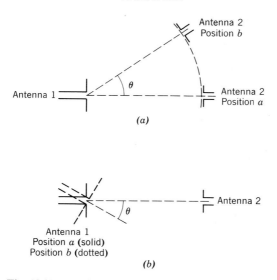

Fig. 12.31   Possible systems for pattern measurement.

If 2 is transmitting and 1 receiving, the power received for the two positions is related by

$$\frac{W_{1b}}{W_{1a}} = \frac{|Z_{12}|_b^2}{|Z_{12}|_a^2}.$$ (10)

Because of reciprocity $|Z_{12}|_a = |Z_{21}|_a$, and similarly for b, so the ratios (9) and (10) are the same. Thus, the same relative power pattern will be measured with antenna 1 transmitting or receiving.

It is, of course, important to remember that the reciprocity relation may be violated if the transmission path contains a medium such as the ionosphere, which may not have strictly bilateral properties. It is obvious that frequency must be kept constant when receiver and transmitter are interchanged. Also, if there are obstacles or other secondary radiators in the field, they must keep their same position relative to the system when the interchange is made. (See Prob. 12.31c.)

Problems

12.31a   Calculate the effective area for a half-wave dipole antenna. Compare with that for the infinitesimal dipole.

12.31b   Calculate the effective area for the small loop antenna.

12.31c   If the antennas are in free space, the pattern of 1 may be measured, as was described in Fig. 12.31a, by moving antenna 2 about the arc of a circle, or, as in Fig. 12.31b, by rotating 1 about an axis to give the same relative position. Explain why the same results might not be obtained by the two methods if there are fixed obstacles in the transmission path.

12.31d For the data of Prob. 12.30b and the radiation resistance of both antennas equal to 50 ohms, calculate $|Z_{12}|$. Now, allowing separation r to vary, find the separation for which Z_{12} becomes comparable to Z_{11}.

12.32 Equivalent Circuit of the Receiving Antenna

For a study of the circuit problem in matching the antenna to a receiver, the second part of the equivalent circuit of Fig. 12.30c is useful and is

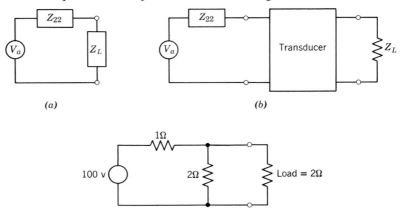

(a)   (b)

(c)

Fig. 12.32 (a) Equivalent circuit of receiving antenna for power transfer calculations. (b) Circuit for receiving antenna coupled to the load through a transducer. (c) Circuit for Prob. 12.32a.

repeated in Fig. 12.32a. In this the internal impedance of the generator Z_{22} is essentially the input impedance of the same antenna if driven at the same terminals.

$$Z_{22} \approx Z_{i2}. \tag{1}$$

This follows by the same argument given for antenna (1) in Art. 12.30, meaning that reaction back through Z_{21} is negligible *when the antenna is driven*.

The voltage generator in Fig. 12.32a is given from Eq. 12.30(2) as $I_1 Z_{21}$, but transmitter current and transfer impedance are not convenient parameters for most calculations, so other forms in terms of the power density of the oncoming wave are preferable. By substitution from Eq.

12.30(4) and Eq. 12.31(2), we can find this voltage in terms of the average Poynting vector or power density of the oncoming wave, P_{av}, the radiation resistance of the receiving antenna R_{r2}, and the effective area A_{e2}. (This effective area is calculated on the assumption of a matched load, but may be a function of the orientation of the antenna with respect to the oncoming wave.)

$$V_a = I_1 Z_{21} = (8R_2 A_{e2} P_{\text{av}})^{\frac{1}{2}}. \tag{2}$$

The equivalent circuit is useful, for example, in computing the transfer of power from the antenna to the useful load through a transmission line which may have discontinuities, matching sections, or filter elements. All these may be lumped together as a transducer, as explained in the preceding chapter (Fig. 12.32b), and the problem from here on is a standard circuit calculation. It must be emphasized, as in any Thévenin equivalent circuit, that the equivalent circuit was derived to tell what happens in the load under different load conditions, and significance cannot be automatically attached to a calculation of power loss in the internal impedance of the equivalent circuit. In the present case, it is tempting to interpret this as the power reradiated or scattered by currents on the receiving antenna, and one would conclude that as much power is scattered under a condition of perfect match as is absorbed in the load. This conclusion is not true, except in special cases where the current distribution may be the same for reception as for transmission.

Problems

12.32a To demonstrate that a power calculation in the internal impedance of a Thévenin equivalent circuit does not necessarily represent the power lost internally, consider a generator of constant voltage 100 volts coupled to a resistance load of 2 ohms through the series-parallel resistances shown in Fig. 12.32c. Calculate the actual power lost in the generator, and compare with that calculated by taking load current flowing through the internal impedance of a Thévenin equivalent circuit.

12.32b An antenna having an input impedance on transmission of $70 + j30$ ohms is used on reception by connecting directly to a 50-ohm transmission line which is perfectly matched to a pure resistance load. The effective area is 0.40 meter^2. Find the power transfer to the load if the antenna is in a plane wave field of 100 microvolts per meter. Compare this with the power that could be obtained with a conjugate match to the antenna impedance.

APPENDIX I

COORDINATE SYSTEMS AND VECTOR RELATIONS

The Rectangular, Cylindrical, and Spherical Coordinate Systems

The three systems utilized in this book are rectangular coordinates, circular cylindrical coordinates, and spherical coordinates. These three are defined briefly here.

The intersection of two surfaces is a line; the intersection of three surfaces is a point; thus the coordinates of a point may be given by stating three parameters, each of which defines a coordinate surface. In rectangular coordinates, the three planes $x = x_1$, $y = y_1$, $z = z_1$ intersect at a point designated by the coordinates x_1, y_1, z_1. The elements of length in the three coordinate directions are dx, dy, and dz, the elements of area are $dx\,dy$, $dy\,dz$, and $dz\,dx$, and the element of volume is $dx\,dy\,dz$.

In the circular cylindrical coordinate system, the coordinate surfaces are (a) a set of circular cylinders (r = constant), (b) a set of planes all passing through the axis (ϕ = constant), (c) a set of planes normal to the axis (z = constant). Coordinates of a particular point may then be given as r_1, ϕ_1, z_1 (Fig. Ia). The r, ϕ, and z coordinates are known respectively as the radius, the azimuthal angle, and the distance along the axis. Elements of length are dr, $r\,d\phi$, dz, and the element of volume is $r\,dr\,d\phi\,dz$. The system shown is a right-hand system in the order of writing r, ϕ, z.

In spherical coordinates the surfaces are (a) a set of spheres (radius r from the origin = constant), (b) a set of cones about the axis (θ = constant), (c) a set of planes passing through the polar axis (ϕ = constant). The intersection of sphere $r = r_1$, cone $\theta = \theta_1$, and plane $\phi = \phi_1$ gives a point whose coordinates are said to be r_1, θ_1, ϕ_1 (Fig. Ib). r is the radius, θ the polar angle or co-latitude, and ϕ is the azimuth angle or longitude. Elements of distance are dr, $r\,d\theta$, and $r \sin \theta\,d\phi$, elements of area are $r\,dr\,d\theta$, $r^2 \sin \theta\,d\theta\,d\phi$, and $r \sin \theta\,d\phi\,dr$, and the element of volume is $r^2 \sin \theta\,dr\,d\theta\,d\phi$.

723

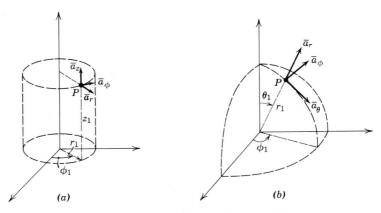

Fig. I   (*a*) System of circular cylindrical coordinates. (*b*) System of spherical coordinates.

In forming the various operations such as divergence and curl in the curvilinear coordinate system, the fundamental definitions are utilized, but we must recognize that the elements of area or length may vary as we change a coordinate, as well as the value of the vector components. As an example, let us find the expression for divergence of $\bar{D}$ in the spherical coordinate system. Consider the radial direction first. Both the radial component D_r and the element of area $r^2 \, d\theta \sin\theta \, d\phi$ change as we move from r to $r + dr$ (Fig. I*c*). Thus the net flux flow out the top over that in at the bottom is

$$ d\psi_r = (r + dr)^2 \sin\theta \, d\theta \, d\phi \left(D_r + \frac{\partial D_r}{\partial r} \, dr \right) - r^2 \sin\theta \, d\theta \, d\phi \, D_r. $$

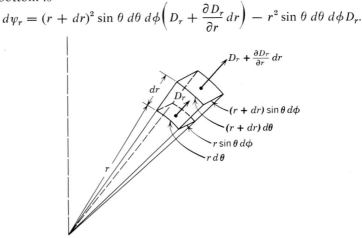

Fig. I(*c*)   Element of volume in spherical coordinates.

To first-order differentials, this leaves

$$d\psi_r = r^2 \sin\theta \, d\theta \, d\phi \frac{\partial D_r}{\partial r} dr + 2r \, dr \sin\theta \, d\theta \, d\phi D_r$$

$$= \sin\theta \, dr \, d\theta \, d\phi \frac{\partial}{\partial r}(r^2 D_r).$$

Note that the same result may be obtained more directly by first forming the product of flux density by area and then taking the rate of change of this product with r:

$$d\psi_r = dr \frac{\partial}{\partial r}(D_r r^2 \sin\theta \, d\theta \, d\phi) = \sin\theta \, dr \, d\theta \, d\phi \frac{\partial}{\partial r}(r^2 D_r).$$

Similarly for the θ and ϕ directions:

$$d\psi_\theta = d\theta \frac{\partial}{\partial\theta}(D_\theta r \sin\theta \, d\phi \, dr) = r \, dr \, d\theta \, d\phi \frac{\partial}{\partial\theta}(\sin\theta \, D_\theta)$$

$$d\psi_\phi = d\phi \frac{\partial}{\partial\phi}(D_\phi r \, d\theta \, dr) = r \, dr \, d\theta \, d\phi \frac{\partial}{\partial\phi}(D_\phi).$$

The divergence is then the total $d\psi$ divided by the element of volume

$$\nabla \cdot \bar{D} = \frac{d\psi_r + d\psi_\theta + d\psi_\phi}{r^2 \sin\theta \, dr \, d\theta \, d\phi}$$

$$\nabla \cdot \bar{D} = \frac{1}{r^2}\frac{\partial}{\partial r}(r^2 D_r) + \frac{1}{r \sin\theta}\frac{\partial}{\partial\theta}(\sin\theta \, D_\theta) + \frac{1}{r \sin\theta}\frac{\partial D_\phi}{\partial\phi}. \tag{1}$$

Corresponding forms for the other operations in this and other coordinate systems are given on the inside back cover.

General Curvilinear Coordinates

Each of the three systems above, and many others utilized in mathematical physics, are orthogonal coordinate systems in that the lines of intersection of the coordinate surfaces are at right angles to one another at any given point. It is possible to develop general expressions for divergence, curl, and other vector operations for such systems which make it unnecessary to begin at the beginning each time a new system is met.

Suppose that a point in space is thus defined in any orthogonal system by the coordinate surfaces q_1, q_2, q_3. These then intersect at right angles and a set of three unit vectors, $\bar{a}_1, \bar{a}_2, \bar{a}_3$, may be placed at this point. These should point in the direction of increasing coordinates. (See Fig. Id.) The three coordinates need not necessarily express directly a distance (consider, for example, the angles of spherical coordinates) so that the differential elements of distance must be expressed:

$$dl_1 = h_1\, dq_1; \qquad dl_2 = h_2\, dq_2, \qquad dl_3 = h_3\, dq_3, \qquad (2)$$

where h_1, h_2, h_3 in the most general case may each be functions of all three coordinates, q_1, q_2, q_3.

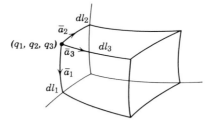

Fig. I(d)   Element in arbitrary orthogonal curvilinear coordinates.

Scalar and Vector Products.   A reference to the fundamental definitions of the two vector multiplications will show that these do not change in form in orthogonal curvilinear coordinates. Thus, for scalar or dot product,

$$\bar{A} \cdot \bar{B} = A_1 B_1 + A_2 B_2 + A_3 B_3, \qquad (3)$$

and, for the vector or cross product,

$$\bar{A} \times \bar{B} = \begin{vmatrix} \bar{a}_1 & \bar{a}_2 & \bar{a}_3 \\ A_1 & A_2 & A_3 \\ B_1 & B_2 & B_3 \end{vmatrix}. \qquad (4)$$

When one of these vectors is replaced by the operator ∇, the foregoing expressions do not hold, as will be shown below.

Gradient.   According to previous definitions, the gradient of any scalar Φ will be a vector whose component in any direction is given by the change of Φ for a change in distance along that direction. Thus

$$\nabla\Phi = \bar{a}_1 \frac{\partial\Phi}{h_1\,\partial q_1} + \bar{a}_2 \frac{\partial\Phi}{h_2\,\partial q_2} + \bar{a}_3 \frac{\partial\Phi}{h_3\,\partial q_3}. \qquad (5)$$

Divergence.   In forming the divergence, it is necessary to account for the variations in surface elements as well as the vector components when one changes a coordinate, as was noted in the preceding section. If the product of surface element by the appropriate component is first formed and then differentiated, both of these changes are taken into account:

$$\nabla \cdot \bar{D} = \frac{1}{h_1 h_2 h_3 \, dq_1 \, dq_2 \, dq_3} \left[dq_1 \frac{\partial}{\partial q_1} (D_1 h_2 h_3 \, dq_2 \, dq_3) \right.$$

$$\left. + dq_2 \frac{\partial}{\partial q_2} (D_2 h_1 h_3 \, dq_1 \, dq_3) + dq_3 \frac{\partial}{\partial q_3} (D_3 h_2 h_1 \, dq_2 \, dq_1) \right]$$

$$\nabla \cdot \bar{D} = \frac{1}{h_1 h_2 h_3} \left[\frac{\partial}{\partial q_1} (h_2 h_3 \, D_1) + \frac{\partial}{\partial q_2} (h_1 h_3 \, D_2) + \frac{\partial}{\partial q_3} (h_2 h_1 \, D_3) \right]. \tag{6}$$

Note that for the spherical coordinate system $dl_1 = dr$, $dl_2 = r \, d\theta$, and $dl_3 = r \sin \theta \, d\phi$, so that $h_1 = 1$, $h_2 = r$, and $h_3 = r \sin \theta$. A substitution of these in (6) leads directly to (1).

Curl. In forming the curl, it is necessary to account for the variations in length elements with changes in coordinates as one integrates about an elemental path. This may again be done by forming the product of length element and proper vector component and then differentiating. The result may be written

$$\nabla \times \bar{H} = \begin{vmatrix} \bar{a}_1 & \bar{a}_2 & \bar{a}_3 \\ \dfrac{\bar{a}_1}{h_2 h_3} & \dfrac{\bar{a}_2}{h_3 h_1} & \dfrac{\bar{a}_3}{h_1 h_2} \\ \dfrac{\partial}{\partial q_1} & \dfrac{\partial}{\partial q_2} & \dfrac{\partial}{\partial q_3} \\ h_1 H_1 & h_2 H_2 & h_3 H_3 \end{vmatrix}. \tag{7}$$

Laplacian. The Laplacian of a scalar, which is defined as the divergence of the gradient of that scalar, may be found by combining (5) and (6):

$$\nabla^2 \Phi = \nabla \cdot \nabla \Phi$$

$$= \frac{1}{h_1 h_2 h_3} \left[\frac{\partial}{\partial q_1} \left(\frac{h_2 h_3}{h_1} \frac{\partial \Phi}{\partial q_1} \right) + \frac{\partial}{\partial q_2} \left(\frac{h_3 h_1}{h_2} \frac{\partial \Phi}{\partial q_2} \right) + \frac{\partial}{\partial q_3} \left(\frac{h_1 h_2}{h_3} \frac{\partial \Phi}{\partial q_3} \right) \right]. \tag{8}$$

Laplacian of Vectors. For the Laplacian of a vector in a system of coordinates other than rectangular, it is convenient to use the vector identity

$$\nabla^2 \bar{F} = \nabla (\nabla \cdot \bar{F}) - \nabla \times \nabla \times \bar{F}. \tag{9}$$

Each of the operations on the right has been defined earlier.

Differentiation of Vectors. The derivative of a vector is sometimes required as in Newton's law for the motion of particles,

$$\bar{F} = m \frac{d\bar{v}}{dt} = m \frac{d}{dt} (\bar{a}_1 v_1 + \bar{a}_2 v_2 + \bar{a}_3 v_3). \tag{10}$$

If this is expanded, we have

$$\frac{\bar{F}}{m} = \bar{a}_1 \frac{dv_1}{dt} + \bar{a}_2 \frac{dv_2}{dt} + \bar{a}_3 \frac{dv_3}{dt} + v_1 \frac{d\bar{a}_1}{dt} + v_2 \frac{d\bar{a}_2}{dt} + v_3 \frac{d\bar{a}_3}{dt} .$$

The last three terms involve changes in the unit vectors, which by definition cannot change magnitude, but may change in direction as one moves

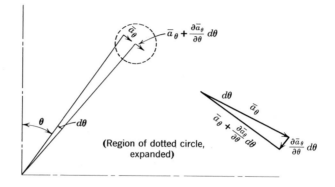

Fig. I(e)

along the coordinate system. Consider for example the fourth term:

$$v_1 \frac{d\bar{a}_1}{dt} = v_1 \left(\frac{\partial \bar{a}_1}{\partial q_1} \frac{dq_1}{dt} + \frac{\partial \bar{a}_1}{\partial q_2} \frac{dq_2}{dt} + \frac{\partial \bar{a}_1}{\partial q_3} \frac{dq_3}{dt} \right).$$

Partials of the form $\partial \bar{a}_1 / \partial q_1$, etc., may not be zero. As an example, consider the term $\partial \bar{a}_\theta / \partial \theta$ in spherical coordinates. From Fig. Ie the vector $d\theta \, \partial \bar{a}_\theta / \partial \theta$ is seen to have magnitude $d\theta$ and has direction given by $-\bar{a}_r$. Thus $\partial \bar{a}_\theta / \partial \theta = -\bar{a}_r$. Other partials of unit vectors in this and the cylindrical coordinate system are listed below.

Coordinates and Derivatives of Unit Vectors for Various Coordinate Systems

Rectangular Coordinates

$$q_1 = x \qquad q_2 = y \qquad q_3 = z$$
$$h_1 = 1 \qquad h_2 = 1 \qquad h_3 = 1$$

All partials of unit vectors $\left(\dfrac{\partial \bar{a}_x}{\partial x} , \dfrac{\partial \bar{a}_x}{\partial y} , \text{etc.} \right)$ are zero.

Cylindrical Coordinates

$$q_1 = r \qquad q_2 = \phi \qquad q_3 = z$$
$$h_3 = 1 \qquad h_2 = r \qquad h_3 = 1$$

All partials of unit vectors are zero except

$$\frac{\partial \bar{a}_r}{\partial \phi} = \bar{a}_\phi \qquad \frac{\partial \bar{a}_\phi}{\partial \phi} = -\bar{a}_r.$$

Spherical Coordinates

$$q_1 = r \qquad q_2 = \theta \qquad q_3 = \phi$$
$$h_1 = 1 \qquad h_2 = r \qquad h_3 = r \sin \theta$$

All partials of unit vectors are zero except

$$\frac{\partial \bar{a}_r}{\partial \theta} = \bar{a}_\theta \qquad \frac{\partial \bar{a}_\theta}{\partial \theta} = -\bar{a}_r$$

$$\frac{\partial \bar{a}_r}{\partial \phi} = \bar{a}_\phi \sin \theta \qquad \frac{\partial \bar{a}_\theta}{\partial \phi} = \bar{a}_\phi \cos \theta \qquad \frac{\partial \bar{a}_\phi}{\partial \phi} = -(\bar{a}_r \sin \theta + \bar{a}_\theta \cos \theta).$$

SKETCH OF THE DERIVATION
OF MAGNETIC FIELD LAWS

In presenting various forms for the laws of static magnetic fields, many of the less obvious steps were left out, and the order was chosen as that most convenient for presentation of the laws rather than that of the logical development. This appendix sketches the omitted steps.

We wish to start from Ampère's law, Eq. 2.24(2), which we may write

$$\bar{H}(x, y, z) = \int \frac{I'(x', y', z')\, \overline{dl}' \times \bar{r}}{4\pi r^3}, \tag{1}$$

by assuming the origin of the coordinate system to be at the current element at each point through the integration. I' is the current in a contributing element $\overline{dl}'$ at point (x', y', z'), and $\bar{r}$ is the vector running from $\overline{dl}'$ to point (x, y, z) at which $\bar{H}$ is to be computed.

$$\bar{r} = \bar{a}_x(x - x') + \bar{a}_y(y - y') + \bar{a}_z(z - z')$$
$$r = \sqrt{(x - x')^2 + (y - y')^2 + (z - z')^2}.$$

We wish to find $\bar{B}$ in terms of the derivatives at the point of observation (x, y, z) of the vector potential $\bar{A}$. It may be shown that

$$\frac{\overline{dl}' \times \bar{r}}{r^3} = \nabla\left(\frac{1}{r}\right) \times \overline{dl}' \tag{2}$$

where ∇ denotes derivatives with respect to x, y, and z. Also, using the vector identity of Prob. 2.28c,

$$\nabla\left(\frac{1}{r}\right) \times \overline{dl}' = \nabla \times \left(\frac{\overline{dl}'}{r}\right) - \frac{1}{r} \nabla \times \overline{dl}'. \tag{3}$$

Since ∇ represents derivatives with respect to x, y, and z, which are not involved in $\overline{dl'}$, the last term is zero. Therefore

$$\bar{B}(x, y, z) = \mu \int \frac{I'(x', y', z')}{4\pi} \nabla \times \left(\frac{\overline{dl'}}{r}\right) = \nabla \times \bar{A}(x, y, z), \qquad (4)$$

where $\bar{A}(x, y, z) = \mu \int \frac{I'(x', y', z') \, \overline{dl'}}{4\pi r}.$ $\qquad (5)$

The curl operation in (4) could be taken outside of the integral since it is with respect to x, y, z, and the integration is with respect to x', y', z'. Thus the vector potential forms of Art. 2.30 have been derived from Ampère's law for which the arbitrary coordinate origin was chosen at the current element for simplicity.

For the next step, let us note the x component of (5):

$$A_x(x, y, z) = \mu \int \frac{I'_x(x', y', z') \, dx'}{4\pi r} = \mu \int_{V'} \frac{i'_x(x', y', z') \, dV'}{4\pi r}. \qquad (6)$$

This may be compared with Poisson's equation and the integral expression for electrostatic potential:

$$\nabla^2 \Phi = -\frac{\rho}{\epsilon}; \qquad \Phi(x, y, z) = \int_{V'} \frac{\rho(x', y', z') \, dV'}{4\pi\epsilon r}. \qquad (7)$$

Although these equations were obtained from a consideration of the properties of electrostatic fields, the second of the two equations (7) may be considered a solution in integral form for the first, for any continuous scalar functions Φ and ρ/ϵ. Consequently, by direct analogy between (6) and (7), we write

$$\nabla^2 A_x = -\mu i_x \qquad (8)$$

$$\nabla^2 \bar{A} = -\mu \bar{i}. \qquad (9)$$

This was the differential equation relating $\bar{A}$ to current density discussed in Art. 2.33. By reversing the steps of that article, the differential equation for magnetic field may be derived from it:

$$\nabla \times \bar{H} = \bar{i}. \qquad (10)$$

And as was shown in Art. 2.29, the integral form may be derived from this by use of Stokes's theorem:

$$\oint \bar{H} \cdot \overline{dl} = I. \qquad (11)$$

There remains the argument for $\nabla \cdot \bar{A} = 0$ used in Art. 2.32. In this it is necessary to make use of the del operator both with respect to the variables x, y, z and with respect to the variables x', y', z'. The former will be denoted

∇, and the latter ∇'. Recall that the integration is with respect to the primed variables. Then

$$\frac{1}{\mu}\nabla \cdot \bar{A} = \nabla \cdot \int_{V'} \frac{\bar{i}'(x', y', z')\, dV'}{4\pi r} = \int_{V'} \nabla \cdot \left(\frac{\bar{i}'(x', y', z')}{r}\right)\frac{dV'}{4\pi}. \tag{12}$$

Using the vector equivalence of Prob. 2.16e:

$$\frac{1}{\mu}\nabla \cdot \bar{A} = -\int_{V'}\left[\frac{\nabla \cdot \bar{i}'(x', y', z')}{r} + \bar{i}'(x', y', z') \cdot \nabla\left(\frac{1}{r}\right)\right]\frac{dV'}{4\pi}.$$

The first term is zero since $\bar{i}'$ is not a function of the x, y, z coordinates. In the latter term, from the definition of r, we can write

$$\nabla\left(\frac{1}{r}\right) = -\nabla'\left(\frac{1}{r}\right).$$

Then $\dfrac{1}{\mu}\nabla \cdot \bar{A} = -\displaystyle\int_{V'} \bar{i}'(x', y', z') \cdot \nabla'\left(\frac{1}{r}\right)\frac{dV'}{4\pi}$

$$= \int_{V'}\left[\frac{1}{r}\nabla' \cdot \bar{i}'(x', y', z') - \nabla' \cdot \frac{\bar{i}'(x', y', z')}{r}\right]\frac{dV'}{4\pi}.$$

In the last step we have again used the vector equivalence of Prob. 2.16e. The first term is zero because we are concerned with direct currents, which, by continuity, give $\nabla' \cdot (\bar{i}') = 0$. The second term is transformable to a surface integral by the divergence theorem:

$$\frac{1}{\mu}\nabla \cdot \bar{A} = \oint_{S'} \frac{\bar{i}'(x', y', z')}{4\pi r} \cdot \overline{dS'}. \tag{13}$$

But, if the surface encloses all the current, as it must, there can be no current flow through the surface and the result in (13) is seen to be zero. Thus all the major laws given have been shown to follow from the original experimental law of Ampère. It should be noted that the argument given is for a homogeneous medium (permeability not a function of position). For an inhomogeneous or anisotropic medium, the equations forming the fundamental starting point are

$$\nabla \times \bar{H} = \bar{i}; \qquad \nabla \cdot \bar{B} = 0. \tag{14}$$

For an anisotropic medium $\bar{B}$ and $\bar{H}$ are not related by a simple constant, as seen in Art. 2.44.

APPENDIX III

MAGNETIC POLARIZATION AND EQUIVALENT CURRENTS

The orbital and spin motions of electrons constitute circulating currents in the classical model and therefore can be represented by magnetic dipole moments. As was seen in Prob. 2.31, torques are exerted on dipole moments $\bar{m}$ when they are in the presence of a magnetic field. The torques tend to align the dipole moments with the applied field. Each dipole produces a magnetic field, the vector potential of which was given by Eq. 2.31(15). It may be written more conveniently for our present purposes as

$$\bar{A}(\bar{r}) = -\frac{\mu_0}{4\pi} \bar{m} \times \nabla_r\left(\frac{1}{|\bar{r} - \bar{r}'|}\right), \tag{1}$$

where the subscript r indicates that derivatives are to be taken with respect to the point of observation which is located by the vector $\bar{r}$ from an arbitrary origin of coordinates. The vector $\bar{r}'$ locates the magnetic dipole relative to the same coordinate origin. The vector potential of an array of dipoles may be found by superposition as

$$\bar{A}(\bar{r}) = -\frac{\mu_0}{4\pi} \sum_i \bar{m}_i \times \nabla_r \frac{1}{|\bar{r} - \bar{r}_i'|}. \tag{2}$$

A magnetic dipole density, also called *magnetization* or *magnetic polarization* may be defined as

$$\bar{M}(\bar{r}') = \lim_{\Delta V \to 0} \frac{\sum_i \bar{m}_i}{\Delta V}, \tag{3}$$

where $\Delta V \to 0$ only in a macroscopic sense. That is, ΔV still contains many dipole moments but is very small compared with the size of the system. Then (2) may be written as

$$\bar{A}(\bar{r}) = -\frac{\mu_0}{4\pi} \int_{V'} \bar{M}(\bar{r}') \times \nabla_r \frac{1}{|\bar{r} - \bar{r}'|} dV' \tag{4}$$

733

where primes denote that the integration is over the volume of the sources. By means of vector identities, (4) can be rearranged into the form

$$\bar{A}(\bar{r}) = \frac{\mu_0}{4\pi} \int_{V'} \frac{\nabla_{r'} \times \bar{M}(\bar{r}')}{|\bar{r} - \bar{r}'|} \, dV' + \frac{\mu_0}{4\pi} \oint_{S} \frac{\bar{M}(\bar{r}') \times \bar{n}}{|\bar{r} - \bar{r}'|} \, dS' \tag{5}$$

where $\bar{n}$ is the (outward) normal to the surface bounding the region of matter, and the subscript r' on the curl operation denotes differentiation with respect to the coordinates of the sources. Let us compare (5) with the equations for the magnetic vector potential resulting from distributions of current density [Eq. 2.30(3)].

$$\bar{A}(\bar{r}) = \frac{\mu_0}{4\pi} \int_{V'} \frac{\bar{i}(\bar{r}')}{|\bar{r} - \bar{r}'|} \, dV'. \tag{6}$$

It is clear that the effect of the dipoles can be represented by a distribution of current density in free space such that

$$\nabla_{r'} \times \bar{M}(\bar{r}') = \bar{i}_b(\bar{r}') \tag{7}$$

and

$$\bar{M}(\bar{r}') \times \bar{n} = \bar{i}_{bs}(\bar{r}'), \tag{8}$$

where $\bar{i}_b(\bar{r}')$ is a volume current density and $\bar{i}_{bs}(\bar{r}')$ is a surface current in amperes per meter width. The subscript b signifies that the currents represent motion of electrons bound to their atoms. The conclusion is that the matter containing the electronic magnetic moments can be replaced by free space and a distribution of volume and surface currents given in terms of the existing magnetization by (7) and (8). The sense in which the currents are equivalent to the polarization is that the same vector potential is found. Thus, since

$$\bar{B} = \nabla \times \bar{A} \tag{9}$$

the correct macroscopic flux density $\bar{B}$ is given by the currents. This is true for points inside and outside the region of matter.

By reasoning similar to that in Art. 2.41 it can be seen that the field acting on a particular dipole moment differs from the macroscopic field given by (9) in that the fields produced by the dipole itself must be excluded. Since the molecule in question is removed, $\bar{B}$ and $\bar{H}$ are related there by μ_0 and the field acting on the dipole can be written as

$$\bar{H}_i = \frac{\bar{B}}{\mu_0} + \kappa \bar{M} \tag{10}$$

where $\bar{B}$ is the macroscopic field and κ is a constant which depends on the nature of the interaction of nearby dipole moments.

The meaning of the surface currents is clarified by considering a rod of magnetizable material as shown in Fig. III. We assume that the rod is homogeneous and is subjected to a magnetic field which exerts torques on the electronic dipole moments so that the dipole vectors are parallel with the axis of the rod. The currents are shown schematically on the end of the rod. The parts of the loops cancelled by parts of other loops are shown by

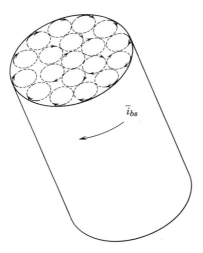

$\bar{i}_{bs}$

Fig. III   Schematic representation of
atomic currents showing cancellations
except on outer surface.

broken lines. The parts of the loops shown by solid lines do not cancel but form a surface current, the direction of which may be seen to be expressed by (8).

The flux density may be related to the true current and equivalent current using the point equivalent of Ampère's law for free space

$$\nabla \times \frac{\bar{B}}{\mu_0} = \bar{i} + \bar{i}_b. \tag{11}$$

And using (7), we see that

$$\nabla \times \frac{\bar{B}}{\mu_0} = \bar{i} + \nabla \times \bar{M}. \tag{12}$$

Thus

$$\nabla \times \left(\frac{\bar{B}}{\mu_0} - \bar{M}\right) = \bar{i}. \tag{13}$$

But we also know that

$$\nabla \times \bar{H} = \bar{i}, \tag{14}$$

so equating (13) and (14), we have

$$\bar{M} = \frac{\bar{B}}{\mu_0} - \bar{H}. \tag{15}$$

If we confine our attention to linear, isotropic media so $\bar{B} = \mu\bar{H}$, we may write (15) as

$$\bar{M} = \left(\frac{\mu}{\mu_0} - 1\right)\bar{H} = \chi_m\bar{H}, \tag{16}$$

where χ_m is called the *magnetic susceptibility* since it is a measure of the susceptibility of the material to magnetic polarization. For nonlinear or anisotropic materials, μ and χ_m are not simple constants.

It was seen in Art. 2.40 that electric field problems involving the dielectric behavior of linear matter are best handled by using the characterizing parameter, permittivity, and the known boundary relations. It is necessary to know the fields in the material to find the polarization. Again, for the magnetic behavior of linear materials, field problems are best solved using the known boundary relations and the permeability μ to characterize the medium. Chapter 9 has an example in which the expression for the permeability is derived from consideration of the behavior of the dipole moments. For materials which may have a residual magnetization when there is no applied external field, the concepts of this appendix are essential.

$\omega\text{-}\beta$ DIAGRAMS FOR VARIOUS TRANSMISSION SYSTEMS

This appendix gives a survey of the $\omega\text{-}\beta$ diagrams for several lossless transmission systems having the indicated equivalent circuits for differential lengths. The propagation constant and attenuation and phase constants are given by

$$\gamma = \alpha + j\beta = \sqrt{ZY}$$

where Z is the series impedance per unit length and Y is the shunt admittance per unit length. The frequencies ω_1 and ω_2 are the resonant frequencies of the series and shunt legs, respectively. Examples of the application of some equivalent circuits are given; examples of the others are found in a wide variety of slow wave structures.

Examples: 1. Uniform transmission line; 2. Plane wave in free space.

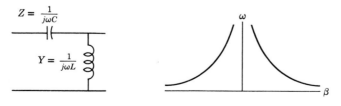

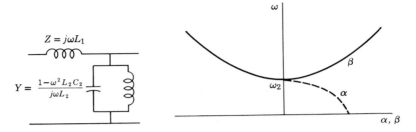

Examples: 1. Transverse electric waveguide mode; 2. Uniform plane wave in
ionized gas without static magnetic field.

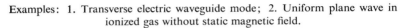

Example: Transverse magnetic waveguide mode.

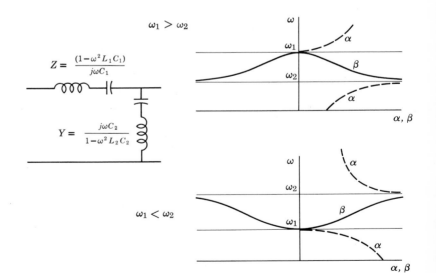

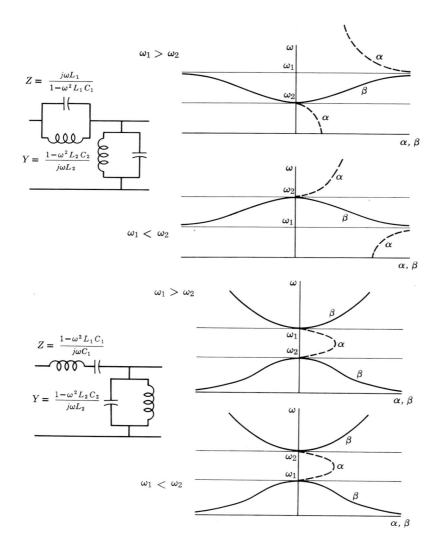

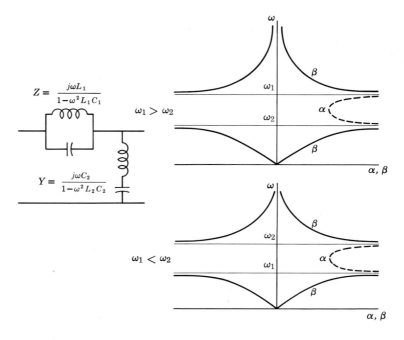

$$Z = \frac{j\omega L_1}{1-\omega^2 L_1 C_1}$$

$$Y = \frac{j\omega C_2}{1-\omega^2 L_2 C_2}$$

$\omega_1 > \omega_2$

$\omega_1 < \omega_2$

INDEX

propagation constant, 45
radial, 453–458
reflections, 27–28, 34, 36, 45
Smith chart, 35–39, 47
standing wave, 33–34, 39–41
table, 445
Transmission line waves, general,
393–400
Transmitting-receiving system,
714–720
Transverse electric waves, see TE
waves
Transverse electromagnetic waves, see
TEM waves
Transverse magnetic waves, see TM
waves
Traveling-wave amplifier, 511
Traveling-wave antennas, 637–638
Triode, electrostatic solution, 318–321
Tyrrell, W. A., 452

Uniaxial crystals, 494
Uniform plane wave, 247
Uniqueness, of field solutions,
258–259
of Laplace solution, 153–154
of network representation, 587
Unpolarized wave, 327–328
Units, cgs practical, 241–242
conversion table, 241
emu, 111
esu, 64–65
Gaussian, 240–241
Heaviside-Lorentz, 241
mks, 65–66, 110–111
rationalized, 66, 240–241
Unit vector, 63, 728–729

Variational formulations, 602
Variables, separation of, 193, 194–195
Vector, 63
complex, 239
differentiation, 728–729
identities, 723–729, end papers
operator, 83
potential, 119–122
Poynting, 243
product, 106–108, 726
radiation, 653

scalar (dot) product, 76–77
summary, end papers
unit, 63, 728–729
Velocity, energy, 48
group, 49–50
of light, end papers
of plane wave, 247
phase, 50
signal, 50
Voltage, 266–267
capacitive drop, 276
comparison with potential difference,
266–267
equivalent for waveguide mode,
584–586
induced by magnetic fields, 228–230
inductive drop, 276
Volume integrals, 76
von Hippel, A. R., 132, 331, 333

Wasow, W. R., 168
Watkins, D. A., 478
Watson, G. N., 208
Wave equation, 25, 246
for guided waves, 374
for transmission line, 25
inhomogenous, 261
one-dimensional, 25, 246, 323
Waveguide, modes, 384
diaphragms, 602
junctions, 591–612
measurement of parameters,
594–597
parameters by analysis, 597–602
ports, 583
Waveguides, below cutoff, 442–445
circular, 429–437
coupling to, 437–439
dielectric, 448–453
discontinuities, 601–602
multimode, 434–437
radiation from, 672
rectangular, 421–429
transmission line technique, 439–442
voltage, current, and impedance, 585
Wave impedance, 345
of TE waves, 409
of TM waves, 404

VECTOR DIFFERENTIAL OPERATIONS

Rectangular Coordinates (x, y, z)

$$\nabla\Phi = \bar{a}_x \frac{\partial\Phi}{\partial x} + \bar{a}_y \frac{\partial\Phi}{\partial y} + \bar{a}_z \frac{\partial\Phi}{\partial z}$$

$$\nabla \cdot \bar{D} = \frac{\partial D_x}{\partial x} + \frac{\partial D_y}{\partial y} + \frac{\partial D_z}{\partial z} = \rho$$

$$\nabla \times \bar{H} = \bar{a}_x\left(\frac{\partial H_z}{\partial y} - \frac{\partial H_y}{\partial z}\right) + \bar{a}_y\left(\frac{\partial H_x}{\partial z} - \frac{\partial H_z}{\partial x}\right) + \bar{a}_z\left(\frac{\partial H_y}{\partial x} - \frac{\partial H_x}{\partial y}\right) = i$$

$$\nabla^2\Phi = \frac{\partial^2\Phi}{\partial x^2} + \frac{\partial^2\Phi}{\partial y^2} + \frac{\partial^2\Phi}{\partial z^2}$$

$$\nabla^2\bar{A} = \bar{a}_x\nabla^2 A_x + \bar{a}_y\nabla^2 A_y + \bar{a}_z\nabla^2 A_z$$

Cylindrical Coordinates (r, ϕ, z)

$$\nabla\Phi = \bar{a}_r \frac{\partial\Phi}{\partial r} + \bar{a}_\phi \frac{1}{r}\frac{\partial\Phi}{\partial \phi} + \bar{a}_z \frac{\partial\Phi}{\partial z}$$

$$\nabla \cdot \bar{D} = \frac{1}{r}\frac{\partial}{\partial r}(rD_r) + \frac{1}{r}\frac{\partial D_\phi}{\partial \phi} + \frac{\partial D_z}{\partial z}$$

$$\nabla \times \bar{H} = \bar{a}_r\left[\frac{1}{r}\frac{\partial H_z}{\partial \phi} - \frac{\partial H_\phi}{\partial z}\right] + \bar{a}_\phi\left[\frac{\partial H_r}{\partial z} - \frac{\partial H_z}{\partial r}\right] + \bar{a}_z\left[\frac{1}{r}\frac{\partial(rH_\phi)}{\partial r} - \frac{1}{r}\frac{\partial H_r}{\partial \phi}\right]$$

$$\nabla^2\Phi = \frac{1}{r}\frac{\partial}{\partial r}\left(r\frac{\partial\Phi}{\partial r}\right) + \frac{1}{r^2}\frac{\partial^2\Phi}{\partial \phi^2} + \frac{\partial^2\Phi}{\partial z^2}$$

$$\nabla^2\bar{A} = \bar{a}_r\left(\nabla^2 A_r - \frac{2}{r^2}\frac{\partial A_\phi}{\partial \phi} - \frac{A_r}{r^2}\right) + \bar{a}_\phi\left(\nabla^2 A_\phi + \frac{2}{r^2}\frac{\partial A_r}{\partial \phi} - \frac{A_\phi}{r^2}\right) + \bar{a}_z(\nabla^2 A_z)$$

Spherical Coordinates (r, θ, ϕ)

$$\nabla\Phi = \bar{a}_r \frac{\partial\Phi}{\partial r} + \bar{a}_\theta \frac{1}{r}\frac{\partial\Phi}{\partial \theta} + \frac{\bar{a}_\phi}{r\sin\theta}\frac{\partial\Phi}{\partial \phi}$$

$$\nabla \cdot \bar{D} = \frac{1}{r^2}\frac{\partial}{\partial r}(r^2 D_r) + \frac{1}{r\sin\theta}\frac{\partial}{\partial \theta}(\sin\theta\, D_\theta) + \frac{1}{r\sin\theta}\frac{\partial D_\phi}{\partial \phi}$$

$$\nabla \times \bar{H} = \frac{\bar{a}_r}{r\sin\theta}\left[\frac{\partial}{\partial \theta}(H_\phi \sin\theta) - \frac{\partial H_\theta}{\partial \phi}\right]$$

$$+ \frac{\bar{a}_\theta}{r}\left[\frac{1}{\sin\theta}\frac{\partial H_r}{\partial \phi} - \frac{\partial}{\partial r}(rH_\phi)\right] + \frac{\bar{a}_\phi}{r}\left[\frac{\partial}{\partial r}(rH_\theta) - \frac{\partial H_r}{\partial \theta}\right]$$

$$\nabla^2\Phi = \frac{1}{r^2}\frac{\partial}{\partial r}\left(r^2\frac{\partial\Phi}{\partial r}\right) + \frac{1}{r^2\sin\theta}\frac{\partial}{\partial \theta}\left(\sin\theta\frac{\partial\Phi}{\partial \theta}\right) + \frac{1}{r^2\sin^2\theta}\frac{\partial^2\Phi}{\partial \phi^2}$$

$$\nabla^2\bar{A} = \bar{a}_r\left[\nabla^2 A_r - \frac{2}{r^2}\left(A_r + \cot\theta\, A_\theta + \csc\theta\frac{\partial A_\phi}{\partial \phi} + \frac{\partial A_\theta}{\partial \theta}\right)\right]$$

$$+ \bar{a}_\theta\left[\nabla^2 A_\theta - \frac{1}{r^2}\left(\csc^2\theta\, A_\theta - 2\frac{\partial A_r}{\partial \theta} + 2\cot\theta\csc\theta\frac{\partial A_\phi}{\partial \phi}\right)\right]$$

$$+ \bar{a}_\phi\left[\nabla^2 A_\phi - \frac{1}{r^2}\left(\csc^2\theta\, A_\phi - 2\csc\theta\frac{\partial A_r}{\partial \phi} - 2\cot\theta\csc\theta\frac{\partial A_\theta}{\partial \phi}\right)\right]$$